WRISTWATCH ANNUAL

2021

THE CATALOG

of

PRODUCERS, PRICES, MODELS,

and

SPECIFICATIONS

BY PETER BRAUN

WITH MARTON RADKAI

ABBEVILLE PRESS PUBLISHERS

New York London

SW
SHOPWORN

ShopWorn: a trusted partner for brands and their authorized retailers to send their past seasons' inventory and be assured those products never end up where they shouldn't.

ShopWorn is the natural evolution of the luxury retail cycle, where brands and their authorized dealers can make room for new inventory on their shelves as ShopWorn buys their past seasons' merchandise.

ShopWorn: a shopping destination for customers who want to be the first to own authentic, unused luxury products but don't want to pay luxury prices.

ShopWorn is the safest place online for customers to find their favorite luxury designer watches, jewelry and other luxury accessories at substantial savings while being guaranteed every item on the site is 100% authentic and never previously owned. No "authenticators" needed because every item on the site came through direct relationships with brands or their authorized retailers.

It's not new: It's past seasons.
It's not pre-owned: It's never-owned.
It's ShopWorn: It's authenticity guaranteed.
Be the First.

www.shopworn.com

(201) 399-7339
info@shopworn.com

CONTENTS

Dear Reader,

The cruel logic of existence is that crises in our private lives generally arise because we simply did not expect or predict them. They are the ones that "came out of nowhere," from the direction in which we were not looking. Crises affecting the collective are different. Individuals or communities cannot be expected to prepare for every single eventuality. As a society, we do expect a certain amount of predictability, because elected and even nonelected leaders are supposed to be prepared for mass casualty events like the covid-19 pandemic.

Well, the heroes and villains in leadership during the year 2020 will be determined and defined by pundits first, and historians later. Suffice to say the obvious for the moment: The coronavirus crisis hit hard, and at the time of writing is still raging. The economic impact is being felt across all industries.

Not that "our" industry was enjoying halcyon days before the pandemic. A look back to 2019 reveals a shift toward online sales, unpleasant stock surpluses, disgruntled retailers, and major changes in the trade fair scene, with Baselworld hemorrhaging major exhibitors due partly to a changing market and partly to the fact that several exhibitors were unhappy with high prices and impossible agreements aimed at locking in clients for years.

And then came the pandemic. Challenges were many, but opportunities were thin on the ground in 2020. By September, the exports from Switzerland had dropped by twelve percent, Europe in general by nineteen percent, and the USA by thirteen percent. The hardest-hit segment was the lower end, which is not that surprising, since the consumers with less income had worries other than buying watches.

The ever-optimistic industry veteran of many crises and successes, Jean-Claude Biver, did note, however, that at least the crisis was not structural, meaning it's not affecting the fundamentals. In one interview with Swiss Radio and Television, he declared seeing more opportunities than he'd seen in the industry since 1982, and notably for the independents. "When you clean an airport, the bigger the vacuum cleaner, the more ground it can cover," he said, with his usual knack for outlandish metaphors, "but it can't do the corners in a turn, so you need a smaller device. Those are the niches in business, and they are an opportunity for the small artisans." Indeed many, including Biver, see a

rebound in 2020. At the time of writing, the Chinese economy has been booming, and that is definitely a positive sign.

As for the independents, they are struggling, but they have several advantages. For one, they are often used to working with shaky financial backing. Secondly, they usually have low overhead and the flexibility to implement new strategies quickly. French clock- and automaton-maker John-Mikaël Flaux told me that despite some financial constraints, the downtime created by the pandemic was good for creativity. Add that to a labor market flooded with talented watchmakers let go by the big brands, and there may well be a lot of free-floating creativity and talent ready to get to work.

Wristwatch Annual is not a sales catalogue, but rather a presentation of what is being done in the industry, which explains why some brands are in the book even though their portfolio hasn't changed a great deal. Every year, though, we try to add new brands without cutting too much from the old-time favorites like Rolex and Patek Philippe. It's not always easy, since an entry in the book is not dependent on the brand advertising with us. That is why every year, for example, Elizabeth Doerr reviews the work of the independents (page 10). Among the new names added to the A-to-Z section are Zero West and Garrick from England, and two Swiss brands, Delma, specialists in diver's watches, and Montres Choisi, a revived brand that serves as Azimuth's "classic" sister brand.

And there is the front section, which features as usual a technical piece, this time covering constant force mechanisms (page 40). When watchmakers want to feel less constrained by space, they turn to building clocks, a segment with its own rules and regulations, literally and figuratively. The article "Timeworks" (page 18) merely gives a hint of the richness of these mechanical works of art. We then look at a key design element that is, strangely, often overlooked, namely watch hands (see page 30). Finally, the watch tech in this edition is devoted to a mechanism that has complication potential: the remontoir or constant force escapement (page 40).

This odd year had a sort of Sleeping Beauty feel to it, but the book got done thanks to a well-integrated team. A special thanks to Ginny Carroll, who proofreads the pages and regulates the workflow as well as any constant force mechanism. Of course, the book couldn't be completed without our advertisers, who trust in the power of a real book filled with durable images that will be read over and over again. Errors do occur, and if you run into one, please make gentle note of it so we correct it. And then enjoy everything else. We'd love to hear from you.

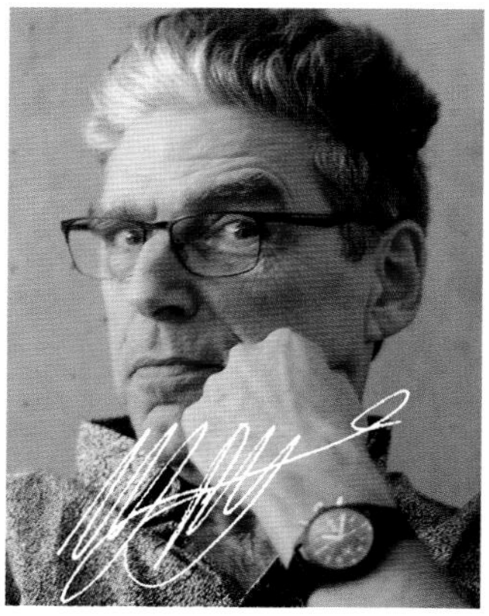

Marton Radkai

This year's *Wristwatch Annual* cover features **Maurice Lacroix's Aikon GMT**. This stainless-steel watch strikes a fair balance between ruggedness and urban chic. It has a diameter of 43 millimeters and a height of just 12 millimeters. It is driven by the in-house automatic ML 165 movement beating at 28,800 vph and has a 42-hour power reserve. The hour, minute, and second hands are joined by a contrasting red hand with a triangular tip that points to the 24-hour scale on a ceramic bezel. The watch is water-resistant to 30 atm. It comes on a steel bracelet but with an additional rubber strap, which can be easily switched thanks to a special easy-change system.

1

2

3

4

THE INDEPENDENT SCENE 2020: YOUTH, AWARDS, CREATIVITY

5

6

ELIZABETH DOERR

The high number of independent watchmakers and boutique brands entering the Grand Prix d'Horlogerie de Genève (GPHG) this year showed that the interest in this horological genre remains active. Watchmakers falling into this category took home eight of the eighteen prizes awarded on November 12, 2020.

While the coronavirus did put a damper on much of the industry, some events, like the GPHG, simply could not be canceled, and so they unfolded in the eerie silence of an empty auditorium with a large online viewership. In Geneva, **Kari Voutilainen**'s streak continues to hold. He won the Men's category with a new variation of the Vingt-8 featuring center sweep seconds called 28SC. This timepiece is outfitted with one of Voutilainen's signature guilloché dials. The Ladies' Complication prize went to Swiss newcomer **Charles Girardier** for a tourbillon with an animated subdial that can be personalized with the owner's initials. Above and beyond that, this watch's impressive dial is decorated with guilloché and high-fire (*grand feu*) enamel enhanced with traditionally crafted silver paillons.

Chronométrie Ferdinand Berthoud, a sub-brand of Chopard that functions like an independent watchmaker, won the Chronometry prize for the second year running, taking home the gold for its fabulous FB 2RE. This is the brand's first watch housed in a round case, which instantly transforms the character. But that is not all that is different about its debut creation: The glorious new C.O.S.C. chronometer-certified movement features two plates of German silver secured by pillars with most of the gear train sandwiched between. As a result, the back of the watch displays a chain-and-fusée assembly and a one-second remontoir d'egalité symmetrically positioned side by side against the backdrop of a gorgeously frosted German silver plate. The clever beauty of the movement's design is not found only in its symmetry, but also in the fact that these two exceptional devices can be admired and appreciated in full.

NORTHERN LIGHTS

A number of independent watchmakers hit the ground running with interesting timepieces in 2020 despite the situation presented by COVID-19's restrictions. Finnish watchmaker and silversmith **Stepan Sarpaneva** pays tribute to his youth with the Sarpaneva × Moomin timepiece, which itself is an homage to Nordic cartoon characters created by Tove Jansson. Crossing the border into Sweden, we find the team of metalsmith Johan Gustafsson and watchmaker Patrik Sjögren (**GoS**) introducing Skadi—named for the Norse goddess of winter—with its gorgeous, blackened Damascus steel and yellow gold case. The

A bouquet of Independent winners: (1) the new Vingt-8 by Kari Voutilainen; (4) bladesmith and watchmaker Johan Gustafsson and Patrik Sjögren (GoS) and their Skadi (2); (3) Charles Girardet's Mysterious Tourbillon Fleur de Sel; (5) Ferdinand Berthoud's masterful Chonomètre FB 2RE; (6) Stepan Sarpaneva's tribute to the Moomin Family comic figures.

PAUL FORREST
SWISS MADE
SCAN QR CODE TO SEE OUR DIAMOND HEART COME TO LIFE
42 JEWEL MOVEMENT WOUND WITH CLASP

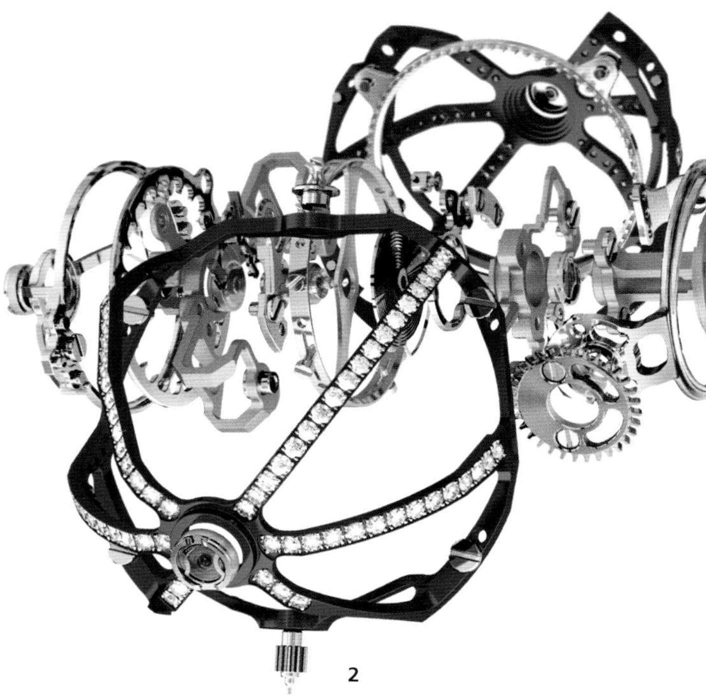

2

1

1 Romain Gauthier reveals more with deep skeletonizing.

2 Purnell's fireworks include two triple-axis tourbillons, six mainsprings, and four barrels.

3 Struthers's Project 248 in the making.

interesting look is topped off by a luminescent blue mother-of-pearl dial and Damascus steel bridges added to the modified ETA Unitas movement visible through the transparent case back.

In Switzerland, independent par excellence **Romain Gauthier** introduced the Insight Micro-Rotor Squelette Carbonium in 2020, adding a new case material to his first automatic watch line. But while this watch might seem very similar to the other versions in this line, it is in fact quite different now that as much material as possible has been removed from the movement, creating very minimal, esthetic skeletonizing on every plate and bridge; the Insight Micro-Rotor Squelette's movement now features an incredible 156 internal angles! The use of "upcycled" carbonium in the case and dials adds even more lightness to the watch, both esthetically and in terms of real weight. The entire effect is superb.

Purnell, whose esthetic concept aims at making visible as much of the mechanical hijinks inside as possible, introduced the Escape II Double Tourbillon in 2020. This prolific wristwatch focuses almost all its energy on two enormous spherical triple-axis tourbillons and a lot of negative space. Featuring six mainsprings in four spring barrels (stacked two and two), one of the most outrageous elements of this watch is the fact that spherical tourbillon cages can be set with diamonds.

ALBION RISING

Heading across the Channel, two English watchmakers introduced new watches in 2020. The husband-and-wife team of **Struthers** introduced its Project 248: referring to the 2 minds, 4 hands, and 8-millimeter watchmaker's lathe they are using to make the first run of five watches, this project encompasses the duo's first in-house movement set to feature a new and improved English lever escapement and a German silver top plate inspired by an 1880s English pocket watch.

3

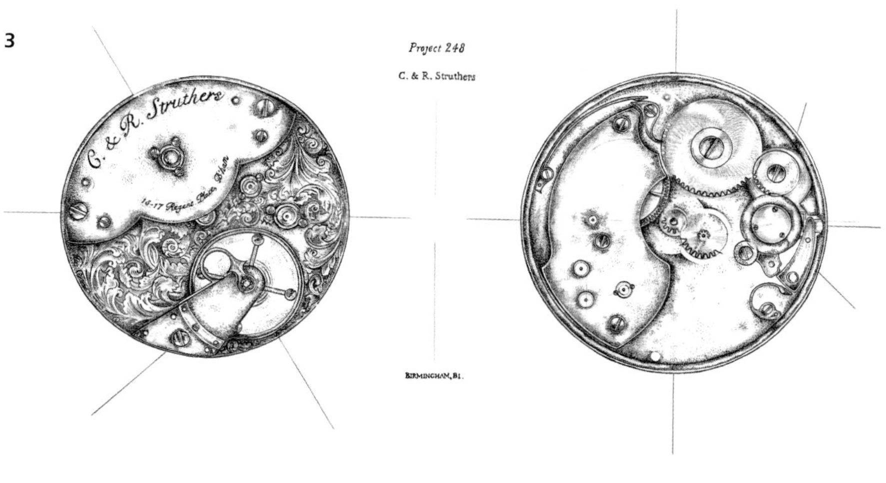

1

2

Garrick presented the S3, an exceedingly captivating open-dialed timepiece powered by a movement developed in collaboration with AHCI member Andreas Strehler. Its look belies the raw power of the movement and focuses on minimal elements to hammer its point home while staying within the loose confines of traditional English watchmaking.

In the lower price ranges, Japan's premier independent watchmaker, **Hajime Asaoka**, who handmakes less than a handful of watches in a year, launched **Kurono Tokyo** in 2019, an affordably priced sub-brand designed by Asaoka that concentrates on the Japanese watchmaker's esthetic codes but utilizes purchased components and movements.

AHCI

The heart piece of the independent scene is the AHCI (Académie Horlogère des Créateurs Indépendents/Horological Academy of Independent Creators), a group of independent creators founded in 1985. The way of these individualistic watchmaker-inventors is indeed anachronistic, and though the products that emerge may not be everyone's cup of tea all of the time, they do attract the attention of collectors of rare taste who follow not only the horological escapades of these 30-odd extraordinary men of varying age and nationality, but also the passion and personality that go into each extremely limited timepiece.

Almost ten years after his last watch, **Bernhard Lederer** introduces the Central Impulse Chronometer, whose movement is built around the concept of the natural escapement invented by Abraham-Louis Breguet and later improved by George Daniels, the purpose of which is to provide the most direct impulse to the balance with the least amount of friction. The Central Impulse Chronometer boasts twin, independent gear trains; each gear train provides one-half of the impulses to the balance wheel every second. A natural escapement is located at the end of each gear train followed by a ten-second remontoir, each providing more consistent force to the natural escapement for a more precise impulse, leading to improved chronometry. The twin gear trains flank the balance wheel, which lies opposite an integrated triple ratchet click winding system, allowing smooth simultaneous winding of each mainspring.

Russian independent **Konstantin Chaykin** brought out the Mars Conquerer in 2020—as well as a new variation of the highly original Joker from the Wristmon line called the

3

1 Konstantin Chaykin's Joker is conquering the world.

2 Bernhard Lederer chose a natural escapement for his natural impulse chronometer.

3 A very streamlined movement: Garrick's S3.

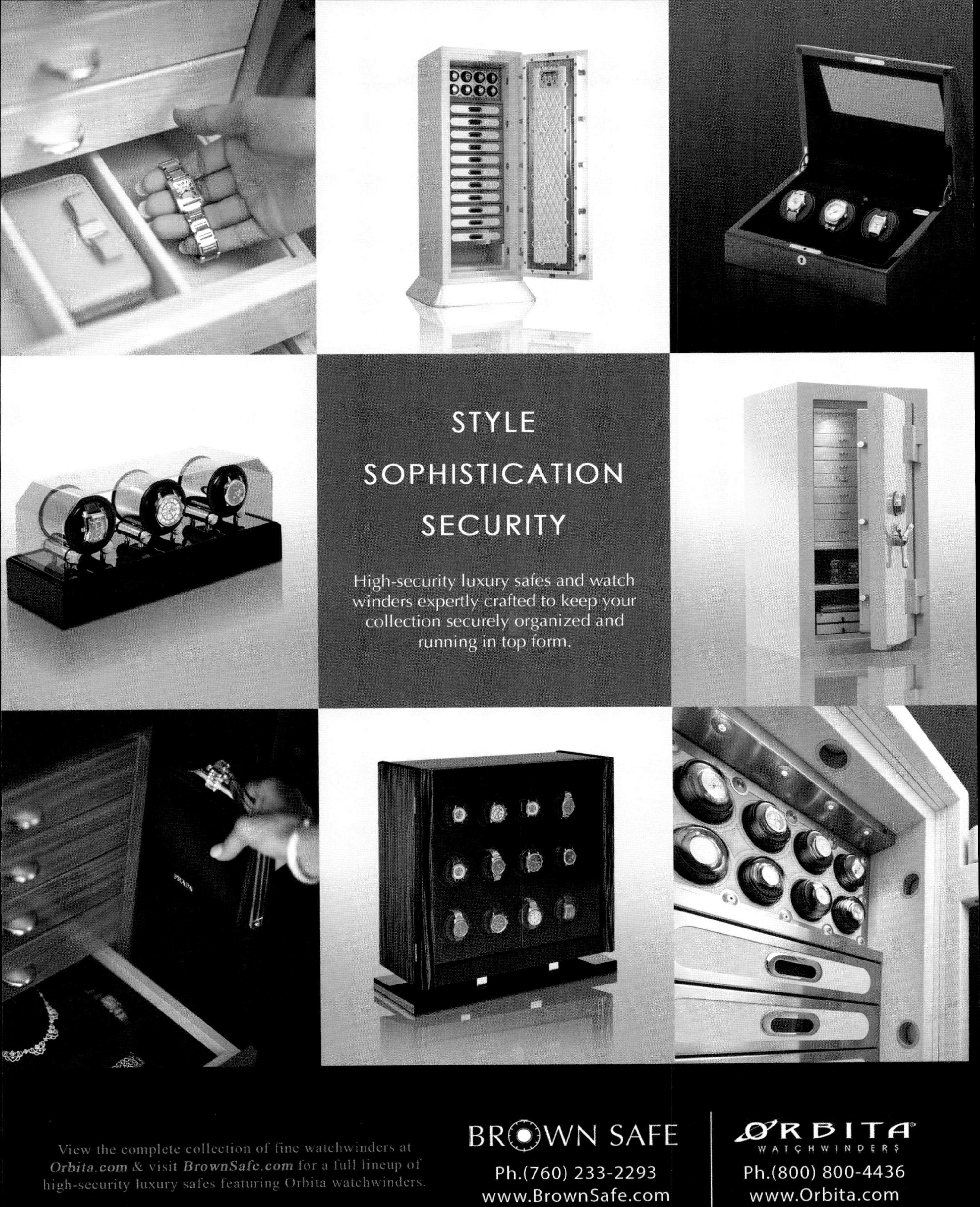
STYLE
SOPHISTICATION
SECURITY
High-security luxury safes and watch winders expertly crafted to keep your collection securely organized and running in top form.
View the complete collection of fine watchwinders at Orbita.com & visit BrownSafe.com for a full lineup of high-security luxury safes featuring Orbita watchwinders.
BROWN SAFE
Ph.(760) 233-2293
www.BrownSafe.com
ORBITA
WATCHWINDERS
Ph.(800) 800-4436
www.Orbita.com

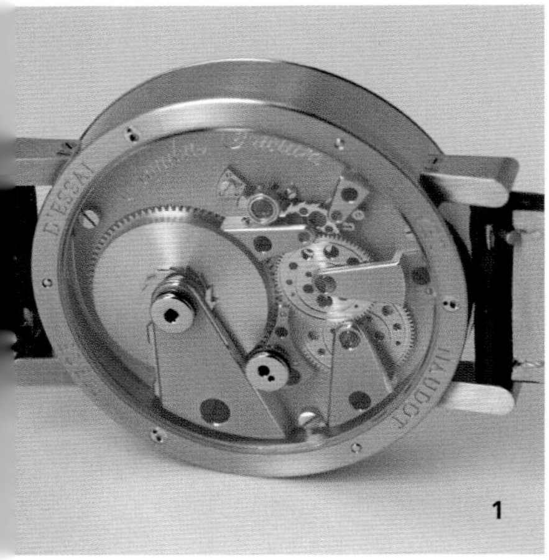

1

2

Mouse King, which combines the Chinese zodiac animal with the fairy tale creature—cleverly crowned by an actual crown.

In other AHCI news, **Marco Lang**, who left his eponymous brand in 2019, was expected to release a new complicated timepiece in a fully different esthetic before the end of 2020 arrives. And just before press time, the news reached us that **Philippe Dufour** has decided to make more of his Simplicity series.

NEWCOMERS

Two notable young independent watchmakers broke out in 2020, entering timepieces in the GPHG and making it through to the final round of the Mechanical Exception category. **Cyril Brivet-Naudot**, an AHCI candidate member, introduced his key-wound Eccentricity. Parisian watchmaker **Theo Auffret**, a winner in 2018 of the F.P. Journe-FHH Young Talent Competition, finalized his Tourbillon à Paris. Both have garnered quite a bit of interest in the community.

But it was perhaps the **Petermann Bédat** team that attracted the most attention at the GPHG, walking away with the Horological Revelation prize for the duo's captivating Seconde Morte timepiece, named 1967 to recall the birth of the quartz watch, with its characteristic second hand "jump." Opposites attract. Gaël Petermann and Florian Bédat, the one a little taciturn, the other loquacious, have known each other since watchmaking school. Their CVs are chock-full of big names—both did long stints at Lange & Söhne, which might explain why their prizewinning first piece features a swan-neck adjustment system. They got the idea to build a dead-beat second complication early on in their collaboration, because it is fairly rare and it has its fans. Also, they were able to tape the knowledge and experience of one of their neighbors at their atelier in Renens, near Lausanne, one Dominique Renaud, of Renaud & Papi fame. There are a number of mechanisms that allow for a dead-beat second—see Habring², for instance, or Arnold & Son. The one chosen by Petermann and Bédat is based on the work of a chaudefonnier watchmaker named Robert Gafner. It features an elegant double anchor looking like an elaborate X. Each side controls a ratchet wheel with deeply angled pallets, a necessity since they otherwise tend to slip out of the ratchet teeth. The one side picks up the energy from the fourth wheel ratchet, while the other side gently nudges the second ratchet wheel, one second at a time. The slow fox-trot of the gears, wheels, and double anchor is contained by a long, fine bridge. The slight arming movement of the system can be seen if you observe the second hand carefully. Before each jump, it takes a little "breath" backward.

Elizabeth Doerr is a freelance journalist specializing in watches and was senior editor of Wristwatch Annual *until the 2010 edition. She is now the editor in chief of* Quill & Pad, *an online magazine that keeps a watch on time (www.quillandpad.com).*

3

The next generation: (1) Cyril Brivet-Naudot's Eccentricity—modern, but with a winding key; (2) a tourbillon to catch the eye; and (3) Gaël Petermann and Florian Bédat started with a deadbeat second.

BALL
OFFICIAL STANDARD
Since 1891
Accuracy under adverse conditions
CHROMED CERAMIC BEZEL
CERTIFIED SWISS CHRONOMETER (COSC)
AUTOMATIC HELIUM RELEASE VALVE
WATER RESISTANT TO 600M (2,000 FT)
REVOLUTIONARY MICRO GAS LIGHTS
SHOCK RESISTANT TO 7,500 GS

1

TIMEWORKS

MARTON RADKAI

On their way from the belfry to the wrist, time-telling devices made a number of stops, where they then flourished into separate but related industries. One of these was the table clock, a device with its own special rules and attributes.

2

1 A table! Clocks by Cartier (left), MB&F (center), and unknown Black Forest clockmakers (Junghans Museum).

2 Hypermodern time-tellers by Hautlence.

3 The old-fashioned clock. *(Photo by Jordan Benton from Pexels)*

The relationship between human beings and time is fraught with questions, doubts, jittery certainties, and physics. Time is truly an ephemeral dimension that can hardly be conceived, grasped, even defined, since it has no body, but merely shows itself by virtue of the transformation of physical manifestations.

St. Augustine (354–430) famously noted that he knew what time was, but when asked, could not describe it. Centuries and thousands of pages later, two brilliant minds, Albert Einstein and the French philosopher Henri Bergson, clashed over the meaning of time. The unresolved conflict is described by scholar and historian of science Jimena Canales in her 2015 book *The Physicist and the Philosopher: Einstein, Bergson and the Debate That Changed Our Understanding of Time*. In a nutshell, she points out that Einstein basically said that time was what the clock said, and Bergson argued that time was more than just the division of the day into equal segments and that without a prior notion of time, clocks would be "bits of machinery with which we would amuse ourselves." Knowing what time it is for Bergson, as Canales points out, "presupposed that the correspondence between the clock and an 'event that is happening' was meaningful for the person involved so that it commanded their attention." In other words, consciously or subconsciously, time for us humans is not just some figure in a vacuum. It means something. The question: What?

Those who manufacture, market, or collect timepieces would probably argue that they are more than just time-tellers. Humans get fascinated by many different things, from other humans to orchids and everything between, including Time (capital T). Which is why, from the clepsydra to the wristwatch, humans have long tried to capture Time in oftentimes elaborate casings: because Time for them means more than just daily routines. The history of interior decorating is filled with clocks that either hung on walls and kept the family on its toes or sat on tables, desks, and mantelpieces, delighting their owners with their ticking or any other animations. The

3

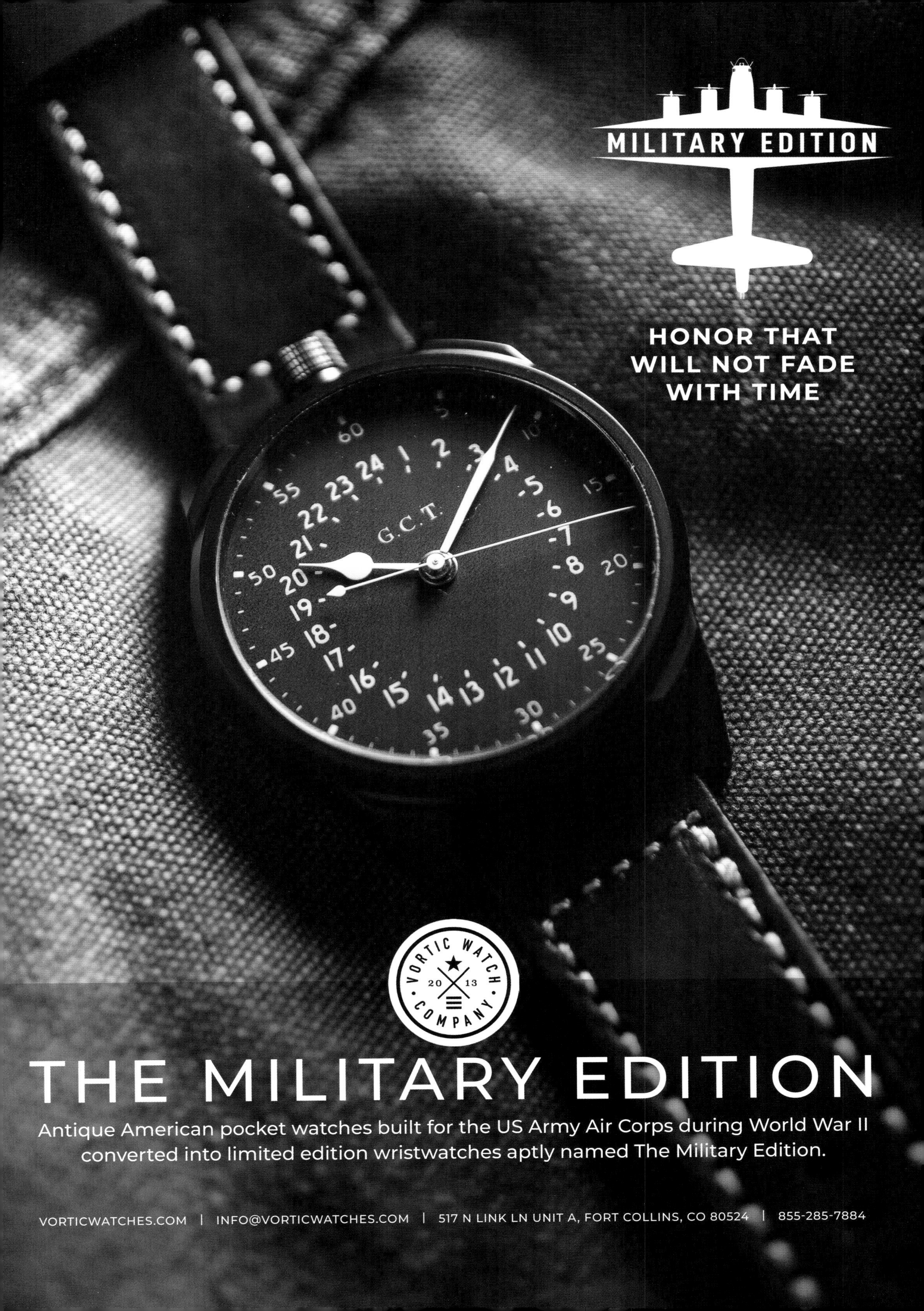
MILITARY EDITION
HONOR THAT WILL NOT FADE WITH TIME
G.C.T.
VORTIC WATCH COMPANY
20 13
THE MILITARY EDITION
Antique American pocket watches built for the US Army Air Corps during World War II converted into limited edition wristwatches aptly named The Military Edition.
VORTICWATCHES.COM | INFO@VORTICWATCHES.COM | 517 N LINK LN UNIT A, FORT COLLINS, CO 80524 | 855-285-7884

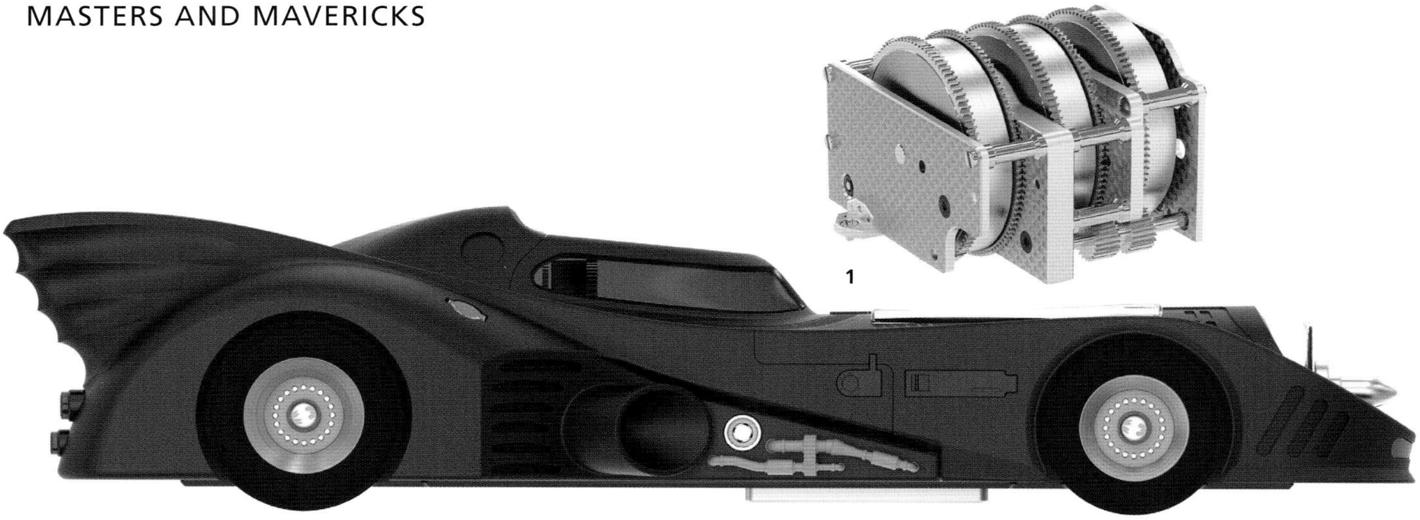

1

1 Studio Kross and Disney: the Batmobile with a three-barrel engine.

2 Jaeger-LeCoultre's enduring Atmos powered by changing temperatures.

watch is a personal friend; the clock is part of the home and hearth.

CAPTIVE TIME

Clockmaking is alive and well, though living somewhat in the shadow of the advertising budgets for watches. There are commercially available, low-cost table clocks to be had, naturally, just as there are mass-produced watches with quartz movements inside. Many people these days wake up to a digital alarm clock, after all, because it does what Einstein said a clock should do: tells time, and without ticking next to your ear all night. The focus here is more on a mechanical clock and its special relationship to the owner and particularly to the manufacturers. Take Mario Tedeschi, CEO of Kross Studio in Geneva. He had never made a clock before being asked by Warner Brothers Consumer Products division to create a limited edition Batmobile clock. "It was a niche product," Tedeschi told me in an interview, "and the challenge was too good to resist. The result is Tim Burton's 1989 vehicle, equipped with a triple-barrel clock running at 21,000 vph inside for a thirty-day power reserve. During the conversation I had the distinct impression that this was not the last clock Studio Kross would be making.

Clocks have a different set of esthetic and engineering rules. "A table clock is not worn on the hand," says Konstantin Chaykin, who is known for wristwatches with stunning animations, like the Cinema. "But a table clock has to complete an interior space, and so has to fit the decorating style correctly." It's one reason he finds it more difficult to sell watches—because clocks have buyers "who want to find a gift for someone or who order something unusual for themselves." Not only will a clock give time, but its style will have meaning for the owner. Are you Art Deco, Art Nouveau, or Baroque? Does hygge reflect your personality, or do you prefer steampunk? Clockmakers have something to slake that desire, and by putting a mechanical clock inside, they are in some ways giving it life.

You might be surprised to find that your favorite brands do produce clocks that epitomize the design concept of the brand as a whole. Jaeger-LeCoultre's Atmos line of table clocks is actually older than the genuinely iconic Reverso. Maintaining the attraction of these timepieces, which began as high-end carriage clocks in 1928, has been quite a feat, precisely because taste in interior decorating is to an extent less conservative than taste in watches. What is most intriguing with the Atmos is surely the fact that winding is done by a gas-filled vessel that expands and contracts with changing temperature and activates a set of bellows. A one-degree centigrade fluctuation in temperature delivers power for two days. The last three Atmos clocks have been designed in a collaboration with the Marc Newson studio. The latest comes enclosed in a Baccarat crystal case that gives the mechanism the feeling of floating in space.

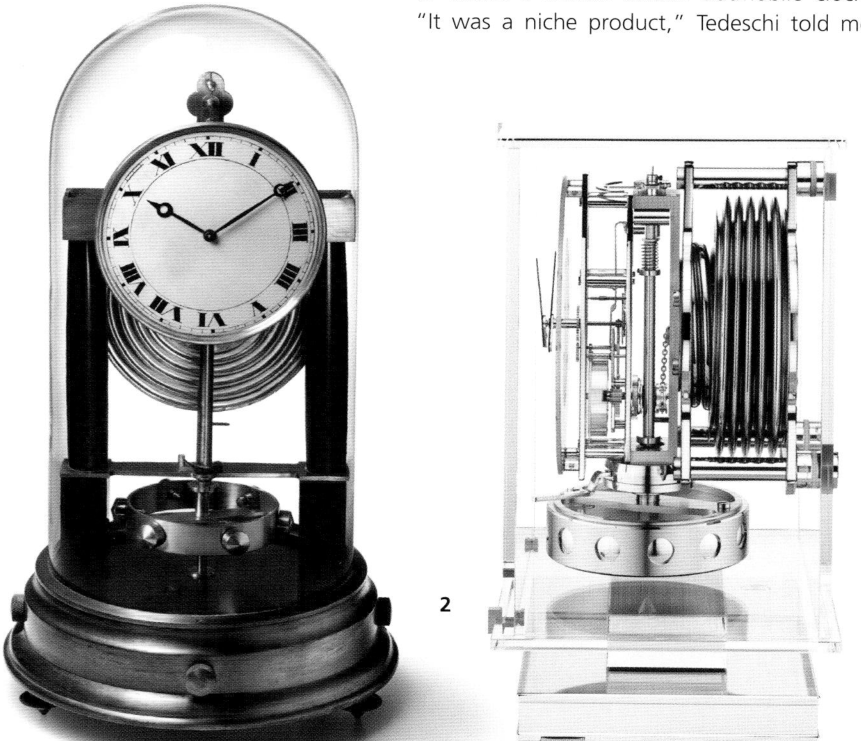

2

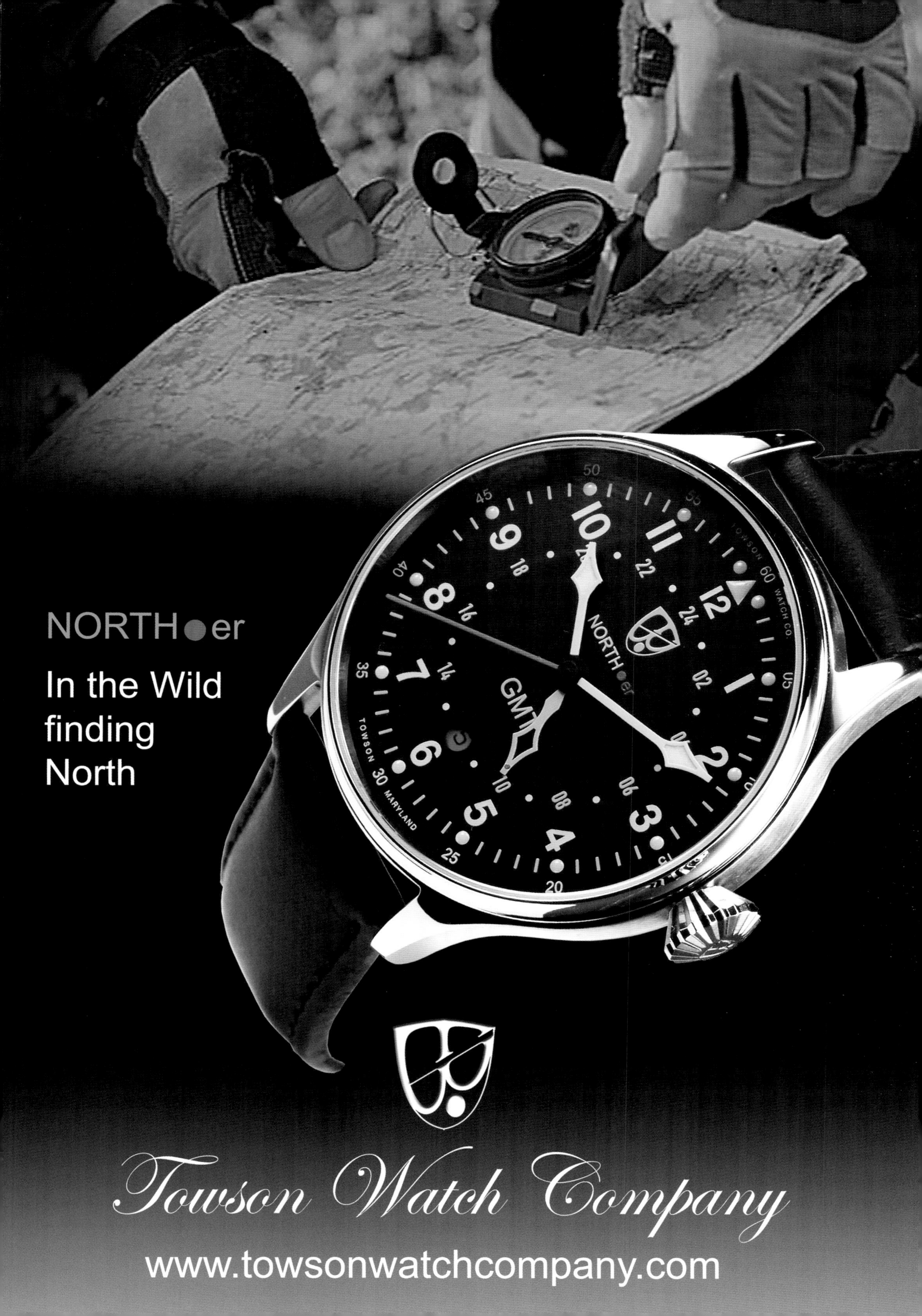

NORTHer
In the Wild
finding
North
Towson Watch Company
www.towsonwatchcompany.com

1

2

Parmigiani is another brand that revels in clockmaking not only to express its technical prowess, but also as a connection to the brand's basic Art Deco flavor. In 2012, the brand launched a collaboration with Lalique to make a fine carriage clock with crystal panels decorated with the typical Fontaine Courtard motif that was a Lalique hallmark back in the 1920s. The mechanism has a power reserve of fifteen days, and the power reserve indicator is connected to the Maltese cross that prevents overwinding. This device has been placed outside the spring barrel.

Rather courageously, Carl Suchy, a young brand that sought its design codes in Austrian architecture of the early twentieth century, also decided to come out with a clock that connects spiritually to the great modernist movement spearheaded by Adolf Loos and Josef Hofmann. The 13-pound Table Waltz is actually a minute and hour repeater that can be silenced if need be. Its vaulted shape recalls the rounded corners of Loos's furniture. It features a variety of materials, such as specially coated brass and silver for the bell. The hand-engraved and cut glass was made by Lobmeyer, a company that had already served the imperial court, as did the original Carl Suchy, and Adolf Loos.

MASTERS OF TIME

The world of clocks is quite diverse. Some manufacturers, such as those mentioned above or the likes of Cartier and Patek Philippe, will focus on design, while others will seek to exhibit their technical prowess—Sattler, a German brand, comes to mind. Others feel the draw of the greenfield, that slightly unsettling impulse to create something from scratch without any predefined form. The artist-engineer is free to make the shape he or she wants. And so the clock becomes an expression of skill and imagination combined.

A recent candidate for the AHCI, John-Mikaël Flaux, who lives in Besançon, France, has been making automatons since childhood. He worked with such brands as Ulysse Nardin and then left the corporate world to give his imagination free rein. His first creations were cars, notably a model based on 1950s race cars, the Time Fury 18. The winding is done in one of the exhaust pipes, while the time is set using a wheel. But watch out: The car will move along the table at about 13 millimeters per hour. Flaux's second major project is even more ambitious: a repeater whose various components are arranged in the shape of a running cheetah.

For Flaux, clocks must tell a story and connect with the owner. Cars are almost typical objects when trying to achieve this goal. Plus, they relate to mechanisms through precise

3
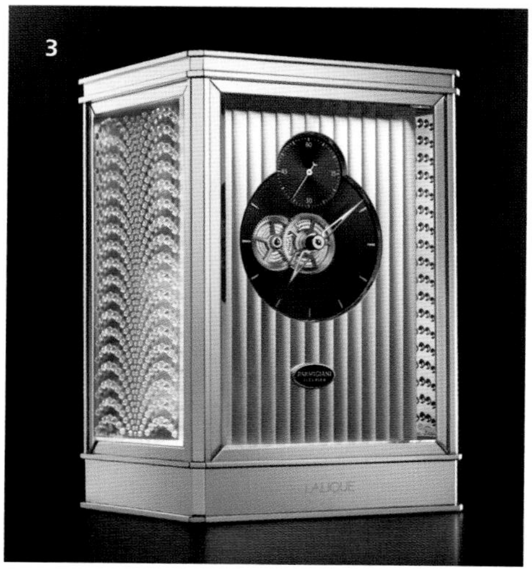

1 John-Mikaël Flaux, builder of clever time-telling automatons.

2 Carl Suchy's Table Waltz keeps the heyday of Viennese design alive.

3 Parmigiani's clocks would fit in the 1930s: above the Lalique carriage clock.

DETROIT WATCH COMPANY
PONTCHARTRAIN
Pontchartrain 1701 Moonphase
42mm case, Swiss automatic
Eta 7751. Exhibition caseback
Exclusively Designed and Assembled by
Detroit Watch Company-Pontchartrain
EXPLORE THE COLLECTION AT
WWW.DETROITWATCHCO.COM
Copyright © 2021, Detroit Watch Company, LLC, All Rights Reserved

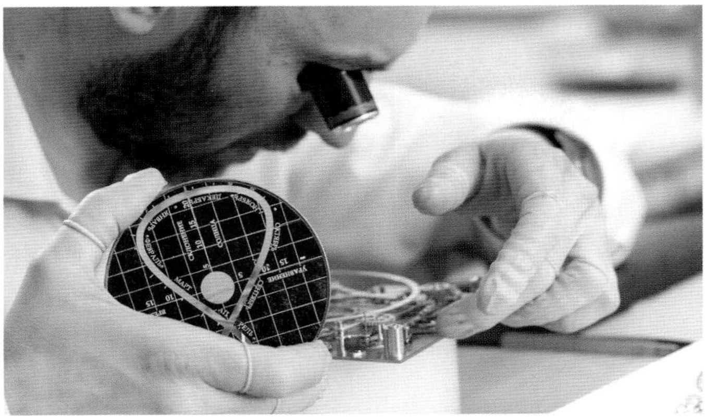

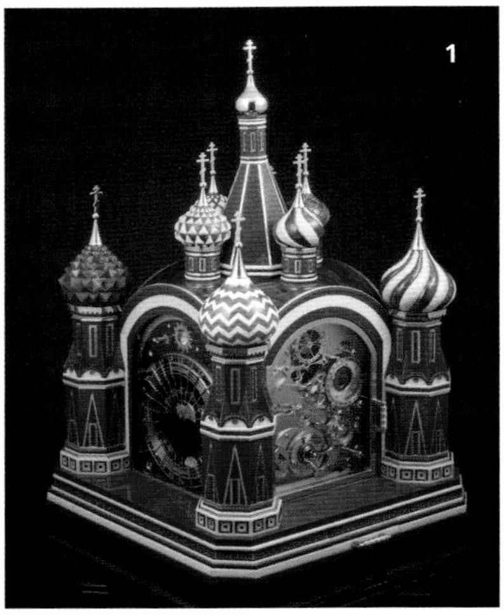

engineering. And Time has a close relationship with speed as well. But there are also other sources of inspiration, like religious traditions. Konstantin Chaykin has built clocks that boast staggering complications. He began his career with one incorporating an indicator of the Orthodox Easter. "I know very well where to start, how to build the clock, and what elements and form it should contain," he told me. "The architectural form of my clocks is very often based on certain architectural models." His first complication developed into the Moscow Computus, a representation of St. Basil's Cathedral built of stones and filled with hair-raising complications on four dials: an analemma showing the movement of the sun through the year, an orbital moon, sunrise and sundown notification, indication of Russia's eleven time zones, world time, the Orthodox Easter—which is at the core of the mechanism's 2,500 components. He also has a visual and aural signal telling the owner when to rewind the clock. Chaykin went on to build a Muslim clock, the Hijra, and a Jewish clock, the Sabbat, each of which represented daunting technical challenges of its own due to the different calendars.

FANTASTIC TIME

Beyond thematic clocks, there are those that are just pure imagination, a clock for clock's sake, one might say. Artists like Miki Eleta have built contraptions that defy the imagination. The entire engine is the clock; space no longer plays a role for these sprawling creations. The beholder is lost in time and space, while the structures function like a three-dimensional Rorschach test. But no matter how complicated, weird, or crazy a clock, it must be crafted to perfection and function as well; otherwise it will take that small step from the sublime to the ridiculous. And the clock is unforgiving when it comes to quality: "If you

Inspiration from religion and cosmos, or pure fantasy. (1) Konstantin Chaykin and his Computus clock; (2) Miki Eleta makes sculptures out of mechanisms, and they work.

PORSCHE DESIGN
CHRONOMETER CERTIFIED
SWISS MADE

1

have a small wheel and you have some tensile errors in it, it's not a problem," says Arnaud Nicole, CEO and artistic director of L'Epée, which has been producing clocks and clock mechanisms since 1839. "Now multiply that by ten and you have an enormous problem. There are very few suppliers that can even supply material of that level of quality." Furthermore, because the mechanisms are generally visible, not even the slightest error is permitted in the surface finishing.

L'Epée (the official name is L'Epée 1839) manufactures a wide range of mechanical clocks. It is also the owner of two other brands, Suisa and Matthew Norman. There are many reasons why people buy clocks, Nicole suggests, one being the fact that "having a decorative object that gives the time is reassuring. It's something you can understand, because there are gears turning, unlike an electric clock, which is entirely controlled by a chip." L'Epée's portfolio includes a number of "real" objects, like an archetypical 1950s race car, the Time Fast D8, which comes in several colors that use original car paint from the era. The back wheels are the winder, which will remind anyone over a certain age of the old friction motors on toy cars. L'Epée also has a range of more traditional carriage clocks, and some highly complicated, modern table clocks, like the Tour-Billon that will increase the heart rate of fans of deep engineering. Pistol, a project in collaboration with the Unnamed Society, is a diamond-studded Colt Bisley on a stand. What exactly it is supposed to promote is unclear, though the press release suggests connections with Pancho Villa and the Mexican revolution.

DYNAMIC TIME

The name L'Epée may have been less known to watch fans prior to 2014. But the company then entered into an explosively creative partnership with one of the most innovative thinkers in the industry, Max Büsser, founder and head of MB&F (see page 215). "The clock, like the mechanical watch before it, needs to morph from a practical object giving time into a real mechanical art piece," he wrote in an email interview. "By deconstructing traditional clockmaking and reconstructing it into a piece of kinetic art which gives time, we clearly responded to a demand that no one was aware of." Pushing the conception envelope is one of his specialties.

Büsser has always understood how to make powerful statements with watches he calls "machines." These large wrist devices never fail to create a strong bond with the owner and raise eyebrows. They can be fun, like the HM6, a kind of space vessel, or deeply touch-

2

1 L'Epée's range: from the Tour-Billon (top left) to pistols and cars to tell time.

2 Max Büsser (MB&F) and Arnaud Nicolas (L'Epée) first collaborated on the Starfleet Explorer.

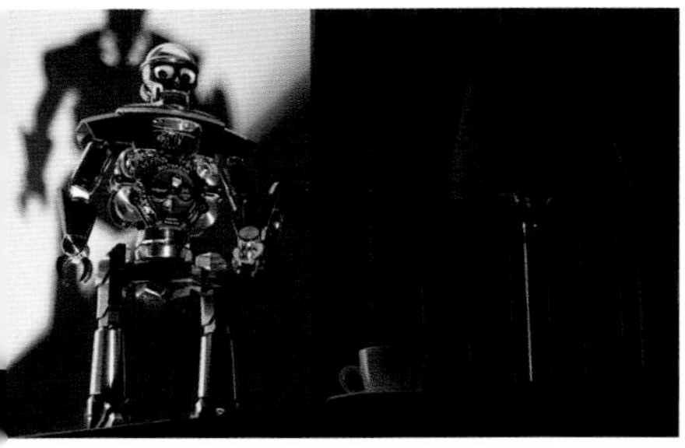

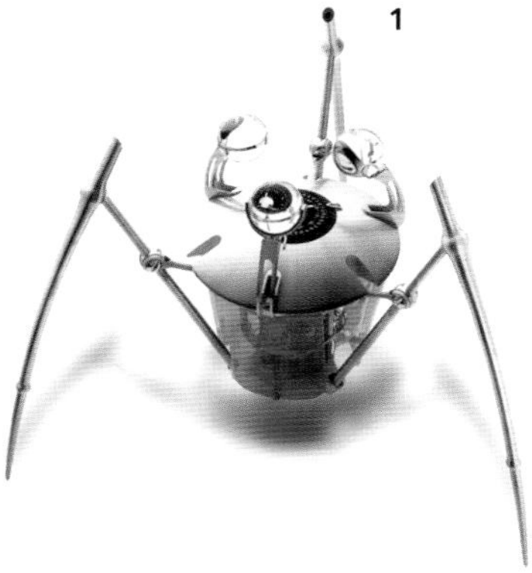

1

ing like the FlyingT in all its iterations, with its little inclined dial under its domed crystal intimately facing the owner. But the creative drive has its own imperatives. Anyone who knows Büsser will also know that there was a single-minded artist, an unruly child, ready to break away from the wrist. "As a creator, clocks give me so much more creative freedom," he says. "No size issue, no water resistance issue, no wearing comfort issue, it is so much more fun and has far fewer boundaries."

The results have probably even surpassed his expectations. The first clock, the Starfleet, opened the floodgates to a series of the most unusual timepieces that basically celebrate all the ideas that continue to inspire and drive MB&F: "Science fiction, robots, animals, they are all themes which resonate with my childhood and I have enjoyed working [with] over the last 15 years." The animals include an extraordinary jellyfish, the Medusa, with its orbiculate body made out of blown Murano glass and available in various colors. It can either stand on delicate glass legs or hang from the ceiling, with the movement inside visible from all sides. The Arachnophobia was inspired by a sculpture of a spider called "Maman," or Mama, that he and Arnaud Nicole saw in Doha: The body is the clock, and the spindly stainless steel legs are not for the faint of heart. Science fiction inspired what Büsser refers to as robocreatures—the TriPod, the T-Rex, and the strangely named Balthazar, a name that ran in his family generations ago, when one of his ancestors determined that all men in the Büsser line would be named after the three wise men, Melchior, Balthazar. or Caspar, a tradition that was changed a few generations ago. At any rate, the workmanship must be and is always top class.

TIME AND TIME AGAIN

The insight that our childhood can influence our choices is basic psychology, but it does bring us back to the idea of time. "Virtually all our L'Epée collaborations have been bought by clients who are not really interested in clocks, and were definitely not planning to purchase a classical clock," says Büsser. Why people disburse tidy sums for such objects is a question that can hardly be answered, but we can summon the spirit of Bergson and Einstein mentioned above. Observing his customers, Büsser notes: "They stem from all over the world and there is no particular sociological trait that differentiates them from others, except maybe that they have remained connected one way or another to their childhood."

And there is another aspect. A clock used as a plain time-giver will keep the rhythm of our days and tell us how much time we have till our next appointment. However, there is another appointment that we usually cannot know, but the beautiful clocks sitting in our homes take us there with every tick and every tock. It reminds us to seize every moment. The French poet Charles Baudelaire expresses this in a dark ode to the clock, which he calls a "sinister god, frightful, impassive, whose finger threatens us and tells us: 'Remember!' "

Threethousandsixhundredtimes per
hour, the Second
Whispers: Remember!—Rapidly, with its
Insect-like voice, Now says: I am Past,
And I sucked out your life with my
abominable trunk!

He may have gotten the hierarchy wrong, because the clock is merely Time's henchman.

2

1 MB&F's clocks are about robots, sci-fi machines, and strange animals.

2 L'Epée's skull clock, a reminder of what happens when our time runs out.

MON 1
AUTOMATIC
200M
Islander
WATCH FEATURES:
• Movement: Seiko NH36 Automatic
• Case: 316L Stainless Steel, 43mm x 14mm thick
• Crystal: Anti-reflective Sapphire
• Bezel: Sapphire luminous bezel insert
• Water Resistant: 200 Meters
• Models Shown: ISL-09 & ISL-10

SHOW OF HANDS

MARTON RADKAI

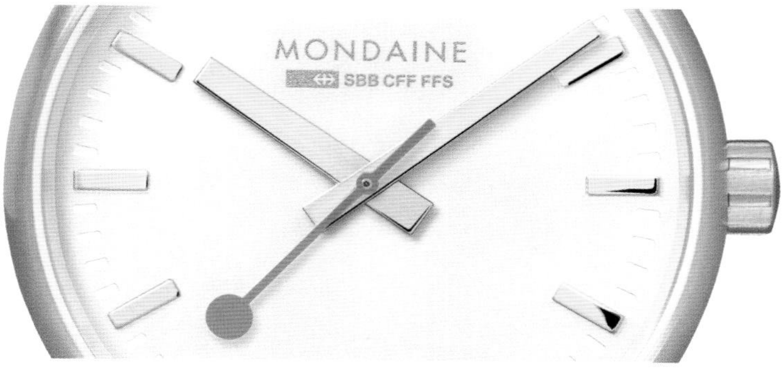

The function of a watch, stripped of all discussions about metaphysics and esthetics, is to give time. But the greatest engine ever beating inside a case will be of no use without the right means to display the time. For most watches, those would be the hands.

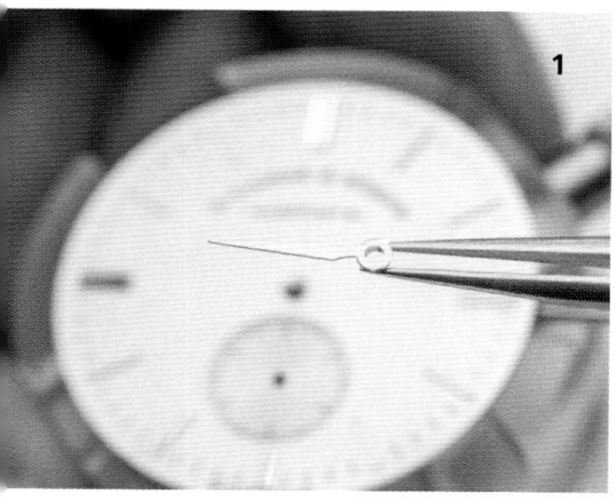

Several years ago, I was invited to see the products of a new brand exhibiting for the first time at Baselworld. These were expensive watches, complicated and imaginative, housed in amazing cases. Obviously, a lot of attention had been paid to detail. But something about one model brought my enthusiasm to a grinding halt, as if someone had just put their hands on a record player. The models I was shown had somewhat stubby, broad, flat, and shiny hands that seemed to cover too much of the dial.

No need to mention the brand, since it would be unfair. Besides, they applied different solutions to other models, such as sanding down one-half of the hand to give it depth or using sleeker hands that did not cover as much space, like open-worked Art Deco hands shaped like the Empire State Building. But it got me thinking about what we sometimes do not really see, even though we are looking.

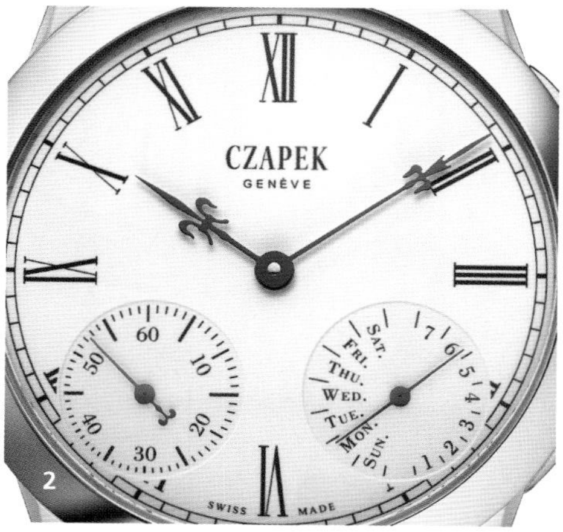

HANDS-ON HANDS

Designing and manufacturing the hands of a watch are difficult. Alexander Peraldi (see interview page 39), who has worked as a designer for several brands, told me that they

1 Lange & Söhne's lancet hand points efficiently.

2 Czapek's fleur-de-lys hands recall the 19th-century DNA of the watch.

3 Clarity above all: the Swiss Railways clock.

The Waldan Heritage Professional, executed in racing green. Individually hand assembled in the United States and powered by an innovative and advanced American built quartz movement, each watch is warrantied for 5 years and fully serviceable. Discover the Waldan story and the new classic.
www.waldanwatches.com
@WaldanWatches
Waldan
WATCHES
SINCE 1979

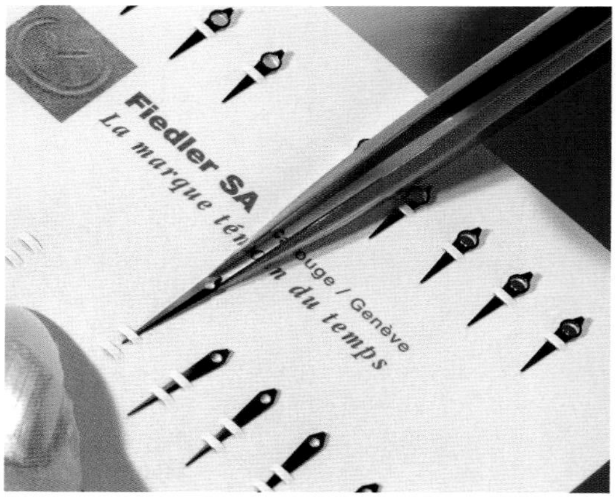

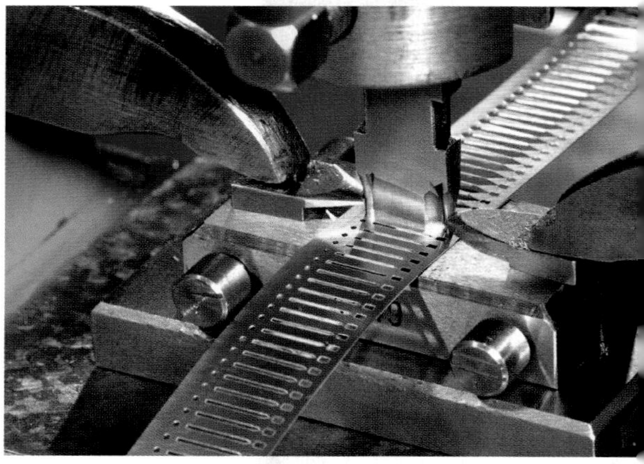

1 The exacting process of hands-making at the family enterprise Fiedler AG; CEO Isabelle Chillier.

Two concepts: ArtyA's artistic dial trumps the hands (2); time at a glance on a Piaget (3).

tend to be last in line for production mainly because one really has to see them on the watch before releasing a new model, and that can mean last-minute changes. "They are like sculptures, they stick out," he says. "The dial and the case have their decoration, the guilloché, for example, but the hands must be clean and perfect." An excellent example of this is, of course, the Mondaine Swiss Railways watch, which was designed originally to be read from afar on station platforms. When the long, rectangular minute hand moves to the rectangular indices, it creates a straight, black, eminently visible line.

The actual manufacturing process is often outsourced simply because of the effort and expense. "There are anywhere between thirty and fifty stages in hand-making," says Isabelle Chillier, owner and CEO of Fiedler SA, one of a few remaining specialized factories in Switzerland. "Some are visible, like the polishing, the machining of the edges, the galvanizing; many are not." The Geneva-based enterprise, which employs about 180 people, has been in her family for four generations already. The company works for many of the top brands but is not allowed to disclose which ones.

The first step following a feasibility study is called *canonage*, which involves stamping out a rough hand including the tubular part at the back that will be friction-fitted onto the cannon pinion that turns the hands. Some hands, particularly the smaller ones on subdials, are fitted with a tube at a later stage. Hands can be made of many different materials: steel, brass, bronze, gold, or even titanium (for lightness). Afterward, they are shaped and polished, and given their coating or treatment if the client demands it. It's all in all an arduous process, with up to 60 percent waste. Because the hands are so exposed, the finishing must be absolutely impeccable, says Isabelle Chillier. "The technical possibilities have changed everything," she continues. "The expectations of the client are higher and the controls are stricter. In the old days they didn't have the measurement methods we have today, so the hands in a series might have been a little different." Another fact she points out is a shift in the culture of customers. Asian buyers, who make up a large segment of the market, are often guided by a philosophy that demands perfection in physical appearance.

CHOOSING THE HAND

Watch hands must give the time, everyone agrees. But they must be an added value to the look of a watch, says Itay Noy (see page 184), who, for over twenty years, has been designing watches that have gathered a fairly strong fan club for their unique look. "They should harmonize with the shape, color, and the sizes of the case, dial, and strap," he told me in a written interview. "They may also have something

1

2

3

Bespoke hands:

1 DeBethune DB21 Maxichrono.

2 Itay Noy ReOrder.

3 Harry Winston Opus X.

4 Kudoke 2 with double pear minute hand.

5 Urban Jürgensen Alfred.

6 Hands change the Reverso: sober pencils vs. sportive dauphines.

more to say about the timepiece, and last but not least they do have to give the time." In his ReOrder, for example, the minute hand looks like a hair-thin tuning fork of sorts, while a short, red seconds hand turns in a recess in the middle of the dial to leave as much space for the hours to appear in their little apertures.

Noy's concept is echoed by many I have spoken to in the industry, in particular one of the mavericks, Denis Flageolet, co-founder of De Bethune (see page 136). "The hands are essential to the whole esthetics of the watch," he says. "I have to draw each hand with respect to the look of the whole. This is how you deduce the full character of the watch just from reading the time."

Flageolet is a radical. The striking watches his company produces in small but exclusive batches are proof enough of his creative and technical derring-do. He believes firmly that unless you make your own hands, you cannot call yourself a *manufacture*.

4

5

Be that as it may: Most brands do outsource to companies like Fiedler, in part because they have their well-established codes, says Alexandre Peraldi, and they will not, and cannot, deviate much from them, since customers usually balk at brands that stray too far from their pedigree. They often resort to standard hands as well, since they are obviously well-tested and effective, but they have to determine the length and whether or not to alter them a little. Some hands even go back to the nineteenth century, like the Breguets with their little round loop just beneath the pointer, or the *poires* with a pear-shaped loop. Urban Jürgensen's Alfred model has an in-house, blued Breguet hour hand with an extra-large loop, for example, which effectively highlights the minute hand as it crosses it. Fans of old pocket watches will see the very decorated hands named after Louis XV and Louis XVI. When it released its first watch, the new brand Czapek did go to the trouble of equipping their Quai des Bergues with fleur-de-lys hands from the model watch they had used for their first-born.

The effect of different hands is well illustrated by Jaeger-LeCoultre's choice of hands. It uses swordlike dauphine hands or slight

6

Aire Parlay GMT Blue Watch.
Case Size: 42mm
Signature RED GOLD(r) Collection.
CHRIS AIRE

1

2

variations thereof for its Masters and Reverso lines. These pointy hands with a raised crest are fairly common, because they meet numerous demands. They were made by Universo in 1930 and have become genuine reference points for the consumer. The long tapering triangle draws the eye dynamically from the center of the dial toward the numerals. Compare with the more staid "pencil" hands on the Polaris line, which are essentially rectangular with a triangular tip. These hands are used to great effect on the Reverso Classic models, which is a touch less sportive than the Reverso Tribute line, perhaps because they are in tune with the geometric lines and the right angles of the watch dial.

Cathedral hands will be familiar to many, especially collectors of military-style watches. The hour hand billows into an oval divided into three compartments, much like a stained-glass window with a needle end that rests over the numerals, while the minute hand is long and rectangular. This offers extra space for luminescent materials. Other tool watches, like pilot's and diver's watches also focus on strong visibility and usually have larger hands, sometimes with a slit down the middle. This can be clearly seen on the Panerai Luminor Submersibles, for example, or many Hanhart watches. Companies like Ball and Deep Blue even have space for tritium gas tubes on the hands to ensure bright and continuous illumination. Some have even become icons in their own right, like the "snowflake" hands that Tudor used on its diver's watches for the French and American navies and which are now on the Black Bay and Pelagos lines. This lozenge filled with Superluminova on the hour hand may not be to everyone's liking, but it identifies the brand from afar.

MAKING A MARK

Most brands, even the high-end ones, seem perfectly content with tapping into the huge world of existing watch hands. Other brands

Hands for lighting:

1 Hanhart's Primus (left) with syringe hands and Pioneer with cathedral hands (right).

2 The Panerai Luminor Submersible.

3 Tudor snowflakes: more than a logo.

4 Ball watches are lit by tritium gas–filled tubes.

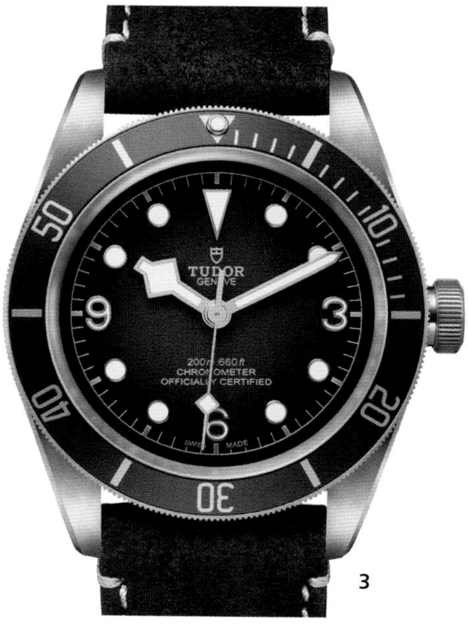

3

4

HANDY FACTS:

Watches started out by having only hour hands. The minute hands came at the end of the seventeenth century.

The second hand was added but only because it indicated visually that the watch was working and for doctors to take a person's pulse.

The rear section of the seconds hand reaches across the cannon pinion to improve balance.

The standard "ten past ten" hands position forms a smile on the dial and does not hide the logo.

Finally, have you ever wondered where the clockwise direction came from? The answer: The sundial in the northern hemisphere. The sun crossing from east to west made the shadow of the gnomon "turn" from left to right.

1

2

3

4

use the hands almost as a logo, like Tudor, mentioned above. The hour, minute, and power reserve hands on F.P. Journe's watches, for instance, are shaped like long, stretched-out drops ending in an elegant tip, and they scream Journe. Laurent Ferrier has chosen hands shaped like an assegai, narrow at the start and bulging slightly toward the middle, before tapering to a point. It is unique to his brand. And who can forget the knife-shaped hands on several collections *chez* ArtyA?

Some watches have even made the hands an integral part of the story they are telling. Ulysse Nardin's Freak and Azimuth's Predator, two models that have a strong resemblance, have totally integrated the movement and hands and turned the dial into a science fiction tale. Vacheron Constantin had a watch called Mercator, whose hands were a divider pointing to a retrograde minute and retrograde hour scale. It was a bit hard to read, but the idea was thrilling. And finally, in this short list of amazing hands, one needs to mention the double retrogrades invented by Thomas Prescher, where rising and falling scimitars, samurai swords, dragons, a geisha, or any number of birds point to the minutes and hours.

There is no single philosophy of watch hands. How time is indicated is a world of its own and could fill books. I merely touched on the minute and hour hands and how they are made, with just a passing reference to other hands. They all have their own requirements. The ultimate goal, however, was to give an introduction and to raise awareness of this aspect of watch design, which has a special fascination and occasionally falls through the cracks.

Special hand:

1 Bovet's squiggly hands fit the engraving.

2 Normal is not in ArtyA's vocabulary.

3 F.P. Journe's watches demand a special hand.

4 Ulysse Nardin's eternal Freak.

5 Thomas Prescher's Geisha offers time and beauty.

5

DESIGNING HANDS

Alexandre Peraldi was director of design at Baume & Mercier for seventeen years and head of watch design at Cartier for another thirteen. In 2018, he went freelance to widen his horizons and work on other product families.

Marton Radkai: *How do you go about designing the hands?*

Alexandre Peraldi: It's actually the most difficult part, because the hands always come at the end. First you draw the case, the dial, the strap, and you outline the hands, but they are really the last things you will draw. It's tough, because you don't have much time to make a prototype, we don't have the time to test ten different examples.

MR: *Are there any guidelines you can follow?*

AP: Hands must be readable. I see many younger designers who don't respect the proportions. What they're doing is great, but you can't read the time. And that is the key. Sometimes there are just indices and no numbers, so it is up to the hands to give you the time.

MR: *Is there some Golden Rule you can follow?*

AP: I did speak to technicians who suggested a ratio that was supposed to be exact, but in the end, it's your eye and experience that is the judge. For example, if you enlarge the hour hand, it does not have to be as long anymore. There are all sorts of details that will impact that ratio, like the location of the minute chapter ring, the dial, and so on.

MR: *Doesn't it depend on the watch?*

AP: Yes, because the hands are in fact just another part of the whole watch. With a very sparsely furnished dial, for example, the hands will become extremely important. In my career as a watch designer, I often had to change the hands at the end, because they took up too much space on the dial. Or they were just too drab for everything around it.

MR: *What are the challenges facing major brands?*

AP: At Cartier, there was not much leeway because they had two or three codes. At Baume & Mercier every watch had its style. We looked through old models, some just drawings, that were difficult to replicate even with today's technologies.

MR: *A luxury brand is less adventurous?*

AP: Cartier has survived with Roman numerals and stick hands for over a century. The smaller brands or new ones are exploring and being very creative until they find the thing that really catches on, then they'll evolve with that.

MR: *Have you ever seen watches that simply failed on the market?*

AP: Sometimes you see a watch with a well-designed case, the hands and the dial are each well done, but the three elements don't fit together. And the year after, it's gone. It's not surprising, as Raymond Lœwy [French-American industrial designer] said: "Ugly sells poorly." Okay, sometimes you see something abominable that sells, but it's for other reasons. It's exceptional, it might have a great movement. But ultimately people will tire of it.

MR: *When do you know you have a perfect set of hands?*

AP: When they are perfect, and that's complicated. I've borrowed a saying by Antoine de St. Exupéry: "You've reached perfection not when there's nothing more to add, but when there's nothing more to remove." It's tough to design something beautiful, but it is also tough to improve something that's mediocre. And you have to be able to delay a project if that happens.

MR: *So, you have to slaughter the golden calf.*

AP: Exactly.

REGULATION

MARTON RADKAI

Since the earliest days of applied horology, scientists, engineers, dabblers, and tinkerers have done their best to achieve precision in time-telling. Perfection is impossible, of course, but on the way, they have devised all sorts of fascinating mechanisms to mitigate the nefarious impact of plain old physics and gravity.

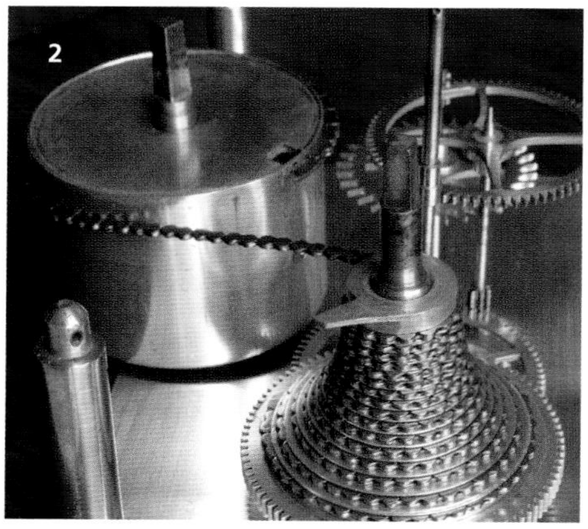

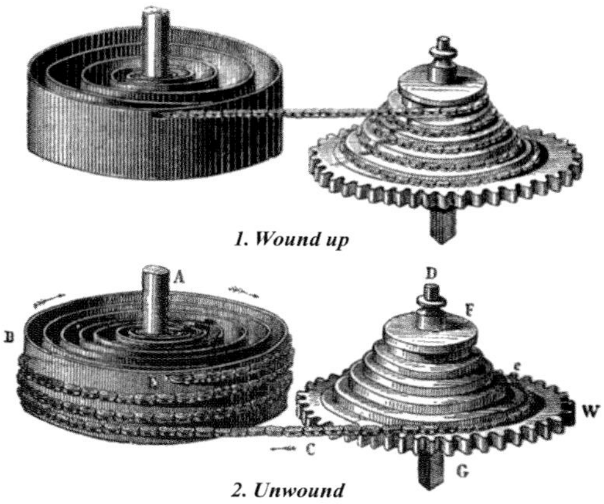

It may be a frightful simplification, but at its very core, watchmaking, and indeed mechanics, can be summed up as an obsessive confrontation with the necessity of controlling energy delivered to a system that is supposed to divide units of time into equal portions. The history is fascinating. In the thirteenth century, a mechanism was invented for tower clocks to regulate the force generated by dropping weights. The verge and foliot (VF) involved stopping and releasing a crown-shaped escape wheel with two pallets attached to a rod (verge) placed horizontally across the wheel. The oscillation of a cross-beam (the foliot) at the top of the verge could be adjusted by moving weights at each end.

SHIFTING GOALPOSTS

The mainspring as a source of power was then developed in the first half of the fifteenth century. It allowed watchmakers to miniaturize movements and pack them into smaller watches, but it also created a new set of challenges. One was uncontrolled power from the spring; the other was too little as the spring unwound. So the regulators needed regulation, a mechanism to make the force coming from the spring more constant.

One solution was the stackfreed (derived from *starke Feder*, a strong spring), which used a kind of leaf spring to press a wheel onto a cam that mechanically absorbed any excess power coming from the driving spring. At about the same time, in the late fifteenth century, a clever and simple mechanism was invented that would soon put paid to the stackfreed: the so-called fusée and chain. Imagine a bicycle chain ring at the pedals and the cone-shaped gear sprockets set on the back wheel that picks up the cyclist's energy. The strong torque at the beginning of the spring's energy release pulls the small gear, and gradually, as the torque weakens, the chain winds onto the larger, lower

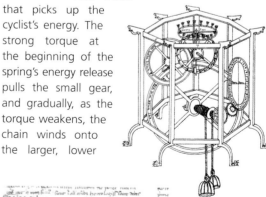

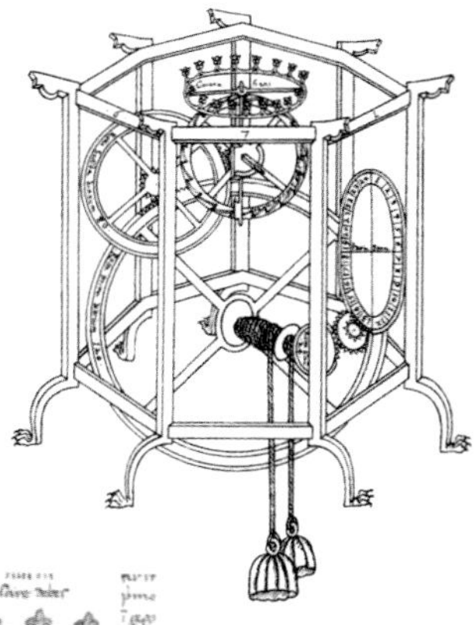

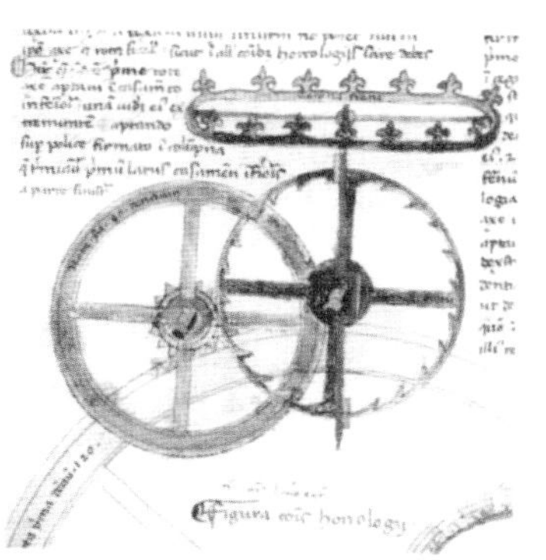

1 Philip the Good's famous clock (circa 1430) featuring a verge and foliot escapement.

2 Tried and true: fusée and chain mechanisms equalize the torque.

3 Early design (circa 1364) of verge and foliot mechanisms by Giovanni de Dondi.

1

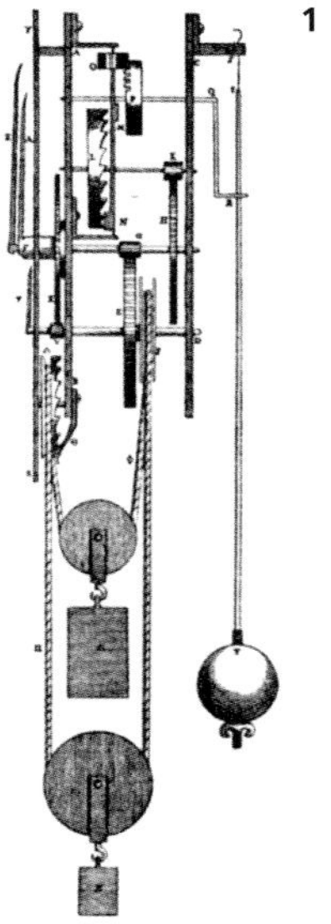

section, just as a bicycle chain does when you switch to lower gears. It was not ideal, but it was good enough to equalize the energy from a mainspring for centuries in clock towers and later in pocket watches.

Meanwhile an almost unknown scientist and mathematician from the region of Toggenburg in Switzerland was building complex astronomical clocks and working on his own systems to control the flow of energy. The peripatetic Jost Bürgi (1552–1632), who is known for having contributed to the concept of logarithms, built a verge with a *second* foliot that moved in the opposite direction to increase stability and precision. He also added a separate sprung mechanism that would collect the energy from the verge and dispense it in even bursts. This is a key idea behind constant force devices.

A NEW ERA

In 1656, Christiaan Huygens built his famous pendulum clock based on a concept by Galileo, which vastly increased the precision of clocks. It was followed by two other seminal horological inventions that would further improve mechanical time-telling, namely the anchor escapement and the hairspring. These provided the necessary predictability to the movements, and they offered an even greater opportunity to make "portable" watches.

The need for constant force to maintain the amplitude of the balance wheel remained, however, and other systems were devised. For his H4 marine chronometer, John Harrison thought of placing a secondary winding mechanism between the mainspring and the escapement. It would get wound up every seven and a half minutes and dish out the energy in neat, equal portions, a concept which would be further refined in the twenty-first century, as we'll see.

2

Another very clever mechanism was invented at about the same time. The Geneva stop-work or Maltese cross allows for only the "best" section of the mainspring to be used for power. It is composed of two components, each screwed onto the spring barrel. The one on the arbor is circular with a recessed stem; the other is shaped like a Maltese cross, but can have four or more branches, depending on the length of the mainspring. Each branch represents one winding turn, i.e., eight hours of power reserve, but one oddly shaped branch will stop the winding up or down of the spring.

MODERN TIMES

Advances in material science improved the performance of springs and balance wheels in wristwatches and clocks, and gradually disposed of the need for constant force mechanisms. They continued to be used in tower clocks, for example, to compensate for changes in oil viscosity and the impact of the

3

4

1 Christiaan Huygens and his pendulum clock.

2 Jost Bürgi, mathematician, improved the verge and foliot.

3 Marine clock (early 18th century) with fusée and chain mechanism.

4 Geneva stopwork system is visible on a Ferdinand Berthoud.

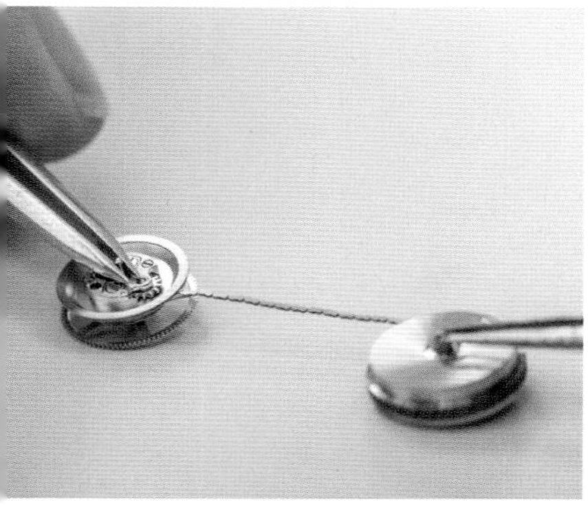

1

weather on heavy hands. Any watchmaker worth their salt, however, will look for some reason to make life more complicated. As for watch fans, many live for the complications.

Not surprisingly, these mechanisms, which have such a rich history, were resuscitated. The first company to build a fusée and chain into a modern watch was Lange & Söhne, in 1994, with its Pour le Mérite. "The chain was like a bicycle chain, but it took a year to make," says Product Manager Anthony de Haas. "The tiny pins holding the links together kept falling out, no one knew how to adjust the chain, so it didn't hang, and finding the right tolerance for the links was impossible." Ultimately, someone came up with the idea of sanding the pins so they would hold by themselves. And a veteran Swiss watchmaker with experience restoring old pocket watches suggested assembling the chain with fine silk paper between the links and setting the paper alight at the end. The paper will burn up, leaving the thinnest of tolerances possible.

Lange added a few extra devices to improve the functioning of the watch—notably, a planetary gear system that permits rewinding without interrupting the power supply. And instead of a simple Geneva stop-work, the company created two separate mechanisms to ensure that only the best torque range of the mainspring is used. This initial attempt was then repeated for the very complicated Tourbograph in 2005 and has since become something of a standard.

Other brands have resorted to the fusée and chain as an expression of can-do. Breguet's Tradition line has the 7047 Tourbillon Fusée with all the traditional codes of the brand. But while Lange and Breguet kept much of the system hidden from the viewer, Zenith placed one fairly boldly on the dial side of its Academy Georges Favre-Jacot, released in 2014 for the company's 150th anniversary. The fusée and chain, which is held in place with angular bridges at the top of the dial, gives a distinctly steampunk look. Only top-notch materials were used, naturally, and the pull of each link of chain was calculated by computer, which allows for optimal functionality. It does make one wonder how the watchmakers of old managed to build these devices.

It took a small, independent watchmaker to think up a solution for innovating the mechanism. In Romain Gauthier's Logical One, every section of the watch seems to have been kept separate for better visibility. Even the spring barrel on the back is open for a viewing. On the left side of the dial is the fusée and chain,

2

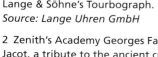

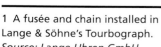

1 A fusée and chain installed in Lange & Söhne's Tourbograph. *Source: Lange Uhren GmbH*

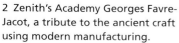

2 Zenith's Academy Georges Favre-Jacot, a tribute to the ancient craft using modern manufacturing.

WEMPE
IRON WALKER
Glashütte I/SA | self-winding diver's watch | stainless steel
certified chronometer | water-resistant to 30 bar | $ 3,450
700 FIFTH AVENUE & 55TH STREET • NEW YORK • 212.397.9000 • WEMPE.COM
HAMBURG BERLIN DUESSELDORF FRANKFURT MUNICH LONDON MADRID PARIS VIENNA

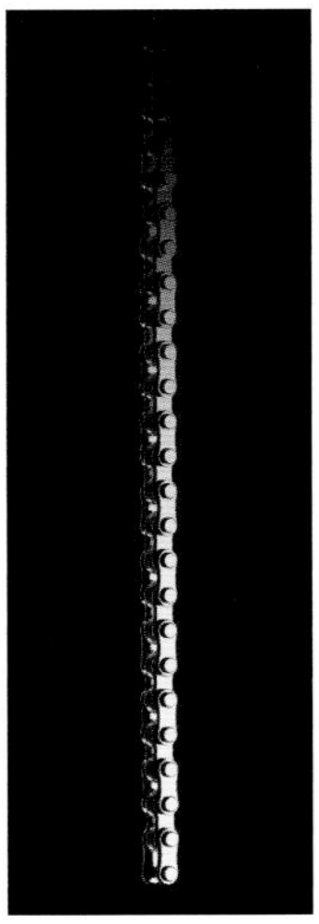

1

1 In Romain Gauthier's Logical One, the fusée and chain are on a single plane.

2 Ferdinand Berthoud's added a remontoir d'égalité to its FB 3RE; it picks up incoming power and delivers it in one second bursts to the balance.

2

reconceived to be on a single plane rather than wandering up and down a wedding-cake-like spindle. The latter was replaced by a snail-shaped cam that slowly draws in the chain without stacking it up. This means a shorter chain, hence larger links, which are made of synthetic ruby—less prone to wear and tear. A pusher-driven winder on the left side ensures easy and smooth winding of the complex device.

GEARING UP

Optimizing the fusée and chain also seemed a worthy idea for Ferdinand Berthoud Chronométrie, a subsidiary of Chopard. Their design includes a groove on the driving barrel to stabilize the unwinding of the chain. Then, in 2020, they released their FB 3RE, which picked up the GPHG Chronometry Prize at the Grand Prix d'Horlogerie in Geneva.

The watch is remarkable. The sober dial belies the engineering beauty of the movement, which can be seen through the transparent case back. Clearly visible at the top are the fusée and chain with the Maltese Cross. In the middle, a large balance wheel. And in the lower third, a strange-looking escapement, the *remontoir d'égalité*, literally an "equalizing winder." It is composed of a small spring mounted coaxially underneath the escape wheel. The spring coils when the arm of a three-pronged component at the top of the escape pinion comes to rest against a pallet affixed to an adjacent pinion. The arm is released when the reuleaux-shaped (a triangle with rounded sides) ruby cam on the escape pinion nudges the pallet fork and releases a second's worth of energy toward the seconds wheel. This way, any unevenness that survived the fusée is, or should be, neutralized. And yes, it does produce a deadbeat second!

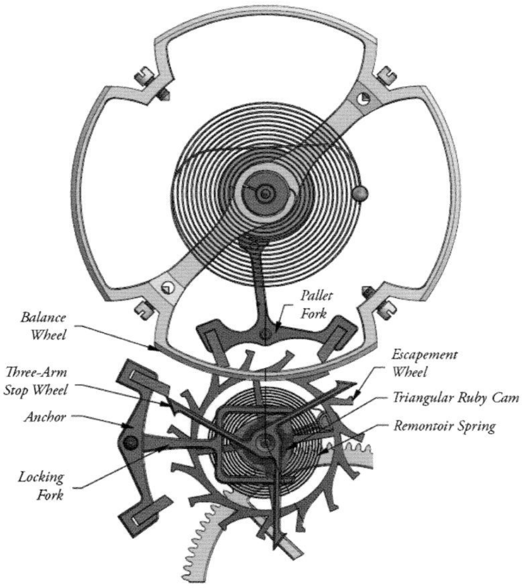

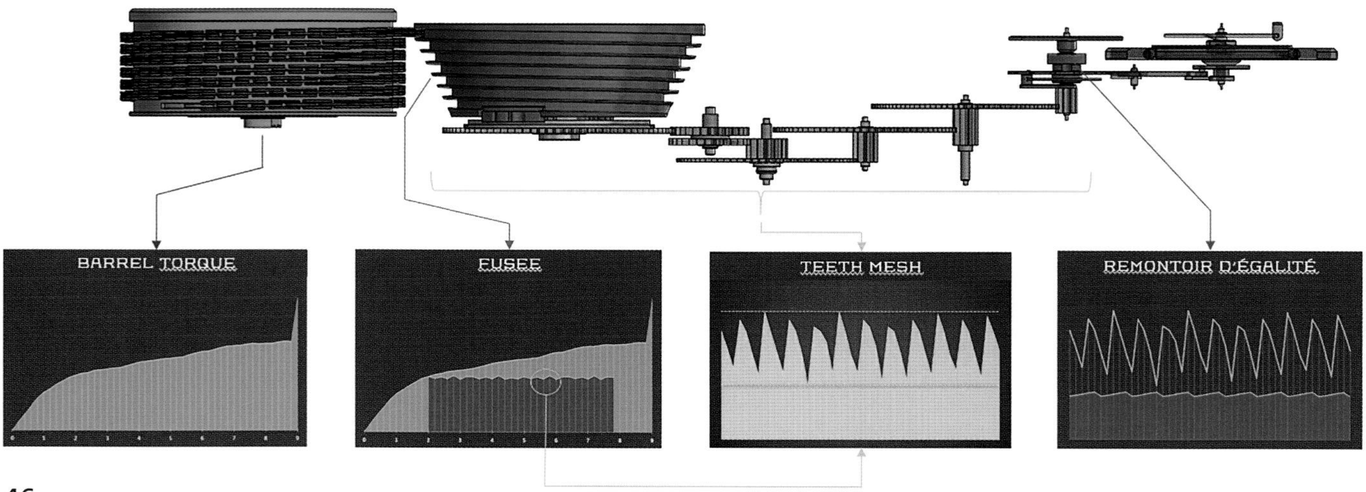

ORIS
AQUIS
PRESSURE RESISTANT
30BAR / 300M
5 DAYS
30
20

1

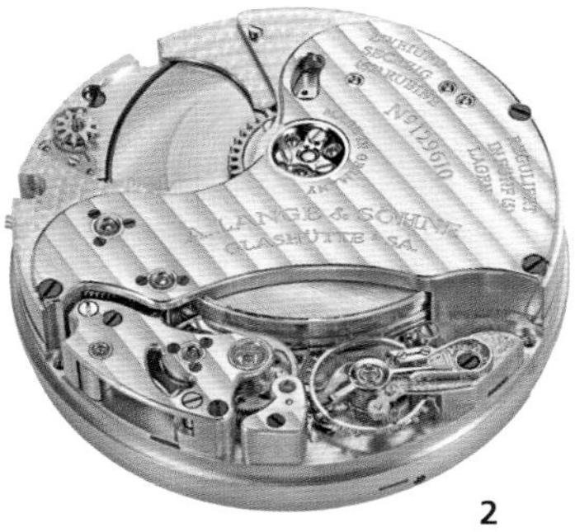

2

One must render unto Caesar, however: The man who first built a remontoir into a wristwatch was François-Paul Journe, in his Tourbillon Souverain. His solution, which has reappeared notably in the recent Chronomètre à resonance, was ingenious, as befits Journe: A secondary wheel on a lever is used to stop the seconds wheel, while a long blade spring, charged from the main wheelwork, passes one second worth of energy on to the escapement, which then releases the secondary wheel. The deadbeat second effect is there, too, but the Journe remontoir actually disengages when the energy from the mainspring is too weak, and the seconds resume their sweep display informing the wearer that it's time to rewind the watch.

TAMING THE DRAGON

The remontoir systems described above are mostly used to achieve greater chronometric precision. Lange & Söhne has also used them to make the impossible possible, however. The Lange 31, released in 2005, has, as the name suggests, a thirty-one-day power reserve. "We had read a magazine article talking about power reserves of eight days, ten days," Product Manager de Haas remembers from an "agenda-free" weekly meeting with his team. "I said, if you manage to make a watch that you wind only once a month, you'll be king. It was a joke."

The idea took root, and soon they were working on a movement with two 25-millimeter barrels each containing a six-foot spring—amazing for a watch. "The problem was that on day one, there was far too much power, but none on day twenty-two," says de Haas. This required a remontoir, inspiration for which was found by examining the huge pendulum clock ticking away in the company's main building in Glashütte. The resulting device makes use of a secondary spring and an escapement system to stop, not the seconds wheel, but rather a second minute wheel, which is then released by a single-toothed anchor wheel. The mechanism is somewhat hidden in the back of the massive watch, but its effect can be seen on the dial, where the subsidiary seconds sweep along, while the minute hand ticks away every ten seconds.

While working on the Lange 31, another idea germinated at Lange that would cause them to reach into the remontoir drawer once again for help. The Zeitwerk, which meant to replicate the digital hour and minutes clock at the stunning Semper opera house in nearby Dresden, featured three number disks to be switched instantaneously. This action needed lots of power, and the first mainspring used in Zeitwerks had an eight-pound pull capacity. "The Lange 31 was Marathon Man," jokes de Haas, "the Zeitwerk was a bodybuilder."

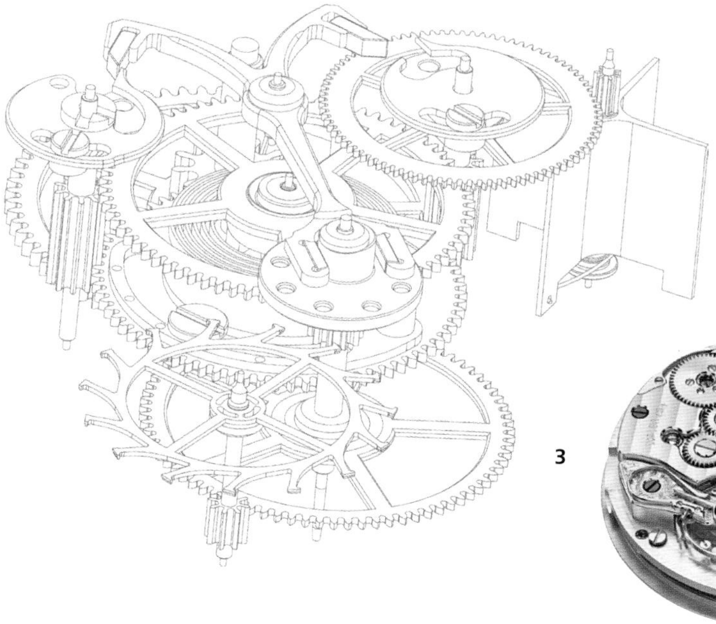

3

1 Journe's Caliber 1520 features two remontoirs that decouple when power drops to a certain level.

2 The remontoir of the Lange 31 controls power from the huge mainspring and drives the minute wheel.

3 A fan brake (far right) burns off excess torque in Lange's complex Zeitwerk system.

An entirely separate remontoir system had to be designed. The remontoir spring, wound by the seconds wheel, accumulates the energy necessary to move the three disks. Once a minute, a Y-shaped lever holds and then releases the pent-up torque on one side, while blocking the movement on the other. To protect the mechanism from a kind of mechanical power surge, the extra torque is sent to a fly governor, or fan brake, that whirls and is slowed by friction with air. The Zeitwerk's intricate mechanism recalls those used to drive some tower clocks and bells.

THE GREAT ESCAPE

Whatever their function, the key idea behind a remontoir system is to separate the mainspring's vigor from the delicate needs of the escapement and thus to maintain steady amplitude. Most use a secondary spring like those of the systems mentioned above. That is also the case with such spectacular watches as the Constant Force Tourbillon made by Arnold & Son. The remarkable innovator Andreas Strehler also invented a system with a satellite arm with a star-shaped wheel at the end that moves along an arc in six-degree increments. The arm essentially picks up the power of the mainspring, coils the intermediary spring underneath it, and releases little bursts of energy to the seconds wheel farther below on the pinion. None of these systems are directly connected to the escapement, the actual heartbeat of the watch.

It was Nicholas Déhon, then a Rolex employee, who came up with a wild idea while sitting in a train station in 1997 absentmindedly snapping his ticket back and forth. The ticket was collecting energy when bent, and releasing the same energy (Hooke's Law) when it snapped the other way. Rolex wasn't that thrilled by the idea, but his next employer, Girard-Perregaux, was amenable to developing an escapement that would drive the balance wheel directly using the buckling spring. In 2013, they came out with their Constant Escapement L.M. This unique mechanism occupies the lower half of the dial. It is composed of a graceful butterfly-shaped silicon component affixed to the escapement system. A 14-micron thread runs across it horizontally. As it snaps, it moves two rocker levers that transmit the impulse to the two balance wheels. The chronometry is excellent, but only time will tell if such a mechanism will survive or simply be a brilliant flash in the pan.

Constant force systems are a major challenge to the ingenuity of watchmakers. "Berthoud himself in his own book talked about the remontoir as probably 'one of the most promising devices to increase accuracy,'" says Jonathan Richard, marketing manager at Ferdinand Berthoud, "but it was very complicated to adjust and a lot of watchmakers gave up the idea of developing it, especially when the tourbillon was developed as a regulating force."

Still, as a number of brands have shown, modern tools and research have made it possible to build and optimize them. They have undoubtedly lots of room to evolve. Take the little company called Oscillon. They have developed one based on the mechanism used to retract vacuum cleaner cables. And just because mechanical devices will never be perfectly precise, that doesn't make them any less attractive to the watchmaker and the consumer. Striving for ever greater precision in the face of quartz's implacable supremacy in that domain still seems like a worthy cause, a little reminiscent of John Henry's duel with the steam drill, though with a happier outcome. This could be a new horizon for the creative engineer.

1

2

1 Andreas Strehler's curious mechanism with a star gear "walking" along an arc.

2 Nicholas Déhon's snapping train ticket becomes a stunning reality in Girard-Perregaux's Constant Escapement L.M.

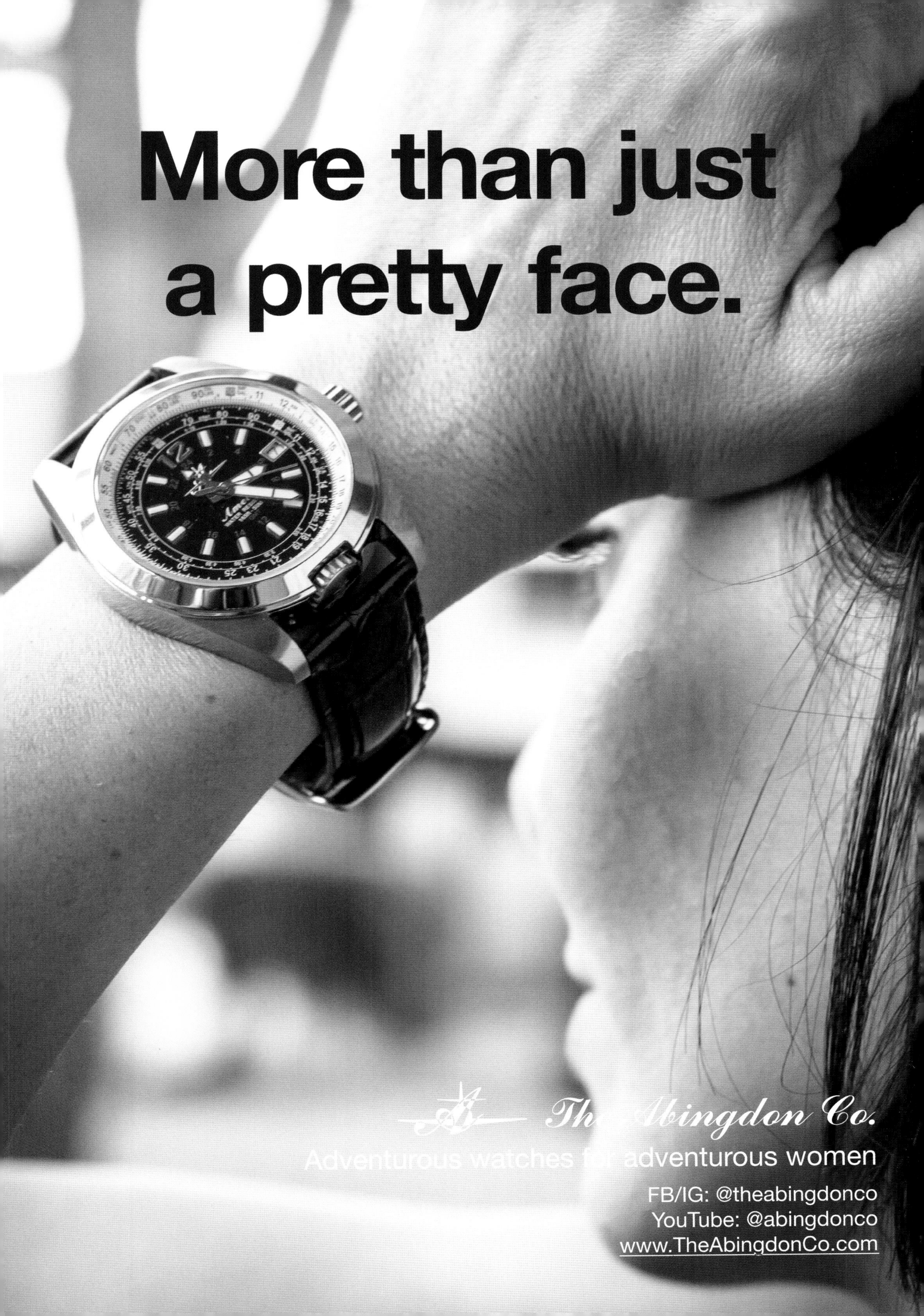
More than just
a pretty face.
The Abingdon Co.
Adventurous watches for adventurous women
FB/IG: @theabingdonco
YouTube: @abingdonco
www.TheAbingdonCo.com

A. LANGE & SÖHNE

In summer 2015, A. Lange & Söhne inaugurated a new *manufacture* in Glashütte. It was a big enough event for German chancellor Angela Merkel to attend. It was a particularly nice capstone for the work of Walter Lange, who died in January 2017 after a life of outstanding entrepreneurship.

Lange, as the company is known for short, exemplifies the steady, careful, and effective way Germans tend to develop their businesses. On December 7, 1990, on the exact day 145 years after the firm was founded by his great-grandfather Ferdinand Adolph Lange, Walter Lange re-registered the brand A. Lange & Söhne in its old hometown of Glashütte. Ferdinand Adolph had originally launched the company as a way to provide work to the local population. And shortly after German reunification in 1990, that is exactly what Glashütte needed as well.

Lange is known for its unique esthetic and mechanical codes. The three-quarter plate and all other structural components are made of German silver. The balance cock is always engraved by hand. The movements are all developed and manufactured by the company and are decorated and assembled by hand with the fine adjustment done in five positions. Patented innovations are always welcome, like the Lange large date, the SAX-O-MAT with an automatic "zero reset" for the second hand, or the three different patented constant force escapements (Lange 31, Zeitwerk, and the Richard Lange Jumping Second). Of the sixty-four newly developed calibers, almost all are equipped with an in-house balance spring.

The entry-level family is the classic three-hand Saxonia, while the Lange 1, introduced in 1994, is considered the collection flagship. The anniversary year, 2019, was celebrated with a collection of ten models in white gold dedicated to the milestones of that Lange family. Late in the year, the company created a stir among watch fans when the Odysseus, with a custom automatic movement and weekday and date display, staked a claim in the sports watch club. The stainless steel model has now been joined by a white gold model with an integrated leather or rubber strap, taking daily sports routine to the high end, as it were.

Lange Uhren GmbH
Ferdinand-A.-Lange-Platz 1
D-01768 Glashütte
Germany

Tel.:
+49-35053-44-0

E-mail:
info@lange-soehne.com

Website:
www.lange-soehne.com

Founded:
1990

Number of employees:
750 employees, almost half of whom are watchmakers

U.S. distributor:
A. Lange & Söhne
645 Fifth Avenue
New York, NY 10022
800-408-8147

Most important collections/price range:
Lange 1 / $35,400 to $335,800; Saxonia / $15,500 to $62,100; 1815 / $24,800 to $236,900; Richard Lange / $33,900 to $231,500; Zeitwerk / $79,300 to $128,100; Odysseus / $28,000

Odysseus

Reference number: 363.179
Movement: automatic, Lange Caliber L155.1; ø 32.9 mm, height 6.2 mm; 31 jewels; 28,800 vph; hand-engraved balance cock, 1 screw-mounted gold chaton, swan-neck fine adjustment; parts finished and assembled by hand; 50-hour power reserve
Functions: hours, minutes, subsidiary seconds; large date, weekday
Case: steel, ø 40.5 mm, height 11.1 mm; sapphire crystal; transparent case back; water-resistant to 12 atm
Band: stainless steel, folding clasp
Price: $28,800

Odysseus

Reference number: 363.179
Movement: automatic, Lange Caliber L155.1; ø 32.9 mm, height 6.2 mm; 31 jewels; 28,800 vph; hand-engraved balance cock, 1 screw-mounted gold chaton, swan-neck fine adjustment; parts finished and assembled by hand; 50-hour power reserve
Functions: hours, minutes, subsidiary seconds; large date, weekday
Case: white gold, ø 40.5 mm, height 11.1 mm; sapphire crystal; transparent case back; water-resistant to 12 atm
Band: rubber, buckle
Price: $40,600

Lange 1

Reference number: 191.032
Movement: manually wound, Lange Caliber L121.3; ø 30.6 mm, height 5.7 mm; 47 jewels; 21,600 vph; 8 screw-mounted gold chatons, swan-neck fine adjustment, hand-engraved balance cock, hand-finished and -assembled; 72-hour power reserve
Functions: hours, minutes, subsidiary seconds; power reserve indicator; large date
Case: pink gold, ø 38.5 mm, height 9.8 mm; sapphire crystal; transparent case back; water-resistant to 3 atm
Band: reptile skin, buckle
Price: $37,200
Variations: yellow or white gold ($37,200); platinum ($37,200)

WOLF

ESTᴰ 1834

PROTECT YOUR LEGACY

BRITISH RACING GREEN

WOLF1834.COM

Lange 1 Time Zone

Reference number: 116.029
Movement: manually wound, Lange Caliber L031.1; ø 34.1 mm, height 6.7 mm; 54 jewels; 21,600 vph; 3 screw-mounted gold chatons; zone time (hours, minutes) with day/night indication and city ring, forward-switchable; 72-hour power reserve
Functions: hours, minutes, subsidiary seconds; 12-hour display (2nd time zone); power reserve indicator; day/night indicator for both time zones; large date
Case: white gold, ø 41.9 mm, height 11 mm; sapphire crystal; transparent case back; water-resistant to 3 atm
Band: reptile skin, buckle
Price: $50,400; **Variations:** pink gold with light dial ($50,400); platinum ($64,300)

Lange 1 Tourbillon Perpetual Calendar

Reference number: 720.038F
Movement: automatic, Lange Caliber L082.1; ø 34.1 mm, height 7.8 mm; 76 jewels; 21,600 vph; 1-minute tourbillon with movement side stop function, off-center balance, 6 screw-mounted gold chatons; 50-hour power reserve
Functions: hours, minutes, subsidiary seconds; day/night indicator; perpetual calendar with large date, weekday, month, moon phase, leap year
Case: white gold, ø 41.9 mm, height 12.2 mm; sapphire crystal; transparent case back; water-resistant to 3 atm; **Band:** reptile skin, folding clasp
Price: $335,800
Variations: pink gold with light dial ($335,800)

Saxonia Large Date

Reference number: 381.029
Movement: automatic; Lange Caliber L086.8; ø 30.4 mm, height 5.2 mm; 40 jewels; 21,600 vph; hand-engraved balance cock, screw balance, swan-neck fine adjustment; 72-hour power reserve
Functions: hours, minutes, subsidiary seconds; large date
Case: white gold, ø 38.5 mm, height 9.6 mm; sapphire crystal; transparent case back; water-resistant to 3 atm
Band: reptile skin, buckle
Price: $15,500
Variations: pink gold ($15,500)

Saxonia Moon Phase

Reference number: 384.031
Movement: automatic, Lange Caliber L086.5; ø 30.4 mm, height 5.2 mm; 40 jewels; 21,600 vph; hand-engraved balance cock, screw balance, swan-neck fine adjustment; 72-hour power reserve
Functions: hours, minutes, subsidiary seconds; large date, moon phase
Case: pink gold, ø 40 mm, height 9.8 mm; sapphire crystal; transparent case back; water-resistant to 3 atm
Band: reptile skin; buckle
Price: $30,900
Variations: white gold ($30,900)

Datograph Auf/Ab

Reference number: 405.031
Movement: manually wound, Lange Caliber L951.7; ø 30.6 mm, height 8.1 mm; 46 jewels; 18,000 vph; 4 screw-mounted gold chatons, swan-neck fine adjustment, hand-engraved balance cock; 60-hour power reserve
Functions: hours, minutes, subsidiary seconds; power reserve indicator; flyback chronograph with precisely jumping minute counter; large date
Case: pink gold, ø 41 mm, height 13.4 mm; sapphire crystal; transparent case back; water-resistant to 3 atm
Band: reptile skin, buckle
Price: $73,000
Variations: platinum ($94,400)

Datograph Perpetual Tourbillon

Reference number: 740.056
Movement: manually wound, Lange Caliber L952.2; ø 32.6 mm, height 9 mm; 59 jewels; 18,000 vph; 1-minute tourbillon; swan-neck fine adjustment, hand-engraved intermediate wheel and tourbillon cock; 50-hour power reserve; **Functions:** hours, minutes, subsidiary seconds; day/night indicator, power reserve indicator; flyback chronograph with precisely jumping minutes; perpetual calendar with large date, weekday, month, moon phase, leap year
Case: white gold, ø 41.5 mm, height 14.6 mm; sapphire crystal; transparent case back; water-resistant to 3 atm; **Band:** reptile skin, folding clasp
Price: $287,800; limited to 100 pieces
Variations: platinum, black dial ($299,800)

Triple Split

Reference number: 424.038F
Movement: manually wound, Lange Caliber L132.1; ø 30.6 mm, height 9.4 mm; 46 jewels; 21,600 vph; off-center balance, in-house hairspring, column-wheel control of chronograph; 5 screw-mounted gold chatons; 55-hour power reserve
Functions: hours, minutes, subsidiary seconds; large date; power reserve indicator; flyback chronograph with triple flyback hand for reference measurements up to 12 hours, precisely jumping minute counter with double hand, continuous chrono hours
Case: white gold, ø 43.2 mm, height 15.6 mm; sapphire crystal; transparent case back; water-resistant to 3 atm; **Band:** reptile skin, folding clasp in white gold
Price: $146,300; limited to 100 pieces

Zeitwerk

Reference number: 140.029
Movement: manually wound, Lange Caliber L043.1; ø 33.6 mm, height 9.3 mm; 68 jewels; 18,000 vph; 2 screw-mounted gold chatons, constant force escapement (remontoir), hand-engraved balance cock; 36-hour power reserve
Functions: hours, minutes (digital, jumping), subsidiary seconds; power reserve indicator
Case: white gold, ø 41.9 mm, height 12.6 mm; sapphire crystal; transparent case back; water-resistant to 3 atm
Band: reptile skin, buckle
Price: $79,300
Variations: pink gold with silver-colored dial ($79,300)

Zeitwerk Minute Repeater

Reference number: 147.028
Movement: manually wound; Lange Caliber L043.5; ø 37.7 mm, height 10.9 mm; 93 jewels; 18,000 vph; 3 screw-mounted gold chatons, three-quarter plate, constant force escapement (remontoir), hand-engraved balance cock; 36-hour power reserve
Functions: hours, minutes (digital, jumping), subsidiary seconds; power reserve indicator, minute repeater
Case: white gold, ø 44.2 mm, height 14.1 mm; sapphire crystal; transparent case back; water-resistant to 3 atm; **Band:** reptile skin, folding clasp
Price: $83,300; limited to 30 pieces
Variations: platinum ($83,300)

1815 Auf/Ab

Reference number: 234.026
Movement: manually wound, Lange Caliber L051.2; ø 30.6 mm, height 4.6 mm; 29 jewels; 21,600 vph; 7 screw-mounted gold chatons, three-quarter plate, screw balance, hand-engraved balance cock, components hand-finished and -assembled; 55-hour power reserve
Functions: hours, minutes, subsidiary seconds; power reserve indicator
Case: white gold, ø 39 mm, height 8.7 mm; sapphire crystal; transparent case back; water-resistant to 3 atm
Band: reptile skin, buckle
Price: $30,900
Variations: yellow or pink gold ($30,900)

1815 Annual Calendar

Reference number: 238.032
Movement: manually wound, Lange Caliber L051.3; ø 30.6 mm, height 5.7 mm; 26 jewels; 21,600 vph; 3 screw-mounted gold chatons, hand-engraved balance cock, parts finished and assembled by hand; 72-hour power reserve
Functions: hours, minutes, subsidiary seconds; annual calendar with date, weekday, month, moon phase
Case: pink gold, ø 40 mm, height 10.1 mm; sapphire crystal; transparent case back; water-resistant to 3 atm
Band: reptile skin, buckle
Price: $41,200
Variations: white gold ($41,200)

Richard Lange Jumping Seconds

Reference number: 252.029
Movement: manually wound, Lange Caliber L094.1; ø 33.6 mm, height 6 mm; 50 jewels; 21,600 vph; zero-reset mechanism, constant force escapement (remontoir); 42-hour power reserve
Functions: hours (off-center), minutes (off-center), large seconds (jumping); winding reminder
Case: white gold, ø 39.9 mm, height 10.6 mm; sapphire crystal; transparent case back; water-resistant to 3 atm
Band: reptile skin, buckle
Price: $75,100
Variations: pink gold with silver-colored dial, limited to 100 pieces ($78,600); platinum ($84,200)

Caliber L155.1 Datomatic

Automatic; swan-neck fine adjustment; stop-seconds mechanism, platinum oscillating mass; single spring barrel; 50-hour power reserve
Functions: hours, minutes, subsidiary seconds; date, weekday
Diameter: 32.9 mm
Height: 6.2 mm
Jewels: 31, including a screw-mounted gold chaton
Balance: glucydur with regulating screws
Frequency: 28,800 vph
Balance spring: made in-house
Remarks: hand-finished and -assembled components; 312 parts

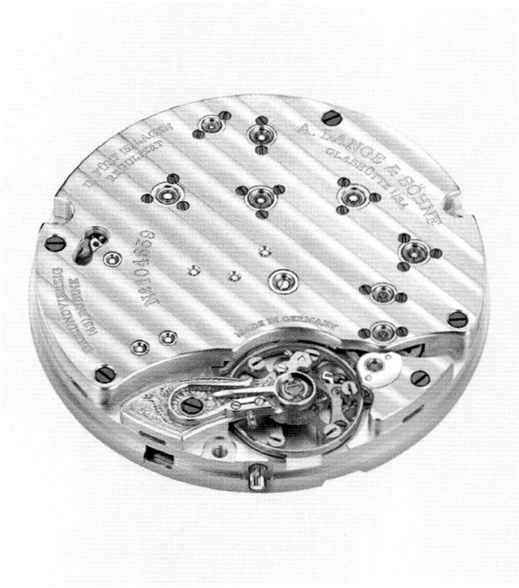

Caliber L121.1

Manually wound; stop-seconds mechanism, 8 screw-mounted gold chatons, swan-neck fine adjustment; double spring barrel; 72-hour power reserve
Functions: hours, minutes, subsidiary seconds; power reserve indicator; large date
Diameter: 30.6 mm
Height: 5.7 mm
Jewels: 43
Balance: glucydur with eccentric adjustment cams
Frequency: 21,600 vph
Balance spring: made in-house
Shock protection: Kif
Remarks: plates and bridges of untreated German silver, decorated and assembled mostly by hand, hand-engraved balance cock

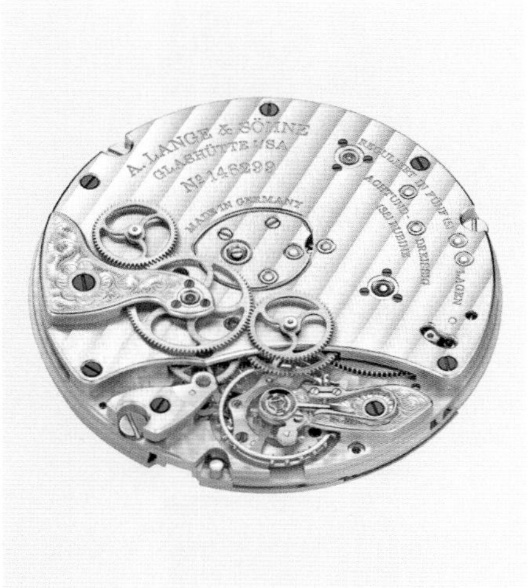

Caliber L141.1

Manually wound; stop-seconds mechanism, 3 screw-mounted gold chatons, swan-neck fine adjustment; single spring barrel; 38-hour power reserve
Functions: hours, minutes, subsidiary seconds; 2nd time zone, 2 day/night indicators, power reserve indicator, daylight saving time
Diameter: 34.1 mm
Height: 6.7 mm
Jewels: 38
Balance: glucydur with eccentric adjustment cams
Frequency: 21,600 vph
Hairspring: made in-house Kif
Remarks: German silver plates and bridges hand-finished and -assembled, hand-engraved balance cock

Caliber L082.1

Automatic; 1-minute tourbillon with patented stop-seconds mechanism; unidirectional gold rotor with platinum oscillating mass; single spring barrel; 38-hour power reserve
Functions: hours, minutes, subsidiary seconds; day/night indicator; perpetual calendar with large date, weekday, month, moon phase, leap year
Diameter: 34.1 mm; **Height:** 7.8 mm
Jewels: 76, including 6 in screw-mounted gold chatons and 1 diamond capstone
Balance: glucydur with eccentric adjustment cams
Frequency: 21,600 vph
Balance spring: made in-house
Remarks: hand-engraved intermediate wheel cock and balance cock; 624 parts

Caliber L086.5

Automatic; single spring barrel; 72-hour power reserve
Functions: hours, minutes, subsidiary seconds; large date, moon phase
Diameter: 30.4 mm
Height: 5.2 mm
Jewels: 40
Balance: glucydur
Frequency: 21,600 vph
Balance spring: made in-house
Remarks: German silver plates, hand-engraved balance cock; 325 parts

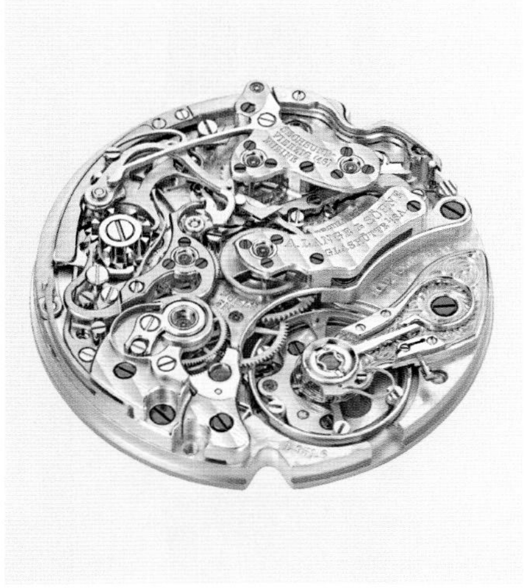

Caliber L951.6

Manually wound; stop-seconds mechanism, jumping minute counter; single spring barrel; 60-hour power reserve
Functions: hours, minutes, subsidiary seconds; power reserve indicator; flyback chronograph; large date
Diameter: 30.6 mm; **Height:** 7.9 mm
Jewels: 46
Balance: glucydur with weighted screws
Frequency: 18,000 vph
Hairspring: made in-house
Shock protection: Incabloc
Remarks: three-quarter plate of untreated German silver, mostly hand-assembled and decorated according to highest quality standards, hand-engraved balance cock; 451 parts

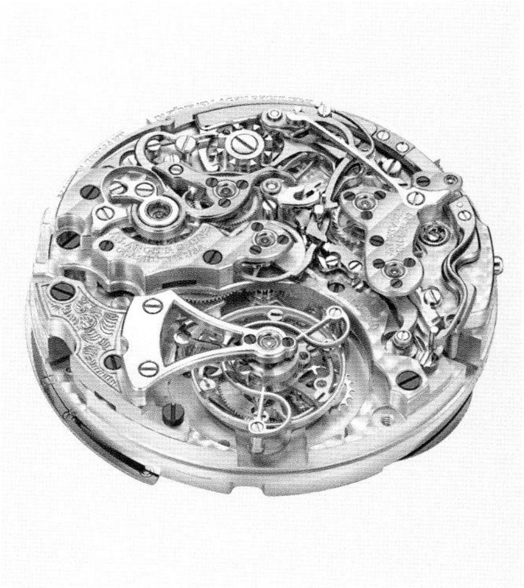

Caliber L952.2

Manually wound; 1-minute tourbillon; single spring barrel; 50-hour power reserve
Functions: hours, minutes, subsidiary seconds; day/night indicator, power reserve indicator; flyback chronograph with precisely jumping minute counter; perpetual calendar with large date, weekday, month, moon phase, leap year
Diameter: 32.6 mm; **Height:** 9 mm
Jewels: 58, including 5 screw-mounted gold chatons, 1 diamond capstone
Balance: glucydur with weighted screws
Frequency: 18,000 vph
Balance spring: made in-house; **Remarks:** German silver plates and bridges, hand-engraved intermediate wheel cock and balance cock; 729 parts

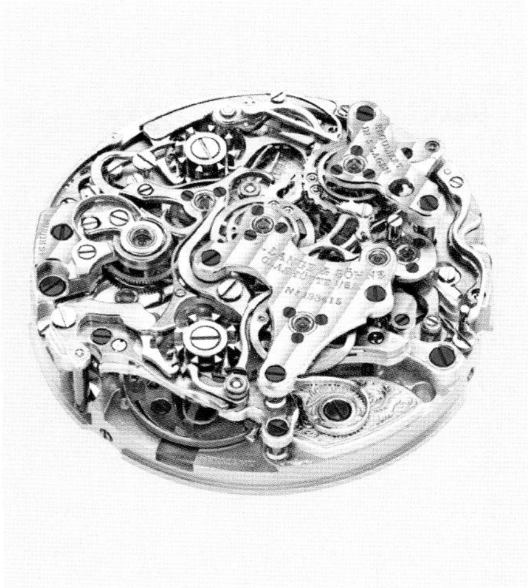

Caliber L132.1

Manually wound; column-wheel control of chronograph functions; single spring barrel; 55-hour power reserve
Functions: hours, minutes, subsidiary seconds; power reserve indicator; flyback chronograph, with triple flyback for comparative time measurements up to 12 hours, precisely jumping chrono and flyback minute counter, continuous chrono and split-second hour counter
Diameter: 30.6 mm; **Height:** 9.4 mm
Jewels: 46, including 5 screw-mounted gold chatons, glucydur with eccentric adjustment cams
Frequency: 21,600 vph
Balance spring: made in-house
Remarks: German silver plates and bridges, hand-engraved balance cock; 567 parts

Caliber L043.8

Manually wound; jumping minute, constant force mechanism (remontoir), patented barrel spring mechanism, stop-seconds mechanism; single spring barrel; 72-hour power reserve
Functions: hours, minutes (digital, jumping), subsidiary seconds; power reserve indicator, acoustic signal every 10 minutes and on the hour (with switch-off mechanism); date
Diameter: 37 mm; **Height:** 8.9 mm
Jewels: 70
Balance: glucydur with eccentric adjustment cams
Frequency: 18,000 vph
Balance spring: made in-house with hairspring clamp
Shock protection: Incabloc; **Remarks:** three-quarter plate of German silver; 516 parts

Caliber L043.5

Manually wound; 3 screw-mounted gold chatons, constant force mechanism (remontoir), stop-seconds mechanism, chiming mechanism; single spring barrel; 36-hour power reserve
Functions: hours. minutes (digital, jumping), subsidiary seconds; power reserve indicator, minute repeater (rings decimally)
Diameter: 37.7 mm; **Height:** 10.9 mm
Jewels: 93
Balance: glucydur with eccentric adjustment cams
Frequency: 18,000 vph
Hairspring: made in-house
Shock protection: Incabloc
Remarks: hand-engraved balance cock, hand-decorated and -assembled; 771 parts

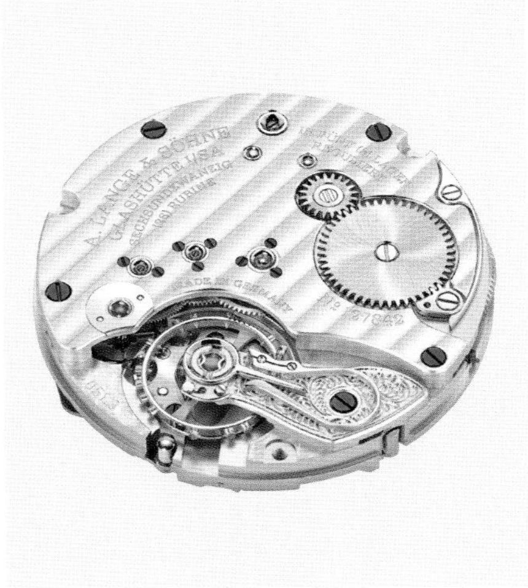

Caliber L051.3

Manually wound; swan-neck fine adjustment; stop-seconds mechanism; German silver plates and bridges; single spring barrel; 72-hour power reserve
Functions: hours, minutes, subsidiary seconds; annual calendar with date, weekday, month, moon phase
Diameter: 30.6 mm
Height: 5.7 mm
Jewels: 26, including 3 screw-mounted gold chatons
Balance: glucydur with weighted screws
Frequency: 21,600 vph
Balance spring: made in-house
Remarks: hand-finished and -assembled, hand-engraved balance cock; 345 parts

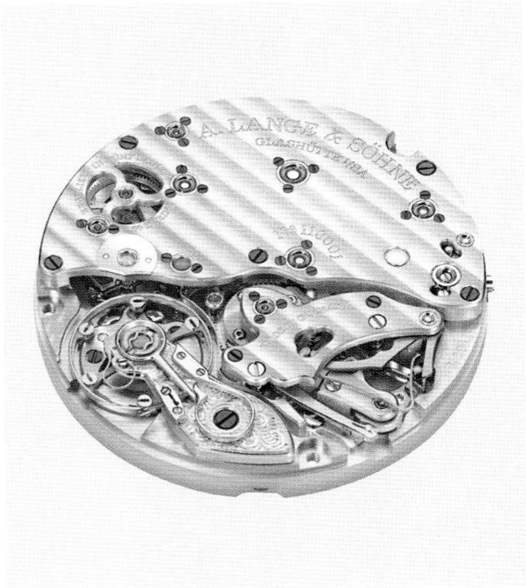

Caliber L094.1

Manually wound; constant force mechanism (remontoir), swan-neck fine adjustment, stop-seconds mechanism; single spring barrel; 42-hour power reserve
Functions: hours, minutes (off-center), large seconds (jumping), rewind reminder
Diameter: 33.6 mm
Height: 6 mm
Jewels: 50, including 8 screw-mounted gold chatons
Balance: glucydur with weighted screws
Frequency: 21,600 vph
Balance spring: made in-house
Remarks: plates and bridges of untreated German silver, hand-engraved balance cock; 390 parts

ALEXANDER SHOROKHOFF

The ultimate goal for the watch connoisseur may be realizing one's own ideas for timepieces. In the first stages of his life, Alexander Shorokhoff, born in Moscow in 1960, was an engineer and then an architect with his own construction company. This turned out to be an excellent platform to begin expanding into the field of fine timepieces. In 1992, shortly after the demise of the Soviet Union, Shorokhoff founded a distribution company in Germany to market Russia's own Poljot watches. This gave him the insight and practice needed to launch phase two of his plan: establishing his own manufacturing facilities for an independent watch brand under his own name.

At Shorokhoff Watches, three main creative lines are bundled under the general concept "Art on the Wrist": Heritage, Avantgarde, and Vintage. The three lines share a design with a distinctly artistic orientation. They all focus on technical quality, sophisticated hand-engraving, and the cultural backdrop. "We consider watches not only as timekeepers, but also as works of art," says Alexander Shorokhoff. It's a statement that can be seen in the watches. The brand is at home in the world of international and Russian art and culture. Each dial is designed down to the smallest detail. The engraving and finishing of the movements are unique as well.

All of them are taken apart in Alzenau, reworked, and then reassembled with great care, which is why the brand has stamped each watch with "Handmade in Germany." Some of the modules used in these timepieces were developed by the company itself. Before a watch leaves the *manufacture,* it is subjected to strict quality control. The timepiece's functionality must be given the cleanest bill of health before it can be sent out to jewelers around the world.

Alexander Shorokhoff Uhrenmanufaktur
Hanauer Strasse 25
63755 Alzenau
Germany

Tel.:
+49-6023-919-93

E-mail:
info@alexander-shorokhoff.de

Website:
www.alexander-shorokhoff.de

Founded:
2003

Number of employees:
16

Annual production:
approx. 1,500 watches

Distributor:
About Time Luxury Group
210 Bellevue Avenue
Newport, RI 02840
401-846-0598

Most important collections/price range:
Heritage / starting at approx. $4,500;
Avantgarde / starting at approx. $1,500;
Vintage / starting at approx. $800

Avantgarde Levels

Reference number: AS.DT03-3
Movement: automatic, Caliber 2671.AS (base ETA 2671); ø 17.5 mm, height 4.8 mm; 25 jewels; 28,800 vph; 2 independent movements with hand-engraved oscillating masses; 42-hour power reserve
Functions: hours, minutes (double), sweep seconds; date
Case: stainless steel, ø 46.5 mm, height 12.5 mm; sapphire crystal; transparent case back; water-resistant to 5 atm
Band: ostrich leather, buckle
Price: $4,200; limited to 99 pieces

Avantgarde "Kandy 2"

Reference number: AS.KD-AVG02
Movement: automatic, ETA Caliber 2892-A2; ø 26.2 mm, height 3.6 mm; 21 jewels; 28,800 vph; hand-engraved oscillating mass; 47-hour power reserve
Functions: hours, minutes, sweep seconds; date
Case: stainless steel with black PVD coating, with yellow gold inserts, 41 mm × 41 mm, height 9 mm; sapphire crystal; water-resistant to 3 atm
Band: calfskin, buckle
Price: $3,800; limited to 100 pieces

Avantgarde "Kandy"

Reference number: AS.KD02-4G
Movement: automatic, ETA Caliber 2892-A2; ø 26.2 mm, height 3.6 mm; 21 jewels; 28,800 vph; hand-engraved oscillating mass; 47-hour power reserve
Functions: hours, minutes, sweep seconds; date
Case: stainless steel with black PVD coating, with red gold inserts, 41 × 41 mm, height 9 mm; sapphire crystal; water-resistant to 3 atm
Band: reptile skin, buckle
Price: $3,750
Variations: various dials

Avantgarde "Los Craneos 2"

Reference number: AS.DT02-2
Movement: automatic, Caliber 2671.AS (base ETA 2671); ø 17.5 mm, height 4.8 mm; 25 jewels; 28,800 vph; 2 independent movements with hand-engraved oscillating masses; 42-hour power reserve
Functions: hours, minutes (double), sweep seconds; date
Case: stainless steel, ø 46.5 mm, height 12.5 mm; sapphire crystal; transparent case back; water-resistant to 5 atm
Band: ostrich leather, buckle
Price: $3,950; limited to 88 pieces

Avantgarde Revolution AVG

Reference number: AS.REV-AVG
Movement: automatic, Caliber 2671.AS (base ETA 2671); ø 17.5 mm, height 4.8 mm; 25 jewels; 28,800 vph; hand-engraved oscillating mass; 42-hour power reserve
Functions: hours, minutes, sweep seconds; date
Case: stainless steel, ø 43.5 mm, height 11.55 mm; sapphire crystal; transparent case back; water-resistant to 5 atm
Band: deerskin, buckle
Remarks: movement case is positioned off-center in case under single sapphire crystal
Price: $5,200; limited to 100 pieces

Avantgarde Tourbillon Picassini

Reference number: AS.TU55-1TM
Movement: manually wound, Concepto Caliber 8950; ø 30.4 mm, height 5.8 mm; 27 jewels; 28,800 vph; 1-minute tourbillon; hand-engraved and -embellished; 60-hour power reserve
Functions: hours, minutes, subsidiary seconds (on tourbillon cage)
Case: stainless steel with yellow gold Inserts, 41 × 41 mm, height 12.5 mm; sapphire crystal; water-resistant to 3 atm
Band: reptile skin, buckle
Price: $33,000; limited to 5 pieces

Avantgarde Colibri

Reference number: AS.KD01-CBR
Movement: automatic, ETA Caliber 2892-A2; ø 25.6 mm, height 3.6 mm; 21 jewels; 28,800 vph; hand-engraved and -finished oscillating weight; 47-hour power reserve
Functions: hours, minutes, sweep seconds
Case: stainless steel with yellow gold inserts, 41 × 41 mm, height 12.5 mm; sapphire crystal; transparent case back; water-resistant to 3 atm
Band: reptile skin, buckle
Remarks: miniature oil painting on a mother-of-pearl dial
Price: $5,400

Avantgarde Crossing 2

Reference number: AS.JH02-5
Movement: automatic, Dubois Dépraz Caliber 14400A; ø 25.6 mm, height 5.9 mm; 25 jewels; 28,800 vph; blued screws, hand-engraved rotor; 40-hour power reserve
Functions: hours (digital, jumping), minutes (off-center), subsidiary seconds
Case: rose gold–plated stainless steel, ø 43.5 mm, height 11.3 mm; sapphire crystal; transparent case back; water-resistant to 5 atm
Band: reptile skin, buckle
Price: $5,200; limited to 25 pieces

Avantgarde Fairytale

Reference number: AS.LA55-FTL
Movement: manually wound, Caliber 2824.AS (base ETA 2824-2); ø 25.6 mm, height 4.6 mm; 25 jewels; 28,800 vph; hand-engraved and -finished oscillating weight; 49-hour power reserve
Functions: hours, minutes, sweep seconds; date
Case: 14-kt rose gold, ø 39 mm, height 10.6 mm; sapphire crystal; transparent case back; water-resistant to 3 atm
Band: reptile skin, buckle
Remarks: miniature oil painting on mother-of-pearl dial
Price: $5,200; limited to 5 pieces

ALPINA

Alpina essentially grew out of a confederation of watchmakers known as the Alpina Union Horlogère, founded by Gottlieb Hauser. The group expanded quickly to reach beyond Swiss borders into Germany, where it opened a factory in Glashütte. For a while in the 1930s it even merged with Gruen, one of the most important watch companies in the United States.

After World War II, the Allied Forces decreed that the name Alpina could no longer be used in Germany, and so that branch was renamed "Dugena" for Deutsche Uhrmacher-Genossenschaft Alpina, or the German Watchmaker Cooperative Alpina.

Today, Geneva-based Alpina is no longer associated with that watchmaker cooperative of yore. Now a sister brand of Frédérique Constant, it has a decidedly modern collection enhanced with a series of movements designed, built, and assembled in-house: the Tourbillon AL-980, the World Timer AL-718, the Automatic Regulator AL-950, the Small Date Automatic AL-710, and, more recently, the Flyback Chronograph Automatic AL-760, which features the patented Direct Flyback technology. Owners Peter and Aletta Stas have built up an outstanding business over the years, and in 2016 they sold it to Citizen Group, but continue managing the brands until 2020.

Alpina likes to call itself the inventor of the modern sports watch. Its iconic Block Uhr of 1933 and the Alpina 4 of 1938, with an in-house automatic movement, set the pace for all sports watches, with a waterproof stainless steel case, an amagnetic system, and shock absorbers. It continues to produce watches designed to survive a harsh environment. But the brand is also looking at the twenty-first-century customers, whose lives are electronic. In 2015, the company introduced the first Swiss Made "Horological Smartwatch," a brand new category of watch. In June 2020, it contributed the Alpiner X Alive to the trend toward health monitoring in cooperation with Philips Healthcare. The watch features, among other things, a pulsometer.

Alpina Watch International SA
Route de la Galaise, 8
CH-1228 Plan-les-Ouates, Geneva
Switzerland

Tel.:
+41-0-22-860-87-40

E-mail:
info@alpina-watches.com

Website:
alpinawatches.com

Founded:
1883

Number of employees:
100

Annual production:
45,000 watches

U.S. distributor:
Alpina Frederique Constant USA
350 5th Avenue, 29th Floor
New York, NY 10118
646-438-8124
lmellor@usa.frederique-constant.com

Most important collections/price range:
AlpinerX / from approx. $995 to $1,295; Seastrong Diver 300 GMT / from approx. $795 to 995; Startimer Pilot Automatic / from approx. $995 to 1,295

Seastrong Gyre Automatic

Reference number: AL-525LNSB4VG6
Movement: automatic, Caliber AL-525 (base Sellita SW200-1); ø 25.6 mm, height 4.6 mm; 26 jewels; 28,800 vph; 38-hour power reserve
Functions: hours, minutes, sweep seconds; date
Case: composite material of recycled fishing nets and fiberglass, ø 44 mm, height 12 mm; unidirectional bevel with 0-60 scale; sapphire crystal; transparent case back; screw-in crown; water-resistant to 30 atm
Band: textile from recycled PET bottles, buckle
Remarks: comes with additional apple-leather strap; 3 men's and 2 ladies' models limited to 1,883 pieces each
Price: $1,595

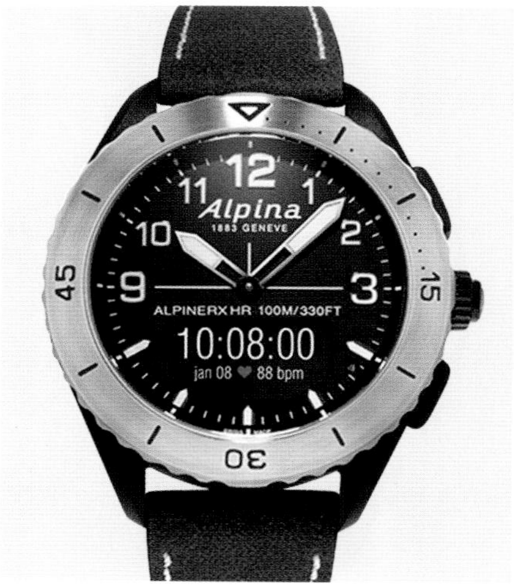

Alpiner X Alive

Reference number: AL-284LBBW5SAQ6
Movement: quartz, microchip, Caliber AL-284
Functions: hours, minutes, altimeter, barometer, compass, GPS, UV indicator, temperature gauge, electronic movement and sleep monitoring, pulsometer, alarm clock, stop watch; world time display; date
Case: composite material (fiberglass), ø 45 mm, height 14 mm; unidirectional stainless steel bezel, 0-60 scale; sapphire crystal; water-resistant to 10 atm
Band: calfskin, buckle
Price: $1,095

Startimer Pilot Heritage

Reference number: AL-525BBG4SH6
Movement: automatic, Caliber AL-525 (base Sellita SW200-1); ø 25.6 mm, height 4.6 mm; 25 jewels; 28,800 vph; 38-hour power reserve
Functions: hours, minutes, sweep seconds; date
Case: stainless steel, ø 44 mm, height 12 mm; sapphire crystal; water-resistant to 10 atm
Band: calfskin, buckle
Price: $1,250

Angelus
Manufacture La Joux-Perret SA
Boulevard des Eplatures 38
2300 La Chaux-de-Fonds
Switzerland

Tel:
+41-32-967-97-97

E-mail:
info@angelus-watches.com

Website:
www.angelus-watches.com

Founded:
1891; relaunched 2011

Number of employees:
about 100, including at the La Joux-Perret manufacture

Distributor:
Angelus USA
510 West 6th Street, Suite 309
Los Angeles, CA 90014
213-622-1133

Most important collections/price range:
U50/U51 / $32,000; various tourbillons / $28,000 to $69,000

ANGELUS

The watch landscape in Switzerland has always been rich in small, vital brands. Many are no longer active, but their names still make for weepy eyes with connoisseurs and collectors. And every now and then, an older company is revived with varying degrees of success. Angelus, founded by Gustave and Albert Stolz in Le Locle in 1891, quickly forged a reputation for complicated watches, notably repeaters and chronographs. The brothers, Catholics, named the brand after the first word of a standard Catholic prayer and the midday church bells.

One of the brand's claims to fame was a two-handed chronograph, which became a hit in the thirties, culminating in a contract with the Hungarian air force in 1940. The company then built a chronograph with a date, and later one of the first digital dates. Meanwhile, it was creating excellent movements, one of which drove Panerai's Mare Nostrum in the fifties. Among its most iconic models was the waterproof repeater/alarm called the Tinkler—a very limited series, hence extremely rare—and, in the seventies, a five-minute repeater, which never really got off the ground due to the quartz crisis, which brought Angelus to its knees . . .

Fast-forward to 2011. La Joux-Perret, a company known for movements and modules and behind Arnold & Son, relaunched the brand. Sébastien Chaulmontet designed the Tourbillon Lumière, which became the breakout watch in 2015, a modern, television-shaped behemoth recalling the travel clocks the company produced at one time. The tourbillon turns in one window, time appears in the other. It struck a chord: modern, slightly dissonant, but with gumption. In 2017, the model reappeared with a Mexican skull (Calavera) dial and accompanied by several other tourbillon models in more standard round watches. Since 2019, the company has been producing a series of high-end skeleton watches with affordable tourbillons and some remarkable diver's watches with tourbillons, a particularly classy way to explore the seabed. At any rate, Angelus is making people talk, and that alone can mean success these days.

U41 Tourbillon Skeleton

Reference number: 0TSBT.O01A
Movement: manually wound, Caliber A-300; ø 32.8 mm, height 4.3 mm; 23 jewels; 28,800 vph; 1-minute flying tourbillon; black DLC-coated, snailed and beveled mainplate and bridges, satin-finished blue skeletonized titanium bridges; 90-hour power reserve
Functions: hours, minutes, subsidiary seconds
Case: annealed stainless steel, ø 42 mm, height 10 mm; sapphire crystal; transparent case back; water-resistant to 3 atm
Band: rubber, buckle
Price: $34,400
Variations: blue or black rubber strap

U20 Ultra-Skeleton Tourbillon

Reference number: 0TCAB.U01A.C004T
Movement: manually wound, Caliber A-250; ø 32.6 mm, height 5.78 mm; 18 jewels; 21,600 vph; 1-minute flying tourbillon; sapphire mainplate, satin-finished blue skeletonized titanium bridges; 90-hour power reserve
Functions: hours, minutes, subsidiary seconds
Case: titanium and NPT carbon fiber, ø 42 mm, height 10.3 mm; sapphire crystal; transparent case back; water-resistant to 3 atm
Band: reptile skin, buckle
Price: $69,900; limited to 18 pieces

U51 Diver Tourbillon

Reference number: 0TDCT.E01A.K008D
Movement: manually wound, Caliber A-310; ø 32.8 mm, height 4.3 mm; 23 jewels; 28,800 vph; 1-minute flying tourbillon; satin-finished plates and bridges; 120-hour power reserve
Functions: hours, minutes, subsidiary seconds
Case: titanium, ø 45 mm, height 12.47 mm; crown-adjustable unidirectional 60-minute timing bezel; sapphire crystal; transparent case back; water-resistant to 30 atm
Band: rubber, buckle
Remarks: 6-spoke design on wheels for rigidity; bi-color chapter ring for better visibility
Price: $42,800; limited to 25 pieces

ANONIMO

Anonimo SA
Chemin des Tourelles 4
CH-2400 Le Locle
Switzerland

Tel.:
+41-22-566-06-06

E-mail:
info@anonimo.com

Website:
anonimo.com

Founded:
1997; moved to Switzerland in 2013

U.S. distributor:
Stroll & Co
1801 Metro Parkway
45459 Dayton, OH
1-800-786-5526
stroll@americaswatchmaker.com

Most important collections/price range:
Epurato, Militare, Nautilo / $2,300 to $5,700

The brand Anonimo was launched in Florence, Italy. Watchmaking has a long history in Florence, going back to one Giovanni de Dondi (1318–1389), who built his first planetarium around 1368, or architect and goldsmith Lorenzo della Volpaia (1446–1512), who worked with calendars and astronomical instruments. And finally, there were the likes of the mathematician Galileo and the incomparable Leonardo da Vinci.

In more recent times, the Italian watch industry has been equipping submarine crews and frogmen with timepieces. The key technology comes from Switzerland, but the specialized know-how for making robust, water-resistant timepieces sprang from small enterprises with special competencies in building cases, notably of bronze. The founders of Anonimo understood this strength and decided to put it in the service of their "anonymous" brand—a name chosen to "hide" the fact that many small, discreet companies are involved in their superbly finished watches.

In 2013, armed with some fresh capital and a new management team, Anonimo came out with three watch families running on Swiss technology: The mechanical movements are a combination of Dubois Dépraz modules and tried-and-true Sellita movements. On the whole, though, the collections reflect exquisite conception and manufacturing, and the quality of the materials is unimpeachable: corrosion-resistant stainless steel, fine bronze, and titanium. The design is definitely vintage, a bit 1960s with a hint of a cushion case, but use of only three numerals—4, 8, and 12, which sketch an A on the dial—is quite modern. On the military models, the crown has been placed in a protected area between the two upper lugs. Thanks to a clever hinge system, that crown can be pressed onto the case for an impermeable fit or released for time setting. The Militare line is also home to a special-edition chronograph to celebrate Anonimo's status as official timer of the World Rally Championship, Italy section. Fans seeking a simpler dial have the Epurato line, including a number of different-colored dials, each with characteristic sunray effect. The Nautilo series was conceived for divers, chic and sportive and able to descend beyond 600 feet. The latest models look back to older Dino Zei Nautilos of the past, with hints of '60s-style cushion cases.

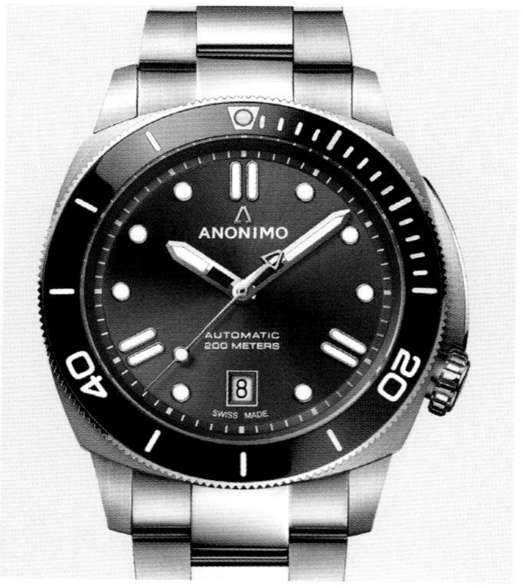

Nautilo 42mm Satin Blue

Reference number: AM-5009.09.103.M01
Movement: automatic, Sellita Caliber SW200-1; ø 25.6 mm, height 4.6 mm; 26 jewels; 28,800 vph; 38-hour power reserve
Functions: hours, minutes, sweep seconds; date
Case: stainless steel, ø 42 mm, height 11.8 mm; unidirectional bezel with ceramic insert, with 0-60 scale; sapphire crystal; transparent case back; screw-in crown; water-resistant to 20 atm
Band: stainless steel, folding clasp with safety catch
Price: $2,800
Variations: calfskin or rubber strap ($2,290)

Militare Chrono Bronze

Reference number: AM-1120.04.001.A01
Movement: automatic, Sellita Caliber SW300 with Dubois Dépraz module 2035M; ø 26.2 mm, height 6.5 mm; 49 jewels; 28,800 vph; 42-hour power reserve
Functions: hours, minutes, subsidiary seconds; chronograph
Case: bronze, ø 43.5 mm, height 14.5 mm; sapphire crystal; transparent case back; water-resistant to 12 atm
Band: calfskin, buckle
Remarks: crown is water-resistant by being pressed onto case by upper lug
Price: $5,080
Variations: different dial colors and case materials

Epurato 42mm

Reference number: AM-4000.01.103.W22
Movement: automatic, Sellita Caliber SW200-1; ø 25.6 mm, height 4.6 mm; 26 jewels; 28,800 vph; 38-hour power reserve
Functions: hours, minutes, sweep seconds; date
Case: stainless steel, ø 42 mm, height 11.6 mm; sapphire crystal; transparent case back; water-resistant to 5 atm
Band: calfskin, buckle
Remarks: galvanic blue dial
Price: $2,480
Variations: various dial colors

Aristo Vollmer GmbH
Erbprinzenstr. 36
D-75175 Pforzheim
Germany

Tel.:
+49-7231-17031

E-mail:
info@aristo-vollmer.de

Website:
www.aristo-uhren.de

Founded:
1907/1998

Number of employees:
16

Annual production:
9,000 watches

Distribution:
retail

U.S. distributor:
Long Island Watch, Marc Frankel
273 Walt Whitman Road, Suite 217
Huntington Station, NY 11746
631-470-0762
www.longislandwatch.com

Most important collections/price range:
Aristo watches starting at $400 up to Vollmer watches at $1,900; Erbprinz watches up to $1,600

ARISTO

"If you lie down with dogs . . ." goes the old saying. And if you work closely with watchmakers . . . you may catch their more beneficial bug and become one yourself. That, at any rate, is what happened to the watch case and metal bracelet manufacturer Vollmer, Ltd., established in Pforzheim, Germany, by Ernst Vollmer in 1922. Third-generation president Hansjörg Vollmer decided he was interested in producing watches as well.

Vollmer, who studied business in Stuttgart, had the experience, but also the connections with manufacturers in Switzerland. He speaks French fluently, another asset. He acquired Aristo and in 1998 launched a series of pilot's watches housed in sturdy titanium cases with bold onion crowns and secured with Vollmer's own light and comfortable titanium bracelets. Bit by bit, thanks to affordable prices and no-nonsense design—reviving some classic dials from World War II—Vollmer's watches caught hold. The collection grew with limited editions and a few chronometers.

In October 2005, Vollmer GmbH and Aristo Watches finally consolidated for a bigger impact. Besides their own lines, they produce quartz watches, automatics, and chronographs under the names Messerschmitt and Aristella. The Aristo brand has been trademarked worldwide and is sold mainly in Europe, North America, and Asia. The collection is divided up into Classic, Design, and Sports, with the mechanical segment further split based on the elements Land, Water, and Air. The timepieces range from quality wristwatches with historical movements from older Swiss production to attractive ladies' watches and replicas of classic military watches, all assembled in Pforzheim. The company also has an established name as a manufacturer of classic pilot's watches. And it took another step toward the higher end of the market by launching the "Erbprinz" series, named after the street where the company also has a workshop for manufacturing metal bracelets.

Messerschmitt 46

Reference number: ME-46H3S
Movement: automatic, Ronda Caliber R150; ø 25.6 mm, height 4.4 mm; 25 jewels; 28,800 vph; 40-hour power reserve
Functions: hours, minutes, sweep seconds
Case: stainless steel, ø 46 mm, height 12 mm; mineral glass; water-resistant to 5 atm
Band: calfskin, buckle
Price: $549

Vintage 47 Pilot

Reference number: 7H98H
Movement: manually wound, Sellita Caliber SW215-1; ø 25.6 mm, height 3.35 mm; 19 jewels; 28,800 vph; 42-hour power reserve
Functions: hours, minutes, sweep seconds
Case: stainless steel, ø 47 mm, height 11 mm; sapphire crystal; water-resistant to 5 atm
Band: calfskin, buckle
Price: $895

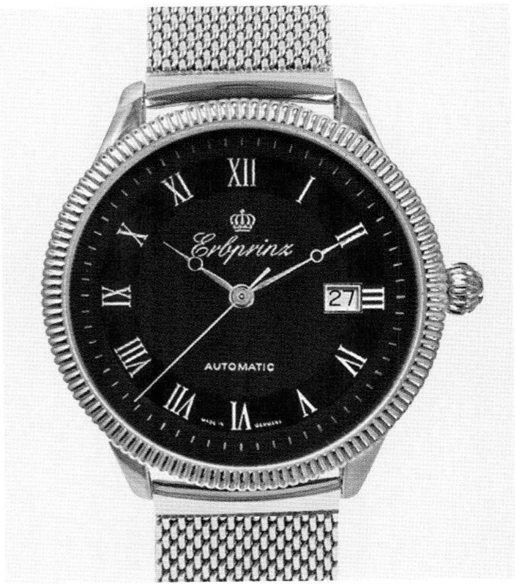

Erbprinz Favorite II

Reference number: F19S
Movement: automatic, Sellita Caliber SW200-1; ø 25.6 mm, height 4.6 mm; 26 jewels; 28,800 vph; 38-hour power reserve
Functions: hours, minutes, sweep seconds; date
Case: stainless steel, ø 41 mm, height 11.2 mm; sapphire crystal
Band: stainless steel Milanese mesh, folding clasp
Price: $650

ARMIN STROM

For more than thirty years, Armin Strom's name was associated mainly with the art of skeletonizing. But this "grandmaster of skeletonizers" then decided to entrust his life's work to the next generation, which turned out to be the Swiss industrialist and art patron Willy Michel.

Michel had the wherewithal to expand the one-man show into a full-blown *manufacture* able to conceive, design, and produce its own mechanical movements. The endeavor attracted Claude Geisler, a very skilled designer, and Michel's own son, Serge, who became business manager. When this triumvirate joined forces, it was able to come up with a technically fascinating movement at the quaint little *manufacture* in the Biel suburb of Bözingen within a brief period of time.

The new movement went on to grow into a family of ten, which forms the backbone of a new collection, including a tourbillon with microrotor—no mean feat for a small firm. The ARF15 caliber of the Mirrored Force Resonance, for example, features two balance wheels placed close enough to influence each other (resonance) and give the movement greater stability. The two oscillating systems are connected by a clutch spring. A similar movement is used in an exclusive, new, minute repeater.

This essential portfolio has given the *manufacture* the industrial autonomy to implement its projects quickly and independently. Armin Strom has additionally created an online configurator (on its homepage) giving fans and collectors the opportunity to personalize their watches. All components can be selected individually and combined, from the dial, hands, and finishing to the straps. The finished product can be picked up at a local dealership or at the manufacturer in Biel/Bienne, including a tour of the place.

Armin Strom AG
Bözingenstrasse 46
CH-2502 Biel/Bienne
Switzerland

Tel.:
+41-32-343-3344

E-mail:
info@arminstrom.com

Website:
www.arminstrom.com

Founded:
2006 (first company 1967)

Number of employees:
22

Annual production:
approx. 400 watches

U.S. representative:
Jean Marc Bories
Head of North America
929-353-5395
Jean-marc@arminstrom.com

Most important collections/price range:
Offers an online configurator for individual design using six in-house movements (manual, power reserve, automatic with or without date, tourbillon, resonance, and skeletons) / $9,900 to $100,000 plus

Minute Repeater Resonance

Reference number: TI19-RMR.SA.AL.M.43.FC
Movement: manually wound, Caliber ARR18; ø 39.4 mm, height 11.35 mm; 51 jewels; 25,200 vph; 2 independent mutually stabilizing regulating systems connected by a resonance clutch spring; finely decorated mainplate and bridges; 96-hour power reserve
Functions: hours, minutes (off-center), subsidiary seconds
Case: titanium, ø 47.7 mm, height 16.1 mm; sapphire crystal; transparent case back; water-resistant to 3 atm
Band: reptile skin, double folding clasp
Remarks: minute repeater visible on dial
Price: $390,000; limited to 10 pieces

Pure Resonance

Reference number: ST17-RW.05.AL.L.14
Movement: manually wound, Caliber ARF16; ø 34.4 mm, height 7.05 mm; 38 jewels; 25,200 vph; 2 independent regulating systems are connected by a resonance clutch spring and mutually stabilize each other; finely decorated mainplate and bridges; 48-hour power reserve
Functions: hours, minutes (off-center), subsidiary seconds
Case: stainless steel, ø 42 mm, height 12 mm; sapphire crystal; transparent case back; water-resistant to 5 atm
Band: reptile skin, buckle
Remarks: comes with extra rubber strap
Price: $50,000

Mirrored Force Resonance

Reference number: RG15-RF.5N
Movement: manually wound, Caliber ARF15; ø 36.6 mm, height 7.7 mm; 43 jewels; 25,200 vph; 2 independent regulating systems are connected by a resonance clutch spring and mutually stabilize each other; movement finely finished; 48-hour power reserve
Functions: hours, minutes (off-center), double subsidiary seconds
Case: rose gold, ø 43.4 mm, height 13 mm; sapphire crystal; transparent case back; water-resistant to 5 atm
Band: reptile skin, buckle
Remarks: comes with extra rubber strap
Price: $55,000; limited to 50 pieces

Gravity Equal Force

Reference number: ST19-GEF.90.AL.M.35
Movement: automatic, Armin Strom Caliber ASB19; ø 35.52 mm, height 11.67 mm; 28 jewels; 25,200 vph; microrotor; spring barrel with constant and limited force mechanism with Maltese cross escapement; finely finished movement; 72-hour power reserve
Functions: hours, minutes (off-center), subsidiary seconds; power reserve indicator
Case: stainless steel, ø 41 mm, height 12.65 mm; sapphire crystal; transparent case back; water-resistant to 3 atm
Band: reptile skin, buckle
Price: $17,500
Variations: with double folding clasp

Skeleton Pure

Reference number: ST15-PW.05
Movement: manually wound, Caliber ARM09-S; ø 36.6 mm, height 6.2 mm; 34 jewels; 18,000 vph; 2 spring barrels, screw balance with gold weight screws, Breguet hairspring, crown wheels visible on dial side; skeletonized plate, gearwheels, and spring barrel bridges, mainplate with blue PVD coating; 168-hour power reserve
Functions: hours, minutes, subsidiary seconds; power reserve indicator
Case: stainless steel, ø 43.4 mm, height 13 mm; sapphire crystal; transparent case back; water-resistant to 5 atm; **Band:** reptile skin, buckle
Remarks: comes with extra rubber strap
Price: $32,400; limited to 100 pieces

Tourbillon Skeleton Earth

Reference number: ST15-TE.90
Movement: manually wound, Caliber ATC11-S; ø 36.6 mm, height 6.2 mm; 24 jewels; 18,000 vph; 1-minute tourbillon, double spring barrel, skeletonized plates, wheels, and bridges, Breguet hairspring, screw balance with gold weight screws, crown wheels visible on dial side; 240-hour power reserve
Functions: hours, minutes, subsidiary seconds
Case: stainless steel with black PVD coating, ø 43.4 mm, height 13 mm; sapphire crystal; transparent case back; water-resistant to 5 atm
Band: reptile skin, double folding clasp
Price: $91,000
Variations: Air ($94,000); Fire ($101,000); Water ($91,000)

Caliber ARR18

Manually wound; 2 separate regulating systems are connected by a resonance clutch spring and mutually stabilize each other; 96-hour power reserve
Functions: hours, minutes; minute repeater
Diameter: 39.4 mm
Height: 11.35 mm
Jewels: 51
Balance: 2 balance wheels oscillating in opposite directions on a single hairspring
Frequency: 25,200 vph
Remarks: movement developed in collaboration with Le Cercle des Horlogers; 408 parts

Caliber ARF15

Manually wound; 2 separate regulating systems are connected by a resonance clutch spring and mutually stabilize each other; single spring barrel, 48-hour power reserve
Functions: hours, minutes (off-center), 2 independent symmetrically mirrored subsidiary seconds
Diameter: 36.6 mm
Height: 7.7 mm
Jewels: 43
Balance: 2 balance wheels oscillating in opposite directions on a single hairspring
Frequency: 25,200 vph
Remarks: 226 components; fine, hand-decorated movement

Caliber ASB19

Automatic; microrotor; spring barrel with constant force escapement (Maltese cross); single spring barrel; 72-hour power reserve
Functions: hours, minutes, subsidiary seconds; power reserve indicator
Diameter: 35.52 mm
Height: 11.67 mm
Jewels: 28
Balance: screw balance with variable inertia
Frequency: 25,200 vph
Remarks: movement decorated by hand; 202 parts

ARNOLD & SON

John Arnold holds a special place among the British watchmakers of the eighteenth and nineteenth centuries because he was the first to organize the production of his chronometers along industrial lines. He developed his own standards and employed numerous watchmakers. During his lifetime, he is said to have manufactured around 5,000 marine chronometers, which he sold at reasonable prices to the Royal Navy and the West Indies merchant fleet. Arnold chronometers were packed in the trunks of some of the greatest explorers, from John Franklin and Ernest Shackleton to Captain Cook and Dr. Livingstone.

As Arnold & Son was once synonymous with precision timekeeping on the high seas, it stands to reason, then, that the modern brand should also focus its design policies on the interplay of time and geography as well as the basic functions of navigation. Independence from The British Masters Group has meant that the venerable English chronometer brand has been reorienting itself, setting its sights on classic, elegant watchmaking. With the expertise of watch manufacturer La Joux-Perret behind it (and the expertise housed in the building behind the complex on the main road between La Chaux-de-Fonds and Le Locle), it has been able to implement a number of new ideas.

There are two main lines: The Royal Collection celebrates John Arnold's art, with luxuriously designed models inspired from past creations with delicate complications, tourbillons or world time displays, or unadorned manual windings featuring the new Caliber A&S 1001 by La Joux-Perret. The Instrument Collection is dedicated to exploring the seven seas and offers a sober look reflecting old-fashioned meters. Typically, these timepieces combine two displays on a single dial: a chronograph with jumping seconds, for example, between the off-center displays of time and the date hand or separate escapements driving a dual time display—left, the sidereal time; right, the solar time; and between the two, the difference. Perhaps the most remarkable timepiece in the collection is the skeletonized Time Pyramid, with a dual power reserve, a crown between the lugs, and an overall modern look.

Arnold & Son
38, boulevard des Eplatures
CH-2300 La Chaux-de-Fonds
Switzerland

Tel.:
+41-32-967-9797

E-mail:
info@arnoldandson.com

Website:
www.arnoldandson.com

Founded:
1995

Number of employees:
approx. 30

U.S. distributor:
Arnold & Son USA
510 West 6th Street, Suite 309
Los Angeles, CA 90014
213-622-1133

Most important collections/price range:
Globetrotter, Time Pyramid, Nebula, TB88, TBR, TE8 (Tourbillon), Time Pyramid, UTTE / from approx. $10,000 to $325,000

DTE (Double Tourbillon Escapement)

Reference number: 1DTAW.S01A.C121R
Movement: manually wound, Arnold & Son Caliber 8513; ø 37.30 mm, height 8.35 mm; 42 jewels; 21,600 vph; NAC-treated mainplate; 1-minute tourbillon with white gold bridges; finely finished parts, skeletonized movement; double spring barrel; 90-hour power reserve
Functions: hours, minutes, seconds on tourbillon; double power reserve indicator
Case: pink gold, ø 43.5 mm, height 12.67 mm with sapphire crystal; sapphire crystal; transparent case back; water-resistant to 3 atm
Band: reptile skin, buckle
Price: $215,800; limited to 28 pieces

DBG Skeleton

Reference number: Reference 1DGAP.S10A.C120P
Movement: manually wound, Arnold & Son Caliber 1309; ø 35 mm, height 3.9 mm; 42 jewels; 21,600 vph; NAC-treated mainplate; double spring barrel, 2 independent gearwheels and escapement systems; 40-hour power reserve
Functions: hours, minutes (double, 2 time zones), sweep seconds; day/night indicator (per time zone)
Case: rose gold, ø 44 mm, height 9.89 mm; sapphire crystal; transparent case back; water-resistant to 3 atm; **Band:** reptile skin, buckle
Remarks: time displayed on 2 tinted sapphire crystal disks; local time can be adjusted to the minute
Price: $38,800; limited to 30 pieces

Nebula 38 Steel

Reference number: 1NEAS.B01A
Movement: manually wound, Arnold & Son Caliber 5101; ø 31.5 mm, height 4.04 mm; 24 jewels; 21,600 vph; skeletonized and finely finished movement with rhodium-plated chapter ring; 90-hour power reserve
Functions: hours, minutes, subsidiary seconds
Case: stainless steel, ø 38 mm, height 8.91 mm; sapphire crystal; transparent case back; water-resistant to 3 atm
Band: calfskin, buckle
Remarks: skeletonized dial
Price: $14,500
Variations: red gold ($25,950)

Ultrathin Tourbillon Koi

Reference number: 1ETAS.B01A.C113S
Movement: manually wound, Arnold & Son Caliber 8200; ø 32 mm, height 2.97 mm; 29 jewels; 28,800 vph; 1-minute flying tourbillon; mainplate with côtes de Genève, hand-engraved tourbillon bridge; 90-hour power reserve; COSC-certified chronometer
Functions: hours, minutes
Case: red gold, ø 42 mm, height 12.23 mm; sapphire crystal; transparent case back; water-resistant to 3 atm
Remarks: miniature painting on black mother-of-pearl, painting engraved by hand
Band: reptile skin, buckle
Price: on request; unique piece

Time Pyramid Black

Reference number: 1TPBS.R01A
Movement: manually wound, Arnold & Son Caliber 1615; ø 37 mm, height 4.4 mm; 27 jewels; 21,600 vph; skeletonized movement; double spring barrel; 90-hour power reserve
Functions: hours, minutes, subsidiary seconds; double power reserve indicator
Case: stainless steel with black DLC coating, ø 44.6 mm, height 10 mm; sapphire crystal; transparent case back; water-resistant to 3 atm
Band: reptile skin, buckle
Remarks: pyramid-shaped movement inspired from table clocks by J. and R. Arnold
Price: $31,900; limited to 50 pieces
Variations: steel ($31,900); red gold ($50,000)

Time Pyramid Tourbillon

Reference number: 1TPBR.T01A
Movement: manually wound, Arnold & Son Caliber 8615; ø 37.60 mm, height 5.70 mm; 31 jewels; 21,600 vph; 1-minute tourbillon; finely finished parts, skeletonized movement; double spring barrel; 90-hour power reserve; **Functions:** hours, minutes, seconds on tourbillon; double power reserve indicator
Case: red gold, ø 44.6 mm, height 10.09 mm; sapphire crystal; transparent case back; water-resistant to 3 atm; **Band:** reptile skin, buckle
Remarks: pyramid-shaped movement inspired from table clocks by J. and R. Arnold; hours on sapphire disk, minutes on rhodium-plated ring
Price: $50,000; limited to 28 pieces
Variations: stainless steel ($39,995)

DSTB

Reference number: 1ATAR.S01A
Movement: automatic, Arnold & Son Caliber 6003; ø 38 mm, height 7.39 mm; 32 jewels; 28,800 vph; true-beat escapement on dial, finely finished movement; 45-hour power reserve
Functions: hours, minutes (off-center), subsidiary seconds (jumping)
Case: red gold, ø 44 mm, height 13 mm; sapphire crystal; transparent case back; water-resistant to 3 atm
Band: reptile skin, buckle
Price: $48,550
Variations: stainless steel ($30,750)

HM Perpetual Obsidian

Reference number: 1GLAR.Z01A.C154A
Movement: manually wound, Arnold & Son Caliber 1512; ø 34 mm, height 5.35 mm; 27 jewels; 21,600 vph; astronomically precise 122-year moon phase; 90-hour power reserve
Functions: hours, minutes; moon phase
Case: pink gold, ø 42 mm, height 11.43 mm; sapphire crystal; transparent case back; water-resistant to 3 atm
Band: reptile skin, buckle
Remarks: gold Mexican obsidian dial, rhodium-plated sculptural moon
Price: $33,650; limited to 28 pieces

Globetrotter

Reference number: 1WTAS.S01A.D137S
Movement: automatic, Arnold & Son Caliber 6022; ø 38 mm, height 6.55 mm (14 mm includes arched bridge and hemisphere); 29 jewels; 28,800 vph; 3D world time display in sculptural hemisphere design; 45-hour power reserve
Functions: hours, minutes; world time indicator (2nd time zone)
Case: stainless steel, ø 45 mm, height 17.2 mm; sapphire crystal; transparent case back; water-resistant to 3 atm
Band: calfskin, buckle
Price: $16,995

ARTYA

Shaking up the staid atmosphere of watchmaking can be achieved in many ways. The conservative approach is to make some small engineering advance and then talk loudly of tradition and innovation. Yvan Arpa, founder of ArtyA watches, does it differently.

This refreshingly candid personality arrived at watchmaking because, after spending his *Wanderjahre* crossing Papua New Guinea on foot and practicing Thai boxing in its native land, any corporate mugginess back home did not quite cut it for him. Instead he turned the obscure brand Romain Jerome into the talk of the industry with novel material choices: "I looked for antimatter to gentrify common matter," he reflects, "like the rust: proof of the passage of time and the sworn enemy of watchmaking."

He founded ArtyA, where he could get his "monster" off the slab as it were, with a divine spark. "I had worked with water, rust, dust, and other elements, and then I really caught fire," says Arpa. Artya's watches hit nerves and drew a gamut of emotional responses. His dials shake up the owner, and are often genuinely unique. They can include real butterfly wings and collages of earth, shells, pigments, or fish scales, or be exquisitely decorated by Bram Ramon. Of late, he has started using mother-of-pearl, which he cuts into skulls that glare spookily from the dial.

Thinking outside of the box is not enough for Arpa. He thinks out of the dial, as illustrated by the Son of Finance Raptor, which features a sleeve-ripping bird of prey staring down from the bezel onto a dial strewn with cut-up banknotes.

One of Arpa's not-so-secret weapons in the fight for market share is his artist wife, Dominique Arpa-Cirpka, who delivers dreamier dials.

Arpa wants us not only to wear a watch, but to reflect on aspects of our world and society, the meaning of money, bullets, skulls, our love-hate relationship with electronics, the passage of time, amour and violence, the beauty of nature frozen in death, and the significance of music.

Luxury Artpieces SA
Route de Thonon 146
CH-1222 Vésenaz
Switzerland

Tel.:
+41-22-752-4940

Website:
www.artya.com

Founded:
2010

Number of employees:
12

Annual production:
at least 365 (one a day)

U.S. distributor:
Contact headquarters for all enquiries.

Most important collections/price range:
Son of a Gun / $8,800 to $167,000; Son of Art / $3,800 to $21,000; Son of Earth / $4,300 to $183,000; Son of Love / $4,300 to $54,500; Son of Sound / $4,300 to $22,110; Son of Gears / $6,550 to $16,550

Horse Enamel

Movement: automatic, A17 highly modified by ArtyA; ø 26.20 mm, height 3.60 mm; 25 jewels
Functions: hours, minutes, sweep seconds
Case: stainless steel, 47 mm, height 14.3 mm; screwed-down case back; water-resistant to 3 atm
Remarks: case completely engraved in neo-Renaissance style by Bram Ramon using bright-cut and regular engraving techniques
Band: reptile skin, buckle
Price: $28,000; unique piece

ArtyA Mother of Pearl Tourbillon

Movement: manually wound, ArtyA; ø 30.6 mm, height 4.5 mm; 21,600 vph; 19 jewels; 1-minute flying tourbillon; 100-hour power reserve
Functions: hours, minutes, seconds on tourbillon cage
Case: stainless steel with black DLC and carbon fiber inserts, 44 mm, height 13 mm; transparent case back; water-resistant to 3 atm
Remarks: hand-engraved bezel in neo-Renaissance style by Bram Ramon; mother-of-pearl dial designed by Yvan Arpa
Band: reptile skin, buckle
Price: $169,000; unique piece

Historic Gold

Movement: manually wound, historical Valjoux 23VZ; ø 29.5 mm, height 5.85 mm; 18,000 vph; 17 jewels; 9-column control of chronograph functions; skeletonized movement; 48-hour power reserve
Functions: hours, minutes
Case: rose gold, 38 mm, height 13.9 mm; transparent case back; water-resistant to 5 atm
Remarks: built around a historic Valjoux movement from around 1938
Band: calfskin, buckle
Price: $38,400; unique piece

Son of Earth Mete-ora

Movement: automatic, ArtyA Aion; ø 26.20 mm, height 3.60 mm; 25 jewels; 28,800 vph; with côtes de Genève; rhodium-plated gold oscillator; COSC-certified; 52-hour power reserve
Functions: hours, minutes, sweep seconds
Case: stainless steel with black DLC, with ArtyOr lateral inserts, ø 44 mm, height 11 mm; engraved and screwed-down case back; water-resistant to 3 atm
Band: calfskin, buckle
Remarks: dial made of Muonionalusta meteorite
Price: $11,000

Black Sunday

Movement: automatic, A17 highly modified by ArtyA; ø 26.20 mm, height 3.60 mm; 25 jewels; 28,800 vph; 52-hour power reserve
Functions: hours, minutes, seconds
Case: stainless steel with PVD treatment, ø 44 mm, height 14.3 mm; silver engraved bezel; transparent case back; water-resistant to 3 atm
Remarks: inspired by a Cypress Hill album; carved in mammoth tusk and water buffalo horn
Band: calfskin, buckle
Price: $28,000

Son of Earth Butterfly Target

Movement: automatic, A17 highly modified by ArtyA; ø 26.20 mm, height 3.60 mm; 25 jewels; 28,800 vph; 52-hour power reserve
Functions: hours, minutes, seconds
Case: stainless steel, ø 44 mm, height 11 mm; engraved and screwed-open case back; water-resistant to 3 atm
Band: calfskin, buckle
Remarks: case and bezel seared by Tesla coil "lightning machine"; dial decorated with real butterfly wing, pigments, leaf gold by artist D. Arpa-Cirpka
Price: $11,200

Son of Gears, Chrono

Movement: automatic wound ArtyA movement; ø 33 mm, height 12 mm; 19 jewels; 21,600 vph; 54-hour power reserve
Functions: hours, minutes, subsidiary seconds; chronograph; date on subdial
Case: stainless steel with black DLC, ø 43 mm, height 14 mm; engraved and screwed-down transparent case back; water-resistant to 3 atm
Band: calfskin, buckle
Remarks: skeletonized dial
Price: $12,000; unique piece
Variations: different case shapes and movement colors

Son of Art Finance Raptor

Movement: automatic, A17 highly modified by ArtyA; ø 26.20 mm, height 3.60 mm; 25 jewels
Functions: hours, minutes, sweep seconds
Case: stainless steel, ø 47 mm, height 14.3 mm; engraved and screwed-on case back; water-resistant to 3 atm
Band: reptile skin, buckle
Remarks: ArtyA unique wrist sculpture featuring hand-engraved eagle pecking at shredded euro bills on the dial
Price: $6,900; unique piece

Son of Sea Fish Scales

Movement: automatic, A17 highly modified by ArtyA; ø 26.20 mm, height 3.60 mm; 25 jewels
Functions: hours, minutes, sweep seconds
Case: stainless steel, ø 47 mm, height 14.3 mm; engraved and screwed-on case back; water-resistant to 3 atm
Band: reptile skin, buckle
Remarks: dial decorated with real fish scales, hand-hammered bezel
Price: $5,500; unique piece

AUDEMARS PIGUET

Manufacture d'Horlogerie
Audemars Piguet
Route de France 16
CH-1348 Le Brassus
Switzerland

Tel.:
+41-21-642-3900

E-mail:
info@audemarspiguet.com

Website:
www.audemarspiguet.com

Founded:
1875

Number of employees:
approx. 1,300

Annual production:
40,000 watches

U.S. distributor:
Audemars Piguet (North America) Inc.
Service Center of the Americas
3040 Gulf to Bay Boulevard
Clearwater, FL 33759

Most important collections/price range:
CODE 11.59 / from approx. $26,000; Millenary / from approx. $28,400; Royal Oak / from approx. $17,800; special concept watches

Jules-Louis Audemars (b. 1851) and Edward-Auguste Piguet (b. 1853) knew they would follow in the footsteps of their fathers and grandfathers and become watchmakers. They were members of the same sports association, sang in the same choir, attended the same vocational school—and both became outstandingly talented watchmakers. The *manufacture,* founded over 140 years ago by these two, is still in family hands, and it has become one of the leading names in the industry.

In the history of watchmaking, only a handful of watches have really achieved cult status. One of them is the Royal Oak by Audemars Piguet. It was born as a radical answer to the global invasion of the quartz watch. Audemars Piguet contacted the designer Gérald Genta to create a watch for a new generation of customers, a sportive luxury timepiece with a modern look, which could be worn every day. The result was a luxurious watch of stainless steel. The octagonal bezel held down with boldly "industrial" hexagonal bolts onto a 39-millimeter case was almost provocative. The watch, big for its time, was nicknamed "Jumbo." It ran on what was then the thinnest automatic movement, a slice 3.05 millimeters high. The second key to the brand's enduring success was no doubt the acquisition of the atelier Renaud et Papi in 1992. APRP, as it is known, specializes in creating and executing complex complications, a skill it lets other brands share in as well.

All good things need to change at some point. At the SIHH 2019, CEO François-Henry Bennahmias presented the "Code 11.59" by Audemars Piguet, a marketing name that suggests deep brand codes cloaked in modern garb. There is the round bezel and case with an octagonal barrel. The sapphire crystal is specially shaped with a double vault. The dials feature special treatments, a subtle reminder of the company's deep knowledge of watch art. And they benefit from a series of new movements, notable in 2020, the Caliber 4401, with column-wheel control of chronograph functions and a flyback mechanism.

Code 11.59 Selfwinding

Reference number: 15210BC.OO.A068CR.01
Movement: automatic, AP Caliber 4302; ø 32 mm, height 4.8 mm; 32 jewels; 28,800 vph; gold rotor, finely finished movement; 70-hour power reserve
Functions: hours, minutes, sweep seconds; date
Case: white gold, ø 41 mm, height 10.7 mm; sapphire crystal; transparent case back; water-resistant to 3 atm
Band: reptile skin, buckle
Price: $26,800

Code 11.59 Selfwinding

Reference number: 26393OR.OO.A616CR.01
Movement: automatic, AP Caliber 4401; ø 32 mm, height 6.8 mm; 40 jewels; 28,800 vph; skeletonized gold rotor, finely finished movement; 70-hour power reserve
Functions: hours, minutes, subsidiary seconds; flyback chronograph; date
Case: rose gold, ø 41 mm, height 12.6 mm; sapphire crystal; transparent case back; water-resistant to 3 atm
Band: reptile skin, buckle
Price: $42,400
Variations: white gold ($42,400)

Code 11.59 Chronograph

Reference number: 26393CR.OO.A009CR.01
Movement: automatic, AP Caliber 4401; ø 32 mm, height 6.8 mm; 40 jewels; 28,800 vph; skeletonized gold rotor, finely finished movement; 70-hour power reserve
Functions: hours, minutes, subsidiary seconds; flyback chronograph; date
Case: white gold, ø 41 mm, height 12.6 mm; sapphire crystal; transparent case back; water-resistant to 3 atm
Band: reptile skin, buckle
Price: $42,400
Variations: rose gold ($42,400)

Code 11.59 Perpetual Calendar

Reference number: 26394OR.OO.D321CR.01
Movement: automatic, AP Caliber 5134; ø 29 mm, height 4.31 mm; 38 jewels; 19,800 vph; skeletonized gold rotor, finely finished movement; 40-hour power reserve
Functions: hours, minutes; perpetual calendar with date, weekday, calendar week, month, moon phase, leap year
Case: rose gold, ø 41 mm, height 10.9 mm; sapphire crystal; transparent case back
Band: reptile skin, folding clasp
Remarks: aventurine dial
Price: $74,500

Code 11.59 Minute Repeater Supersonnerie

Reference number: 26395BC.OO.D321CR.01
Movement: manually wound, AP Caliber 2953; ø 30 mm, height 6 mm; 32 jewels; 21,600 vph; movement finely finished; 72-hour power reserve
Functions: hours, minutes, subsidiary seconds; minute repeater
Case: white gold, ø 41 mm, height 13.5 mm; sapphire crystal
Band: reptile skin, folding clasp
Remarks: volume amplifier for minute repeater using special resonance board; enamel dial
Price: on request

Code 11.59 Tourbillon Openworked

Reference number: 26600OR.OO.D002CR.01
Movement: manually wound, AP Caliber 2948; ø 32.25 mm, height 4.97 mm; 19 jewels; 21,600 vph; flying 1-minute tourbillon; fully skeletonized movement; 80-hour power reserve
Functions: hours, minutes
Case: rose gold, ø 41 mm, height 10.7 mm; sapphire crystal; transparent case back; water-resistant to 3 atm
Band: reptile skin, folding clasp
Price: on request

[RE]MASTER01

Reference number: 26595SR.OO.A032VE.01
Movement: automatic, AP Caliber 4409; ø 32 mm, height 6.82 mm; 40 jewels; 28,800 vph; 70-hour power reserve
Functions: hours, minutes, subsidiary seconds; flyback chronograph
Case: stainless steel, ø 40 mm, height 14.6 mm; rose gold bezel, crown, and pushers; sapphire crystal; transparent case back
Band: calfskin, buckle
Remarks: comes with additional reptile skin strap
Price: $53,100

Royal Oak Chronograph

Reference number: 26315OR.OO.1256OR.01
Movement: automatic, AP Caliber 2385; ø 26.2 mm, height 5.5 mm; 37 jewels; 21,600 vph; completely hand-decorated movement; 40-hour power reserve
Functions: hours, minutes, subsidiary seconds; chronograph; date
Case: rose gold, ø 38 mm, height 11 mm; bezel screwed to case back with 8 white gold screws; sapphire crystal; screw-in crown and pushers; water-resistant to 5 atm
Band: rose gold, folding clasp
Price: $52,700

Royal Oak Chronograph

Reference number: 26315ST.OO.1256ST.01
Movement: automatic, AP Caliber 2385; ø 26.2 mm, height 5.5 mm; 37 jewels; 21,600 vph; hand-decorated movement; 40-hour power reserve
Functions: hours, minutes, subsidiary seconds; chronograph; date
Case: stainless steel, ø 38 mm, height 11 mm; bezel screwed to case back with 8 white gold screws; sapphire crystal; screw-in crown and pushers; water-resistant to 5 atm
Band: stainless steel, folding clasp
Price: $23,800

Royal Oak Chronograph

Reference number: 26315ST.OO.1256ST.02
Movement: automatic, AP Caliber 2385; ø 26.2 mm, height 5.5 mm; 37 jewels; 21,600 vph; hand-decorated movement; 40-hour power reserve
Functions: hours, minutes, subsidiary seconds; chronograph; date
Case: stainless steel, ø 38 mm, height 11 mm; bezel screwed to case back with 8 white gold screws; sapphire crystal; screw-in crown and pushers; water-resistant to 5 atm
Band: stainless steel, folding clasp
Price: $23,800

Royal Oak Chronograph

Reference number: 26331ST.OO.1220ST.01
Movement: automatic, AP Caliber 2385; ø 26.2 mm, height 5.5 mm; 37 jewels; 21,600 vph; hand-decorated movement; 40-hour power reserve
Functions: hours, minutes, subsidiary seconds; chronograph; date
Case: stainless steel, ø 41 mm, height 11 mm; bezel screwed to case back with 8 white gold screws; sapphire crystal; screw-in crown and pusher; water-resistant to 5 atm
Band: stainless steel, folding clasp
Price: $24,300

Royal Oak Selfwinding

Reference number: 15500ST.OO.1220ST.01
Movement: automatic, AP Caliber 4302; ø 32 mm, height 4.8 mm; 32 jewels; 28,800 vph; movement finely finished; 70-hour power reserve
Functions: hours, minutes, sweep seconds; date
Case: stainless steel, ø 41 mm, height 10.4 mm; bezel screwed to case back with 8 white gold screws; sapphire crystal; water-resistant to 5 atm
Band: stainless steel, folding clasp
Price: $19,200

Royal Oak Selfwinding

Reference number: 15500ST.OO.1220ST.01
Movement: automatic, AP Caliber 4302; ø 32 mm, height 4.8 mm; 32 jewels; 28,800 vph; movement finely finished; 70-hour power reserve
Functions: hours, minutes, sweep seconds; date
Case: rose gold, ø 41 mm, height 10.4 mm; bezel screwed to case back with 8 white gold screws; sapphire crystal; water-resistant to 5 atm
Band: stainless steel, folding clasp
Price: $32,000
Variation: stainless steel case ($19,200)

Royal Oak

Reference number: 15502OR.ZZ.1222OR.01
Movement: automatic, AP Caliber 4302; ø 32 mm, height 4.8 mm; 32 jewels; 28,800 vph; 70-hour power reserve
Functions: hours, minutes, sweep seconds; date
Case: rose gold, ø 41 mm, height 10.4 mm; bezel screwed to case back with 8 white gold screws and set with diamonds; sapphire crystal; transparent case back; water-resistant to 5 atm
Band: rose gold, folding clasp
Remarks: case and bracelet set with 610 diamonds; dial set with 466 sapphires
Price: on request

Royal Oak Offshore Chronograph

Reference number: 26480TI.OO.A027CA.01
Movement: automatic, AP Caliber 2385; ø 26.2 mm, height 5.5 mm; 37 jewels; 21,600 vph; hand-decorated movement; 40-hour power reserve
Functions: hours, minutes, subsidiary seconds; chronograph; date
Case: titanium, ø 42 mm, height 12.8 mm; bezel screwed to case back with 8 white gold screws; sapphire crystal; water-resistant to 10 atm
Band: rubber, buckle
Remarks: comes with white rubber strap
Price: $26,800

Royal Oak Offshore Chronograph

Reference number: 26400SO.OO.A335CA.01
Movement: automatic, AP Caliber 3126/3840; ø 29.92 mm, height 7.16 mm; 59 jewels; 21,600 vph; 50-hour power reserve
Functions: hours, minutes, subsidiary seconds; chronograph; date
Case: stainless steel, ø 44 mm, height 14.4 mm; ceramic bezel screwed to case back with 8 white gold screws; sapphire crystal; transparent case back; ceramic crown and pusher, screw-in crown; water-resistant to 10 atm
Band: rubber, buckle
Price: $32,200
Variations: various bands, dials, and cases

Royal Oak Concept Flying Tourbillon GMT

Reference number: 26589IO.OO.D002CA.01
Movement: manually wound, Audemars Piguet Caliber 2954; ø 35.6 mm, height 9.9 mm; 24 jewels; 21,600 vph; flying 1-minute tourbillon; movement finely finished by hand; 237-hour power reserve
Functions: hours, minutes; additional 24-hour display (2nd time zone), crown position indicator for function changes
Case: titanium, ø 44 mm, height 16.1 mm; ceramic bezel screwed to case back with 8 white gold screws; sapphire crystal; transparent case back; ceramic crown and pushers; water-resistant to 10 atm
Band: rubber, folding clasp
Price: on request

Millenary Frosted Gold Philosophique

Reference number: 77266BC.GG.A326CR.01
Movement: automatic, AP Caliber 3140; ø 26.59 mm; 43 jewels; 21,600 vph; 50-hour power reserve
Functions: hours
Case: white gold, 39.5 × 35.4 mm, height 10.9 mm; "frosted gold" bezel and lugs; sapphire crystal; transparent case back; crown with sapphire cabochon
Band: reptile skin, buckle
Price: $29,500

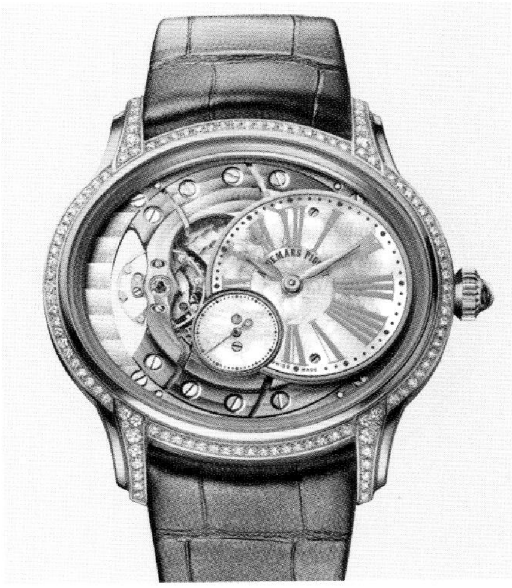

Millenary Frosted Gold Opal Dial

Reference number: 77244OR.GG.1272OR.01
Movement: manually wound, AP Caliber 5201; 32.74 × 28.59 mm, height 4.16 mm; 19 jewels; 21,600 vph; inverted movement design with balance and escapement on dial side; 49-hour power reserve
Functions: hours, minutes, subsidiary seconds
Case: rose gold, 39.5 × 35.4 mm; bezel and lugs set with 116 diamonds; sapphire crystal; transparent case back; crown with sapphire cabochon
Band: reptile skin, buckle
Remarks: mother-of-pearl dial
Price: $28,400

Royal Oak

Reference number: 77351OR.ZZ.1261OR.01
Movement: automatic, AP Caliber 5800; ø 23.3 mm; 28 jewels; 28,800 vph; 50-hour power reserve
Functions: hours, minutes, sweep seconds; date
Case: rose gold, ø 34 mm, height 8.8 mm; bezel screwed to case with 8 white gold screws and set with 40 diamonds; sapphire crystal; transparent case back; screw-in crown; water-resistant to 5 atm
Band: rose gold, folding clasp
Price: $44,500

Royal Oak

Reference number: 77350ST.OO.1261ST.01
Movement: automatic, AP Caliber 5800; ø 23.3 mm; 28 jewels; 28,800 vph; 50-hour power reserve
Functions: hours, minutes, sweep seconds; date
Case: stainless steel, ø 34 mm, height 8.8 mm; bezel screwed to case with 8 white gold screws; sapphire crystal; transparent case back; screw-in crown; water-resistant to 5 atm
Band: stainless steel, folding clasp
Price: $18,300

Caliber 4302

Automatic; bidirectionally winding gold rotor; single spring barrel, 70-hour power reserve
Functions: hours, minutes, sweep seconds; date
Diameter: 32 mm
Height: 4.8 mm
Jewels: 32
Balance: with variable inertia
Frequency: 28,800 vph
Remarks: beveled and polished steel parts, plate with perlage, bridges with côtes de Genève; 257 parts

Caliber 4401

Automatic; column-wheel control of chronograph functions; skeletonized gold rotor; single spring barrel, 70-hour power reserve
Functions: hours, minutes, subsidiary seconds; flyback chronograph; date
Diameter: 32 mm
Height: 6.8 mm
Jewels: 40
Balance: with variable inertia
Frequency: 28,800 vph
Remarks: beveled and polished steel parts, plate with perlage, bridges with côtes de Genève; 367 parts

Caliber 4409

Automatic; column-wheel control of chronograph functions; bidirectional gold winding rotor; single spring barrel, 70-hour power reserve
Functions: hours, minutes, subsidiary seconds; flyback-chronograph
Diameter: 32 mm
Height: 6.82 mm
Jewels: 40
Balance: with variable inertia
Frequency: 28,800 vph
Remarks: beveled and polished steel parts, plate with perlage, bridges with côtes de Genève; 349 parts

Caliber 5134

Automatic; flying spring barrel; 40-hour power reserve
Functions: hours, minutes; perpetual calendar with date, weekday, calendar week, month, moon phase, leap year
Diameter: 29 mm
Height: 4.31 mm
Jewels: 38
Balance: with variable inertia
Frequency: 19,800 vph
Balance spring: flat hairspring
Remarks: hand-decorated movement; gold rotor; 374 parts

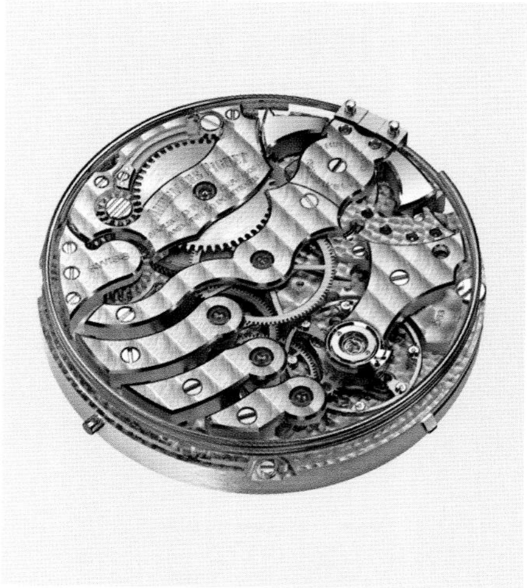

Caliber 2953

Manually wound; single spring barrel, 72-hour power reserve
Functions: hours, minutes, subsidiary seconds; minute repeater
Diameter: 30 mm
Height: 6 mm
Jewels: 32
Balance: with variable inertia
Frequency: 21,600 vph
Remarks: beveled and polished steel parts, plate with perlage, bridges with côtes de Genève; 362 parts

Caliber 2948

Manually wound; flying 1-minute tourbillon; skeletonized movement; single spring barrel, 80-hour power reserve
Functions: hours, minutes
Diameter: 32.25 mm
Height: 4.97 mm
Jewels: 19
Frequency: 21,600 vph
Remarks: black-coated structural parts; 196 parts

AVeritas Watches
105 McLaughlin Road
Suite F
Rochester, NY 14615

Tel.:
585-662-8225

E-mail:
info@averitas.com

Website:
www.averitas.com

Founded:
2006

Number of employees:
3

Annual production:
150–200

Distribution:
direct to consumer

Most important collections/price range:
Primus / $1,489; Dimetior / $3,950; Paerio / $7,995

AVERITAS

J. Michael Brady's interest in watches was sparked by his grandfather's love of mechanical watches. His first career move, however, was engineering and the establishment of a manufacturing company specializing in optical components with micron tolerances. The watches came in 2006, when he created custom timepieces on commissions for close friends. These bespoke watches were powered by traditional mechanical movements supplied by various Swiss manufacturers.

Fast-forward a few years, and Brady decided to formally launch the AVeritas brand he had been considering for quite some time. In 2009, he started making his AVeritas cases using the machines he already owned, with the first fruits of his labors being the Aurora and Primus lines. These were powered by a traditionally finished manually wound Swiss movement placed inside a coin-edge case. These two original designs show just how different the same case can look when framing different dials.

Expanding beyond the original cast of two, Brady has since added another six variations of his original idea. These timepieces all combine traditional forms of watchmaking with bold avant-garde dial designs that appear inspired from nature itself. There are the "thunderbolts" on the Regulator that flash away from the center of the dial, and the swirling pattern on the Lunar Date, which contrasts with old-fashioned cathedral hands. The central dial of the Dimetior, on the other hand, is animated by a blend of two different patterns, one square and rational, like a parquet floor, the other more flowing. At any rate, each watch Brady produces is surprising in its own way. Not being bound to a specific DNA gives Brady a great deal of liberty to create. The watches are all powered by robust ETA movements.

Dimetior

Movement: automatic, modified ETA/Valjoux 7750; ø 30 mm, height 9.2 mm; 25 jewels; 28,800 vph; finely finished with perlage, côtes de Genève, blued screws, custom rotor; 44-hour power reserve
Functions: hours, minutes, subsidiary seconds; 12-hour totalizer; analog date
Case: stainless steel case, crown, and pushers, ø 44 mm at bezel, height 15.1 mm; coin-edge bezel; sapphire crystal; transparent case back; water-resistant to 5 atm
Band: leather, buckle
Price: $3,950; limited to 90 pieces
Variations: various color options

Lunar Date

Movement: automatic, modified ETA Caliber 2892 base; ø 25.6 mm, height 4.1 mm; 26 jewels; 28,800 vph; 42-hour power reserve
Functions: hours, minutes, seconds; moon phase; analog date
Case: stainless steel, ø 42 mm at bezel, height 13 mm; coin-edge bezel; sapphire crystal; transparent case back; water-resistant to 5 atm
Band: leather, buckle
Price: $4,495; limited to 90 pieces

Regulator

Movement: manually wound, modified ETA Caliber 6498; ø 37.2 mm, height 4.5 mm; 17 jewels; 18,000 vph; finely finished movement with côtes de Genève and blued screws; 53-hour power reserve
Functions: hours, minutes, seconds in regulator format
Case: stainless steel, ø 44 mm, height 12.5 mm; sapphire crystal; transparent case back; water-resistant to 5 atm
Remarks: dial decorated with thunderbolt motif
Band: leather, buckle
Price: $4,479

AZIMUTH

Creativity can take on all forms and accept all forms as well. This appears to be the philosophy behind Azimuth, an independent watch brand that has sprouted an eclectic and surprising bouquet of watch designs. For the company, the path is by no means well-beaten: Azimuth always guarantees a raised eyebrow with avant-garde designs for luxury timepieces, with several iconic models like the Mr. Roboto, the Spaceship series, the automobile series and the TT and GT enjoying cult status.

In 2019, Azimuth ventured once again into sci-fi and let itself be inspired by the space travel, cyber-robotics, and interplanetary exploration that are currently woven into the fabric of everyday life. The result was the Azimuth Predator 2.0, which boasts state-of-the-art case construction, unique material treatment, and contemporary design. The spacy esthetics also include an ingenious jumping hour display complemented by a highly stylized, broad minute hand.

In 2020, Azimuth continued with the Astro Boy, which is bound to thrill fans of the vintage manga character from the 1950s and 1960s. Azimuth collaborated with Tezuka/Planetnemo to create an automatic timepiece that tells time by means of Astro Boy's animated arms. The playful nature of Astro Boy is best captured by the artist's impression of him standing sideways and wearing a cheeky smile. For added dimension, the dial has been created with a charcoal-colored *fumé effect,* and Astro Boy is coated with a layer of luminous compound, enabling it to glow in the dark.

Like all great artists, though, Azimuth is capable of doing "serious watches," and for that they purchased a venerable Swiss brand in 2013 called Choisi (see page 226).

Azimuth Watch Co. Sàrl
Rue des Draizes 5
CH-2000 Neuchâtel
Switzerland

Tel.:
+41-79-765-1466

E-mail:
gpi@azimuthwatch.com
chrislong@azimuthwatch.com

Website:
www.azimuthwatch.com

Founded:
2003

Number of employees:
6

U.S. distributor:
About Time Luxury Group
210 Bellevue Avenue
Newport, RI 02840
401-952-4684

Most important collection/price range:
SP-1 / from $1,750

SP-1 Gran Turismo

Reference number: SP.SS.GT.N005
Movement: automatic, ETA 2671; ø 17.2 mm, height 4.80 mm; 28,800 vph
Functions: hours, minutes, seconds
Case: stainless steel with camouflage PVD treatment, 50 mm × 45 mm; water-resistant to 3 atm
Band: calfskin strap, folding clasp
Price: $4,850; limited to 50 pieces
Variations: top case in stainless steel high-gloss polished, gold PVD treatment or black PVD treatment

SP-1 Twin Turbo

Reference number: SP.SS.TT.N001
Movement: manually wound, ETA 2512-1; ø 17.2 mm, height 2.85 mm; 21,600 vph
Functions: hours, minutes; 2 time zones
Case: stainless steel and aluminum, 51 mm × 50 mm; water-resistant to 3 atm
Band: calfskin strap, folding clasp
Remarks: 2 vintage movements
Price: $6,000; limited to 88 pieces
Variations: top hood in gray, anthracite, or red (red limited to 50 pieces)

SP-1 Crazy Rider

Reference number: SP.SS.CR.N004
Movement: automatic, in-house modified; length 47.7 mm, height 4.35 mm; 28,800 vph
Functions: 24-hour chain drive hour system, minutes
Case: stainless steel with PVD treatment, titanium bezel with black PVD treatment, 55 mm × 36 mm; sapphire crystal; water-resistant to 3 atm
Band: calfskin, folding clasp
Price: $5,250
Variations: brown dial

SP-1 Mr. Roboto R2

Reference number: SP.SS.ROT.N001
Movement: automatic, in-house modified, sapphire rotor; ø 32.5 mm, height 6.70 mm; 28,800 vph
Functions: regulator hours, retrograde minutes; GMT
Case: stainless steel, 47 mm x 55 mm; sapphire crystal; water-resistant to 3 atm
Band: calfskin, folding clasp
Price: $6,000
Variations: mid-case in titanium with blue PVD treatment

SP-1 Mr. Roboto Bronzo

Reference number: SP.BR.MRB.L001
Movement: automatic, in-house modified; ø 32.5 mm, height 6.70 mm; 28,800 vph
Functions: regulator hours, retrograde minutes; GMT
Case: bronze, 43 mm × 50 mm; sapphire crystal; water-resistant to 3 atm
Band: calfskin, bronze tang buckle
Price: $7,000; limited to 100 pieces

SP-1 Predator 2.0

Reference number: SP.TI.PR.N001
Movement: manual winding, AZM 769 modified and skeletonized aluminum plates; ø 36.6 mm, height 4.50 mm; 21,600 vph
Functions: jumping hours, minutes, seconds
Case: titanium and stainless steel, diameter 44 mm; domed sapphire crystal; water-resistant to 3 atm
Band: rubber, folding clasp
Remarks: 3D titanium minute hand
Price: $5,850
Variations: movement plates in various colors

Back-in-Time "Save the 1-Ocean Blue"

Reference number: RN.BT.BR.N002
Movement: automatic, in-house modified; ø 34.4 mm, height 4.50 mm; 28,800 vph
Functions: hands in counterclockwise motion
Case: bronze, ø 42 mm, height 14.4 mm; domed sapphire crystal; water-resistant to 3 atm
Band: calfskin, bronze tang buckle
Price: $2,550; limited to 50 pieces
Variations: green dial

Back-in-Time Pilot

Reference number: RN.BT.SS.R001
Movement: automatic, in-house modified (base ETA/Sellita); ø 34.4 mm, height 4.50 mm; 21,600/28,800 vph
Functions: single hand in counterclockwise motion, date
Case: stainless steel, ø 42 mm, height 14.40 mm; domed sapphire crystal; water-resistant to 3 atm
Band: calfskin, buckle
Price: $1,750
Variations: silver, black, blue, anthracite dial colors

Astro Boy

Reference number: RN.AS.SS.L001
Movement: automatic, ETA 2842; ø 25.60 mm, height 4.60 mm; 21,600 vph
Functions: hours, minutes
Case: stainless steel with black PVD treatment, ø 42 mm, height 14.40 mm; domed sapphire crystal; water-resistant to 3 atm
Band: calfskin, folding clasp
Price: $2,400; limited to 50 pieces

BALL WATCH CO.

BALL Watch Company SA
Rue du Châtelot 21
CH-2300 La Chaux-de-Fonds
Switzerland

Tel.:
0041-32-724-53-00

E-mail:
info@ballwatch.ch

Website:
www.ballwatch.com
shop.ballwatch.ch

Founded:
1891

U.S. distribution:
BALL Watch USA
888-660-0691

Most important collections/price range:
Engineer, Fireman, Trainmaster / $1,300 to $6,500

Ball Watch Co. collections trace back to the company's origins and evoke the glorious age when trains puffing smoke and steam crisscrossed America. Companies back then had adopted the General Railroads Timepiece Standards, which included such norms as regulation in at least five positions, precision to within thirty seconds per week, Breguet balance springs, and so on. One of the chief players in developing the standards was Webster Clay Ball, a farmboy-turned-watchmaker from Fredericktown, Ohio. He decided to leave the homestead and apprentice as a watchmaker. He worked as a sales rep for Dueber watch cases, and finally opened the Webb C. Ball Company in Cleveland. In 1891, he added the position of chief inspector of the Lake Shore Lines to his CV. When a hogshead's watch stopped for a few minutes, resulting in a lethal crash near Kipton, Ohio, Ball decided to establish quality benchmarks for watch manufacturing that included amagnetic technology. He also set up an inspection system for the timepieces.

Today, Ball Watch Co. still produces tool-like watches, including divers, although now the manufacturing is done in Switzerland. These rugged, durable watches aim to be "accurate in adverse conditions," so says the company tagline—and at a very good price. Since functionality is a top priority, Ball has developed a number of mechanisms like the SpringLOCK antishock system that prevents the balance spring from unfurling when jostled. Ball has also developed special oils for cold temperatures, and it is one of few brands to use tritium gas tubes to light up dials, hands, and markers. For those who need to read the time accurately in dark places—divers, pilots, commandos, hunters, etc.—this is essential.

Engineer Hydrocarbon Original

Reference number: DM2118B-SCJ-BK
Movement: automatic, Ball Caliber RR1102-CSL; ø 25.6 mm, height 5.05 mm; 25 or 26 jewels; 28,800 vph; 38-hour power reserve; COSC-certified chronometer; SpringLOCK® antishock system
Functions: hours, minutes, sweep seconds; day, date
Case: stainless steel, ø 40 mm, height 14.6 mm; sapphire unidirectional bezel with micro gas tubes; sapphire crystal; crown protection system; water-resistant to 20 atm
Band: stainless steel, folding clasp with extension
Remarks: amagnetic
Price: $3,199

Engineer Hydrocarbon AeroGMT II

Reference number: DG2018C-S3C-BK
Movement: automatic, Ball Caliber RR1201-C; ø 25.6 mm, height 4.1 mm; 21 jewels; 28,800 vph; 42-hour power reserve; COSC-certified chronometer
Functions: hours, minutes, sweep seconds; date; 2nd time zone indication
Case: stainless steel, ø 42 mm, height 13.9 mm; sapphire bidirectional bezel with micro gas tube illumination; sapphire crystal; crown protection system; water-resistant to 10 atm
Band: stainless steel, folding clasp with extension
Remarks: shock-resistant; amagnetic
Price: $3,499
Variations: rubber strap

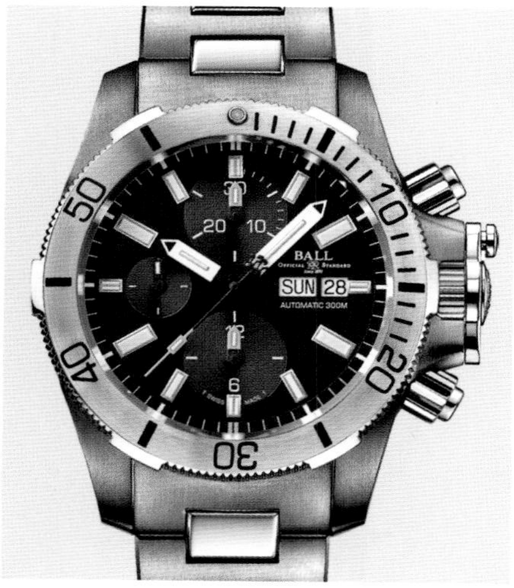

Engineer Hydrocarbon Submarine Warfare Chronograph

Reference number: DC2276A-SJ-BK
Movement: automatic, Ball Caliber RR1402; ø 30 mm, height 7.9 mm; 25 jewels; 28,800 vph; 48-hour power reserve; **Functions:** hours, minutes, subsidiary seconds; day, date; 12-hour chronograph
Case: titanium, ø 42 mm, height 17.9 mm; stainless steel unidirectional bezel; sapphire crystal; crown protection system; water-resistant to 30 atm
Band: tapered titanium and stainless steel, folding clasp with extension
Remarks: micro gas tube illumination; shock-resistant; amagnetic
Price: $3,199; **Variations:** ceramic bezel; stainless steel case; stainless steel bracelet; rubber strap

Engineer Hydrocarbon NEDU

Reference number: DC3026A-S3C-BE
Movement: automatic, Ball Caliber RR1402-C; ø 30 mm, height 7.9 mm; 25 jewels; 28,800 vph; 48-hour power reserve; COSC-certified chronometer
Functions: hours, minutes, subsidiary seconds; day, date; 12-hour chronograph operable underwater
Case: stainless steel, ø 42 mm, height 17.3 mm; patented helium system; ceramic unidirectional bezel; sapphire crystal; crown protection system; water-resistant to 60 atm
Band: titanium/stainless steel, folding clasp with extension
Remarks: micro gas tube illumination; shock-resistant; amagnetic
Price: $4,499; **Variations:** blue dial; rubber strap

Engineer Master II Diver

Reference number: DM3020A-SAJ-BK
Movement: automatic, Ball Caliber RR1102; ø 25.6 mm, height 5.05 mm; 25 or 26 jewels; 28,800 vph; 38-hour power reserve
Functions: hours, minutes, sweep seconds; day, date
Case: stainless steel, ø 42 mm, height 14.6 mm; inner bezel with micro gas tube illumination; sapphire crystal; screw-in crown; water-resistant to 30 atm
Band: stainless steel, folding buckle
Remarks: shock-resistant; amagnetic
Price: $2,499
Variations: rubber strap

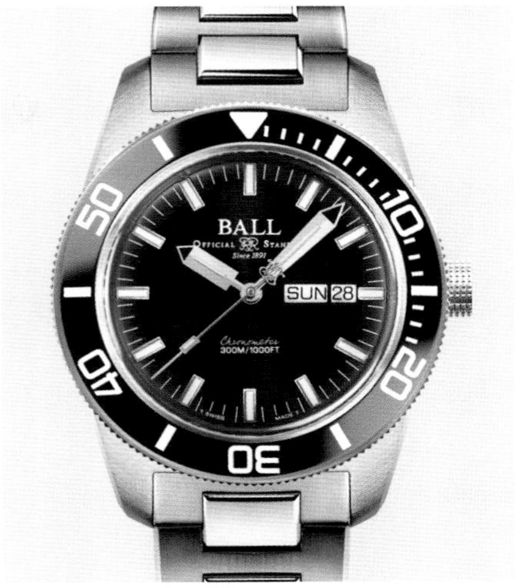

Engineer Master II Skindiver Heritage

Reference number: DM3308A-SC-BK
Movement: automatic, Ball Caliber RR1102-C; ø 25.6 mm, height 5.05 mm; 25 or 26 jewels; 28,800 vph; 38-hour power reserve; COSC-certified chronometer
Functions: hours, minutes, sweep seconds; date
Case: stainless steel, ø 42 mm, height 15.2 mm; unidirectional bezel; mu-metal shield; sapphire crystal; screw-in crown; water-resistant to 10 atm
Band: stainless steel, folding buckle
Remarks: micro gas tube illumination; shock-resistant; amagnetic
Price: $2,799

Engineer Master II Aviator

Reference number: NM1080C-L14A-BK
Movement: automatic, Ball Caliber RR1102; ø 25.6 mm, height 5.05 mm; 25 or 26 jewels; 28,800 vph; 38-hour power reserve
Functions: hours, minutes, sweep seconds; day, date
Case: stainless steel, ø 46 mm, height 11.55 mm; mu-metal shield; antireflective convex sapphire crystal; screw-in crown; water-resistant to 10 atm
Band: calfskin, standard buckle
Remarks: micro gas tube illumination; shock-resistant; amagnetic
Price: $1,999
Variations: stainless steel bracelet; rubber strap

Engineer II Moon Phase

Reference number: NM2282C-LLJ-BK
Movement: automatic, Ball Caliber RR1801; ø 25.6 mm, height 5.05 mm; 25 jewels; 28,800 vph; 42-hour power reserve
Functions: hours, minutes, sweep seconds; date, moon phase
Case: stainless steel, ø 41 mm; luminous moon phase indication; sapphire crystal; screw-in crown; water-resistant to 10 atm
Band: reptile skin strap, standard buckle
Remarks: micro gas tube illumination; Amortiser® antishock system; amagnetic
Price: $1,799
Variations: stainless steel bracelet; blue, gray dial

Engineer II Rainbow

Reference number: NM2028C-L28CJ-BK
Movement: automatic, Ball Caliber RR1103-C; ø 25.6 mm, height 4.6 mm; 25 or 26 jewels; 28,800 vph; 38-hour power reserve; COSC-certified chronometer
Functions: hours, minutes, sweep seconds; magnified date
Case: titanium carbide, ø 43 mm, height 12.4 mm; sapphire crystal; screw-in crown; water-resistant to 10 atm
Band: leather strap, buckle
Remarks: micro gas tube illumination; shock-resistant
Price: $2,199

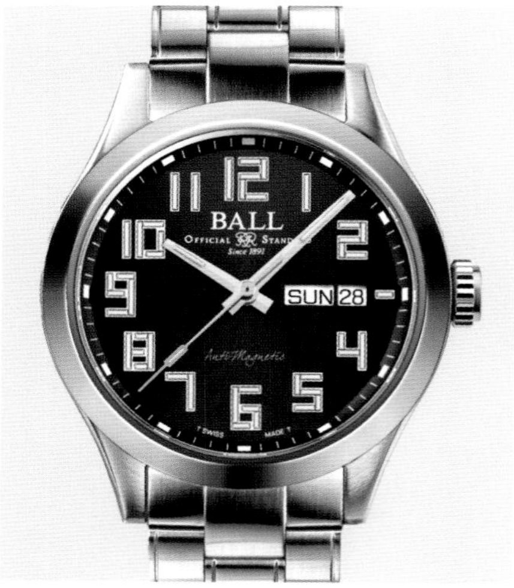

Engineer III StarLight

Reference number: NM2182C-S12-BK1
Movement: automatic, Ball Caliber RR1102; ø 25.6 mm, height 5.05 mm; 25 or 26 jewels; 28,800 vph; 38-hour power reserve
Functions: hours, minutes, sweep seconds; day, date
Case: stainless steel, ø 40 mm, height 13.5 mm; mu-metal shield; sapphire crystal; screw-in crown; water-resistant to 10 atm
Band: stainless steel, folding buckle
Remarks: micro gas tube illumination; Amortiser® antishock system; amagnetic
Price: $1,799
Variations: rubber strap; blue dial

Engineer III Pioneer

Reference number: NM2026C-S15CJ-BK
Movement: automatic, Ball Caliber RR1103-C; ø 25.6 mm, height 4.6 mm; 25 or 26 jewels; 28,800 vph; 38-hour power reserve; COSC-certified chronometer
Functions: hours, minutes, sweep seconds; magnified date
Case: 904L stainless steel, ø 40 mm, height 12.45 mm; sapphire crystal; screw-in crown; water-resistant to 10 atm
Band: 904L stainless steel, folding buckle
Remarks: micro gas tube illumination; shock-resistant; amagnetic
Price: $1,899
Variations: blue dial

Engineer III Bronze

Reference number: NM2186C-L3J-BK
Movement: automatic, Ball Caliber RR1102-SL; ø 25.6 mm, height 5.05 mm; 25 or 26 jewels; 28,800 vph; 38-hour power reserve; SpringLOCK® antishock system
Functions: hours, minutes, sweep seconds; day, date
Case: bronze, ø 43 mm, height 13.45 mm; mu-metal shield; sapphire crystal; screw-in crown; water-resistant to 10 atm
Band: calfskin, standard buckle
Remarks: micro gas tube illumination; Amortiser® antishock system; amagnetic
Price: $2,199

Engineer III Marvelight Bronze Star

Reference number: NM2186C-L4J-GR
Movement: automatic, Ball Caliber RR1102-CSL; ø 25.6 mm, height 5.05 mm; 25 or 26 jewels; 28,800 vph; 38-hour power reserve; COSC-certified chronometer; SpringLOCK® antishock system
Functions: hours, minutes, sweep seconds; day, date
Case: bronze, ø 43 mm, height 13.5 mm; mu-metal shield; sapphire crystal; screw-in crown; water-resistant to 10 atm
Band: calfskin, buckle
Remarks: micro gas tube illumination; Amortiser® antishock system; amagnetic
Price: $2,499
Variations: black or blue dial

Trainmaster Eternity

Reference number: NM2080D-S1J-BE
Movement: automatic, Ball Caliber RR1102; ø 25.6 mm, height 5.05 mm; 25 or 26 jewels; 28,800 vph; 38-hour power reserve
Functions: hours, minutes, sweep seconds; day, date
Case: stainless steel, ø 39.5 mm, height 11.8 mm; sapphire crystal; screw-in crown; transparent case back; water-resistant to 3 atm
Band: stainless steel bracelet, folding buckle
Remarks: micro gas tube illumination; shock-resistant
Price: $2,299
Variations: black dial; reptile skin strap

Trainmaster Legend

Reference number: NM9080D-SJ-SL
Movement: automatic, Ball Caliber RR1103; ø 25.6 mm, height 4.6 mm; 25 or 26 jewels; 28,800 vph; 38-hour power reserve
Functions: hours, minutes, sweep seconds; date
Case: 904L stainless steel, ø 40 mm, height 10.5 mm; sapphire crystal; transparent case back; water-resistant to 3 atm
Band: reptile skin, buckle
Remarks: micro gas tube illumination; shock-resistant
Price: $1,799
Variations: stainless steel bracelet; black dial

Trainmaster Manufacture 80 Hours

Reference number: NM3280D-S1CJ-BK
Movement: automatic, Ball Caliber RRM7309-C; ø 34.24 mm, height 5.16 mm; 25 jewels; 28,800 vph; 80-hour power reserve; COSC-certified chronometer
Functions: hours, minutes, sweep seconds; date
Case: stainless steel, ø 40 mm, height 12.25 mm; sapphire crystal; transparent case back; screw-in crown; water resistant to 5 atm
Band: stainless steel, folding clasp
Remarks: micro gas tube illumination; shock-resistant; amagnetic
Price: $2,799

Trainmaster Standard Time

Reference number: NM3888D-S1CJ-WH
Movement: automatic, Ball Caliber RR1105; ø 25.6 mm, height 4.35 mm; 27 jewels; 28,800 vph; 42-hour power reserve
Functions: hours, minutes, subsidiary seconds; date
Case: stainless steel, ø 39.5 mm, height 11.5 mm; sapphire crystal; transparent case back; screw-in crown; water-resistant to 3 atm
Band: stainless steel bracelet, folding buckle
Remarks: micro gas tube illumination; shock-resistant
Price: $2,499
Variations: reptile skin strap

Fireman Enterprise

Reference number: NM2188C-S5J-BK
Movement: automatic, Ball Caliber RR1103; ø 25.6 mm, height 4.6 mm; 25 or 26 jewels; 28,800 vph; 38-hour power reserve
Functions: hours, minutes, sweep seconds; magnified date
Case: stainless steel, ø 40 mm, height 11.3 mm; sapphire crystal; screw-in crown; water-resistant to 10 atm
Band: stainless steel bracelet, folding clasp
Remarks: micro gas tube illumination; shock-resistant
Price: $999
Variations: white dial; NATO strap

Fireman NightBreaker

Reference number: NM2188C-S13-BE
Movement: automatic, Ball Caliber RR1103; ø 25.6 mm, height 4.6 mm; 25 or 26 jewels; 28,800 vph; 38-hour power reserve
Functions: hours, minutes, sweep seconds; date
Case: stainless steel, ø 40 mm, height 11.3 mm; stainless steel carbide rotating bezel; sapphire crystal; screw-in crown; water-resistant to 10 atm
Band: stainless steel bracelet, folding buckle
Remarks: micro gas tube illumination; Amortiser® antishock system
Price: $1,299
Variations: rubber strap

Fireman Victory

Reference number: NM2098C-S5J-SL
Movement: automatic, Ball Caliber RR1103; ø 25.6 mm, height 4.6 mm; 25 or 26 jewels; 28,800 vph; 38-hour power reserve
Functions: hours, minutes, sweep seconds; date
Case: stainless steel, ø 40 mm, height 11.6 mm; sapphire crystal; screw-in crown; water-resistant to 10 atm
Band: stainless steel bracelet, folding clasp
Remarks: micro gas tube illumination; shock-resistant
Price: $1,499
Variations: black or blue dial; calfskin

Engineer M Marvelight

Reference number: NM2128C-S1C-BE
Movement: automatic, Ball Caliber RRM7309-C; ø 34.24 mm, height 5.16 mm; 25 jewels; 28,800 vph; 80-hour power reserve; COSC-certified chronometer
Functions: hours, minutes, sweep seconds; date
Case: stainless steel, ø 43 mm, height 12.85 mm; sapphire crystal; transparent case back; screw-in crown; water-resistant to 10 atm; Amortiser® antishock system
Band: stainless steel bracelet, folding clasp
Remarks: micro gas tube illumination; shock-resistant; amagnetic
Price: $2,499
Variations: ø 40 mm; black or gray dial; calfskin strap

BAUME & MERCIER

Baume & Mercier, a company founded in 1830, has staked a claim on the market by its ability to keep a finger on the pulse of stylish, urban fashionistas, who are looking for affordable yet remarkable timepieces. Since the early 2000s, it has created a number of noteworthy—and often copied—classics, like the Riviera and the Catwalk.

Joining the Richemont Group has boosted the brand's technical value. In 2018, after four years of development with ValFleurier, the Group's movement manufacturer, and the RIMS research and innovation team, Baume & Mercier released its first in-house *manufacture* movement, the Baumatic Caliber BM12-1975A. In 2020, it added two new complications to the in-house caliber. Models using the caliber boast a five-day power reserve and accuracy of just –4/+6 seconds per day and amagnetism that is about twenty-five times higher than the current ISO norm. This, despite the fact that Baume & Mercier is not permitted to use silicon hairsprings due to patent conflicts. The movement needs servicing only every seven years, which compares favorably to the three to five years required by classic mechanical watches.

The new BM14.1975 AC1/AC2 caliber is used in four of the Clifton models and drives a moon phase plus, in two models, a weekday and date display. In order to make way for the subsidiary dials and apertures, the crosshairs that "ordered" the dial of the simpler three-handers were removed.

The Hampton line was also extended with a series of watches whose rectangular shape recalls Art Deco predecessors. To make sure everyone is served, the company has produced a wide range of timepieces in this line, with dials in various colors. Some are driven by movements. At the top of the line is a steel version with a large date and second time zone. A special system allows the owner to switch bracelets or straps without needing a special tool.

Baume & Mercier
Rue André de Garrini 4
CH-1217 Meyrin
Switzerland

Tel.:
+41-022-580-2948

Website:
www.baume-et-mercier.com

Founded:
1830

Annual production:
100,000 (estimated)

U.S. distributor:
Baume & Mercier
Richemont North America
New York, NY 10022
800-637-2437

Most important collections/price range:
Clifton (men) / $2,200 to $24,500; Classima (men and women) / $990 to $5,950; Hampton (men and women) / $2,500 to $15,000; Linea (women) / $1,950 to $15,750; Promesse (women) / $2,100 to $4,850

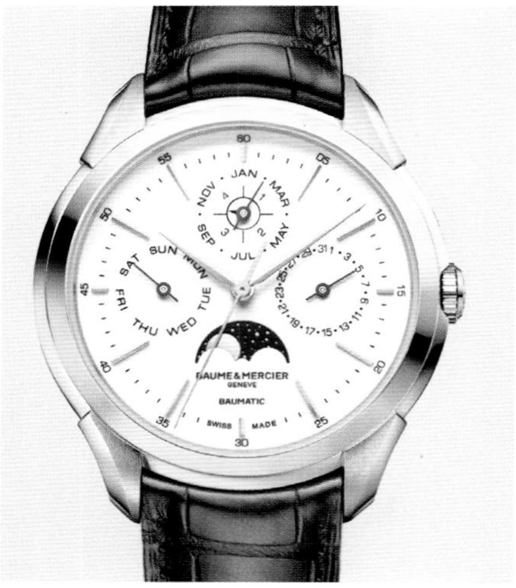

Clifton Baumatic Perpetual Calendar

Reference number: 10583
Movement: automatic, Caliber Baumatic BM13.1975AC2 with Modul Dubois Dépraz 55102; ø 28.2 mm, height 5.8 mm; 21 jewels; 28,800 vph; silicon anchor and escape wheel; balance with variable inertia; skeletonized rotor; 120-hour power reserve
Functions: hours, minutes, sweep seconds; perpetual calendar with date, weekday, month, moon phase, leap year
Case: rose gold, ø 42 mm, height 12.1 mm; sapphire crystal; transparent case back; water-resistant to 5 atm
Band: reptile skin, buckle
Price: $24,700

Clifton Baumatic Day Date Moon Phase

Reference number: 10547
Movement: automatic, Caliber Baumatic BM14.1975AC2; ø 28.2 mm, height 5.7 mm; 21 jewels; 28,800 vph; silicon anchor and escape wheel; balance with variable inertia; skeletonized rotor; 120-hour power reserve
Functions: hours, minutes, sweep seconds; date, weekday, moon phase
Case: rose gold, ø 42 mm, height 12.95 mm; sapphire crystal; transparent case back; water-resistant to 5 atm
Band: reptile skin, buckle
Price: $12,200

Clifton Baumatic Date Moon Phase

Reference number: 10549
Movement: automatic, Caliber Baumatic BM14.1975AC1; ø 28.2 mm, height 5.7 mm; 21 jewels; 28,800 vph; silicon anchor and escape wheel; balance with variable inertia; skeletonized rotor; 120-hour power reserve
Functions: hours, minutes, sweep seconds; date, moon phase
Case: stainless steel, ø 42 mm, height 13.2 mm; sapphire crystal; transparent case back; water-resistant to 5 atm
Band: reptile skin, buckle
Price: $4,050

Clifton Baumatic COSC

Reference number: 10551
Movement: automatic, Caliber Baumatic BM13.1975A COSC; ø 28.2 mm, height 4.2 mm; 21 jewels; 28,800 vph; silicon anchor and escape wheel; balance with variable inertia; skeletonized rotor; 120-hour power reserve; COSC-certified chronometer
Functions: hours, minutes, sweep seconds; date
Case: stainless steel, ø 40 mm, height 11.1 mm; sapphire crystal; transparent case back; water-resistant to 5 atm
Band: stainless steel, folding clasp
Price: $3,150

Clifton Baumatic COSC

Reference number: 10584
Movement: automatic, Caliber Baumatic BM13.1975A COSC; ø 28.2 mm, height 4.2 mm; 21 jewels; 28,800 vph; silicon anchor and escape wheel; balance with variable inertia; skeletonized rotor; 120-hour power reserve; COSC-certified chronometer
Functions: hours, minutes, sweep seconds; date
Case: rose gold, ø 39 mm, height 10.74 mm; sapphire crystal; transparent case back; water-resistant to 5 atm
Band: reptile skin, buckle
Price: $7,200

Hampton Automatic

Reference number: 10528
Movement: automatic, ETA Caliber 2895-2; ø 25.6 mm, height 4.35 mm; 27 jewels; 28,800 vph; 42-hour power reserve
Functions: hours, minutes, subsidiary seconds; date
Case: stainless steel, 31 × 48 mm, height 9.35 mm; sapphire crystal; transparent case back; water-resistant to 5 atm
Band: reptile skin, triple folding clasp
Price: $2,600

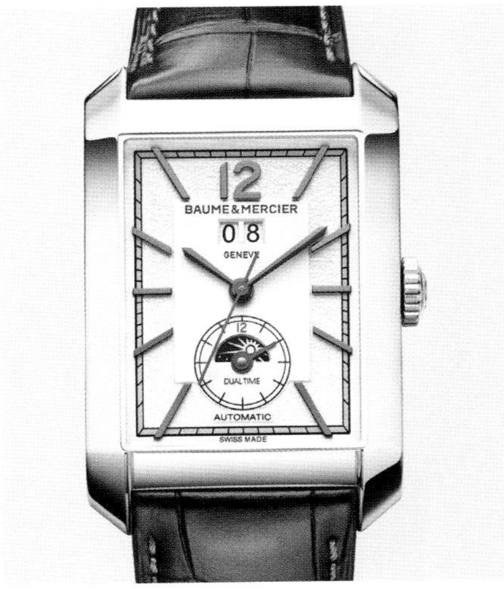

Hampton Automatic Large Date

Reference number: 10523
Movement: automatic, Soprod Caliber TT651; ø 25.6 mm, height 5.25 mm; 21 jewels; 28,800 vph; 42-hour power reserve
Functions: hours, minutes, sweep seconds; additional 12-hour display (2nd time zone) with day/night indicator; large date
Case: stainless steel, 31 × 48 mm, height 10.8 mm; sapphire crystal; transparent case back; water-resistant to 5 atm
Band: reptile skin, triple folding clasp
Price: $4,050

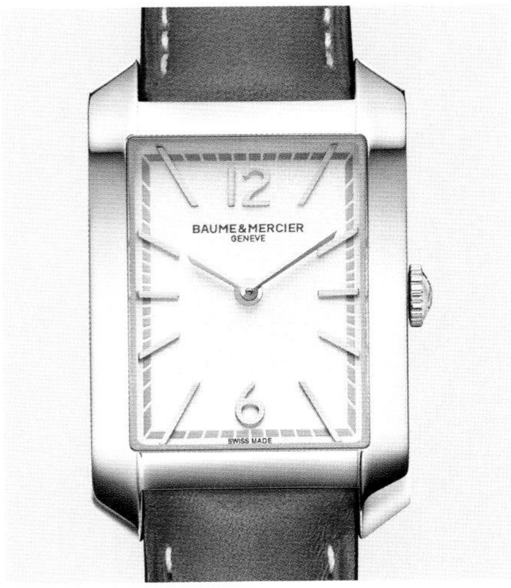

Hampton

Reference number: 10472
Movement: quartz
Functions: hours, minutes
Case: stainless steel, 22.2 × 35 mm, height 8.1 mm; sapphire crystal; water-resistant to 5 atm
Band: calfskin, buckle
Price: $1,500

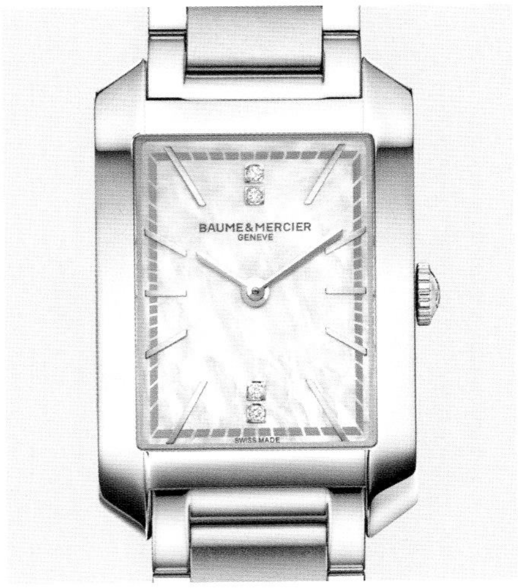

Hampton

Reference number: M0A10474
Movement: quartz
Functions: hours, minutes
Case: stainless steel, 22.2 × 35 mm, height 8.1 mm; sapphire crystal; water-resistant to 5 atm
Band: stainless steel, double folding clasp
Remarks: mother-of-pearl dial with 4 diamond indices
Price: $2,000

BELL & ROSS

If there is such a class as "military chic," Bell & Ross is undoubtedly one of the leaders. The Paris-headquartered brand develops, manufactures, assembles, and regulates its timepieces in a modern factory in La Chaux-de-Fonds in the Jura mountains of Switzerland. The early models had a certain stringency that one might associate with soldierly life, but in the past years, working with outside specialists, the company has ventured into even more complicated watches such as tourbillons and wristwatches with uncommon shapes. This kind of ambitious innovation has only been possible since perfume and fashion specialist Chanel—which also maintains a successful watch line in its own right—became a significant Bell & Ross shareholder and brought the watchmaker access to the production facilities where designers Bruno Belamich and team can create more complicated, more interesting designs for their esthetically unusual "instrument" watches.

What sets Bell & Ross timepieces apart from those of other, more traditional professional luxury makers is their special, roguish look: a delicate balance between striking, martial, and poetic—think Lawrence of Arabia, the gallivanting warrior. And it is this beauty for the eye to behold that makes the company's wares popular with style-conscious "civilians" as well as with the pilots, divers, astronauts, sappers, and other hard-riding professionals drawn to Bell & Ross timepieces for their superior functionality. The latest line, the BR 05, connects two geometric forms, the circular and the square. The result is a watch that gravitates more toward everyday usage, or what the brand calls "Urban Explorers," a modern version of the elemental being that slumbers in everyone.

Bell & Ross Ltd.
8 rue Copernic
F-75116 Paris
France

Tel.:
+33-1-73-73-93-00

E-mail:
sav@bellross.com

Website:
www.bellross.com

Founded:
1992

U.S. distributor:
Bell & Ross, Inc.
605 Lincoln Road, Suite 300
Miami Beach, FL 33139
888-307-7887
information@bellross.com
www.bellross.com

Most important collections/price range:
Instrument BR-X1, BR 01, BR 03, and BR 05 / approx. $3,100 to $200,000

BR 03-92 H.U.D

Reference number: BR0392-HUDCE/SRB
Movement: automatic, Caliber BR-CAL.302 (base ETA 2892-A2); ø 25.6 mm, height 3.6 mm; 21 jewels; 28,800 vph; 42-hour power reserve
Functions: hours, minutes, sweep seconds; date
Case: ceramic, 42 × 42 mm, height 12.3 mm; bezel screwed to monocoque case with 4 screws; sapphire crystal; screw-in crown; water-resistant to 10 atm
Band: rubber, buckle
Remarks: comes with additional textile strap
Price: $3,990

BR 03-92 Grey Lum

Reference number: BR0392-GC3-ST/SCA
Movement: automatic, Caliber BR-CAL.302 (base ETA 2892-A2); ø 25.6 mm, height 3.6 mm; 21 jewels; 28,800 vph; 42-hour power reserve
Functions: hours, minutes, sweep seconds; date
Case: stainless steel, 42 × 42 mm, height 12.3 mm; bezel screwed to monocoque case with 4 screws; sapphire crystal; screw-in crown; water-resistant to 10 atm
Band: calfskin, buckle
Price: $3,400

BR 03-92 Diver Full Lum

Reference number: BR0392-D-C5-CE/SRB
Movement: automatic, Caliber BR-CAL.302 (base ETA 2892-A2); ø 25.6 mm, height 3.6 mm; 21 jewels; 28,800 vph; 42-hour power reserve
Functions: hours, minutes, sweep seconds; date
Case: ceramic, 42 × 42 mm, height 12.3 mm; unidirectional bezel with 0-60 scale; sapphire crystal; screw-in crown; water-resistant to 30 atm
Band: rubber, buckle
Remarks: comes with additional textile strap
Price: $4,500

BR 05 Skeleton Blue

Reference number: BR05A-BLU-SKST
Movement: automatic, Caliber BR-CAL.322 (base ETA 2892-A2); ø 25.6 mm, height 3.6 mm; 21 jewels; 28,800 vph; skeletonized movement and rotor, with blue PVD; 42-hour power reserve
Functions: hours, minutes, sweep seconds
Case: stainless steel, 40 × 40 mm, height 9.8 mm; bezel screwed to monococque case with 4 screws; sapphire crystal; transparent case back; screw-in crown; water-resistant to 10 atm
Band: stainless steel, folding clasp
Price: $6,900; limited to 500 pieces

BR 05 Steel & Gold

Reference number: BR05A-BLSTPG/SSG
Movement: automatic, Caliber BR-CAL.322 (base ETA 2892-A2); ø 25.6 mm, height 3.6 mm; 21 jewels; 28,800 vph; 42-hour power reserve
Functions: hours, minutes, sweep seconds; date
Case: stainless steel, 40 × 40 mm; rose gold bezel screwed to monococque case with 4 screws; sapphire crystal; transparent case back; screw-in crown; water-resistant to 10 atm
Band: stainless steel with rose gold elements, folding clasp
Price: $10,900
Variations: rubber strap ($6,500); stainless steel ($4,400)

BR X1 R.S. 20

Reference number: BRX1-RS20/SRB
Movement: automatic, Caliber BR-CAL.313 (base ETA 2892-A2 with Modul Dubois Dépraz); ø 25.6 mm; 56 jewels; 28,800 vph; skeletonized movement; 42-hour power reserve
Functions: hours, minutes, subsidiary seconds; chronograph; date
Case: titanium and ceramic with rubber inserts, 45 × 45 mm, height 14.8 mm; bidirectional bezel, with 0-60 scale; sapphire crystal; transparent case back; water-resistant to 10 atm
Band: rubber, buckle
Price: on request; limited to 250 pieces

BR V2-93 GMT Blue

Reference number: BRV293-BLUST/SF
Movement: automatic, Caliber BR-CAL.303 (base ETA 2893-2); ø 25.6 mm, height 4.1 mm; 21 jewels; 28,800 vph; 42-hour power reserve
Functions: hours, minutes, sweep seconds; additional 24-hour display (2nd time zone); date
Case: stainless steel, ø 41 mm, height 12.15 mm; bidirectional bezel with aluminum inserts, with 0-24 scale; sapphire crystal; transparent case back; screw-in crown; water-resistant to 10 atm
Band: textile, folding clasp
Price: $3,200
Variations: stainless steel band

BR V2-94 Aéronavale Bronze

Reference number: BRV294-BLU-BR/SCA
Movement: automatic, Caliber BR-CAL.301 (base ETA 2894); ø 28.6 mm, height 6.1 mm; 37 jewels; 28,800 vph; 42-hour power reserve
Functions: hours, minutes, subsidiary seconds; chronograph; date
Case: bronze, ø 41 mm, height 13.9 mm; unidirectional bezel with aluminum inserts, with 0-60 scale; sapphire crystal; transparent case back; screw-in crown and pushers; water-resistant to 10 atm
Band: calfskin, folding clasp
Price: $5,200

BR V3-94 Black Steel

Reference number: BRV394-BLST/SST
Movement: automatic, Caliber BR-CAL.301 (base ETA 2894); ø 28.6 mm, height 6.1 mm; 37 jewels; 28,800 vph; 42-hour power reserve
Functions: hours, minutes, subsidiary seconds; chronograph; date
Case: stainless steel, ø 43 mm; unidirectional bezel with aluminum inserts, with 0-60 scale; sapphire crystal; transparent case back; screw-in crown; water-resistant to 10 atm
Band: stainless steel, folding clasp
Price: $4,500
Variations: calfskin strap

BLANCPAIN

In its advertising, the Blancpain watch brand has always proudly declared that, since 1735, the company has never made quartz watches and never will. Indeed, Blancpain is Switzerland's oldest watchmaker, and by sticking to its ideals, the company was put out of business by the "quartz boom" of the 1970s.

The Blancpain brand we know today came into being in the mid-eighties, when Jean-Claude Biver and Jacques Piguet purchased the venerable name. The company was subsequently moved to the Frédéric Piguet watch factory in Le Brassus, where it quickly became largely responsible for the renaissance of the mechanical wristwatch. This success caught the attention of the Swatch Group—known at that time as SMH. In 1992, it swooped in and purchased both companies to add to its portfolio. Movement fabrication and watch production were melded to form the Blancpain Manufacture in mid-2010.

But being quartz-less does not mean being old-fashioned. Over the past several years, Blancpain president Marc A. Hayek has put a great deal of energy into developing the company's technical originality. He is frank about the fact that making new calibers did harness most of Blancpain's creative potential, leaving little to apply to its existing collection of watches. Still, in terms of complications, Blancpain watches have always been in a class of their own. Furthermore, the farsighted move now means that other brands in the family have outstanding movements at their disposal, notably the Z9 from Harry Winston.

The Blancpain portfolio has been growing and subtly modernizing with each new model. The watches feature the company's own basic movement and a choice of manual or automatic winding, like the new collection, the Fifty Fathoms Bathyscaphe, a modern interpretation of the classic diver's watch of 1953. The product families were all consolidated into four families: the Villeret, the legendary Fifty Fathoms diver's watches, a graceful series for women, and a collection of unique pieces that express the brand's artistic and watchmaking prowess.

Blancpain SA
Le Rocher 12
CH-1348 Le Brassus
Switzerland

Tel.:
+41-21-796-3636

Website:
www.blancpain.com

Founded:
1735

U.S. distributor:
Blancpain
The Swatch Group (U.S.), Inc.
1200 Harbor Boulevard
Weehawken, NJ 07086
201-271-4680

Most important collections/price range:
L'Evolution, Villeret, Fifty Fathoms, Le Brassus, Women / $9,800 to $400,000

Villeret Carrousel Répétition Minutes

Reference number: 00235-3631-55B
Movement: automatic, Blancpain Caliber 235; ø 32.8 mm, height 9.1 mm; 54 jewels; 21,600 vph; escapement with 1-minute flying carrousel
Functions: hours, minutes; minute repeater
Case: pink gold, ø 45 mm, height 15.35 mm; sapphire crystal; transparent case back
Band: reptile skin, folding clasp
Remarks: enamel dial
Price: $412,100

Villeret Tourbillon Carrousel

Reference number: 2322-3631-55B
Movement: manually wound, Blancpain Caliber 2322; ø 35.3 mm, height 5.85 mm; 70 jewels; 21,600 vph; escapement system with flying 1-minute tourbillon and 1-minute carrousel with differential compensation; 3 spring barrels, 168-hour power reserve
Functions: hours, minutes; power reserve indicator (on rear); date
Case: pink gold, ø 44.6 mm, height 11.94 mm; sapphire crystal; transparent case back; water-resistant to 3 atm
Band: reptile skin, folding clasp
Remarks: enamel dial
Price: $319,000

Villeret Tourbillon Volant Heure Sautante Minute Rétrograde

Reference number: 66260-3633-55B
Movement: manually wound, Blancpain Caliber 260MR; ø 32 mm, height 5.85 mm; 40 jewels; 21,600 vph; flying 1-minute tourbillon; 144-hour power reserve
Functions: hours (digital, jumping), minutes (retrograde)
Case: pink gold, ø 42 mm, height 11 mm; sapphire crystal; transparent case back; water-resistant to 3 atm
Band: reptile skin, folding clasp
Remarks: enamel dial
Price: $148,800

Villeret Quantième Complet

Reference number: 6654-3640-55B
Movement: automatic, Blancpain Caliber 6654; ø 32 mm, height 5.5 mm; 28 jewels; 28,800 vph; 2 spring barrels, 72-hour power reserve
Functions: hours, minutes, sweep seconds; full calendar with date, weekday, month, moon phase
Case: pink gold, ø 40 mm, height 10.94 mm; sapphire crystal; transparent case back; water-resistant to 3 atm
Band: reptile skin, folding clasp
Price: $25,700
Variations: pink gold Milanese bracelet ($45,000)

Villeret Grande Date Jour Rétrograde

Reference number: 6668-3642-55B
Movement: automatic, Blancpain Caliber 6950GJ; ø 32 mm, height 5.27 mm; 40 jewels; 28,800 vph; 72-hour power reserve
Functions: hours, minutes, sweep seconds; large date, weekday (retrograde)
Case: pink gold, ø 40 mm, height 11.1 mm; sapphire crystal; transparent case back; water-resistant to 3 atm
Band: reptile skin, folding clasp
Remarks: opaline dial
Price: $24,500

Villeret Ultraplate

Reference number: 6224-3642-55B
Movement: automatic, Blancpain Caliber 1150; ø 26.2 mm, height 3.25 mm; 28 jewels; 28,800 vph; 100-hour power reserve
Functions: hours, minutes, sweep seconds; date
Case: pink gold, ø 38 mm, height 8.35 mm; sapphire crystal; transparent case back; water-resistant to 3 atm
Band: reptile skin, folding clasp
Price: $17,400
Variations: pink gold-Milanese bracelet ($35,600); stainless steel with reptile skin strap ($14,300); stainless steel bracelet ($16,700)

Fifty Fathoms Automatique

Reference number: 5015-12B30-98
Movement: automatic, Blancpain Caliber 1315; ø 30.6 mm, height 5.65 mm; 35 jewels; 28,800 vph; silicon hairspring; 120-hour power reserve
Functions: hours, minutes, sweep seconds; date
Case: titanium, ø 45 mm, height 15.4 mm; unidirectional bezel with sapphire crystal inserts, with 0-60 scale; sapphire crystal; transparent case back; water-resistant to 30 atm
Band: titanium, folding clasp
Price: $18,300
Variations: blue dial and bezel

Fifty Fathoms Automatic

Reference number: 5015-3603C-63B
Movement: automatic, Blancpain Caliber 1315; ø 30.6 mm, height 5.65 mm; 35 jewels; 28,800 vph; silicon hairspring; 120-hour power reserve
Functions: hours, minutes, sweep seconds; date
Case: red gold, ø 45 mm, height 15.4 mm; unidirectional bezel with sapphire crystal inlay, with 0-60 scale; sapphire crystal; transparent case back; water-resistant to 30 atm
Band: textile, buckle
Price: $35,800
Variations: titanium

Fifty Fathoms Nageurs de Combat

Reference number: 5015E-1130-B52A
Movement: automatic, Blancpain Caliber 1315; ø 30.6 mm, height 5.65 mm; 35 jewels; 28,800 vph; silicon spring; 120-hour power reserve
Functions: hours, minutes, sweep seconds; date
Case: stainless steel, ø 45 mm, height 15.7 mm; unidirectional bezel with sapphire crystal insert, with 0-60 scale; sapphire crystal; transparent case back; screw-in crown; water-resistant to 30 atm
Band: textile, buckle
Price: $15,500; limited to 300 pieces

Fifty Fathoms Bathyscaphe Quantième Complet

Reference number: 5054-1110-B52A
Movement: automatic, Blancpain Caliber 6654.P; ø 32 mm, height 5.48 mm; 28 jewels; 28,800 vph; 72-hour power reserve
Functions: hours, minutes, sweep seconds; full calendar with date, weekday, month, moon phase
Case: stainless steel, ø 43 mm, height 13.9 mm; unidirectional bezel with ceramic insert, with 0-60 scale; sapphire crystal; transparent case back; water-resistant to 30 atm
Band: textile, folding clasp
Price: $14,800

Fifty Fathoms Bathyscaphe Chronograph Flyback

Reference number: 5200-1110-70B
Movement: automatic, Blancpain Caliber F385; ø 31.8 mm, height 6.65 mm; 37 jewels; 36,000 vph; silicon hairspring; 50-hour power reserve
Functions: hours, minutes, subsidiary seconds; flyback chronograph; date
Case: ceramic, ø 43 mm, height 14.85 mm; unidirectional bezel, with 0-60 scale; sapphire crystal; water-resistant to 30 atm
Band: stainless steel, buckle
Price: $17,400
Variations: textile strap ($17,200)

Air Command

Reference number: AC01-1130-63A
Movement: automatic, Blancpain Caliber F388B; ø 31.8 mm, height 6.65 mm; 35 jewels; 28,800 vph; 50-hour power reserve
Functions: hours, minutes; flyback chronograph
Case: stainless steel, ø 42.5 mm, height 13.77 mm; bidirectionally rotating bezel with ceramic inlay, with 0-60 scale; sapphire crystal; transparent case back; water-resistant to 3 atm
Band: calfskin, buckle
Price: $19,800; limited to 500 pieces

Villeret Women Quantième Moonphase

Reference number: 6126-2987-55B
Movement: automatic, Blancpain Caliber 913QL; ø 23.7 mm, height 4.5 mm; 20 jewels; 28,800 vph; 40-hour power reserve
Functions: hours, minutes, sweep seconds; date, moon phase
Case: red gold, ø 33.2 mm, height 10.2 mm; bezel set with diamonds; sapphire crystal; transparent case back; water-resistant to 3 atm
Band: reptile skin, folding clasp
Remarks: dial set with 8 diamonds
Price: $22,900

Villeret Women Date

Reference number: 6127-4628-55B
Movement: automatic, Blancpain Caliber 1151; ø 27.4 mm, height 3.25 mm; 28 jewels; 28,800 vph; 100-hour power reserve
Functions: hours, minutes, sweep seconds; date
Case: stainless steel, ø 33.2 mm, height 9.15 mm; bezel set with diamonds; sapphire crystal; transparent case back; water-resistant to 3 atm
Band: reptile skin, buckle
Price: $14,100

Villeret Women Ultraplate

Reference number: 6104-2987-55A
Movement: automatic, Blancpain Caliber 913; ø 21 mm, height 3.28 mm; 20 jewels; 28,800 vph; 40-hour power reserve
Functions: hours, minutes, sweep seconds
Case: pink gold, ø 29.2 mm, height 9.2 mm; sapphire crystal; transparent case back; water-resistant to 10 atm
Band: reptile skin, buckle
Price: $17,000

Caliber F385

Automatic; column-wheel control of chronograph functions; single spring barrel, 50-hour power reserve
Functions: hours, minutes, subsidiary seconds; flyback chronograph; date
Diameter: 31.8 mm
Height: 6.65 mm
Jewels: 37
Balance: silicon
Frequency: 36,000 vph
Balance spring: flat hairspring
Shock protection: Kif
Remarks: finely worked movement, bridges with côtes de Genève

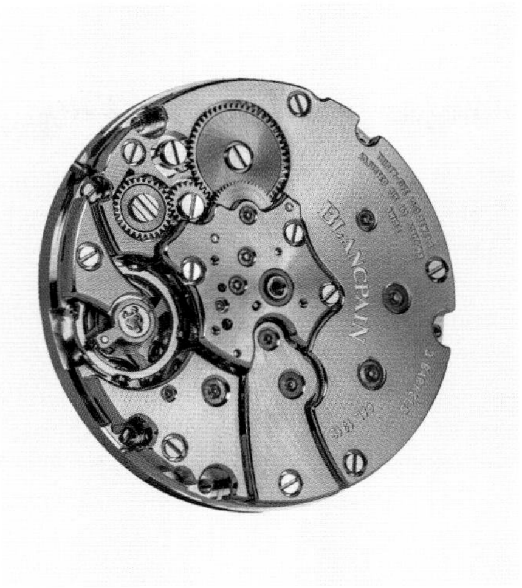

Caliber 1315

Automatic; 3 spring barrels, 120-hour power reserve
Functions: hours, minutes, sweep seconds; date
Diameter: 30.6 mm
Height: 5.65 mm
Jewels: 35
Frequency: 28,800 vph
Balance: silicon
Shock protection: Kif
Remarks: 227 parts

Caliber 913

Automatic; single spring barrel, 40-hour power reserve
Functions: hours, minutes, sweep seconds
Diameter: 21 mm
Height: 3.28 mm
Jewels: 20
Balance: glucydur
Frequency: 28,800 vph
Remarks: 174 parts

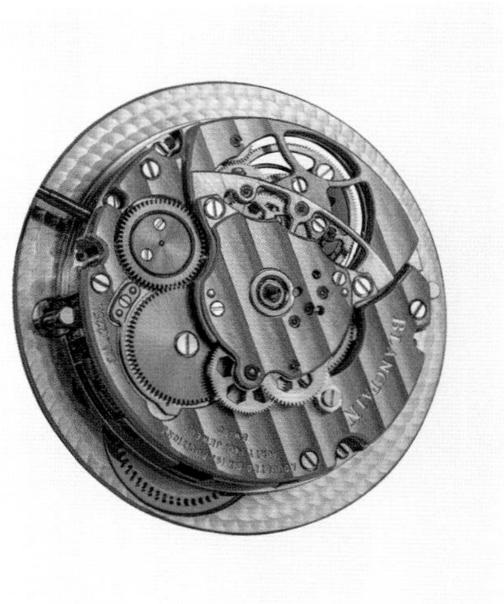

Caliber 225L

Automatic; flying 1-minute carrousel, 2 separate gear works; single spring barrel, 120-hour power reserve
Functions: hours, minutes; date, moon phase
Diameter: 31.9 mm
Height: 6.86 mm
Jewels: 40
Balance: glucydur with screw balance
Frequency: 28,800 vph
Balance spring: silicon
Shock protection: Kif
Remarks: 281 parts

Caliber 242

Automatic; flying 1-minute tourbillon with silicon balance and pallet fork horns; peripheral rotor at edge of movement; quadruple spring barrel, 288-hour power reserve
Functions: hours, minutes; power reserve indicator (on rear)
Diameter: 30.6 mm
Height: 6.1 mm
Jewels: 43
Balance: silicon
Frequency: 21,600 vph
Remarks: finely finished movement, hand-guillochéed bridges; 243 parts

Caliber 6654

Automatic; double spring barrel, 72-hour power reserve
Functions: hours, minutes, sweep seconds; full calendar with date, weekday, month, moon phase
Diameter: 32 mm
Height: 5.48 mm
Jewels: 28
Frequency: 28,800 vph
Shock protection: Kif
Remarks: 321 parts

BORGWARD

Borgward
Zeitmanufaktur GmbH & Co. KG
Markgrafenstrasse 16
D-79588 Efringen-Kirchen
Germany

Tel.:
+49-7628-805-7840

E-mail:
manufaktur@borgward.ag

Website:
www.borgward.ag

Founded:
2010

Number of employees:
3

Annual production:
approx. 180

Distribution:
Please contact Borgward directly for enquiries.

Most important collections:
P100, B2300, FiftySeven, FortyOne, Heritage Steam

It is not unusual for prospective watch brand founders to search for the name of a dormant or even defunct horological company to connect their business with a glorious past. Watchmaker Jürgen Betz looked elsewhere when he launched a series of watches under the name Borgward. This former automobile company had a reputation for outstanding quality, reliability, and durability. For connoisseurs and fans, Borgward meant technical prowess, perfect styling, and precision engineering.

Carl F. Borgward began his career as an automobile designer in 1924, when he built a small three-wheeled van. In the early 1930s, he took over the Hansa-Lloyd automobile factory and went on to conquer a global market with the Lloyd, Goliath, and Borgward brands. The real Borgward legend, however, began in the 1950s with the "Goddess," the famed Isabella Coupé, whose elegant lines and state-of-the-art technology heralded a new era in automotive design in Germany. In 1961, the company went bankrupt due to poor management. But the legend lives on and became the inspiration for Betz when building his Borgward watch B511. Support came from his friend Eric Borgward, grandson of Carl. Since then, Borgward Zeitmanufaktur has produced three collections: the B511 limited to 511 pieces, the P100 limited to 1,890 pieces, and the B2300 limited to 1,942 pieces. They are all "made in Germany" but based on Swiss technology. At the heart of each watch is either an ETA 2824 with three hands and calendar or the famous ETA 7750 Valjoux chronograph automatic.

In 2018, Betz came out with a special series, the 41, named for the aluminum-bodied Borgward that raced at Le Mans sixty-five years earlier, in 1953. That car, restored, was again at the Le Mans Classic race in 2018, with a sponsorship from the brand, which, of course, did not exist back in the day.

BIG FiftySeven

Reference number: BIG57.CL.09
Movement: automatic, ETA Caliber 7750; ø 30 mm, height 7.9 mm; 25 jewels; 28,800 vph; skeletonized oscillating weight, finely finished with côtes de Genève; 42-hour power reserve
Functions: hours, minutes; chronograph; date, weekday
Case: stainless steel, ø 44 mm, height 15.9 mm; sapphire crystal; transparent case back; water-resistant to 5 atm
Band: calfskin, buckle
Price: $3,125
Variations: various dial colors

FiftySeven

Reference number: B57.CL.07
Movement: automatic, ETA Caliber 7750; ø 30 mm, height 7.9 mm; 25 jewels; 28,800 vph; blackened oscillating weight, movement with perlage and côtes de Genève; 42-hour power reserve
Functions: hours, minutes; chronograph; date, weekday
Case: stainless steel, ø 40 mm, height 15.9 mm; sapphire crystal; transparent case back; water-resistant to 5 atm
Band: calfskin, buckle
Price: $2,999
Variations: stainless steel Milanese mesh bracelet ($3,199); various dial colors

Deluxe Chronograph

Reference number: Deluxe.CL
Movement: automatic, ETA Caliber 7751; ø 30 mm, height 7.9 mm; 25 jewels; 28,800 vph; mainplate with perlage, bridges with côtes de Genève, blackened oscillating weight; 46-hour power reserve
Functions: hours, minutes, subsidiary seconds; additional 24-hour display; chronograph; full calendar with date, weekday, month, moon phase
Case: stainless steel, ø 42.5 mm, height 14 mm; sapphire crystal; transparent case back; water-resistant to 10 atm
Band: calfskin, buckle
Price: $7,959
Variations: stainless steel band ($8,165); various dial colors

FortyOne 24H

Reference number: FORTY24.HA.01.V10
Movement: manually wound, Borgward Caliber B24H (base ETA 6498-1); ø 36.6 mm, height 4.5 mm; 17 jewels; 18,000 vph; finely finished with côtes de Genève; 46-hour power reserve
Functions: 24 hours, minutes, subsidiary seconds
Case: stainless steel, ø 44 mm, height 12.5 mm; sapphire crystal; transparent case back; water-resistant to 5 atm
Band: calfskin, buckle
Remarks: recalls the Borgward Hansa RS 1500 no. 41 that raced at Le Mans in 1953
Price: $2,090; limited to 41 pieces
Variations: stainless steel bracelet ($2,250)

FortyOne Deluxe

Reference number: FORTY.VK.04
Movement: automatic, ETA Caliber 7751; ø 30 mm, height 7.9 mm; 25 jewels; 28,800 vph; finely finished with côtes de Genève; 42-hour power reserve
Functions: hours, minutes, subsidiary seconds; additional 24-hour display (2nd time zone); chronograph; full calendar with date, weekday, month
Case: stainless steel, ø 42.5 mm, height 14.5 mm; sapphire crystal; transparent case back; water-resistant to 5 atm
Band: calfskin, buckle
Remarks: recalls the Borgward Hansa RS 1500 no. 41 that raced at Le Mans in 1953
Price: $6,840
Variations: stainless steel bracelet ($7,040)

FortyOne 1953 Medium

Reference number: FORTY53.CL.04
Movement: automatic, ETA Caliber 7753; ø 30 mm, height 7.9 mm; 25 jewels; 28,800 vph; finely finished with côtes de Genève; 42-hour power reserve
Functions: hours, minutes, subsidiary seconds; chronograph
Case: stainless steel, ø 36 mm, height 15.5 mm; sapphire crystal; transparent case back; water-resistant to 5 atm
Band: calfskin, buckle
Remarks: recalls the Borgward Hansa RS 1500 no. 41 that raced at Le Mans in 1953
Price: $3,210; **Variations:** stainless steel band ($3,420)

P100 Automatic Silver

Reference number: P100.AL.02
Movement: automatic, ETA Caliber 2824-2; ø 25.6 mm, height 4.6 mm; 25 jewels; 28,800 vph; mainplate with perlage, bridges with côtes de Genève, blackened oscillating weight; 42-hour power reserve
Functions: hours, minutes, sweep seconds; date
Case: stainless steel, ø 40 mm, height 12 mm; sapphire crystal; transparent case back; water-resistant to 5 atm
Band: calfskin, buckle
Price: $1,630

P100 Medium Automatic Diamond

Reference number: P100.AMDIAK.05.MIL
Movement: automatic, ETA Caliber 2824-2; ø 25.6 mm, height 4.6 mm; 25 jewels; 28,800 vph; mainplate with perlage, bridges with côtes de Genève, blackened oscillating weight; 42-hour power reserve
Functions: hours, minutes, sweep seconds; date
Case: stainless steel, ø 36 mm, height 10 mm; bezel set with diamonds; sapphire crystal; transparent case back; water-resistant to 5 atm
Band: stainless steel Milanese mesh, folding clasp
Price: $4,490

New Heritage Steam Medium

Reference number: NHS.AM.01
Movement: automatic, ETA Caliber 2824-2; ø 25.6 mm, height 4.6 mm; 25 jewels; 28,800 vph; blackened oscillating weight, movement with perlage and côtes de Genève; 42-hour power reserve
Functions: hours, minutes, sweep seconds; date
Case: stainless steel, ø 38 mm, height 12.5 mm; bezel in bronze; sapphire crystal; transparent case back; water-resistant to 5 atm
Band: calfskin, buckle
Price: $1,990; limited to 98 pieces
Variations: stainless steel Milanese mesh bracelet

BOVET

Bovet Fleurier S.A.
Le Château, CP20
CH-2112 Môtiers
Switzerland

Tel.:
+41-22-731-4638

E-mail:
info@bovet.com

Website:
www.bovet.com

Founded:
1822

Annual production:
around 800 timepieces

U.S. distributor:
Bovet LLC North America
305-974-4826

Most important collections/price range:
Amadeo Fleurier, Dimier, Pininfarina, Récital, Sportster / $18,500 to $1,000,000

If any brand can claim real connections to China, it is Bovet, founded by Swiss businessman Edouard Bovet. Bovet emigrated to Canton, China, in 1818 and sold four watches of his own design there. On his return to Switzerland in 1822, he set up a company for shipping his Fleurier-made watches to China. The company name, pronounced "Bo Wei" in Mandarin, became a synonym for "watch" in Asia and at one point had offices in Canton. For more than eighty years, Bovet and his successors supplied the Chinese ruling class with valuable timepieces.

In 2001, the brand was bought by entrepreneur Pascal Raffy. He ensured the company's industrial independence by acquiring several other companies as well, notably the high-end watchmaker Swiss Time Technology (STT) in Tramelan, which he renamed Dimier 1738. In addition to creating its own line of watches, this *manufacture* produces complex technical components such as tourbillons for Bovet watches. Assembly of Bovet creations takes place at the headquarters in the thirteenth-century Castle of Môtiers in Val-de-Travers not far from Fleurier.

Bovet is an equal opportunity manufacturer of fine watches for men and women. These high-end timekeepers do have several distinctive features. The first is intricate dial work, featuring not only complex architecture in the men's series, but also intricate guilloché patterns and very fine enameling techniques, as in the Poppies, where 138 diamonds meet bold red grand-feu poppies, a work by artist and jewelry designer Ilgiz Fazulzyanov. The latest development is a case shaped like a slant-top desk, which makes for easy reading of time.

The second special feature is placement of the lugs and crown at 12 o'clock, recalling Bovet's tasteful pocket watches of the nineteenth century. On some models, the wristbands are made to be easily removed so the watch can be worn on a chain or cord. Other watches convert to table clocks, and the Amadeo Fleurier Miss Audrey series can even be worn as a necklace.

Amadéo Tourbillon

Reference number: AIFSQ035-G123467
Movement: manually wound, Bovet Caliber 14BM02A1; ø 29.10 mm, height 3.6 mm; 21,600 vph; 7-day power reserve
Functions: hours, minutes, seconds on tourbillon, reversed hand-fitting, power reserve indicator
Case: red gold, ø 45 mm, height 14.30 mm; Amadéo convertible system sapphire crystal; transparent case back; water-resistant to 3 atm
Band: reptile skin, buckle
Remarks: hand-engraved case, bezel and bow with floral motif (*fleurisannes*); Amadéo system lets wearer turn the watch into a table clock, pendant, or pocket watch without tools
Price: $273,500; unique piece

Récital 26 Brainstorm Chapter Two

Reference number: R26C2001
Movement: manually wound, Bovet Caliber 17DM04-3FPL; ø 39 mm, height 15.70 mm; 21,600 vph; 1-minute double-sided flying tourbillon; spherical winding system; 10-day power reserve; **Functions:** hours, minutes, seconds on tourbillon, moon phase, 2nd time zone with rotating hemispherical city indicator
Case: sapphire crystal and titanium, ø 47.80 mm, height 15.95 mm; sapphire crystal; transparent case back; water-resistant to 3 atm; **Band:** reptile skin, buckle
Remarks: "slant-top desk" case; convex quartz dial; convertible case
Price: $383,500; limited to only 10 movements with blue quartz dial
Variations: aventurine blue, green quartz dial, sunshine collection, evolutive dial (unique piece)

Virtuoso VII

Reference number: ACQPR012
Movement: manually wound, Bovet Caliber 13BM12AIQPR; ø 29.10 mm; 21,600 vph; hand-engraved bridges and plates; 5-day power reserve
Functions: hours, minutes, subsidiary seconds (on both sides); perpetual calendar (retrograde) with date, month, weekday, leap year; power reserve indicator
Case: gray gold, ø 43.30 mm, height 11.25 mm; red gold or white gold chain; sapphire crystal; transparent case back; water-resistant to 3 atm
Band: reptile skin, buckle
Remarks: guilloché in lotus pattern
Price: $89,000
Variations: green guilloché or blue circular brushed dial; hand-engraved case, bezel, buckle and bow

Classique Extra-Thin Tourbillon

Reference: 5367PT 2Y 9WU
Movement: automatic, Breguet Caliber 581; ø 36 mm, height 3 mm; 33 jewels; 28,800 vph; minute tourbillon, silicon pallet lever and hairspring; hubless peripheral rotor; 80-hour power reserve
Functions: hours, minutes, small second (on tourbillon cage)
Case: platinum, ø 41 mm, height 7.45 mm; sapphire crystal; back with viewing window; water-resistant to 3 atm
Band: reptile leather, folding clasp
Remarks: enamel dial
Price: $161,800

Classique Extra-Thin Tourbillon Skeletonized

Reference: 5395PT RS 9WU
Movement: automatic, Breguet Caliber 581SQ; ø 36 mm, height 3 mm; 33 jewels; 28,800 vph; 1-minute tourbillon, silicon anchor and hairspring; hubless peripheral winding rotor; movement completely skeletonized; 80-hour power reserve
Functions: hours, minutes, small second (on tourbillon cage)
Case: platinum, ø 41 mm, height 7.7 mm; sapphire crystal; back with viewing window; water-resistant to 3 atm; **Band:** reptile leather, folding clasp
Remarks: sapphire crystal dial
Price: $240,600
Variations: rose gold ($225,200)

Classique Dame

Reference: 9068BR 52 976 DD00
Movement: automatic, Breguet Caliber 591A; ø 25.6 mm; 25 jewels; 28,800 vph; silicon escapement and hairspring; 38-hour power reserve
Functions: hours, minutes, central second; date
Case: pink gold, ø 33.5 mm, height 7.55 mm; bezel and lugs set with 88 diamonds; sapphire crystal; case back with window; crown with ruby cabochon; water-resistant to 3 atm
Band: reptile leather, buckle
Remarks: mother-of-pearl dial
Price: $26,600
Variations: white gold ($26,600)

Tradition Dame

Reference number: 7038BR 18 9V6 D00D
Movement: automatic, Breguet Caliber 505 SR; ø 33 mm; 38 jewels; 21,600 vph; silicon Breguet hairspring and lever pallets; 50-hour power reserve
Functions: hours, minutes (off-center), subsidiary seconds (retrograde)
Case: rose gold, ø 37 mm, height 11.85 mm; bezel set with 68 diamonds; sapphire crystal; transparent case back; crown with ruby cabochon; water-resistant to 3 atm
Band: reptile skin, buckle set with 19 diamonds
Price: $38,100
Variations: white gold ($38,900)

Tradition Seconde Rétrograde

Reference number: 7097BB G1 9WU
Movement: automatic, Breguet Caliber 505 SR1; ø 33 mm; 38 jewels; 21,600 vph; silicon Breguet hairspring and lever pallets; 50-hour power reserve
Functions: hours, minutes (off-center), subsidiary seconds (retrograde)
Case: rose gold, ø 40 mm, height 11.65 mm; sapphire crystal; transparent case back; water-resistant to 3 atm
Band: reptile skin, folding clasp
Price: $33,500 (white gold/silvered dial)
Variations: rose gold/silvered dial ($32,700); white gold/blue dial ($33,500)

Tradition Grande Complication

Reference number: 7047PT 11 9ZU
Movement: manually wound, Breguet Caliber 569; ø 35.7 mm, height 10.82 mm; 43 jewels; 18,000 vph; Breguet silicon hairspring, constant force regulation with fusée and chain, minute tourbillon; 50-hour power reserve
Functions: hours, minutes; power reserve indicator
Case: platinum, ø 41 mm, height 15.95 mm; sapphire crystal; back with window; water-resistant to 3 atm
Band: reptile leather, folding clasp
Price: $189,700
Variations: rose gold/gray face/black dial ($175,600)

Marine Date

Reference: 5517TI G2 TZ0
Movement: automatic, Breguet Caliber 777A; ø 33.8 mm; 26 jewels; 28,800 vph; silicon pallets and hairspring; 55-hour power reserve
Functions: hours, minutes, sweep seconds; date
Case: titanium, ø 40 mm, height 11.5 mm; sapphire crystal; transparent case back
Band: titanium, folding clasp
Price: $19,900
Variations: alligator skin or rubber strap ($17,300); rose or white gold/strap ($28,600); rose or white gold bracelet ($49,100)

Marine Chronograph

Reference number: 5527BB Y2 9WV
Movement: automatic, Breguet Caliber 582QA; ø 32.7 mm; 28 jewels; 28,800 vph; silicon pallets and hairspring; 48-hour power reserve
Functions: hours, minutes, subsidiary seconds; chronograph; date
Case: white gold, ø 42.3 mm, height 13.85 mm; sapphire crystal; transparent case back; screw-in crown; water-resistant to 10 atm
Band: rubber strap, folding clasp
Price: $33,800
Variations: alligator skin ($33,800); rose or white gold bracelet ($56,300); titanium on alligator/rubber ($21,500); titanium on bracelet ($24,100)

Marine Alarme Musicale

Reference number: 5547BR 12 9ZU
Movement: automatic, Breguet Caliber 518F/1; ø 27.1 mm; 36 jewels; 28,800 vph; silicon pallets and hairspring; 45-hour power reserve
Functions: hours, minutes, sweep seconds; additional 24-hour display (2nd time zone), power reserve indicator for chimes; alarm (adjustable to the minute); date
Case: rose gold, ø 40 mm, height 13.05 mm; sapphire crystal; transparent case back; water-resistant to 5 atm
Band: reptile skin, folding clasp
Price: $39,900; **Variations:** rubber strap ($39,900); white gold ($39,900); white or rose gold bracelet ($60,300); titanium on reptile skin/rubber ($28,600); titanium bracelet ($31,200)

Marine Équation Marchante

Reference number: 5887BR 12 9WV
Movement: automatic, Breguet Caliber 581DPE; ø 37.2 mm; 57 jewels; 28,800 vph; 1-minute tourbillon; silicon anchor, escape wheel and hairspring; 80-hour power reserve
Functions: hours, minutes, subsidiary seconds (on tourbillon cage); running equation of time; perpetual calendar with date (retrograde), weekday, month
Case: rose gold, ø 43.9 mm, height 11.75 mm; sapphire crystal; transparent case back; water-resistant to 10 atm
Band: reptile skin, folding clasp
Price: $215,000
Variations: platinum ($230,400)

Marine Dame 9518

Reference number: 9518BR 52 984 D000
Movement: automatic, Breguet Caliber 591A; ø 25.6 mm; 25 jewels; 28,800 vph; silicon Breguet hairspring and escapement, gold oscillating weight set with 31 diamonds; 38-hour power reserve
Functions: hours, minutes, sweep seconds; date
Case: rose gold, ø 33.8 mm, height 9.89 mm; bezel set with 50 diamonds; sapphire crystal; transparent case back; water-resistant to 5 atm
Band: reptile skin, folding clasp
Remarks: hand-guillochéed mother-of-pearl dial
Price: $34,900
Variations: white gold ($34,900); stainless steel ($20,000)

Marine Dame 9517

Reference number: 9517ST E2 984
Movement: automatic, Breguet Caliber 591A; ø 25.6 mm; 25 jewels; 28,800 vph; silicon Breguet hairspring and escapement, gold oscillating weight set with 31 diamonds; 38-hour power reserve
Functions: hours, minutes, sweep seconds; date
Case: stainless steel, ø 33.8 mm, height 9.89 mm; sapphire crystal; transparent case back; water-resistant to 5 atm
Band: reptile skin, folding clasp
Remarks: mother-of-pearl dial
Price: $17,700

Héritage Tourbillon

Reference number: 5497BR 12 9V6
Movement: manually wound, Breguet Caliber 187H; ø 26 mm; 21 jewels; 18,000 vph; 1-minute tourbillon; 50-hour power reserve
Functions: hours, minutes (off-center), subsidiary seconds (on tourbillon cage)
Case: platinum, 35 mm × 42 mm; sapphire crystal; water-resistant to 3 atm
Band: reptile skin, folding clasp
Price: $142,900
Variations: rose gold ($127,900)

Type XXI Chrono Cadran Vintage

Reference number: 3817ST X2 3ZU
Movement: automatic, Breguet Caliber 584 Q/2; ø 30 mm; 26 jewels; 28,800 vph; silicon hairspring and escapement, central minute totalizer; 48-hour power reserve
Functions: hours, minutes, subsidiary seconds; additional 24-hour display (2nd time zone); flyback chronograph; date
Case: stainless steel, ø 42 mm, height 15.2 mm; unidirectional bezel, 0-60 scale; sapphire crystal; transparent case back; water-resistant to 10 atm
Band: calfskin
Price: $13,900

Type XXI Chronograph

Reference number: 3810TI H2 TZ9
Movement: automatic, Breguet Caliber 584 Q/2; ø 30 mm; 26 jewels; 28,800 vph; silicon hairspring and escapement, central minute totalizer; 45-hour power reserve
Functions: hours, minutes, subsidiary seconds; additional 24-hour display (2nd time zone); flyback chronograph; date
Case: titanium, ø 42 mm, height 15.2 mm; unidirectional bezel, 0-60 scale; sapphire crystal; transparent case back; water-resistant to 10 atm
Band: titanium, folding clasp
Price: $15,400; **Variations:** stainless steel on alligator strap ($11,800); stainless steel on bracelet ($13,400); rose gold on alligator strap ($20,900)

Reine de Naples

Reference number: 8918BB 5P 964 D00D
Movement: automatic, Breguet Caliber 537/3; ø 19.7 mm; 26 jewels; 21,600 vph; silicon balance wheel, escapement, and hairspring; 45-hour power reserve
Functions: hours, minutes
Case: white gold, 28.45 × 36 mm, height 10.05 mm; bezel and flange set with 117 diamonds; sapphire crystal; transparent case back; crown with ruby cabochon; water-resistant to 3 atm; **Band:** reptile skin, folding clasp set with 26 diamonds
Remarks: mother-of-pearl dial with hand-guillochéed gold field and drop-shaped diamonds
Price: $36,100; **Variations:** rose gold ($35,100); yellow gold ($34,000)

Reine de Naples

Reference number: 8928BR 5W 944 DD0D
Movement: automatic, Breguet Caliber 586/1; ø 19.7 mm; 29 jewels; 21,600 vph; silicon hairspring and pallet forks; 38-hour power reserve
Functions: hours, minutes
Case: rose gold, 24.95 × 33 mm, height 10.05 mm; bezel, flange, and lugs set with139 diamonds; sapphire crystal; transparent case back; crown with diamond cabochon; water-resistant to 3 atm
Band: reptile skin, folding clasp set with 26 diamonds
Remarks: mother-of-pearl dial
Price: $35,100
Variations: white gold ($36,100)

Reine de Naples "Jour Nuit"

Reference number: 8998BR 11 974 D00D
Movement: automatic, Breguet Caliber 78CS; ø 19.7 mm; 45 jewels; 25,200 vph; silicon hairspring; 57-hour power reserve
Functions: hours, minutes; additional 24-hour display, day/night indication on a peripheral plate with a visible escapement
Case: rose gold, 32 × 40.05 mm, height 10.8 mm; bezel and flange set with 143 diamonds; sapphire crystal; transparent case back; crown with a diamond cabochon; water-resistant to 3 atm
Band: reptile skin, triple folding clasp
Remarks: hand-guillochéed gold dial
Price: $122,900
Variations: white gold ($123,900)

BREITLING

In 1884, Léon Breitling opened his workshop in St. Imier in the Jura Mountains and immediately began specializing in integrated chronographs. His business strategy was to focus consistently on instrument watches with a distinctive design. High quality standards and the rise of aviation completed the picture.

Today, Breitling's relationship with air sports and commercial and military aviation is clear from its brand identity. The watch company hosts a series of aviation days, owns an aerobatics team, and sponsors several aviation associations.

The unveiling of its own, modern chronograph movement at Basel in 2009 was a major milestone in the company's history and also a return to its roots. The new design was to be "100 percent Breitling" and industrially produced in large numbers at a reasonable cost. Although Breitling's operations in Grenchen and in La Chaux-de-Fonds both boast state-of-the-art equipment, the contract for the new chronograph was awarded to a small team in Geneva. By 2006, the brand-new Caliber B01 had made the COSC grade with flying colors, and it has enjoyed great popularity ever since. For the team of designers, the innovative centering system on the reset mechanism that requires no manual adjustment was one of the great achievements. Since then, the in-house caliber has evolved, but the cost for the company was immense. Ultimately, owner Théodore Schneider, in the second generation, decided to put management in the hands of Georges Kern of IWC fame. Together with the new owners, the investment company CVC Capital Partners, Kern decided to expand the brand beyond the pilot watch niche and look to the untapped markets in the Far East. The new collections were streamlined and given more defined profiles, a recipe he brought in from his IWC days. The winged logo was replaced mostly with a coquettish "B." Prices range from around $3,500 to the $10,000 region, and that includes ladies' watches. No more quartz, only mechanical. The company will also be making its own chronographs using the B1 movement and movements from outside vendors.

Breitling
Léon Breitling-Strasse 2
2540 Grenchen
Switzerland

Tel.:
+41-32-654-5454

E-mail:
sales@breitlingusa.com

Website:
www.breitling.com

Founded:
1884

Annual production:
700,000 (estimated)

U.S. distributor:
Breitling U.S.A. Inc.
206 Danbury Road
Wilton, CT 06897
203-762-1180
www.breitling.com

Most important collections:
Navitimer, Aviator 8, Avenger, Premier, Chronomat, Superocean Heritage, Superocean, Professional

---

Navitimer B01 Chronograph 46

Reference number: AB0127211B1X1
Movement: automatic, Breitling Caliber B01; ø 30 mm, height 7.2 mm; 47 jewels; 28,800 vph; column-wheel control of chronograph functions; 70-hour power reserve; COSC-certified chronometer
Functions: hours, minutes, subsidiary seconds; chronograph; date
Case: stainless steel, ø 46 mm, height 14.51 mm; bidirectional bezel, with integrated slide rule and tachymeter scale; sapphire crystal; transparent case back; water-resistant to 3 atm
Band: calfskin, buckle
Price: $8,305

Navitimer B01 Chronograph 46

Reference number: AB0127211C1A1
Movement: automatic, Breitling Caliber B01; ø 30 mm, height 7.2 mm; 47 jewels; 28,800 vph; column-wheel control of chronograph functions; 70-hour power reserve; COSC-certified chronometer
Functions: hours, minutes, subsidiary seconds; chronograph; date
Case: stainless steel, ø 46 mm, height 14.51 mm; bidirectional bezel, with integrated slide rule and tachymeter scale; sapphire crystal; transparent case back; water-resistant to 3 atm
Band: stainless steel, folding clasp
Price: $9,250

Navitimer B01 Chronograph 43

Reference number: AB0121211G1P1
Movement: automatic, Breitling Caliber B01; ø 30 mm, height 7.2 mm; 47 jewels; 28,800 vph; column-wheel control of chronograph functions; 70-hour power reserve; COSC-certified chronometer
Functions: hours, minutes, subsidiary seconds; chronograph; date
Case: stainless steel, ø 43 mm, height 14.22 mm; bidirectional bezel, with integrated slide rule and tachymeter scale; sapphire crystal; water-resistant to 3 atm
Band: reptile skin, buckle
Price: $8,680
Variations: stainless steel band ($9,250)

Navitimer Chronograph 41

Reference number: U13324211B1X1
Movement: automatic, Breitling Caliber 13 (base ETA 7750); ø 30 mm, height 7.8 mm; 25 jewels; 28,800 vph; 48-hour power reserve
Functions: hours, minutes, subsidiary seconds; chronograph; date
Case: stainless steel, ø 41 mm, height 14.44 mm; bidirectional rose gold bezel, with integrated slide rule and tachymeter scale; sapphire crystal; water-resistant to 3 atm
Band: calfskin, buckle
Price: $7,710

Superocean Héritage B01 Chronograph 44

Reference number: AB0162121B1S1
Movement: automatic, Breitling Caliber B01; ø 30 mm, height 7.2 mm; 47 jewels; 28,800 vph; 70-hour power reserve; COSC-certified chronometer
Functions: hours, minutes, subsidiary seconds; chronograph; date
Case: stainless steel, ø 44 mm, height 15.5 mm; unidirectional bezel with ceramic insert; sapphire crystal; screw-in crown; water-resistant to 20 atm
Band: rubber, folding clasp
Price: $7,665
Variations: stainless steel band ($7,990)

Superocean Héritage B01 Chronograph 44

Reference number: AB0162121G1A1
Movement: automatic, Breitling Caliber B01; ø 30 mm, height 7.2 mm; 47 jewels; 28,800 vph; 70-hour power reserve; COSC-certified chronometer
Functions: hours, minutes, subsidiary seconds; chronograph; date
Case: stainless steel, ø 44 mm, height 15.5 mm; unidirectional bezel with ceramic insert; sapphire crystal; screw-in crown; water-resistant to 20 atm
Band: stainless steel Milanese mesh, folding clasp
Price: $7,990
Variations: rubber strap ($7,665)

Superocean Héritage Chronograph 44

Reference number: U13313121B1S1
Movement: automatic, Breitling Caliber 13 (base ETA 7750); ø 30 mm, height 7.9 mm; 25 jewels; 28,800 vph; 42-hour power reserve; COSC-certified chronometer
Functions: hours, minutes, subsidiary seconds; chronograph; date, weekday
Case: stainless steel, ø 44 mm, height 15.65 mm; unidirectional rose gold bezel with ceramic insert, with 0-60 scale; sapphire crystal; screw-in crown; water-resistant to 20 atm
Band: rubber, folding clasp
Price: $7,295

Superocean Héritage B20 Automatic 44

Reference number: AB2030161C1S1
Movement: automatic, Breitling Caliber B20 (base Tudor MT 5612); ø 31.8 mm, height 6.5 mm; 28 jewels; 28,800 vph; 70-hour power reserve; COSC-certified chronometer
Functions: hours, minutes, sweep seconds; date
Case: stainless steel, ø 44 mm, height 14.55 mm; unidirectional bezel with ceramic insert; sapphire crystal; screw-in crown; water-resistant to 20 atm
Band: rubber, folding clasp
Price: $4,660
Variations: black strap dial; stainless steel Milanese mesh bracelet ($4,985)

Superocean Héritage B20 Automatic 42

Reference number: UB2010121B1A1
Movement: automatic, Breitling Caliber B20 (base Tudor MT 5612); ø 31.8 mm, height 6.5 mm; 28 jewels; 28,800 vph; 70-hour power reserve; COSC-certified chronometer
Functions: hours, minutes, sweep seconds; date
Case: stainless steel, ø 42 mm, height 14.35 mm; unidirectional rose gold bezel with ceramic insert; sapphire crystal; screw-in crown; water-resistant to 20 atm
Band: stainless steel Milanese, folding clasp
Price: $6,040

Premier B01 Chronograph 42

Reference number: AB0118221G1P2
Movement: automatic, Breitling Caliber B01; ø 30 mm, height 7.2 mm; 47 jewels; 28,800 vph; column-wheel control of chronograph functions; 70-hour power reserve; COSC-certified chronometer
Functions: hours, minutes, subsidiary seconds; chronograph; date
Case: stainless steel, ø 42 mm, height 13.65 mm; sapphire crystal; transparent case back; water-resistant to 10 atm
Band: reptile skin, buckle
Price: $8,150

Premier B01 Chronograph 42 Norton

Reference number: AB0118A21B1X1
Movement: automatic, Breitling Caliber B01; ø 30 mm, height 7.2 mm; 47 jewels; 28,800 vph; column-wheel control of chronograph functions; 70-hour power reserve; COSC-certified chronometer
Functions: hours, minutes, subsidiary seconds; chronograph; date
Case: stainless steel, ø 42 mm, height 13.65 mm; sapphire crystal; transparent case back; water-resistant to 10 atm
Band: calfskin, buckle
Remarks: special edition for British motorcycle manufacturer Norton
Price: $8,500

Premier B01 Chronograph 42 Bentley

Reference number: AB0118A11L1X1
Movement: automatic, Breitling Caliber B01; ø 30 mm, height 7.2 mm; 47 jewels; 28,800 vph; column-wheel control of chronograph functions; 70-hour power reserve; COSC-certified chronometer
Functions: hours, minutes, subsidiary seconds; chronograph; date
Case: stainless steel, ø 42 mm, height 13.65 mm; sapphire crystal; transparent case back; water-resistant to 10 atm
Band: calfskin, buckle
Remarks: special edition in cooperation with British automaker Bentley
Price: $8,500

Premier Chronograph 42

Reference number: A13315351C1A1
Movement: automatic, Breitling Caliber 13 (base ETA 7750); ø 30 mm, height 7.9 mm; 25 jewels; 28,800 vph; 42-hour power reserve; COSC-certified chronometer
Functions: hours, minutes, subsidiary seconds; chronograph; date
Case: stainless steel, ø 42 mm, height 13.8 mm; sapphire crystal; water-resistant to 10 atm
Band: stainless steel, folding clasp
Price: $6,550

Chronomat B01 42

Reference number: AB0134101G1A1
Movement: automatic, Breitling Caliber B01; ø 30 mm, height 7.2 mm; 47 jewels; 28,800 vph; column-wheel control of chronograph functions; 70-hour power reserve; COSC-certified chronometer
Functions: hours, minutes, subsidiary seconds; chronograph; date
Case: stainless steel, ø 42 mm, height 15.1 mm; unidirectional bezel with 0-60 scale; sapphire crystal; transparent case back; screw-in crown; water-resistant to 20 atm
Band: stainless steel, folding clasp
Price: $8,100

Chronomat B01 42

Reference number: AB01343A1L1A1
Movement: automatic, Breitling Caliber B01; ø 30 mm, height 7.2 mm; 47 jewels; 28,800 vph; column-wheel control of chronograph functions; 70-hour power reserve; COSC-certified chronometer
Functions: hours, minutes, subsidiary seconds; chronograph; date
Case: stainless steel, ø 42 mm, height 15.1 mm; unidirectional bezel with 0-60 scale; sapphire crystal; transparent case back; screw-in crown; water-resistant to 20 atm
Band: stainless steel, folding clasp
Price: $8,100

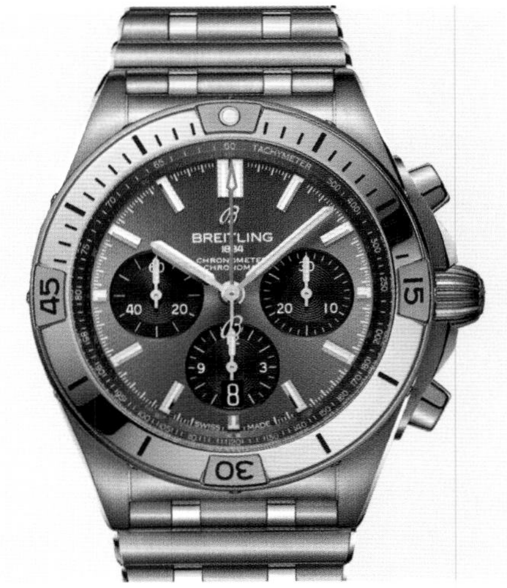

Chronomat B01 42

Reference number: UB0134101B1U1
Movement: automatic, Breitling Caliber B01; ø 30 mm, height 7.2 mm; 47 jewels; 28,800 vph; column-wheel control of chronograph functions; 70-hour power reserve; COSC-certified chronometer
Functions: hours, minutes, subsidiary seconds; chronograph; date
Case: stainless steel, ø 42 mm, height 15.1 mm; unidirectional rose gold bezel with 0-60 scale; sapphire crystal; transparent case back; screw-in crown, rose gold crown and pushers; water-resistant to 20 atm
Band: stainless steel with rose gold elements, folding clasp
Price: $12,100

Avenger Chronograph 45 Night Mission

Reference number: V13317101L1X1
Movement: automatic, Breitling Caliber 13 (base ETA 7750); ø 30 mm, height 7.9 mm; 25 jewels; 28,800 vph; 42-hour power reserve; COSC-certified chronometer
Functions: hours, minutes, subsidiary seconds; chronograph; date
Case: titanium with black PLC, ø 45 mm, height 16.46 mm; unidirectional bezel with 0-60 scale; sapphire crystal; screw-in crown; water-resistant to 30 atm
Band: textile, buckle
Price: $5,835

Avenger Automatic GMT 45 Night Mission

Reference number: V32395101B1X1
Movement: automatic, Breitling Caliber 32 (base ETA 2893-2); ø 25.6 mm, height 4.1 mm; 21 jewels; 28,800 vph; 42-hour power reserve
Functions: hours, minutes, sweep seconds; additional 24-hour display (2nd time zone); date
Case: titanium with black DLC, ø 45 mm, height 12.31 mm; unidirectional bezel with 0-60 scale; sapphire crystal; screw-in crown; water-resistant to 30 atm
Band: textile, buckle
Price: $4,795

Caliber B01

Automatic; column-wheel control of chronograph functions; vertical clutch; single spring barrel; COSC-certified chronometer; 70-hour power reserve
Functions: hours, minutes, subsidiary seconds; chronograph; date
Diameter: 30 mm
Height: 7.2 mm
Jewels: 47
Balance: glucydur
Frequency: 28,800 vph

Caliber B04

Automatic; column-wheel control of chronograph functions; vertical clutch; single spring barrel; COSC-certified chronometer; 70-hour power reserve
Functions: hours, minutes, subsidiary seconds; additional 24-hour display (2nd time zone); chronograph; date
Diameter: 30 mm
Height: 7.4 mm
Jewels: 47
Balance: glucydur
Frequency: 28,800 vph

Caliber B05

Automatic; column-wheel control of chronograph functions; vertical clutch; time zone disk connected to hand mechanism by planetary transmission; single spring barrel; COSC-certified chronometer; 70-hour power reserve
Functions: hours, minutes, subsidiary seconds; world time display (crown-set 2nd time zone); chronograph; date
Diameter: 30 mm
Height: 8.1 mm
Jewels: 56
Balance: glucydur
Frequency: 28,800 vph

BREMONT

Bremont watches have adventure in their DNA, as it were, but adventure with a bit of Anglo-Saxon understatement. They have been worn by a number of people who have exhibited their taste for derring-do, like polar explorer Ben Saunders or Levison Wood, who was the first person to walk the length of the Nile. And it's hardly any wonder, since the brand is the brainchild of brothers Nick and Giles English, themselves dyed-in-the-wool pilots and restorers of vintage airplanes. The brand name has a wild story as well: To avoid a storm, the brothers were forced to land their vintage biplane in a field in southern France. The farmer, a former World War II pilot, was more than happy to put them up for the night. His name: Antoine Bremont.

These British-made timepieces hit the market in 2007 and hit a nerve in those seeking a watch that tells the time and expresses some smoldering attraction to danger, perhaps. They use sturdy, COSC-certified automatic movements from Switzerland, some modified, hardened steel, a patented shock-absorbing system, and a rotor whose design recalls a flight of planes. The brand has sought its inspiration from such British icons as the Spitfire, Bletchley Park (where the German codes were broken during World War II), or Jaguar sports cars and, at the time of publishing, Stephen Hawking. The brand also partnered with Boeing to produce an elegant range of watches on an organic polymer strap. Water sport is another area Bremont has explored, with models inspired by the legendary J-Class yachts, like the ladies' model AC I 32, and a special set devoted to the America's Cup.

The watches have been manufactured in Henley-on-Thames since 2010. In 2017, Bremont became the first official timekeeper for the Henley Royal Regatta, one of Great Britain's top rowing events.

Bremont Watch Company
P.O. Box 4741
Henley-on-Thames
RG9 9BZ
Oxfordshire
United Kingdom

Tel.:
+44-800-817-4281

E-mail:
info@bremont.com

Website:
www.bremont.com

Founded:
2002

Number of employees:
100+

Annual production:
several thousand watches

U.S. distributor:
Bremont Inc.
501 Madison Avenue
New York, NY 10022
855-273-6668
Michael.Pearson@bremont.com
Anthony.kozlowsky@bremont.com

Most important collections/price range:
ALT1, Armed Forces collection, Bremont Boeing, Bremont Jaguar, MB, SOLO, Supermarine, U-2, and limited editions / $3,600 to $42,500

Alt1-P2 Jet

Movement: automatic, Caliber BE-53AE (base Valjoux 7753); ø 30 mm, height 7.9 mm; 27 jewels; 28,800 vph; modified winding rotor; ISO 3159-certified chronometer; 42-hour power reserve
Functions: hours, minutes, subsidiary seconds; chronograph; date
Case: stainless steel with black DLC, ø 43 mm, height 16 mm; sapphire crystal; transparent case back; water-resistant to 10 atm
Band: calfskin, buckle
Price: $5,595
Variations: with stainless steel DLC-coated bracelet

Alt1-C Griffon

Movement: automatic, Caliber BE-50AE (base Valjoux 7750); ø 30 mm, height 7.9 mm; 25 jewels; 28,800 vph; modified winding rotor; ISO 3159-certified chronometer; 42-hour power reserve
Functions: hours, minutes, subsidiary seconds; chronograph; date
Case: stainless steel, ø 43 mm, height 16 mm; sapphire crystal; transparent case back; water-resistant to 10 atm
Band: calfskin, buckle
Price: $6,695
Variations: with stainless steel DLC-coated bracelet

MBII

Movement: automatic, Caliber BE-36AE (base Sellita SW300); ø 25.6 mm, height 3.6 mm; 25 jewels; 28,800 vph; soft iron cage for amagnetic protection; ISO 3159-certified chronometer; 38-hour power reserve
Functions: hours, minutes, sweep seconds; date
Case: stainless steel, ø 43 mm, height 12 mm; crown-activated inner bezel with 0-60 scale; sapphire crystal; transparent case back; water-resistant to 10 atm
Band: textile, buckle
Remarks: aluminum case barrel with DLC coating in different colors, configurable.
Price: $4,995

BRM
(Bernard Richards Manufacture)
2 Impasse de L'Aubette
ZA des Aulnaies
F-95420 Magny en Vexin
France

Tel.:
+33-1-61-02-00-25

Website:
www.brm-manufacture.com

Founded:
2003

Number of employees:
20

Annual production:
approx. 2,000 pieces

U.S. distributor:
BRM Manufacture North America
25 Highland Park Village, Suite 100-777
Dallas, TX 75205
214-231-0144
usa@brm-manufacture.com

Price range:
$3,000 to $150,000

BRM

For Bernard Richards, the true sign of luxury lies in "technical skills and perfection in all stages of manufacture." The exterior of the product is of course crucial, but all of BRM's major operations for making a wristwatch—such as encasing, assembling, setting, and polishing—are performed by hand in his little garage-like factory located outside Paris in Magny-sur-Vexin.

BRM is devoted to the ultra-mechanical look with the *haute-horlogerie* feel of high-end materials. His inspiration at the start came from the 1940s, the age of axle grease, pinups, real pilots, and a can-do attitude. The design: three dimensions visible to the naked eye, big mechanical landscapes. The inside: custom-designed components, fitting perfectly into Richards's automotive ideal. Gradually, though, Richards has been modernizing.

BRM's unusual timepieces have mainly been based on the tried and trusted ETA movements. The new GTM, featuring a printed and UV-treated world on the dial, runs on one, for example. But Richards has set lofty goals for himself and his young venture, for he intends to set up a true *manufacture* in his French factory. His BiRotor model is thus outfitted with the Precitime, an autonomous caliber conceived and manufactured on French soil. The movement features BRM's shock absorbers mounted on the conical springs of its so-called Isolastic system. Plates and bridges are crafted in ARCAP, rotors are made of Fortale and tantalum. The twin rotors, found at 12 and 6 o'clock, are mounted on double rows of ceramic bearings that require no lubrication.

When not building eccentric timepieces, Richards lets BRM aficionados do their own thing: When visiting the BRM website, they can construct a V12-44-BRM model on their own.

GMT6

Movement: automatic, ETA Caliber 2824/2 modified in-house; ø 25.6 mm, height 4.6 mm; 25 jewels; 28,800 vph; skeletonized dial; 38-hour power reserve
Functions: hours, minutes, seconds; 24-hour time zone (numbers printed on bezel rim); date
Case: titanium with black PVD, ø 46 mm, height 10 mm; 24 reference flags printed on bezel, user rotates home flag to hour hand to compute time in other zones; steel crown and lugs; crystal sapphire; transparent case back; screw-in crown; water-resistant to 5 atm
Remarks: UV-treated white world map printed on dial
Band: leather, buckle
Price: $6,950

R46

Movement: automatic, heavily modified ETA Caliber 2161; ø 38 mm; 35 jewels; 28,800 vph; 48-hour power reserve; patented Isolastic system with 3 shock absorbers; Fortale HR, tantalum and aluminum rotor; hand-painted Gulf colors
Functions: hours, minutes, sweep seconds; power reserve indication
Case: Makrolon with rose gold crown and strap lugs, ø 46 mm, height 10 mm; sapphire crystal; antireflective on both sides; exhibition case back; water-resistant to 3 atm
Band: leather, buckle
Price: $24,750; limited to 30 pieces

V12-46-TSAABL

Movement: automatic, ETA Valjoux Caliber 7753 modified in-house; ø 30 mm, height 7.90 mm; 27 jewels; 28,800 vph; skeletonized dial; shock absorbers connected to movement, 3 vertical, 3 horizontal; 42-hour power reserve
Functions: hours, minutes, subsidiary seconds; chronograph; date with 10-hour corrector
Case: titanium with stainless steel crown and strap lugs, ø 46 mm, height 12 mm; sapphire crystal; antireflective on both sides; transparent case back; screw-in crown; water-resistant to 10 atm
Band: calfskin, folding clasp
Price: $16,700
Variations: hands and springs in different colors on request

BULGARI

Although Bulgari is one of the largest jewelry manufacturers in the world, watches have always played an important role for the brand. The purchase of Daniel Roth and Gérald Genta in the Vallée de Joux opened new perspectives for its timepieces, thanks to specialized production facilities and the watchmaking talent in the Vallée de Joux—especially where complicated timepieces are concerned. In March 2011, luxury goods giant Louis Vuitton Moët Hennessy (LVMH) secured all the Bulgari family shares in exchange for 16.5 million LVMH shares and a say in the group's future. The financial backing of the mega-group boosted the company's strategy to become fully independent.

In mid-2013, Jean-Christophe Babin, the man who turned TAG Heuer into a leading player in sports watches, was chosen to head the venerable brand. He pushed for integration, meaning the company now builds complete watches, including its own cases and dials, and a number of outstanding calibers, like the 168 automatic based on a design by the great nineteenth-century watchmaker Jean Frédéric Leschot.

Under the bold leadership of Guido Terrini, the watch division has also been pushing the envelope with a series of increasingly thin and complicated automatics. After the tourbillon in 2014 came a minute repeater in 2016, which is 3.12 millimeters high and whose dial features slotted indices for better sound transmission. The 5.15-millimeter-high Octo Finissimo Automatic, with the Caliber BVL 138, was the talk of Baselworld in 2017. The chronograph GMT is another feat of streamlining. It is 6.9 millimeters high, wound with a hubless peripheral rotor, and features an hour hand that can be quickly and easily clicked through the time zones.

Bulgari Horlogerie SA
rue de Monruz 34
CH-2000 Neuchâtel
Switzerland

Tel.:
+41-32-722-7878

E-mail:
info@bulgari.com

Website:
www.bulgari.com

Founded:
1884 (Bulgari Horlogerie was founded in the early 1980s as Bulgari Time)

U.S. distributor:
Bulgari Corporation of America
555 Madison Avenue
New York, NY 10022
212-315-9700

Most important collections/price range:
Bulgari-Bulgari / from approx. $4,700 to $30,300; Diagono / from approx. $3,200; Octo / from approx. $9,500 to $690,000 and above; Daniel Roth and Gérald Genta collections

Octo Finissimo Automatic

Reference number: BGO40C3PSSXTAUTO
Movement: automatic, Bulgari Caliber BVL 138 Finissimo; ø 36 mm, height 2.23 mm; 23 jewels; 21,600 vph; platinum microrotor; finely finished with côtes de Genève; 60-hour power reserve
Functions: hours, minutes, subsidiary seconds
Case: stainless steel, ø 40 mm, height 5.15 mm; sapphire crystal; transparent case back
Band: stainless steel, folding clasp
Price: $11,900
Variations: titanium ($13,200); rose gold case and bracelet ($45,700)

Octo Finissimo Automatic

Reference number: BGO40BPPGLXTAUTO
Movement: automatic, Bulgari Caliber BVL 138 Finissimo; ø 36 mm, height 2.23 mm; 23 jewels; 21,600 vph; platinum microrotor; finely finished with côtes de Genève; 60-hour power reserve
Functions: hours, minutes, subsidiary seconds
Case: rose gold, ø 40 mm, height 5.15 mm; sapphire crystal; transparent case back
Band: reptile skin, buckle
Price: $22,100
Variations: stainless steel ($11,900); titanium ($13,200)

Octo Finissimo Automatic

Reference number: BGO40BPCCXTAUTO
Movement: automatic, Bulgari Caliber BVL 138 Finissimo; ø 36 mm, height 2.23 mm; 23 jewels; 21,600 vph; platinum microrotor; finely finished with côtes de Genève; 60-hour power reserve
Functions: hours, minutes, subsidiary seconds
Case: ceramic, ø 40 mm, height 5.15 mm; sapphire crystal; transparent case back
Band: ceramic, folding clasp
Price: $16,100
Variations: titanium ($13,200); rose gold with rose gold band ($45,700); stainless steel ($11,900)

Octo Finissimo Automatic

Reference number: BGO40BPSSXTAUTO
Movement: automatic, Bulgari Caliber BVL 138 Finissimo; ø 36 mm, height 2.23 mm; 23 jewels; 21,600 vph; platinum microrotor; finely finished with côtes de Genève; 60-hour power reserve
Functions: hours, minutes, subsidiary seconds
Case: stainless steel, ø 40 mm, height 5.15 mm; sapphire crystal; transparent case back
Band: stainless steel, folding clasp
Price: $11,900
Variations: titanium ($13,900); ceramic ($16,100); rose gold ($20,400)

Octo L'Originale

Reference number: BGOP41BGL
Movement: automatic, Bulgari Caliber BVL 191; ø 26.2 mm, height 3.8 mm; 26 jewels; 28,800 vph; finely finished with côtes de Genève; 42-hour power reserve
Functions: hours, minutes, sweep seconds; date
Case: rose gold, ø 41.5 mm, height 10.5 mm; lower bezel and crown in stainless steel with black DLC; sapphire crystal; transparent case back; water-resistant to 10 atm
Band: rubber, folding clasp
Price: $24,300
Variations: stainless steel with black DLC ($7,200)

Octo L'Originale Velocissimo Chronograph

Reference number: BGOP41BGLCH
Movement: automatic, Bulgari Caliber BVL 328 Velocissimo (base Zenith "El Primero"); ø 30 mm, height 6.62 mm; 31 jewels; 36,000 vph; column-wheel control of chronograph functions, silicon escapement; 50-hour power reserve
Functions: hours, minutes, subsidiary seconds; chronograph; date
Case: rose gold, ø 41.5 mm, height 13.07 mm; lower bezel, crown, and pushers in stainless steel with black DLC; sapphire crystal; transparent case back; water-resistant to 10 atm; **Band:** rubber, folding clasp
Price: $24,000; **Variations:** stainless steel with black DLC ($10,500)

Octo L'Originale Velocissimo Chronograph

Reference number: BGO41C14TVDCH
Movement: automatic, Bulgari Caliber BVL 328 Velocissimo (base Zenith "El Primero"); ø 30 mm, height 6.62 mm; 31 jewels; 36,000 vph; column-wheel control of chronograph functions, silicon escapement; 50-hour power reserve
Functions: hours, minutes, subsidiary seconds; chronograph; date
Case: titanium, ø 41 mm, height 13.07 mm; sapphire crystal; transparent case back; water-resistant to 10 atm
Band: rubber, folding clasp
Price: $10,200

Octo L'Originale

Reference number: BGO41PBBSGVD
Movement: automatic, Bulgari Caliber BVL 191; ø 26.2 mm, height 3.8 mm; 26 jewels; 28,800 vph; finely finished with côtes de Genève; 42-hour power reserve
Functions: hours, minutes, sweep seconds; date
Case: stainless steel with black DLC coating, ø 41.5 mm, height 10.5 mm; red gold lower bezel and crown; sapphire crystal; transparent case back; water-resistant to 10 atm
Band: rubber, folding clasp
Price: $8,650

Octo Roma

Reference number: OC41C5SPGLD
Movement: automatic, Bulgari Caliber BVL 191; ø 26.2 mm, height 3.8 mm; 26 jewels; 28,800 vph; finely finished with côtes de Genève; 42-hour power reserve
Functions: hours, minutes, sweep seconds; date
Case: stainless steel, ø 41 mm, height 10.5 mm; rose gold lower bezel and crown; sapphire crystal; transparent case back; water-resistant to 10 atm
Band: stainless steel, folding clasp
Price: $7,800
Variations: comes with different cases, straps, and dials

Octo Finissimo Automatic Ceramica

Reference number: BGO40BCCXTAUTO
Movement: automatic, Bulgari Caliber BVL 138 Finissimo; ø 36 mm, height 2.23 mm; 23 jewels; 21,600 vph; platinum microrotor; finely finished with côtes de Genève; 60-hour power reserve
Functions: hours, minutes, subsidiary seconds
Case: ceramic, ø 40 mm, height 5.15 mm; sapphire crystal; transparent case back
Band: ceramic, folding clasp
Price: $15,600

Octo Finissimo Skeleton

Reference number: BGO40CCXTSK
Movement: manually wound, Bulgari Caliber BVL 128SK; ø 36 mm, height 2.35 mm; 28,800 vph; skeletonized bridges and plates; 65-hour power reserve
Functions: hours, minutes, subsidiary seconds; power reserve indicator
Case: ceramic, ø 40 mm, height 5.37 mm; sapphire crystal; transparent case back; screw-in crown; water-resistant to 3 atm
Band: ceramic, folding clasp
Price: $24,700

Octo Finissimo Chronograph

Reference number: BGO42C14TTXTCHGMT
Movement: automatic, Bulgari Caliber BVL 318 Finissimo; ø 36 mm, height 3.3 mm; 37 jewels; 21,600 vph; hubless peripheral rotor with platinum oscillating mass; column-wheel control of chronograph functions; finely finished with côtes de Genève; 60-hour power reserve; **Functions:** hours, minutes, subsidiary seconds; additional 24-hour display (2nd time zone); chronograph
Case: titanium, ø 42 mm, height 6.9 mm; sapphire crystal; transparent case back; water-resistant to 3 atm
Band: titanium, folding clasp
Remarks: currently the thinnest automatic chronograph movement
Price: $17,600; **Variations:** reptile skin band

Octo Finissimo Skeleton

Reference number: BGO40CCXTSK
Movement: manually wound, Bulgari Caliber BVL 128SK; ø 36 mm, height 2.35 mm; 28,800 vph; skeletonized bridges and plates; 65-hour power reserve
Functions: hours, minutes, subsidiary seconds; power reserve indicator
Case: ceramic, ø 40 mm, height 5.37 mm; sapphire crystal; transparent case back; screw-in crown; water-resistant to 3 atm
Band: ceramic, folding clasp
Price: $24,700

Octo Finissimo Tourbillon Automatic

Reference number: BGO42CCXTSKAUTO
Movement: automatic, Bulgari Caliber BVL 288; ø 36 mm, height 1.95 mm; 24 jewels; 21,600 vph; flying 1-minute tourbillon; hubless peripheral rotor; 55-hour power reserve
Functions: hours, minutes
Case: carbon composite, ø 42 mm, height 3.95 mm; sapphire crystal; transparent case back; water-resistant to 3 atm
Band: carbon composite, double folding clasp
Remarks: currently the thinnest mechanical automatic watch with tourbillon
Price: $130,000

Octo Grande Sonnerie

Reference number: OC44CPGLTBGSQP
Movement: automatic, Bulgari Caliber BVL 5307; 82 jewels; 1-minute tourbillon; 48-hour power reserve
Functions: hours, minutes; minute repeater; dual power reserve indicator; perpetual calendar with date, weekday, month, moon phase, leap year
Case: carbon, ø 44 mm; sapphire crystal; rose gold crown and pushers
Band: reptile skin, folding clasp
Price: $833,000; limited to 3 pieces

Bulgari Bulgari

Reference number: BB41C3BSD/MB
Movement: automatic, Bulgari Caliber BVL 191; ø 26.2 mm, height 3.8 mm; 26 jewels; 28,800 vph; finished with côtes de Genève; 42-hour power reserve
Functions: hours, minutes, sweep seconds; date
Case: bronze, ø 41 mm, height 8.7 mm; sapphire crystal; water-resistant to 5 atm
Band: rubber, folding clasp
Price: $5,600

Bulgari Bulgari

Reference number: BB41C3BSD/MB
Movement: automatic, Bulgari Caliber BVL 191; ø 26.2 mm, height 3.8 mm; 26 jewels; 28,800 vph; finished with côtes de Genève; 42-hour power reserve
Functions: hours, minutes, sweep seconds; date
Case: stainless steel with black DLC coating, ø 41 mm, height 8.7 mm; sapphire crystal; water-resistant to 5 atm
Band: rubber, folding clasp
Price: $4,100

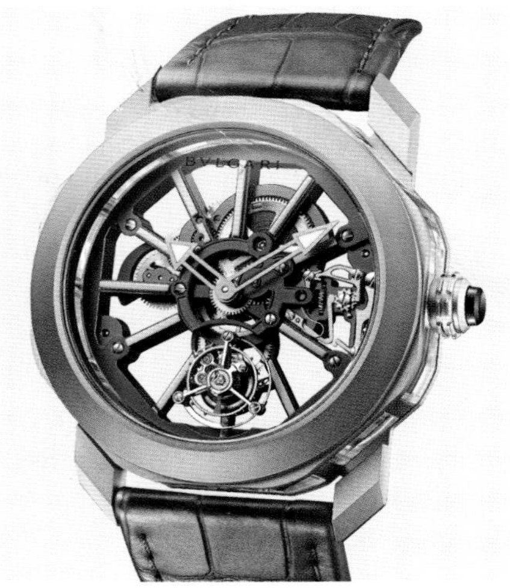

Octo Roma Tourbillon Sapphire

Reference number: BGO44PGLTBSK/BLUE
Movement: manually wound, Bulgari Caliber BVL 206; ø 34 mm, height 5 mm; 21,600 vph; flying 1-minute tourbillon; skeletonized movement, bridges with blue DLC coating; 64-hour power reserve
Functions: hours, minutes
Case: rose gold, ø 44 mm, height 12.45 mm; sapphire crystal; transparent case back; water-resistant to 5 atm
Band: reptile skin, folding clasp
Price: $89,000

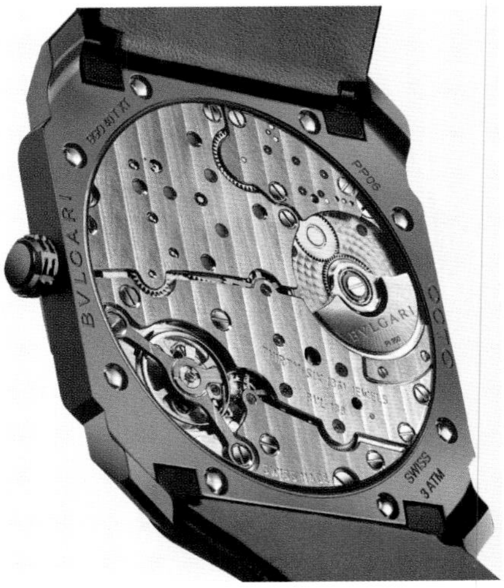

Caliber BVL 138 Finissimo

Automatic; flying platinum microrotor; flying single spring barrel, 60-hour power reserve
Functions: hours, minutes, subsidiary seconds; date
Diameter: 36 mm
Height: 2.23 mm
Jewels: 23
Balance: glucydur
Frequency: 21,600 vph
Balance spring: flat hairspring index for fine adjustment
Shock protection: Incabloc
Remarks: finely finished with côtes de Genève

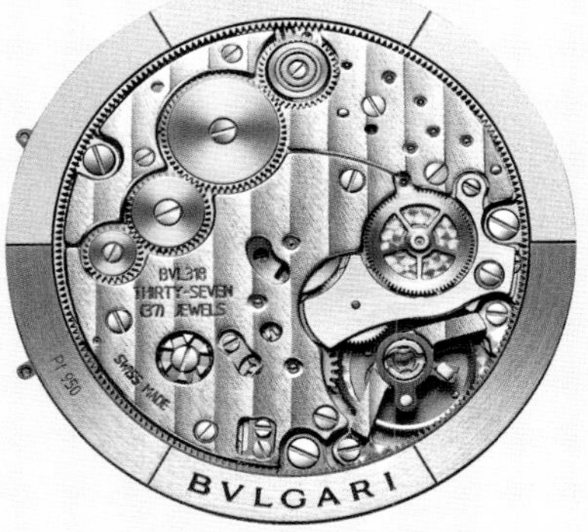

Caliber BVL 318 Finissimo

Automatic; hubless peripheral rotor with platinum oscillating mass; column-wheel control of chronograph functions; flying spring barrel; 60-hour power reserve
Functions: hours, minutes, subsidiary seconds; additional 24-hour display (2nd time zone); chronograph
Diameter: 36 mm; **Height:** 3.3 mm
Jewels: 37
Balance: glucydur
Frequency: 21,600 vph
Balance spring: flat hairspring index for fine adjustment
Shock protection: Incabloc
Remarks: finely finished with côtes de Genève; currently the thinnest chronograph movement

Caliber BVL 288

Automatic; flying 1-minute tourbillon; hubless peripheral rotor; single spring barrel, 55-hour power reserve
Functions: hours, minutes
Diameter: 36 mm
Height: 1.95 mm
Jewels: 24
Frequency: 21,600 vph
Remarks: engine of the thinnest automatic wristwatch—including a tourbillon

CARL F. BUCHERER

While luxury watch brand Carl F. Bucherer is still rather young, the Lucerne-based Bucherer jewelry dynasty behind it draws its vast know-how from more than ninety years of experience in the conception and design of fine wristwatches.

In 2005, Bucherer joined its Sainte-Croix-headquartered partner, Techniques Horlogères Appliquées SA (THA), to manufacture its own movement. THA was integrated into the Bucherer Group and the watch company renamed Carl F. Bucherer Technologies SA (CFBT). The Sainte-Croix operation is led by technical director Dr. Albrecht Haake, who oversees a staff of about twenty. Dr. Haake is currently focusing much of his energy on furthering the capacities at the workshop. "Industrialization is not a question of cost, but rather a question of quality," says Haake.

The Swiss company also expanded its Lengnau location to create a competence center that can focus on manufacturing its own movements as well as in-house watches. The famed automatic caliber with the peripheral rotor went through a thorough revamping process with the idea of industrializing it. For its 130th birthday, in 2018, the company decided to create a special "floating" tourbillon for its Manero collection. Not only does it feature a hubless peripheral rotor but the power transmission to the tourbillon is done from the side, making it invisible to the observer, a very subtle technology that has greatly contributed to the brand's fame. And in 2019, Bucherer launched the appropriately named Heritage collection. It is composed of timepieces like the Heritage BiCompax Annual Chronograph and the Heritage Tourbillon Double Peripheral that draw inspiration from the brand's historical models and give them a modern look.

Bucherer AG
Carl F. Bucherer
Langensandstrasse 27
CH-6002 Lucerne
Switzerland

Tel.:
+41-41-369-7070

E-mail:
info@carl-f-bucherer.com

Website:
www.carl-f-bucherer.com

Founded:
1919; repositioned under the name Carl F. Bucherer in 2001

Number of employees:
approx. 200

Annual production:
approx. 30,000 watches

U.S. distributor:
Carl F. Bucherer North America
1805 South Metro Parkway
Dayton, OH 45459
937-291-4366
info@cfbna.com

Most important collections/price range:
Patravi, Manero, Alacria, and Pathos / core price segment $5,000 to $30,000

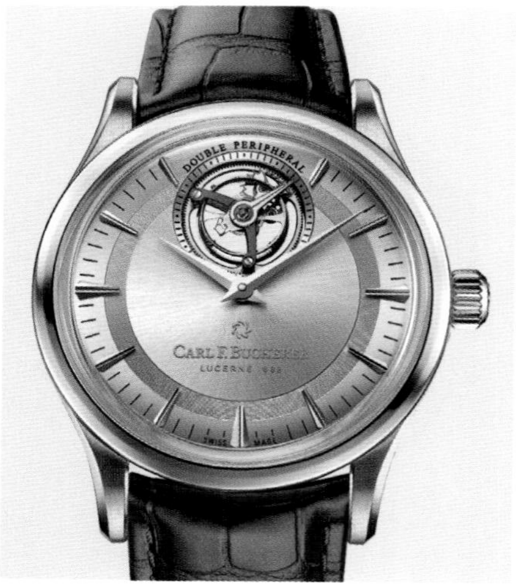

Heritage Tourbillon Double Peripheral

Reference number: 00.10802.03.13.01
Movement: automatic, Caliber CFB T3000; ø 36.5 mm, height 4.6 mm; 32 jewels; 21,600 vph; silicon escapement; flying 1-minute tourbillon with invisible peripheral drive, hubless peripheral rotor with rose gold oscillating mass; hand-engraved white gold bridge; COSC-certified chronometer; 65-hour power reserve
Functions: hours, minutes, subsidiary seconds (on tourbillon cage)
Case: rose gold, ø 42.5 mm, height 11.9 mm; sapphire crystal; transparent case back; water-resistant to 3 atm; **Band:** reptile skin, folding clasp
Price: $88,888; limited to 88 pieces

Heritage BiCompax Annual Chronograph

Reference number: 00.10803.07.42.01
Movement: automatic, Caliber CFB 1972; ø 30 mm, height 7.3 mm; 47 jewels; 28,800 vph; 42-hour power reserve
Functions: hours, minutes, subsidiary seconds; chronograph; annual calendar with large date, month
Case: stainless steel, ø 41 mm, height 14.05 mm; rose gold bezel, crown, and pushers; sapphire crystal; transparent case back; water-resistant to 3 atm
Band: calfskin, folding clasp
Price: $11,000

Heritage BiCompax Annual Chronograph

Reference number: 00.10803.08.12.01
Movement: automatic, Caliber CFB 1972; ø 30 mm, height 7.3 mm; 47 jewels; 28,800 vph; 42-hour power reserve
Functions: hours, minutes, subsidiary seconds; chronograph; annual calendar with large date, month
Case: stainless steel, ø 41 mm, height 14.05 mm; sapphire crystal; transparent case back; water-resistant to 3 atm
Band: rubber, folding clasp
Price: $7,200

Manero Tourbillon Double Peripheral

Reference number: 00.10920.03.13.01
Movement: automatic, Caliber CFB T3000; ø 36.5 mm, height 4.6 mm; 32 jewels; 21,600 vph; silicon escapement; flying 1-minute tourbillon with invisible peripheral drive, hubless peripheral rotor with tungsten oscillating mass; COSC-certified chronometer; 65-hour power reserve
Functions: hours, minutes, subsidiary seconds (on tourbillon cage)
Case: rose gold, ø 43.1 mm, height 11.57 mm; sapphire crystal; transparent case back; water-resistant to 3 atm
Band: reptile skin, folding clasp
Price: $68,000

Manero Peripheral

Reference number: 00.10917.03.33.01
Movement: automatic, Caliber CFB A2050; ø 30.6 mm, height 5.28 mm; 33 jewels; 28,800 vph; hubless peripheral rotor with tungsten oscillating mass; COSC-certified chronometer; 55-hour power reserve
Functions: hours, minutes, subsidiary seconds; date
Case: rose gold, ø 40.6 mm, height 11.2 mm; sapphire crystal; transparent case back; water-resistant to 3 atm
Band: reptile skin, folding clasp
Price: $16,600

Manero Peripheral

Reference number: 00.10917.08.73.11
Movement: automatic, Caliber CFB A2050; ø 30.6 mm, height 5.28 mm; 33 jewels; 28,800 vph; hubless peripheral rotor with tungsten oscillating mass; COSC-certified chronometer; 55-hour power reserve
Functions: hours, minutes, subsidiary seconds; date
Case: stainless steel, ø 40.6 mm, height 11.2 mm; bezel set with 60 diamonds; sapphire crystal; transparent case back; water-resistant to 3 atm
Band: reptile skin, folding clasp
Remarks: mother-of-pearl dial
Price: $9,700

Manero Flyback

Reference number: 00.10919.03.33.01
Movement: automatic, Caliber CFB 1970; ø 30.4 mm, height 7.9 mm; 25 jewels; 28,800 vph; 42-hour power reserve
Functions: hours, minutes, subsidiary seconds; flyback chronograph; date
Case: rose gold, ø 43 mm, height 14.45 mm; sapphire crystal; transparent case back; water-resistant to 3 atm
Band: reptile skin, folding clasp
Price: $16,900

Manero Flyback

Reference number: 00.10919.08.33.01
Movement: automatic, Caliber CFB 1970; ø 30.4 mm, height 7.9 mm; 25 jewels; 28,800 vph; 42-hour power reserve
Functions: hours, minutes, subsidiary seconds; flyback chronograph; date
Case: stainless steel, ø 43 mm, height 14.45 mm; sapphire crystal; transparent case back; water-resistant to 3 atm
Band: reptile skin, folding clasp
Price: $6,200

Manero AutoDate Love

Reference number: 00.10922.08.73.21
Movement: automatic, Caliber CFB 1971, ø 26.2 mm, height 4.35 mm; 31 jewels; 28,800 vph; 42-hour power reserve
Functions: hours, minutes, subsidiary seconds; date
Case: stainless steel, ø 35.3 mm, height 9.15 mm; sapphire crystal; transparent case back; water-resistant to 3 atm
Band: stainless steel, folding clasp
Remarks: mother-of-pearl dial
Price: $4,000
Variations: rose gold set with diamonds ($14,400)

Patravi ScubaTec Black

Reference number: 00.10632.28.33.01
Movement: automatic, Caliber CFB 1950.1; ø 26.2 mm, height 4.6 mm; 25 jewels; 28,800 vph; COSC-certified chronometer; 38-hour power reserve
Functions: hours, minutes, sweep seconds; date
Case: titanium with black DLC coating, ø 44.6 mm, height 13.45 mm; unidirectional bezel with ceramic insert, with 0-60 scale; sapphire crystal; screw-in crown, helium valve; water-resistant to 50 atm
Band: rubber with textile inlay, folding clasp with extension link
Price: $7,200
Variations: stainless steel with stainless steel bracelet ($6,700); stainless steel with rubber strap ($6,200)

Patravi ScubaTec "Black Manta"

Reference number: 00.10632.28.33.99
Movement: automatic, Caliber CFB 1950.1; ø 26.2 mm, height 4.6 mm; 25 jewels; 28,800 vph; COSC-certified chronometer; 38-hour power reserve
Functions: hours, minutes, sweep seconds; date
Case: titanium with black DLC coating, ø 44.6 mm, height 13.45 mm; unidirectional bezel with ceramic insert, 0-60 scale; sapphire crystal; screw-in crown; helium valve; water-resistant to 50 atm
Band: rubber with recycled textile insert, folding clasp with extension link
Price: $7,200; **Variations:** stainless steel with stainless steel bracelet ($6,700); stainless steel with rubber strap ($6,200); rose gold and stainless steel with rubber strap ($9,600)

Patravi TravelTec

Reference number: 00.10620.08.33.02
Movement: automatic, Caliber CFB 1901.1; ø 28.6 mm, height 7.3 mm; 39 jewels; 28,800 vph; COSC-certified chronometer; 42-hour power reserve
Functions: hours, minutes, subsidiary seconds; 3 time zone display; chronograph; date
Case: stainless steel, ø 46.6 mm, height 15.5 mm; pusher-activated, bidirectional inner bezel with 24-hour division for a 3rd time zone; sapphire crystal; screw-in crown; water-resistant to 5 atm
Band: rubber, folding clasp
Price: $10,900

CFB T3000

Automatic; floating 1-minute tourbillon; silicon escapement, bidirectional peripheral tungsten rotor turning on edge of movement, on spring-based bearings; precision adjustment mechanism; single spring barrel; COSC-certified chronometer; 65-hour power reserve
Functions: hours, minutes, subsidiary seconds; date
Diameter: 36.5 mm
Height: 4.6 mm
Jewels: 32
Balance: glucydur
Frequency: 21,600 vph
Balance spring: flat hairspring
Shock protection: Incabloc

CFB A2050

Movement: automatic; bidirectional peripheral tungsten rotor turning on edge of movement, on spring-based bearings; precision adjustment mechanism; single spring barrel, 55-hour power reserve
Base caliber: CFB A2000
Functions: hours, minutes, subsidiary seconds; date
Diameter: 30.6 mm
Height: 5.28 mm
Jewels: 33
Balance: glucydur
Frequency: 28,800 vph
Balance spring: flat hairspring
Shock protection: Incabloc

CFB A1000

Movement: automatic; bidirectional peripheral tungsten rotor turning on edge of movement, on spring-based bearings; precision adjustment mechanism; single spring barrel, 55-hour power reserve
Functions: hours, minutes, subsidiary seconds, large date
Diameter: 32 mm; **Height:** 6.3 mm
Jewels: 33; **Balance:** glucydur
Frequency: 21,600 vph
Balance spring: flat hairspring
Shock protection: Incabloc
Related calibers: CFB A1002 (with large date, weekday, power reserve indicator), CFB A1003 (with large date, weekday)

Carl Suchy & Söhne
Prinz-Eugen-Strasse 48/Top 3
A-1010 Wien
Austria

Tel.:
+43-660-75-24-331

E-mail:
office@carlsuchy.com

Website:
www.carlsuchy.com

Founded:
1822/2017

Distribution:
Retail

Most important collection:
Waltz N°1

CARL SUCHY & SÖHNE

Carl Suchy & Söhne, founded in 1822, was a successful clock and pocket watch maker with a presence in Vienna and Prague and workshops in La Chaux-de-Fonds. The products were the ultimate in fashion at the time, the somewhat restrained, bourgeois Biedermeier style, which found favor well beyond Vienna's borders. The clocks and pocket watches were the buzz at international trade fairs and world exhibitions and became coveted status symbols. Everyone with a name or title, from Kaiser Franz Joseph I to Sigmund Freud, owned a Carl Suchy, supplier to the Kaiser's and King's court, a very special branding.

The brand was revived in 2016 by a Viennese businessman with experience in "curating art," the kind of person with a wealth of creative ideas and knowledge. Instead of pretending that Carl Suchy would continue in the same Biedermeier vein, the brand sought the more timeless look of the Viennese Modern movement ushered in by architect Alfred Loos, whose main idea was encapsulated in a 1910 essay entitled "Ornament and Crime," in which he comes up with this stunning formulation: "Cultural evolution is equivalent to the removal of ornament from articles in daily use." The coming-out model, the Waltz N°1, was designed in a dialogue between CEO Robert Punkenhofer and a young graduate from the ECAL in Lausanne, Miloš Ristin. It was to express "Viennese elegance and savoir vivre," says the CEO.

The final product was supervised by the outstanding Swiss watchmaker, Marc Jenni. It was not a spectacular watch at first glance. All the value was in the detailed finishings of the thin case, the lugs, and the silk-leather strap. The dial features a calming geometrical pattern with perpendicular guilloché on one half and a vertical guilloché on the other. It's not a static visual: At 6 o'clock, a small second disk turns, breaking up the pattern, but "clicking in place" twice each minute. Time for the Waltz N°1 is driven by a Vaucher Fleurier automatic caliber. The model was skeletonized for the second version.

Waltz N°1

Reference number: 200052
Movement: automatic, Vaucher Caliber VMF 5401; ø 30 mm, height 2.6 mm; 29 jewels; 21,600 vph; microrotor; finely finished movement; 48-hour power reserve
Functions: hours, minutes, subsidiary seconds (on a revolving disk)
Case: stainless steel, ø 40 mm, height 9.3 mm; sapphire crystal; transparent case back; crown with ceramic insert; water-resistant to 3 atm
Band: reptile skin, double folding clasp
Remarks: dial with horizontal and vertical guilloché pattern
Price: $8,950
Variations: black or blue dial; case with black PVD

Waltz N°1 Gold

Reference number: 200059
Movement: automatic, Vaucher Caliber VMF 5401; ø 30 mm, height 2.6 mm; 29 jewels; 21,600 vph; microrotor; finely finished movement; 48-hour power reserve
Functions: hours, minutes, subsidiary seconds (on a revolving disk)
Case: yellow gold, ø 40 mm, height 9.3 mm; sapphire crystal; transparent case back; crown with ceramic insert; water-resistant to 3 atm
Band: reptile skin, double folding clasp
Remarks: dial with horizontal and vertical guilloché pattern
Price: $17,900; limited to five pieces
Variations: black or blue dial

Waltz N°1 Skeleton

Reference number: 200058
Movement: automatic, Vaucher Caliber VMF 5401/180; ø 30 mm, height 2.6 mm; 29 jewels; 21,600 vph; microrotor; fully skeletonized dial; 48-hour power reserve
Functions: hours, minutes, subsidiary seconds (on a revolving disk)
Case: stainless steel, ø 40 mm, height 9.3 mm; sapphire crystal; transparent case back; crown with ceramic insert; water-resistant to 3 atm
Band: reptile skin, double folding clasp
Remarks: dial skeletonized along the vertical and horizontal guilloché lines
Price: $22,950; limited to five pieces
Variations: silver dial

CARTIER

Since the Richemont Group's founding, Cartier has played an important role in the luxury concern as its premier brand and instigator of turnover. Although it took a while for Cartier to find its footing and convince the male market of its masculinity, any concerns about Cartier's seriousness and potential are being dispelled by facts. The company is growing by leaps and bounds—a components manufacturing site employing 400 people is being built at the growing Richemont campus in Meyrin (Geneva). Carole Forestier-Kasapi, who heads watchmaking, has driven the vertical integration of the brand with a host of outstanding calibers, beginning with the 1904 MC, a reference to the year in which Louis Cartier developed the first wristwatch made for men—a pilot's watch custom designed for his friend and early pioneer of aviation, Alberto Santos-Dumont.

The automatic movement is a largely unadorned yet efficient machine, powered by twin barrels. The central rotor sits on ceramic ball bearings, and the adjustment of the conventional escapement is by an excenter screw. It is available for chronographs or diver's watches. But mainly, it has positioned Cartier as one of the most effective makers of high-end watches in a very competitive industry.

In a period that values vintage, the Cartier brand has an advantage. More than a century of watchmaking has provided it with a steady stream of models to revive and modernize. This year, Cartier resurrected the Pasha, a watch originally released in 1985, but based on a watch designed in the 1930s for the Pasha of Marrakech as a water-resistant timepiece, because he liked to keep an eye on the time while taking a bath. The striking features: a round bezel, a square minute track, and the four cardinal hours as Arab numerals. The modern elements are an interchangeable strap system and the sapphire crystal in the back, so the wearer can show off the 1847 MC caliber inside. Also new this year is an asymmetrical Tank, a very catchy interpretation of a watch that keeps returning to the market as a success story.

Cartier
1201 Genève
Switzerland

E-mail:
contact.na@cartier.com

Website:
www.cartier.com

Founded:
1847

Number of employees:
approx. 1,300 (watch manufacturing)

U.S. distributor:
Cartier North America
645 Fifth Avenue
New York, NY 10022
1-800-CARTIER
www.cartier.us

Most important collections:
Santos de Cartier, Panthère de Cartier, Baignoire, Tank, Ballon Bleu de Cartier, Drive de Cartier, Calibre de Cartier, Clé de Cartier, Ronde de Cartier, Pasha de Cartier

Pasha de Cartier

Reference number: WGPA0014
Movement: automatic, Cartier Caliber 1847 MC; ø 25.6 mm; 23 jewels; 28,800 vph; 40-hour power reserve
Functions: hours, minutes, sweep seconds
Case: rose gold, ø 35 mm, height 9.37 mm; sapphire crystal; crown with screw cap and sapphire cabochon; water-resistant to 10 atm
Band: reptile skin, folding clasp
Remarks: comes with additional reptile skin strap
Price: $14,300

Pasha de Cartier

Reference number: WSPA0010
Movement: automatic, Cartier Caliber 1847 MC; ø 25.6 mm; 23 jewels; 28,800 vph; 40-hour power reserve
Functions: hours, minutes, sweep seconds; date
Case: stainless steel, ø 41 mm, height 9.55 mm; sapphire crystal; crown with screw-down cap and spinel cabochon; water-resistant to 10 atm
Band: reptile skin, folding clasp
Remarks: comes with additional reptile skin strap
Price: $6,200

Pasha de Cartier

Reference number: WGPA0007
Movement: automatic, Cartier Caliber 1847 MC; ø 25.6 mm; 23 jewels; 28,800 vph; 40-hour power reserve
Functions: hours, minutes, sweep seconds; date
Case: yellow gold, ø 41 mm, height 9.55 mm; sapphire crystal; crown with screw-down cap and sapphire cabochon; water-resistant to 10 atm
Band: reptile skin, folding clasp
Remarks: comes with additional reptile skin strap
Price: $16,600

Santos de Cartier ADLC

Reference number: WSSA0037
Movement: automatic, Cartier Caliber 1847 MC; ø 25.6 mm; 23 jewels; 28,800 vph; 40-hour power reserve
Functions: hours, minutes, sweep seconds; date
Case: stainless steel, ø 39.8 mm, height 9.08 mm; bezel with black ADLC; sapphire crystal; crown with spinel cabochon; water-resistant to 10 atm
Band: stainless steel, double folding clasp
Remarks: comes with rubber strap with QuickSwitch rapid changing system
Price: $7,400

Santos de Cartier ADLC

Reference number: WSSA0039
Movement: automatic, Cartier Caliber 1847 MC; ø 25.6 mm; 23 jewels; 28,800 vph; 40-hour power reserve
Functions: hours, minutes, sweep seconds; date
Case: stainless steel with black ADLC, ø 39.8 mm, height 9.38 mm; bezel with black ADLC; sapphire crystal; crown with spinel cabochon; water-resistant to 10 atm
Band: reptile skin, double folding clasp
Remarks: comes with rubber strap with QuickSwitch rapid changing system
Price: $7,650

Santos Dumont XL

Reference number: WGSA0032
Movement: manually wound, Cartier Caliber 430 MC; ø 20.55 mm, height 2.1 mm; 18 jewels; 21,600 vph
Functions: hours, minutes
Case: pink gold, 33.9 × 46.6 mm, height 7.5 mm; sapphire crystal; crown with sapphire cabochon
Band: reptile skin, buckle
Price: $15,600
Variations: stainless steel ($5,850); stainless steel with pink gold bezel ($8,100)

Santos Dumont XL

Reference number: WSSA0032
Movement: manually wound, Cartier Caliber 430 MC; ø 20.55 mm, height 2.1 mm; 18 jewels; 21,600 vph
Functions: hours, minutes
Case: stainless steel, 33.9 × 46.6 mm, height 7.5 mm; sapphire crystal; crown with spinel cabochon
Band: reptile skin, buckle
Price: $5,850
Variations: pink gold ($15,600); stainless steel with rose gold bezel ($8,100)

Santos Dumont XL

Reference number: W2SA0017
Movement: manually wound, Cartier Caliber 430 MC; ø 20.55 mm, height 2.1 mm; 18 jewels; 21,600 vph
Functions: hours, minutes
Case: stainless steel, 33.9 × 46.6 mm, height 7.5 mm; rose gold bezel; sapphire crystal; crown with spinel cabochon
Band: reptile skin, buckle
Price: $8,100
Variations: rose gold ($15,600); stainless steel ($5,850)

Santos Dumont Limited Edition

Reference number: WGSA0027
Movement: manually wound, Cartier Caliber 430 MC; ø 20.55 mm, height 2.1 mm; 18 jewels; 21,600 vph
Functions: hours, minutes
Case: yellow gold, 31.4 × 43.5 mm, height 7.3 mm; sapphire crystal; crown with sapphire cabochon
Band: reptile skin, buckle
Price: $14,300; limited to 300 pieces

Santos Dumont Limited Edition

Reference number: W2SA0015
Movement: manually wound, Cartier Caliber 430 MC; ø 20.55 mm, height 2.1 mm; 18 jewels; 21,600 vph
Functions: hours, minutes
Case: stainless steel, 31.4 × 43.5 mm, height 7.3 mm; bezel in yellow gold; sapphire crystal; crown with spinel cabochon
Band: reptile skin, buckle
Price: $7,250; limited to 500 pieces

Santos Dumont Limited Edition

Reference number: WGSA0034
Movement: manually wound, Cartier Caliber 430 MC; ø 20.55 mm, height 2.1 mm; 18 jewels; 21,600 vph
Functions: hours, minutes
Case: platinum, 31.4 × 43.5 mm, height 7.3 mm; sapphire crystal; crown with ruby cabochon
Band: reptile skin, buckle
Price: $18,700; limited to 100 pieces

Rotonde de Cartier Double Tourbillon Mystérieux Squelette

Reference number: WHRO0039
Movement: manually wound, Cartier Caliber 9465 MC; ø 39.7 mm, height 6.28 mm; 21,600 vph; skeletonized movement with integrated Roman numerals; double tourbillon located between 2 sapphire disks; 52-hour power reserve; Geneva Seal
Functions: hours, minutes (off-center)
Case: platinum, ø 45 mm, height 12.4 mm; sapphire crystal; transparent case back; crown with sapphire cabochon; water-resistant to 3 atm
Band: reptile skin, double folding clasp
Price: on request; limited to 30 pieces

Tank Asymétrique

Reference number: WHTA0012
Movement: manually wound, Cartier Caliber 9623 MC; 17.8 × 32 mm, height 4.2 mm; 22 jewels; 28,800 vph; skeletonized movement with integrated Roman numerals; 48-hour power reserve
Functions: hours, minutes
Case: platinum, 26.2 × 39.5 mm, height 7.82 mm; sapphire crystal; transparent case back; crown with sapphire cabochon
Band: reptile skin, buckle
Price: $30,100; limited to 100 pieces

Tank Asymétrique

Reference number: WGTA0042
Movement: manually wound, Cartier Caliber 1917 MC; 12.9 × 16 mm, height 2.9 mm; 19 jewels; 21,600 vph; 38-hour power reserve
Functions: hours, minutes
Case: platinum, 26.1 × 47.2 mm, height 6.38 mm; sapphire crystal; transparent case back; crown with ruby cabochon
Band: reptile skin, buckle
Price: $61,000; limited to 100 pieces

Tank Asymétrique

Reference number: WHTA0011
Movement: manually wound, Cartier Caliber 9623 MC; 17.8 × 32 mm, height 4.2 mm; 22 jewels; 28,800 vph; skeletonized movement with integrated Roman numerals; 48-hour power reserve
Functions: hours, minutes
Case: rose gold, 26.2 × 47.2 mm, height 7.82 mm; sapphire crystal; transparent case back; crown with sapphire cabochon
Band: reptile skin, buckle
Price: $70,000; limited to 100 pieces

Calibre de Cartier Diver Blue

Reference number: WSCA0010
Movement: automatic, Cartier Caliber 1904 MC; ø 25.6 mm, height 4 mm; 27 jewels; 28,800 vph; 2 spring barrels, 47-hour power reserve
Functions: hours, minutes, subsidiary seconds; date
Case: stainless steel, ø 42 mm, height 11 mm; unidirectional bezel with blue DLC, with 0-60 scale; sapphire crystal; screw-in crown; water-resistant to 30 atm
Band: calfskin with rubber covering, buckle
Price: $7,900

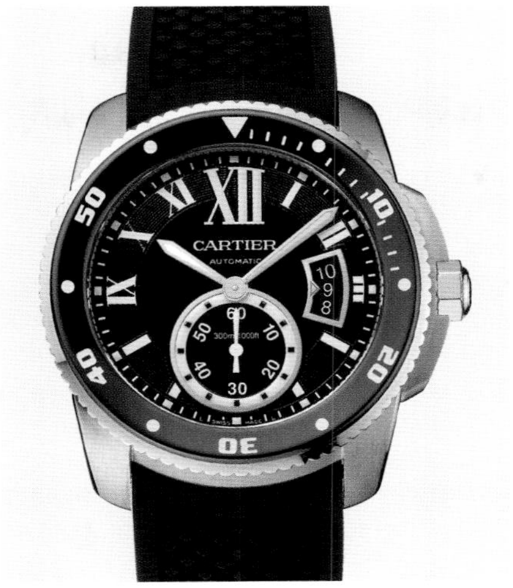

Calibre de Cartier Diver

Reference number: W7100056
Movement: automatic, Cartier Caliber 1904 MC; ø 25.6 mm, height 4 mm; 27 jewels; 28,800 vph; 2 spring barrels, 47-hour power reserve
Functions: hours, minutes, subsidiary seconds; date
Case: stainless steel, ø 42 mm, height 11 mm; unidirectional bezel with black DLC, with 0-60 scale; sapphire crystal; screw-in crown; water-resistant to 30 atm
Band: rubber, buckle
Price: $7,900
Variations: completely coated in black DLC ($8,950)

Calibre de Cartier Diver

Reference number: WSCA0006
Movement: automatic, Cartier Caliber 1904 MC; ø 25.6 mm, height 4 mm; 27 jewels; 28,800 vph; 2 spring barrels, 47-hour power reserve
Functions: hours, minutes, subsidiary seconds; date
Case: stainless steel with black DLC, ø 42 mm, height 11 mm; unidirectional bezel with 0-60 scale; sapphire crystal; screw-in crown; water-resistant to 30 atm
Band: rubber, buckle
Price: $8,950

Drive de Cartier

Reference number: WSNM0004
Movement: automatic, Cartier Caliber 1904-PS MC; ø 24.9 mm, height 4.5 mm; 27 jewels; 28,800 vph; 48-hour power reserve
Functions: hours, minutes, subsidiary seconds; date
Case: stainless steel, 40 × 41 mm, height 11.3 mm; sapphire crystal; water-resistant to 3 atm
Band: reptile skin, double folding clasp
Price: $6,250
Variations: black dial; rose gold ($16,600)

Drive de Cartier

Reference number: WGNM0003
Movement: automatic, Cartier Caliber 1904-PS MC; ø 24.9 mm, height 4.5 mm; 27 jewels; 28,800 vph; 48-hour power reserve
Functions: hours, minutes, subsidiary seconds; date
Case: rose gold, 40 × 41 mm, height 11.3 mm; sapphire crystal; water-resistant to 3 atm
Band: reptile skin, double folding clasp
Price: $16,600
Variations: stainless steel ($6,250)

Drive de Cartier Extra-Flat

Reference number: WSNM0011
Movement: manually wound, Cartier Caliber 430 MC; ø 20 mm, height 2.15 mm; 18 jewels; 21,600 vph; 43-hour power reserve
Functions: hours, minutes
Case: stainless steel, 38 × 39 mm, height 6.6 mm; sapphire crystal; water-resistant to 3 atm
Band: reptile skin, buckle
Price: $5,600
Variations: yellow gold ($14,200)

CHANEL

Chanel
135, avenue Charles de Gaulle
F-92521 Neuilly-sur-Seine Cedex
France

Tel.:
+33-1-41-92-08-33

Website:
www.chanel.com

Founded:
1914

Distribution:
retail and 200 Chanel boutiques worldwide

U.S. distributor:
Chanel Fine Jewelry and Watches
600 Madison Avenue, 19th Floor
New York, NY 10022
212-715-4741
www.chanel.com

Most important collections:
J12, Première, Boy.Friend, Monsieur de Chanel

After putting the occasional jewelry watch onto the market earlier, family-owned Chanel opened its own horology division in 1987, a move that gave the brand instant access to the world of watchmaking art. While the brand's first collections were directed exclusively at its female clientele, it was actually with the rather simple and masculine J12 that Chanel finally achieved a breakthrough. That was in 1999, over twenty years ago. The designer was Jacques Helleu. The J12 collection showpiece, the Rétrograde Mystérieuse, was a stroke of genius—courtesy of the innovative think tank Renaud et Papi. Its sleek ceramic case and complex mechanics instantly propelled Chanel into the world of *haute horlogerie*.

It was designer Arnaud Chastaingt who created the new J12.1. It still comes in brilliant white ceramic, but a black limited edition has been added as well. Inside is a new movement built by Kenissi, a joint venture Chanel shares with Tudor and Breitling. It no longer has a silicon hairspring, and it has returned to the soft iron cage to protect from magnetic fields.

In the past few years, the brand turned its attention to a younger, dynamic crowd with the "Vendôme" rectangular Boy.Friend, whose diamond-studded version won the Ladies' Prize at the 2018 edition of the GPHG. The Monsieur de Chanel is a purist, 40-millimeter watch with jumping hour and retrograde minutes driven by the Caliber 1. By the same token, it keeps returning to the J12, which put it's *haute horlogerie* products on the map. The new Paradoxe has an almost Pierrot look, with its black-and-white ceramic combinations. As for the X-Ray, it is a genuine diamond-studded jewel that doubles as a fine skeleton watch. It's price tag makes it exclusive, and, besides, only twelve pieces have been made.

J12 Paradoxe

Reference number: H6515
Movement: automatic, Chanel Caliber 12.1; ø 26 mm, height 4.99 mm; 28 jewels; 28,800 vph; winding rotor with tungsten oscillating weight; 70-hour power reserve; COSC-certified chronometer
Functions: hours, minutes, sweep seconds; date
Case: seamlessly poured black-and-white ceramic, ø 38 mm, height 12 mm; stainless steel bezel with bicolor ceramic insert, with 0-60 scale; sapphire crystal; screw-in crown, with ceramic cabochon; water-resistant to 20 atm
Band: ceramic, double folding clasp
Remarks: bicolor ceramic dial
Price: $8,050

J12-20

Reference number: H6476
Movement: automatic, Chanel Caliber 12.1; ø 26 mm, height 4.99 mm; 28 jewels; 28,800 vph; winding rotor with tungsten weight; 70-hour power reserve; COSC-certified chronometer
Functions: hours, minutes, sweep seconds
Case: ceramic, ø 38 mm, height 12 mm; stainless steel bezel with ceramic insert, with 0-60 scale; sapphire crystal; screw-in crown, with ceramic cabochon; water-resistant to 20 atm
Band: ceramic, double folding clasp
Remarks: dial set with 12 diamonds
Price: $7,750; anniversary edition limited to 2,020 pieces

J12 X-Ray

Reference number: H6249
Movement: manually wound, Chanel Caliber 3.1; 19.7 × 23.3 mm; 21 jewels; 28,800 vph; movement mounted on sapphire crystal mainplate; 55-hour power reserve
Functions: hours, minutes
Case: sapphire crystal, ø 38 mm, height 12 mm; bezel in white gold, set with 46 baguette-cut diamonds; sapphire crystal; crown in white gold with diamond cabochon; water-resistant to 3 atm
Band: sapphire crystal, triple folding clasp in white gold, set with 34 diamonds
Remarks: sapphire crystal dial set with 12 diamonds
Price: $626,000; limited to 12 pieces

Chopard & Cie. SA
8, rue de Veyrot
CH-1217 Meyrin (Geneva)
Switzerland

Tel.:
+41-22-719-3131

E-mail:
info@chopard.ch

Website:
www.chopard.ch

Founded:
1860

Distribution:
160 boutiques

U.S. distributor:
Chopard USA
75 Valencia Ave, Suite 1200
Coral Gables, FL 33134
1-800-CHOPARD
www.us.chopard.com

Most important collections/price range:
L.U.C / from \$7,950; Happy Sport / from \$4,240; Imperiale / from \$5,490; Classic Racing / from \$4,950; Alpine Eagle / from \$9,760

CHOPARD

The Chopard *manufacture* was founded by Louis-Ulysse Chopard in 1860 in the tiny village of Sonvillier in the Jura mountains of Switzerland. In 1963, it was purchased by Karl Scheufele, a goldsmith from Pforzheim, Germany, and revived as a producer of fine watches and jewelry.

The past seventeen years have seen a breathtaking development, when Karl Scheufele's son, Karl-Friedrich, and his sister, Caroline, decided to create watches with in-house movements, thus restoring the old business launched by Louis-Ulysse back in the nineteenth century.

In 1996, out of nowhere, Chopard opened up its watchmaking *manufacture* in the sleepy town of Fleurier in the Val-de-Travers, which had not yet experienced the revival of the mechanical watch. Focus on vertical integration drove the opening of a second building, Fleurier Ebauches SA, a hub of movement kits, including the L.U.C series. Chopard now has a line-up of eleven calibers, ranging from simple three-hander automatics to a tourbillon, a perpetual calendar, chronographs, an ultra-high-frequency chronometer, and a minute repeater.

The company's latest collection presented in October 2019 is called Alpine Eagle, a modernized version of the St. Moritz from the 1980s. The latter is the first watch project by then co-president Karl-Friedrich Scheufele, who had to convince his father, Karl, to actually manufacture the watch. For the new version, it was his son's turn to do the convincing. And he got vigorous support from his grandfather.

L.U.C Full Strike

Reference number: 168604-3001
Movement: manually wound, L.U.C Caliber 08.01-L; ø 37.2 mm, height 7.97 mm; 63 jewels; 28,800 vph; sapphire crystal gong; 60-hour power reserve; Geneva Seal, COSC-certified chronometer
Functions: hours, minutes, subsidiary seconds; power reserve indicator, minute repeater
Case: stainless steel, ø 42.5 mm, height 11.55 mm; sapphire crystal; transparent case back
Band: reptile skin, folding clasp
Price: on request; limited to 10 pieces

L.U.C Flying T Twin

Reference number: 161978-5001
Movement: automatic, L.U.C Caliber 96.24-L; ø 27.4 mm, height 3.3 mm; 25 jewels; 25,200 vph; flying 1-minute tourbillon, 2 spring barrels, microrotor; 65-hour power reserve; Geneva Seal, COSC-certified chronometer
Functions: hours, minutes, subsidiary seconds (on tourbillon cage)
Case: rose gold, ø 40 mm, height 7.2 mm; sapphire crystal; transparent case back; water-resistant to 3 atm
Band: reptile skin, buckle
Remarks: case made of certified fair-traded gold; hand-guillochéed rose gold dial
Price: on request; limited to 50 pieces

L.U.C Perpetual Chrono

Reference number: 161973-9001
Movement: manually wound, L.U.C Caliber 03.10-L; ø 33 mm, height 8.32 mm; 42 jewels; 28,800 vph; German silver mainplate and balance cock; 60-hour power reserve; Geneva Seal, COSC-certified chronometer
Functions: hours, minutes, sweep seconds; day/night indicator; flyback chronograph; perpetual calendar with large date, weekday, month, moon phase, leap year
Case: platinum, ø 45 mm, height 15.06 mm; sapphire crystal; transparent case back; water-resistant to 3 atm
Band: reptile skin, folding clasp
Price: on request; limited to 20 pieces

L.U.C Quattro

Reference number: 161926-1002
Movement: manually wound, L.U.C Caliber 98.01-L; ø 28.6 mm, height 3.7 mm; 39 jewels; 28,800 vph; 4 spring barrels, swan-neck fine adjustment, gold rotor; 216-hour power reserve; Geneva Seal, COSC-certified chronometer
Functions: hours, minutes, subsidiary seconds; power reserve indicator; date
Case: white gold, ø 43 mm, height 8.84 mm; sapphire crystal; transparent case back; water-resistant to 5 atm
Band: reptile skin, buckle
Price: $25,800; limited to 50 pieces
Variations: rose gold ($24,900)

L.U.C All in One

Reference number: 161925-9003
Movement: manually wound, L.U.C Caliber 05.01-L; ø 33 mm, height 11.75 mm; 42 jewels; 28,800 vph; 1-minute tourbillon; 170-hour power reserve; Geneva Seal, COSC-certified chronometer
Functions: hours, minutes, subsidiary seconds; day/night indicator, power reserve indicator, time equation, sunrise/sunset (on movement side); perpetual calendar with large date, weekday, month, orbital astronomical moon phase, leap year
Case: white gold, ø 46 mm, height 18.5 mm; sapphire crystal; transparent case back; water-resistant to 3 atm
Band: reptile skin, buckle
Price: on request; limited to 10 pieces

Mille Miglia GTS Power Control

Reference number: 168566-3011
Movement: automatic, Chopard Manufacture Caliber 01.08-C; ø 28.8 mm, height 4.95 mm; 40 jewels; 28,800 vph; 60-hour power reserve; COSC-certified chronometer
Functions: hours, minutes, sweep seconds; power reserve indicator; date
Case: stainless steel, ø 43 mm, height 11.43 mm; sapphire crystal; transparent case back; screw-in crown; water-resistant to 10 atm
Band: calfskin, folding clasp
Price: $6,800; limited to 500 pieces

Mille Miglia GTS Azzurro Chrono

Reference number: 168571-3007
Movement: automatic, ETA Caliber 7750; ø 30.4 mm, height 7.9 mm; 25 jewels; 28,800 vph; 48-hour power reserve; COSC-certified chronometer
Functions: hours, minutes, subsidiary seconds; chronograph; date
Case: stainless steel, ø 44 mm, height 13.79 mm; sapphire crystal; water-resistant to 10 atm
Band: calfskin, folding clasp
Price: $7,400; limited to 750 pieces

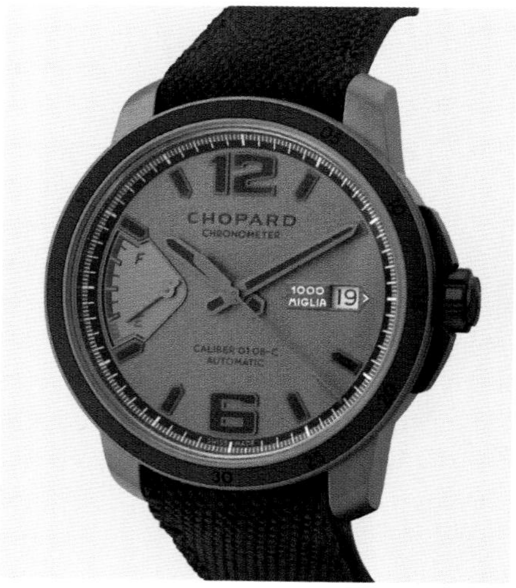

Mille Miglia GTS Power Control Grigio Speciale

Reference number: 168566-3007
Movement: automatic, Chopard Manufacture Caliber 01.08-C; ø 28.8 mm, height 4.95 mm; 40 jewels; 28,800 vph; 60-hour power reserve; COSC-certified chronometer
Functions: hours, minutes, sweep seconds; power reserve indicator; date
Case: titanium, ø 43 mm, height 11.43 mm; sapphire crystal; transparent case back; screw-in crown; water-resistant to 10 atm
Band: textile, folding clasp
Price: $8,220; limited to 1,000 pieces

Mille Miglia Classic Chronograph

Reference number: 168589-3002
Movement: automatic, ETA Caliber 2894-2; ø 28.6 mm, height 6.1 mm; 37 jewels; 28,800 vph; 42-hour power reserve; COSC-certified chronometer
Functions: hours, minutes, subsidiary seconds; chronograph; date
Case: stainless steel, ø 42 mm, height 12.67 mm; sapphire crystal; transparent case back; screw-in crown; water-resistant to 5 atm
Band: rubber, buckle
Price: $5,260

Mille Miglia 2020 Race Edition

Reference number: 168589-6002
Movement: automatic, ETA Caliber 2894-2; ø 28.6 mm, height 6.1 mm; 37 jewels; 28,800 vph; 42-hour power reserve; COSC-certified chronometer
Functions: hours, minutes, subsidiary seconds; chronograph; date
Case: stainless steel, ø 42 mm, height 12.67 mm; rose gold bezel; sapphire crystal; transparent case back; screw-in crown; water-resistant to 5 atm
Band: calfskin, folding clasp
Price: $8,400

L.U.C Perpetual Twin

Reference number: 161976-5003
Movement: automatic, L.U.C Caliber 96.22-L; ø 33 mm, height 6 mm; 29 jewels; 28,800 vph; 2 spring barrels, microrotor in gold with heavy-metal oscillating mass; with côtes de Genève; 65-hour power reserve; COSC-certified chronometer
Functions: hours, minutes, subsidiary seconds; perpetual calendar with large date, weekday, month, leap year
Case: rose gold, ø 43 mm, height 11.47 mm; sapphire crystal; transparent case back; water-resistant to 3 atm
Band: reptile skin, buckle
Price: $49,800

L.U.C GMT One

Reference number: 168579-3001
Movement: automatic, L.U.C Caliber 01.10-L; ø 31.9 mm, height 5.95 mm; 31 jewels; 28,800 vph; bridges with côtes de Genève; 60-hour power reserve; COSC-certified chronometer
Functions: hours, minutes, sweep seconds; additional 24-hour display (2nd time zone); date
Case: stainless steel, ø 42 mm, height 11.71 mm; sapphire crystal; transparent case back; water-resistant to 5 atm
Band: reptile skin, buckle
Price: $9,880
Variations: rose gold ($20,000)

L.U.C Time Traveler One

Reference number: 161942-5001
Movement: automatic, L.U.C Caliber 01.05-L; ø 35.3 mm, height 6.52 mm; 39 jewels; 28,800 vph; 60-hour power reserve; COSC-certified chronometer
Functions: hours, minutes, sweep seconds; world time (2nd time zone); date
Case: rose gold, ø 42 mm, height 12.09 mm; crown-activated scale ring, with reference city names; sapphire crystal; transparent case back; water-resistant to 5 atm
Band: reptile skin, buckle
Price: $24,200
Variations: stainless steel ($13,700)

L.U.C Chrono One Flyback

Reference number: 168596-3002
Movement: automatic, L.U.C Caliber 03.03-L; ø 28.8 mm, height 7.6 mm; 45 jewels; 28,800 vph; gold rotor; 60-hour power reserve; COSC-certified chronometer
Functions: hours, minutes, subsidiary seconds; flyback chronograph; date
Case: titanium, special alloy (Titalyt), steel, ø 42 mm, height 13.42 mm; sapphire crystal; transparent case back; water-resistant to 10 atm
Band: reptile skin, buckle
Price: $29,100; limited to 100 pieces

L.U.C Perpetual Twin

Reference number: 168561-3001
Movement: automatic, L.U.C Caliber 96.22-L; ø 33 mm, height 6 mm; 29 jewels; 28,800 vph; 2 spring barrels, microrotor in gold with heavy-metal oscillating mass; with côtes de Genève; 65-hour power reserve; COSC-certified chronometer
Functions: hours, minutes, subsidiary seconds; perpetual calendar with large date, weekday, month, leap year
Case: stainless steel, ø 43 mm, height 11.47 mm; sapphire crystal; transparent case back; water-resistant to 3 atm
Band: reptile skin, buckle
Price: $24,700

L.U.C Lunar One

Reference number: 161927-5001
Movement: automatic, L.U.C Caliber 96.13-L; ø 33 mm, height 6 mm; 32 jewels; 28,800 vph; 65-hour power reserve; Geneva Seal, COSC-certified chronometer
Functions: hours, minutes, subsidiary seconds; additional 24-hour display (2nd time zone); perpetual calendar with large date, weekday, month, orbital moon phase display, leap year
Case: rose gold, ø 43 mm, height 11.47 mm; sapphire crystal; transparent case back; water-resistant to 5 atm
Band: reptile skin, folding clasp
Price: $59,800
Variations: platinum ($59,800)

L.U.C XPS Twist QF

Reference number: 161945-1001
Movement: automatic, L.U.C Caliber 96-26-L; ø 27.4 mm, height 3.3 mm; 29 jewels; 28,800 vph; microrotor in gold; 2 spring barrels, 65-hour power reserve; COSC-certified chronometer, Qualité Fleurier
Functions: hours, minutes, subsidiary seconds; date
Case: white gold, ø 40 mm, height 7.2 mm; sapphire crystal; transparent case back; screw-in crown; water-resistant to 3 atm
Band: reptile skin, buckle
Remarks: case made of gold with Fairmined certification
Price: $19,900; limited to 250 pieces
Variations: yellow gold ($19,900)

Alpine Eagle Large

Reference number: 298600-3001
Movement: automatic, L.U.C Caliber 01.01-C; ø 28.8 mm, height 4.95 mm; 31 jewels; 28,800 vph; 60-hour power reserve; COSC-certified chronometer
Functions: hours, minutes, sweep seconds; date
Case: stainless steel, ø 41 mm, height 9.7 mm; bezel screwed to case with 8 screws; sapphire crystal; transparent case back; water-resistant to 10 atm
Band: stainless steel, folding clasp
Price: $12,800
Variations: rose gold bezel ($19,700); various dial colors

Alpine Eagle Large

Reference number: 298600-3002
Movement: automatic, L.U.C Caliber 01.01-C; ø 28.8 mm, height 4.95 mm; 31 jewels; 28,800 vph; 60-hour power reserve; COSC-certified chronometer
Functions: hours, minutes, sweep seconds; date
Case: stainless steel, ø 41 mm, height 9.7 mm; bezel screwed to case with 8 screws; sapphire crystal; transparent case back; water-resistant to 10 atm
Band: stainless steel, folding clasp
Price: $12,800
Variations: rose gold bezel ($19,700); various dial colors

Alpine Eagle Large

Reference number: 298600-6001
Movement: automatic, L.U.C Caliber 01.01-C; ø 28.8 mm, height 4.95 mm; 31 jewels; 28,800 vph; 60-hour power reserve; COSC-certified chronometer
Functions: hours, minutes, sweep seconds; date
Case: stainless steel, ø 41 mm, height 9.7 mm; rose gold bezel screwed to case with 8 screws; sapphire crystal; transparent case back; water-resistant to 10 atm
Band: stainless steel with rose gold elements, folding clasp
Price: $19,700

Alpine Eagle XL Chrono

Reference number: 298609-3002
Movement: automatic, L.U.C Caliber 03.05-C; ø 28.8 mm, height 7.6 mm; 45 jewels; 28,800 vph; 60-hour power reserve; COSC-certified chronometer
Functions: hours, minutes, subsidiary seconds; flyback-chronograph; date
Case: stainless steel, ø 44 mm, height 14 mm; bezel screwed to case with 8 screws; sapphire crystal; transparent case back; water-resistant to 10 atm
Band: stainless steel, folding clasp
Price: $19,200

Caliber L.U.C 96.24-L

Automatic; flying 1-minute tourbillon; gold microrotor; double spring barrel, 65-hour power reserve; Geneva Seal, COSC-certified chronometer
Functions: hours, minutes
Diameter: 27.4 mm
Height: 3.3 mm
Jewels: 25
Balance: glucydur
Frequency: 25,200 vph
Balance spring: flat hairspring, Nivarox 1
Remarks: 190 parts

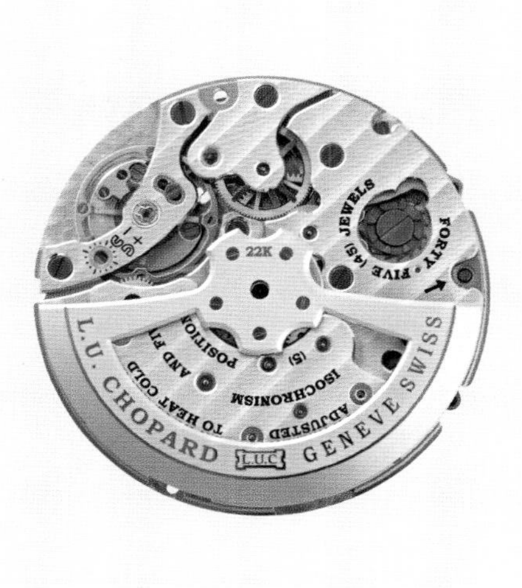

Caliber L.U.C 03.03-L

Automatic; column-wheel control of chronograph functions, vertical chronograph clutch, stop-seconds mechanism with automatic zero-reset; skeletonized gold rotor; single spring barrel, 60-hour power reserve; COSC-certified chronometer
Functions: hours, minutes, subsidiary seconds; flyback chronograph; date
Diameter: 28.8 mm
Height: 7.6 mm
Jewels: 45
Balance: Variner with 4 weighted screws
Frequency: 28,800 vph
Balance spring: flat hairspring
Remarks: perlage on mainplate, beveled bridges with côtes de Genève; 359 parts

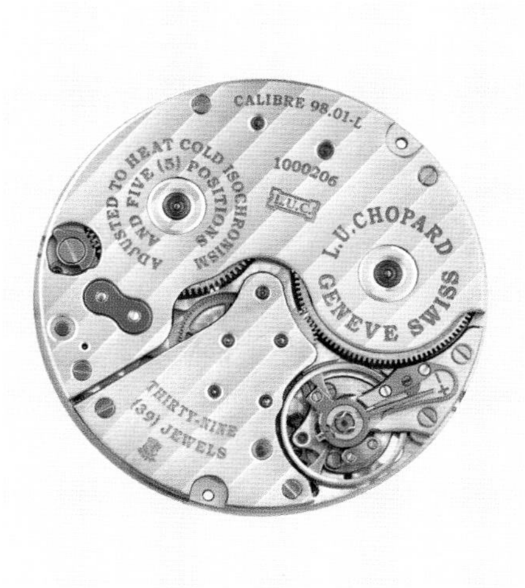

Caliber L.U.C 98.01-L

Manually wound; swan-neck fine regulation; quadruple spring barrel running in twin series barrel springs, 216-hour power reserve; Geneva Seal, COSC-certified chronometer
Functions: hours, minutes, subsidiary seconds; power reserve indicator; date
Diameter: 28.6 mm
Height: 3.7 mm
Jewels: 39
Frequency: 28,800 vph
Balance spring: Breguet hairspring
Remarks: 223 parts

Caliber L.U.C 01.01-C

Automatic; single spring barrel, 60-hour power reserve; COSC-certified chronometer
Functions: hours, minutes, sweep seconds; date
Diameter: 28.8 mm
Height: 4.95 mm
Jewels: 31
Balance: glucydur
Frequency: 28,800 vph
Balance spring: flat spring, Nivarox 1
Remarks: 207 parts

Caliber L.U.C 03.10-L

Manually wound; German silver mainplate and balance cock; single spring barrel, 60-hour power reserve; Geneva Seal, COSC-certified chronometer
Functions: hours, minutes, sweep seconds; day/night indicator; flyback chronograph; perpetual calendar with large date, weekday, month, moon phase, leap year
Diameter: 33 mm
Height: 8.32 mm
Jewels: 42
Balance: Variner with 4 weighted screws
Frequency: 28,800 vph
Balance spring: flat hairspring

Caliber L.U.C 96.22-L

Automatic; flying 1-minute tourbillon (not assembled in the image); gold microrotor; double spring barrel, 65-hour power reserve; COSC-certified chronometer
Functions: hours, minutes, subsidiary seconds; perpetual calendar with large date, weekday, month, leap year
Diameter: 33 mm
Height: 6 mm
Jewels: 29
Balance: glucydur
Frequency: 28,800 vph
Balance spring: flat spring, Nivarox 1
Remarks: carefully hand-decorated movement
Remarks: German silver plate and balance cock; 533 parts

CHRISTOPHE CLARET

Individuals like Christophe Claret eat, drink, and breathe watchmaking and have developed careers based on pushing the envelope to the very edge of what's possible. At twenty-three, the Lyon-born Claret was in Basel, where he was spotted by the late Rolf Schnyder of Ulysse Nardin and commissioned to make a minute repeater with jacquemarts. In 1989, he opened his *manufacture*, with a state-of-the-art machining area. Indeed, Claret embraces wholeheartedly the potential in modern tools to create the precise pieces needed to give physical expression to exceedingly complex ideas.

Over the years, Claret created complications and movements for many major brands, like Ulysse Nardin and Harry Winston.

Twenty years after establishing his business, Claret finally launched his own complex watches: models like the DualTow, with its hours and minutes on two tracks, minute repeater, and complete view of the great ballet of cams and levers inside. Then came the Adagio, again a minute repeater, with a clear dial that has room for a second time zone and large date. In 2011, Claret wowed the watch world with a humorous, on-the-wrist gambling machine telling time and playing blackjack, craps, or roulette. The Poker takes the concept further, offering roulette on the back and a pack of fifty-two cards buried inside the watch allowing three people to play a few rounds of Texas Hold'em.

The stunning X-TREM-1 is one of Claret's perennial favorite warhorses, a turbocharged DualTow with two spheres controlled by magnets hovering along the numeral tracks to tell the time plus a tourbillon.

The list goes on and on. Whatever Claret produces—the Margot, for women, the art-laden Aventicum, or the Angelico, a complex tourbillon with a fusée and carbon nanofiber cable escapement—his signature is always present: a total dedication to power mechanics and an infallible sense of style.

Christophe Claret SA
Route du Soleil d'Or 2
CH-2400 Le Locle
Switzerland

Tel.:
+41-32-933-0000

E-mail:
info@christopheclaret.com

Website:
www.christopheclaret.com

Founded:
manufacture 1989, brand 2009

Number of employees:
70

Distribution:
Contact the *manufacture* directly.

Most important collections:
Traditional complications (Maestro/Mecca/Allegro/Aventicum/Maestoso/Kantharos/Soprano), Extreme line (X-TREM-1), gaming watches (Poker/Baccara/Blackjack), and ladies' complications line (Margot, Layla, Marguerite)
Prices are given in Swiss francs at near parity.

Poker

Reference number: MTR.PCK05.001-020
Movement: automatic, Christophe Claret Caliber PCK 05; ø 38.6 mm, height 9.92 mm; 72 jewels; 28,800 vph; striking mechanism (gong); 2 spring barrels, 72-hour power reserve
Functions: hours, minutes; pusher-activated mechanical random generator with a sonorous signal
Case: titanium with black PVD, ø 45 mm, height 15.95 mm; sapphire crystal; transparent case back; water-resistant to 3 atm
Band: reptile skin, double folding clasp
Remarks: random generator and 52-card pack for Texas Hold'em with identification and display of flops and rivers (front); roulette on rear
Price: CHF 164,000; limited to 12 pieces

X-Trem-1

Reference number: MTR.FLY11.180-188
Movement: manually wound, Christophe Claret Caliber FLY11; 26.6 × 46.4 mm, height 11.94 mm; 66 jewels; 21,600 vph; 2 separate spring barrels for movement and time indication; flying tourbillon on ball bearing, with 30° tilt; central pusher for rapid correction; 50-hour power reserve
Functions: hours, minutes (linear display using steel beads hovering in lateral meshed tubes)
Case: titanium with blue PVD and Damascus steel, 40.8 × 56.8 mm, height 15 mm; sapphire crystal; transparent case back
Band: reptile skin, folding clasp
Price: CHF 268,000; limited to 8 pieces

Angelico

Reference number: MTR.DTC08.000-010
Movement: manually wound, Christophe Claret Caliber DTC08; ø 41.1 mm, height 14.2 mm; 62 jewels; 18,000 vph; 1-minute tourbillon with chronometer escapement, power regulation with carbon nanofiber cable and fusée; 2 serially ordered spring barrels, 72-hour power reserve; **Functions:** hours (digital, jumping), minutes (index tip); additional 24-hour display (2nd time zone), day/night indicator
Case: titanium, red gold, ø 45.5 mm, height 17.45 mm; sapphire crystal; transparent case back; water-resistant to 3 atm; **Band:** reptile skin, folding clasp
Price: CHF 238,000; limited to 10 pieces
Variations: titanium, limited to 10 pieces (CHF 218,000)

Chronoswiss AG
Löwenstrasse 16b
CH-6004 Lucerne
Switzerland

Tel.:
+41-41-552-2100

E-mail:
shopmanager@chronoswiss.com

Website:
www.chronoswiss.com

Founded:
1983

Number of employees:
approx. 30

Annual production:
up to 4,000 wristwatches

U.S. distributor:
Chronoswiss US Service Office
Shami Fine Watchmaking
155 Willowbrook Blvd., Suite 320
Wayne, NJ 07470
973-785-0004

Most important collections/price range:
Approx. 30 models including Regulator, Flying Regulator, Sirius Chronograph Moon Phase, Sirius Chronograph Skeleton, Sirius Artist, Timemaster Big Date, Timemaster Chronograph GMT / approx. $4,650 to $47,000

CHRONOSWISS

Chronoswiss has been assembling its signature watches—which boast such features as coin edge bezels and onion crowns—since 1983. Founder Gerd-Rüdiger Lang loved to joke about having "the only Swiss watch factory in Germany," as the brand used Swiss technology with concepts and designs "made in Germany," in Karlsfeld, near Munich, to be precise.

Lang also created regulator watches in the 1980s, a pioneering idea that found many fans of new ways to tell the time. Whether in a rectangular or round case, with a tourbillon or without, the off-center dial became the absolute identity of Chronoswiss watches and remains so to this day. It was a remarkable bit of inspiration and somewhat anachronistic back then.

Chronoswiss has always been a little on the edge of the industry in terms of style and technical developments. It created the enduring *manufacture* caliber C.122—based on an old Enicar automatic movement with a patented rattrapante mechanism—and its Chronoscope chronograph has earned a solid reputation for technical prowess. The Pacific and Sirius models, additions to the classic collection, point the company in a new stylistic direction designed to help win new buyers and the attention of the international market.

In March 2012, a Swiss couple, Oliver and Eva Ebstein, purchased Chronoswiss and moved the company headquarters to Lucerne, Switzerland, but without changing the essential codes of the brand. Recent models reveal the brand to be faithful to its regulator and coin edges, and the large crown, though the dial has acquired a three-dimensional design. The Flying Regulator and the Regulator Jumping Hour find the minute hand hovering freely over the dial, with the hours and seconds on bridges. In-house calibers beat inside, and increasingly the staid look is giving way to modern designs, daring skeletonizing feats, and bold colors.

Open Gear ReSec

Reference number: CH-6926-BLGO
Movement: automatic, Chronoswiss Caliber C.301; ø 36.5 mm; 28,800 vph; dial-side hand gear train (transmission wheel); finely finished movement; 42-hour power reserve
Functions: hours (off-center), minutes, subsidiary seconds (retrograde)
Case: stainless steel with blue CVD coating, ø 44 mm, height 13.35 mm; sapphire crystal; transparent case back; water-resistant to 10 atm
Band: reptile skin, folding clasp
Remarks: hand-guillochéed dial
Price: $9,900; limited to 50 pieces

Open Gear ReSec

Reference number: CH-6926-REBK
Movement: automatic, Chronoswiss Caliber C.301; ø 36.5 mm; 28,800 vph; dial-side hand gear train (transmission wheel); finely finished movement; 42-hour power reserve
Functions: hours (off-center), minutes, subsidiary seconds (retrograde)
Case: red gold, ø 44 mm, height 13.35 mm; sapphire crystal; transparent case back; water-resistant to 10 atm
Band: reptile skin, folding clasp
Remarks: hand-guillochéed dial
Price: $9,900; limited to 50 pieces

Flying Regulator Open Gear

Reference number: CH-8753-YEBK
Movement: automatic, Chronoswiss Caliber C.299; ø 35.2 mm; height 6.11 mm; 31 jewels; 28,800 vph; dial-side hand gear train (transmission wheel); finely finished movement; 42-hour power reserve
Functions: hours (off-center), minutes, subsidiary seconds
Case: stainless steel, ø 41 mm, height 13.85 mm; sapphire crystal; transparent case back; water-resistant to 10 atm
Band: reptile skin, folding clasp
Remarks: hand-guillochéed dial
Price: $10,500; limited to 35 pieces

Flying Regulator Open Gear

Reference number: CH-8753-SISI
Movement: automatic, Chronoswiss Caliber C.299; ø 35.2 mm, height 6.11 mm; 31 jewels; 28,800 vph; hand mechanism (transmission wheel) relocated to dial side; finely finished movement; 42-hour power reserve
Functions: hours (off-center), minutes, subsidiary seconds
Case: stainless steel, ø 41 mm, height 13.85 mm; sapphire crystal; transparent case back; water-resistant to 10 atm
Band: reptile skin, folding clasp
Price: $6,680
Variations: pink gold ($16,300)

ReSec Classic

Reference number: CH-8783-BKBR
Movement: automatic, Chronoswiss Caliber C.302; ø 25.6 mm, height 4.35 mm; 27 jewels; 28,800 vph; finely finished movement; 42-hour power reserve
Functions: hours, minutes, subsidiary seconds (retrograde); large date
Case: stainless steel, ø 41 mm, height 12.7 mm; sapphire crystal; transparent case back; water-resistant to 10 atm
Band: stainless steel, folding clasp
Price: $5,600
Variations: blue dial

Regulator Classic Carbon Racer

Reference number: CH-8773-CARE
Movement: automatic, Chronoswiss Caliber C.295; ø 25.6 mm, height 4.35 mm; 27 jewels; 28,800 vph; 42-hour power reserve
Functions: hours (off-center), minutes, subsidiary seconds
Case: stainless steel, ø 41 mm, height 12.7 mm; sapphire crystal; transparent case back; water-resistant to 10 atm
Band: stainless steel, folding clasp
Remarks: carbon dial
Price: $4,700

Regulator Classic Blue Steel

Reference number: CH-8776-BL
Movement: automatic, Chronoswiss Caliber C.295; ø 25.6 mm, height 4.35 mm; 27 jewels; 28,800 vph; 42-hour power reserve
Functions: hours (off-center), minutes, subsidiary seconds
Case: stainless steel with blue PVD, ø 41 mm, height 12.7 mm; sapphire crystal; transparent case back; water-resistant to 10 atm
Band: reptile skin, folding clasp
Price: $4,900

Flying Regulator Night and Day Limited Edition

Reference number: CH-8763-BLOR
Movement: automatic, Chronoswiss Caliber C.296; ø 25.2 mm, height 4.35 mm; 31 jewels; 28,800 vph; skeletonized rotor; finely finished movement; 42-hour power reserve
Functions: hours (off-center), minutes, subsidiary seconds; sculptural day/night indicator; date
Case: stainless steel, ø 41 mm, height 13.85 mm; sapphire crystal; transparent case back; water-resistant to 10 atm
Band: reptile skin, folding clasp
Remarks: hand-guillochéed dial
Price: $7,350; limited to 50 pieces

Flying Regulator Night and Day

Reference number: CH-8763-BLBL
Movement: automatic, Chronoswiss Caliber C.296; ø 25.2 mm, height 4.35 mm; 27 jewels; 28,800 vph; skeletonized rotor; finely finished movement; 42-hour power reserve
Functions: hours (off-center), minutes, subsidiary seconds; day/night indicator; date
Case: stainless steel, ø 41 mm, height 13.85 mm; sapphire crystal; transparent case back; water-resistant to 10 atm
Band: reptile skin, folding clasp
Remarks: winner of 2019 Red Dot Design Award
Price: $6,950

Flying Grand Regulator Skeleton

Reference number: CH-6725S-REBK
Movement: manually wound, Chronoswiss Caliber C.677S; ø 37.2 mm, height 4.5 mm; 17 jewels; 18,000 vph; screw balance, swan-neck fine adjustment; skeletonized mainplate, bridges, and gearwheels; finely finished movement; 46-hour power reserve
Functions: hours (off-center), minutes, subsidiary seconds
Case: stainless steel with black DLC coating, ø 44 mm, height 12.48 mm; sapphire crystal; transparent case back; water-resistant to 3 atm
Band: reptile skin, folding clasp
Price: $10,300; limited to 30 pieces

Flying Grand Regulator

Reference number: CH-6725-YEBK
Movement: manually wound, Chronoswiss Caliber C.678; ø 37.2 mm, height 4.5 mm; 17 jewels; 18,000 vph; screw balance, swan-neck fine adjustment; finely finished movement; 46-hour power reserve
Functions: hours (off-center), minutes, subsidiary seconds
Case: stainless steel with black DLC coating, ø 44 mm, height 12.48 mm; sapphire crystal; transparent case back; water-resistant to 3 atm
Band: reptile skin, folding clasp
Price: $9,900; limited to 30 pieces

Flying Grand Regulator

Reference number: CH-6723-BLBL
Movement: manually wound, Chronoswiss Caliber C.678; ø 37.2 mm, height 4.5 mm; 17 jewels; 18,000 vph; screw balance, swan-neck fine regulation; finely finished movement; 46-hour power reserve
Functions: hours (off-center), minutes, subsidiary seconds
Case: stainless steel, ø 44 mm, height 12.48 mm; sapphire crystal; transparent case back; water-resistant to 3 atm
Band: reptile skin, folding clasp
Price: $8,500

Flying Regulator Manufacture

Reference number: CH-1243.3-BLBL
Movement: automatic, Chronoswiss Caliber C.122; ø 26.8 mm, height 5.3 mm; 30 jewels; 21,600 vph; skeletonized rotor; finely finished movement; 40-hour power reserve
Functions: hours (off-center), minutes, subsidiary seconds
Case: stainless steel, ø 40 mm, height 12 mm; sapphire crystal; transparent case back; water-resistant to 3 atm
Band: reptile skin, buckle
Remarks: winner of 2019 Red Dot Design Award
Price: $7,200
Variations: black DLC treatment ($7,750); pink gold ($16,950)

Lunar Chronograph

Reference number: CH-7541LR
Movement: automatic, Chronoswiss Caliber C.755 (base ETA 7750); ø 30 mm, height 7.9 mm; 25 jewels; 28,800 vph; perlage on movement, côtes de Genève, skeletonized rotor; finely finished movement; 46-hour power reserve
Functions: hours, minutes, subsidiary seconds; chronograph; date, moon phase
Case: pink gold, ø 41 mm, height 15.45 mm; sapphire crystal; transparent case back; water-resistant to 3 atm
Band: reptile skin, buckle
Price: $19,150
Variations: stainless steel ($7,950)

Opus Chronograph

Reference number: CH-7543S
Movement: automatic, Chronoswiss Caliber C.741 S (base ETA 7750); ø 30 mm, height 7.9 mm; 25 jewels; 28,800 vph; entirely skeletonized movement with ribbing; 46-hour power reserve
Functions: hours, minutes, subsidiary seconds; chronograph; date
Case: stainless steel, ø 41 mm, height 15.45 mm; sapphire crystal; transparent case back; water-resistant to 3 atm
Band: reptile skin, buckle
Remarks: skeletonized dial
Price: $10,400
Variations: pink gold ($22,950)

CLAUDE MEYLAN

Claude Meylan
Route de l'Hôtel de Ville 2
CH-1344 L'Abbaye
Switzerland

Tel.:
+41-21 841 14 57

E-mail:
info@claudemeylan.ch

Website:
www.claudemeylan.ch

Founded:
originally mid-18th century; revived in mid-20th century and purchased in 2011

Number of employees:
7

Annual production:
approx. 1,000 pieces

Most important collections/price range:
Tortue, Lac, Lionne, l'Abbaye / $4,500 to $6,850; Légendes series / up to $33,000

In the quest for recognition, many companies, especially the smaller ones, look for a niche in which they can excel. The Swiss brand Claude Meylan, located in L'Abbaye near Joux Lake in the heart of watch country, specializes in skeletonization, which is the art of removing as much material as possible from bridges, plates, the dial, even the hands. The exercise is not just for fun. First, it transforms a watch, making it transparent and allowing a view of the mechanical innards. Second, it allows for imaginative designs using what's left of the material, notably the bridges. These can be either abstract or representative.

Skeletonization has become popular in recent years, but it's not as simple as it might sound. As the various metal components are hollowed out and properly finished with chamfering and sanding, the tensions within the material change. This can then have a deleterious effect on the functioning of the mechanism, since the bridges and plates are in fact used to hold and stabilize the movement.

In 1988, Claude Meylan founded his company. It was taken over soon after by another watchmaker, Henri Berney, who kept up the old tradition. In 2011, the next CEO, Philippe Belais, took charge. He also heads Vaudaux, a maker of high-end boxes and cases in Geneva.

Claude Meylan's products, which show many different aspects of the art of skeletonization, live up to the brand's tagline: "Sculptors of time." The company has five main collections, all relating in some way to the region: Lac, for Joux Lake; l'Abbaye; Légendes, exploring local tales; Lionne, the river that flows by the workshops; and, finally, Tortue, whose tonneau case is reminiscent of a turtle. The latter features delicate vine-like elements spreading across the movement. A smaller series is devoted to women's watches, notably the Valentine with a diamond pavé on the microrotor and a striking blood-red section to honor the love.

Tortue Lady, Valentine

Reference number: 6080-PF
Movement: automatic, Caliber 7.75CM17; ø 26.5 mm, height 5 mm; 25 jewels; 28,800 vph; 38-hour power reserve; microrotor with 68 pavé diamonds
Functions: hours, minutes
Case: stainless steel, ø 31 × 31 mm, height 11 mm; sapphire crystal; transparent case back; water-resistant to 3 atm
Band: technical satin, buckle
Price: $6,900

Lac

Reference number: 6144-MR
Movement: manually wound, Unitas Caliber 6497; ø 36.6 mm, height 4.5 mm; 17 jewels; 18,000 vph; rhodium-plated black bridges; 46-hour power reserve
Functions: hours (hand-cut into rotating dial), minutes
Case: stainless steel, ø 42 mm, height 11 mm; sapphire crystal; transparent case back; water-resistant to 3 atm
Band: leather, buckle
Price: $4,750
Variations: blue or brown dials

Tortue Rainbow

Reference number: 6047-NO
Movement: manually wound, Claude Meylan Caliber 165CM14; ø 40 mm, height 4.5 mm; 17 jewels; 18,000 vph; open-worked dial, black and orange scheme, orange cathedral hands; 42-hour power reserve
Functions: hours, minutes
Case: stainless steel with black PVD, ø 40 × 40 mm, height 11 mm; sapphire crystal; transparent case back; water-resistant to 3 atm
Band: rubber, buckle
Price: $5,980
Variations: comes with different colors: yellow, green, blue, purple, indigo, and red

Montres Corum Sàrl
Rue du Petit-Château 1
Case postale 374
CH-2301 La Chaux-de-Fonds
Switzerland

Tel.:
+41-32-967-0670

E-mail:
info@corum.ch

Website:
www.corum-watches.com

Founded:
1955

Number of employees:
160 worldwide

Annual production:
16,000 watches

U.S. distributor:
Montres Corum USA
CWJ BRANDS
1551 Sawgrass Corporate Parkway
Suite 109
Sunrise, FL 33323
954-279-1220
www.corum.ch

Most important collections/price range:
Admiral's Cup, Golden Bridge, Bubble, and Heritage, Romvlvs and Artisan, 150 models in total /approx. $1,500 to over $1,000,000

CORUM

Founded in 1955, Switzerland's youngest luxury watch brand, Corum, celebrated sixty years of unusual—and sometimes outlandish—case and dial designs in 2015. The brand has had quite a busy history, but still by and large remains true to the collections launched by founders Gaston Ries and his nephew René Bannwart: the Admiral's Cup, Bridges, and Heritage. Among Corum's most iconic pieces is the legendary Golden Bridge baguette, or stick, movement, which has received a complete makeover in recent years with the use of modern materials and complicated mechanisms. It is built around the idea of concentrating all parts along a straight axis in the middle of a rectangular dial. The development of these extraordinary movements required great watchmaking craftsmanship.

The Bridges collection has always been an eye-catcher. It was originally the brainchild of the great watchmaker Vincent Calabrese, though these types of movements trace back further in time. Its introduction was a milestone in watchmaking history. And the Golden Bridge recently acquired a new highlight in the Golden Bridge Tourbillon Panoramique, with all components appearing to float in thin air.

Corum's vision is expressed in its logo: a key facing the sky, which symbolizes both the mysteries to be discovered as well as openness to the new. As such, it keeps an open mind when it comes to its target groups. The sporty Admiral's Cup collection is divided into two families: the classical Legend and the more athletic AC-One 45. The colorful nautical number flags have returned to the Admiral's Cup dials. For a more popular experience of watch-wearing, the company revived the remarkable Bubble, which earned its moniker from the domed shape of the crystal, allowing room for all sorts of dial decoration. And in the year of the coronavirus, it managed to come out with a stunning concept watch, a skeleton timepiece, the Lab 2, which seems to do away with bridges altogether.

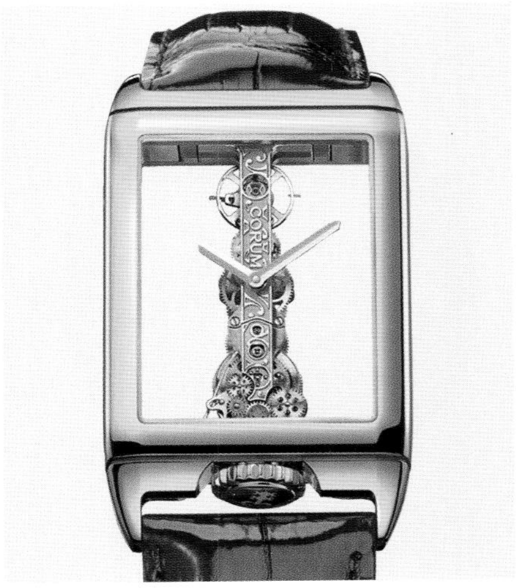

Golden Bridge Rectangle

Reference number: B113/04145
Movement: manually wound, Caliber CO 113; 4.9 × 34 mm, height 3 mm; 19 jewels; 28,800 vph; baguette movement, hand-engraved bridges and mainplate in gold; 40-hour power reserve
Functions: hours, minutes
Case: rose gold, 29.5 × 42.2 mm, height 9.3 mm; sapphire crystal; transparent case back; water-resistant to 3 atm
Band: reptile skin, triple folding clasp
Price: $35,000

Golden Bridge Classic

Reference number: B113/01043
Movement: manually wound, Caliber CO 113; 4.9 × 34 mm, height 3 mm; 19 jewels; 28,800 vph; baguette movement, bridges and mainplate in gold; 40-hour power reserve
Functions: hours, minutes
Case: rose gold, 34 × 51 mm, height 10.9 mm; sapphire crystal; transparent case back; water-resistant to 3 atm
Band: reptile skin, buckle
Price: $33,800

Golden Bridge Round 43

Reference number: B113/03951
Movement: manually wound, Caliber CO 113; 4.9 × 34 mm, height 3 mm; 19 jewels; 28,800 vph; baguette movement, bridges and mainplate in gold; 40-hour power reserve
Functions: hours, minutes
Case: titanium with black DLC, ø 43 mm, height 8.8 mm; sapphire crystal; transparent case back; rose gold crown; water-resistant to 3 atm
Band: rubber, triple folding clasp
Remarks: baguette movement flanked with 3D microstructures
Price: $23,800

Admiral 42 Automatic Bronze Blue

Reference number: A395/04034
Movement: automatic, Caliber CO 395 (base ETA 2895-2); ø 25.9 mm, height 4.35 mm; 27 jewels; 28,800 vph; 42-hour power reserve
Functions: hours, minutes, subsidiary seconds; date
Case: bronze, ø 42 mm, height 10 mm; sapphire crystal; transparent case back; water-resistant to 5 atm
Band: reptile skin, triple folding clasp
Price: $4,700

Admiral 42 Automatic All Black

Reference number: A395/04007
Movement: automatic, Caliber CO 395 (base ETA 2895-2); ø 25.9 mm, height 4.35 mm; 27 jewels; 28,800 vph; 42-hour power reserve
Functions: hours, minutes, subsidiary seconds; date
Case: stainless steel with black PVD, ø 42 mm, height 10 mm; sapphire crystal; transparent case back; water-resistant to 5 atm
Band: rubber, triple folding clasp
Price: $5,200; limited to 100 pieces

Admiral 38 Automatic

Reference number: A082/04125
Movement: automatic, Caliber CO 082 (base ETA 2892-A2); ø 25.9 mm, height 3.6 mm; 21 jewels; 28,800 vph; 42-hour power reserve
Functions: hours, minutes, sweep seconds; date
Case: rose gold, ø 38 mm, height 9.3 mm; bezel set with 72 diamonds; sapphire crystal; transparent case back; water-resistant to 5 atm
Band: rubber, triple folding clasp
Price: $12,800

Admiral AC-One 45 Openworked Tourbillon

Reference number: A298/03901
Movement: automatic, Caliber CO 298; ø 25.6 mm; 39 jewels; 28,800 vph; 1-minute tourbillon; skeletonized movement; 42-hour power reserve
Functions: hours, minutes, subsidiary seconds; power reserve indicator; chronograph with 3-minute counter
Case: red gold, ø 45 mm, height 14.3 mm; bezel with black DLC coating; sapphire crystal; transparent case back; water-resistant to 10 atm
Band: rubber with textile layer, triple folding clasp
Price: $65,800; limited to 18 pieces

Admiral AC-One 45 Openworked Automatic

Reference number: A297/03897
Movement: automatic, Caliber CO 297; ø 25.6 mm; 39 jewels; 28,800 vph; skeletonized movement; 42-hour power reserve
Functions: hours, minutes, subsidiary seconds; power reserve indicator; chronograph with 3-minute counter
Case: titanium, ø 45 mm, height 14.3 mm; sapphire crystal; transparent case back; water-resistant to 10 atm
Band: rubber with textile layer, triple folding clasp
Remarks: skeletonized dial
Price: $25,700

Heritage Artisans Coin Watch

Reference number: C082/03956
Movement: automatic, Caliber CO 082 (base ETA 2892-A2); ø 25.6 mm, height 3.6 mm; 21 jewels; 28,800 vph; 42-hour power reserve
Functions: hours, minutes
Case: silver with PVD, ø 43 mm, height 7.4 mm; sapphire crystal; crown with diamond cabochon
Band: reptile skin, buckle
Remarks: dial and case back made of a gold double eagle coin and partially blackened
Price: $19,000

LAB 01 Damascus Steel Green

Reference number: Z410/03954
Movement: automatic, Caliber CO 410; 30 × 32 mm; 27 jewels; 28,800 vph; microrotor; partially skeletonized dial; 50-hour power reserve
Functions: hours, minutes
Case: stainless steel with black DLC, case sides in rubber, 39.89 × 55 mm, height 11.75 mm; sapphire crystal; transparent case back; water-resistant to 5 atm
Band: rubber, buckle
Remarks: skeletonized dial
Price: $16,800; limited to 99 pieces

LAB 02 Rose Gold

Reference number: Z300/03999
Movement: manually wound, Caliber CO 300; ø 37.2 mm; 33 jewels; 21,600 vph; flying 1-minute tourbillon; completely skeletonized movement; 55-hour power reserve
Functions: hours, minutes; power reserve indicator; date
Case: rose gold, ø 45 mm, height 13.4 mm; sapphire crystal; transparent case back; water-resistant to 3 atm
Band: reptile skin, triple folding clasp
Price: $202,340

Bubble 47 Chronograph

Reference number: L771/03904
Movement: automatic, Caliber CO 771 (base Sellita SW500); ø 29.9 mm, height 7.9 mm; 28 jewels; 28,800 vph; 55-hour power reserve
Functions: hours, minutes, subsidiary seconds; chronograph with crown pusher control; date
Case: titanium, ø 47 mm, height 20.8 mm; sapphire crystal; transparent case back; water-resistant to 10 atm
Band: rubber, buckle
Remarks: vaulted sapphire crystal
Price: $6,900

Romulus Billionaire

Reference number: R374/03461
Movement: manually wound, Caliber CO 374; ø 32.7 mm; 17 jewels; 21,600 vph; flying 1-minute tourbillon; skeletonized movement; 90-hour power reserve
Functions: hours, minutes
Case: white gold, ø 44 mm, height 10.25 mm; bezel and lugs set with 154 diamonds and 44 rubies; sapphire crystal; transparent case back; water-resistant to 3 atm
Band: reptile skin, buckle
Price: $395,000

Golden Bridge Round 39

Reference number: B113/03651
Movement: manually wound, Caliber CO 113; 4.9 × 34 mm, height 3 mm; 19 jewels; 28,800 vph; baguette movement, hand-engraved gold bridges and mainplate; 40-hour power reserve
Functions: hours, minutes
Case: white gold, set with 76 diamonds, ø 39 mm, height 8.8 mm; bezel set with 82 diamonds; sapphire crystal; transparent case back; water-resistant to 3 atm
Band: reptile skin, triple folding clasp
Remarks: dial set with 60 diamonds
Price: $111,900

Golden Bridge Miss

Reference number: B113/03844
Movement: manually wound, CO 113 × 4.9 × 34 mm, height 3 mm; 19 jewels; 28,800 vph; baguette movement, hand-engraved bridges and mainplate in gold; 40-hour power reserve
Functions: hours, minutes
Case: white gold, set with 245 diamonds; 21 × 43 mm, height 11.19 mm; sapphire crystal; transparent case back; water-resistant to 3 atm
Band: reptile skin, buckle
Price: $42,000

CUERVO Y SOBRINOS

CyS SA
Via Carlo Maderno 54
CH-6825
Switzerland

Tel.:
+41 21-552-18-82

E-mail:
contact@cuervoysobrinos.com

Website:
www.cuervoysobrinos.com

Founded:
1882

Annual production:
3,500 watches

Distributor:
Provenance Gems LLC
ines@provenancegems.com
800-305-3869

Most important collections/price range:
Historiador, Prominente, Torpedo, Robusto / $2,000 to $20,000; higher for perpetual calendars and tourbillon models

Many brands have been going vintage to surf a wave of nostalgia in an age of techno-frigidity. Cuervo y Sobrinos, however, never really left that track. The brand originated with Ramón Rio y Cuervo and his sister's sons (that would be his nephews, the "sobrinos" of the brand name) kept a watchmaking workshop and an elegant store on Quinta Avenida, where they sold fine Swiss pocket watches—and more modest American models as well. With the advent of tourism from the coast of Florida, their business developed with wristwatches, whose dials Don Ramón soon had printed with *Cuervo y Sobrinos*—"Cuervo and Nephews."

An Italian watch enthusiast, Marzio Villa, resuscitated Cuervo y Sobrinos in 2002 and started manufacturing in the Italian-speaking region of Switzerland and in cooperation with various Swiss watchmakers. The tagline "Latin heritage, Swiss manufacture" says it all. These timepieces epitomize—or even romanticize—the island's heyday. The lines are at times elegant and sober, or blatantly vintage with fissured dial effect, like the Robusto line, or radiate the ease of those who still have time on their hands, like the Prominente, which is expressed in the long but narrow Doble Tiempo that comfortably hugs the wrist. This particular model is run by two ETA movements. Colors hint at cigar leaves and sepia photos in frames of old gold, or even coffee with lots of cream. The Vuelo series is perhaps the most modern of watches, often with complex dial indications, like the GMT. And in the Historiador collection, perhaps the most authentically vintage is the Tradicion, with a champagne dial and a very "rational" grid pattern on the dial

---

Prominente Doble Tiempo

Reference number: 1124.1ACG
Movement: automatic, 2 Caliber CYS 5205 movements (base ETA 2678); ø 17.2 mm, height 5.35 and 4.8 mm; 25 jewels; 28,800 vph; 38-hour and 44-hour power reserve; rotor with CyS engraving; 2nd movement modified for 24-hour display; guilloché dial
Functions: hours, minutes; 2nd 24-hour display; day, date
Case: stainless steel, 52 × 30.5 mm, height 9.5 mm; sapphire crystal; transparent case back affixed with 6 screws; water-resistant to 3 atm
Band: reptile skin, folding clasp
Price: $5,450

Vuelo GMT

Reference number: 3204.1B
Movement: automatic, Caliber CYS 5123 (base Sellita 330); ø 25.6 mm, height 4.1 mm; 21 jewels; 28,800 vph; 42-hour power reserve; rotor with fan decoration and CyS engraving
Functions: hours, minutes, sweep seconds; central 2nd 24-hour display (2nd time zone); date at 3 o'clock
Case: stainless steel, ø 44, height 11.4 mm; sapphire crystal; screw-down transparent case back; water-resistant to 3 atm
Band: stainless steel, folding clasp
Price: $5,050
Variation: cream-colored dial

Tradicion

Reference number: 3195.1TR.C
Movement: automatic, Caliber CYS 5102 (base ETA Caliber 2893-1); ø 25.60 mm, height 3.6 mm; 21 jewels; 28,800 vph; rose gold–plated "frappage" grid decoration on dial, 42-hour power reserve; engraved oscillating weight
Functions: hours, minutes, sweep seconds; date
Case: stainless steel, ø 40 mm, height 10.1 mm; bubble-style sapphire crystal; screwed-down transparent case back with watch number printed on the sapphire crystal; water-resistant to 3 atm
Band: calfskin, buckle
Price: $4,250; limited to 882 pieces

Czapek & Cie.
18 Rue de la Corraterie
CH-1204 Geneva
Switzerland

Tel.:
+41 22 557 41 41

E-mail:
info@czapek.com

Website:
www.czapek.com

Founded:
2012

U.S. distributor:
Horology Works
11 Flagg Road
West Hartford, CT 06117
860-986-9676
info@horologyworks.com

Most important collections/price range:
Quai des Bergues men's and ladies' watches / from $12,000 to $45,800;
Place Vendôme / up to $226,000; Faubourg de Cracovie / up to $26,800

CZAPEK & CIE.

Born in Bohemia (Czech Republic today) in 1811, watchmaker Frantiszek Czapek fought in the failed Polish insurrection of 1832 against Russia and then fled to Geneva. In 1839, he joined another Pole, Antoine de Patek, in a business venture. When the contract expired in 1845, Patek decided on a partnership with Jean Philippe, inventor of the keyless watch. Czapek went on to become purveyor of watches to Emperor Napoleon III and author of a book on watches. Then he vanished without a trace sometime in the late 1860s.

His "resurrection" is due to entrepreneur, art specialist, and occasional watch collector Harry Guhl, who registered the name and set up a management team that included Xavier de Roquemaurel and Sébastien Follonier. They chose Czapek's model No. 3430 as a model upon which to build up a new brand. It is an intriguing piece with elongated Roman numerals, elegant fleur-de-lys hands, and two oddly placed subdials at 7:30 and 4:30, one for small seconds, the other featuring a clever double hand for the seven-day power reserve and days of the week.

The team's claim to fame is collaborating with friends of the brand to create new models, which are always implemented by outstanding Swiss suppliers like Donzé for the grand-feu dials with the secret signature, and Aurélien Bouchet for the fine fleur-de-lys hands.

Since the company's coming-out in November 2015, Czapek has launched a few models that rapidly created a buzz: the Quai des Bergues won the Public Prize of the Grand Prix d'Horlogerie de Genève a year later. Next came the Place Vendôme in homage to the great square in Paris where Czapek actually had a boutique. The Faubourg de Cracovie, 2018, is a classic chronograph, but with a grand-feu dial and, once again, the fine hands that reach all the way back to Czapek's day. The latest piece, the Antarctique, fits in well with the current trend for sportive watches.

Antarctique

Reference number: Terre Adèlie
Movement: automatic, Czapek Caliber SXH5; ø 30 mm, height 4.2 mm; 28 jewels; 28,800 vph; microrotor of recycled gold, balance with gold regulating cams, skeletonized bridges; finely finished movement; 56-hour power reserve; COSC-certified chronometer
Functions: hours, minutes, sweep seconds; date
Case: stainless steel, ø 40.5 mm, height 10.6 mm; sapphire crystal; transparent case back; water-resistant to 12 atm
Band: stainless steel, folding clasp
Remarks: bracelet with special easy-release system
Price: $18,900
Variations: various dial colors; calfskin or rubber strap

Quai des Bergues

Reference number: 33bis
Movement: manually wound, Czapek Caliber SXH1; ø 32 mm, height 4.75 mm; 31 jewels; 21,600 vph; finely finished movement; 168-hour power reserve
Functions: hours, minutes, subsidiary seconds; power reserve indicator; weekday
Case: pink gold, ø 42.5 mm, height 11.8 mm; sapphire crystal; transparent case back; water-resistant to 3 atm
Band: reptile skin, buckle
Remarks: enamel dial
Price: $28,200

Faubourg de Cracovie

Reference number: King
Movement: automatic, Czapek Caliber SXH3; ø 30 mm, height 6.95 mm; 42 jewels; 36,000 vph; column-wheel control of chronograph functions; finely finished movement; 65-hour power reserve; COSC-certified chronometer
Functions: hours, minutes, subsidiary seconds; chronograph; date
Case: stainless steel, ø 41.5 mm, height 13.5 mm; sapphire crystal; transparent case back; water-resistant to 5 atm
Band: reptile skin, folding clasp
Remarks: hand-made guilloché on gold dial
Price: $28,800; limited to 18 pieces

DAMASKO

When it comes to sheer toughness, Damasko has built up quite a track record ever since its founding in 1994, in Germany. But it's not visible at first glance.

These unadorned watches with clean, sharp lines are almost archetypical watches. They are robust, indestructible even, and will not need much servicing.

The company's claim to fame lies in its choice of materials, such as polycrystalline silicon hairsprings and components made of a special ice-hardened steel. This special patent involves adding nitrogen and carbon to the molten stainless steel and then cooling it quickly. The resulting material, which has been used in machines like the space shuttle, is extremely hard and does not corrode easily, so these are watches that will keep their look for a long time.

In fact, the research done by this small brand, located near Regensburg in southern Germany, has generated over one hundred patents for the brand, as well as registered samples and designs. The "German" look means well-groomed dials and an immediate view of the time, thanks to contrasting hues.

These watches boast outstanding technical quality, which combines with a very clear stylistic concept. The collection includes an array of model families ranging from very classical-functional pilot watches to a line of timeless sportive chronographs, and to some very elegant watches for daily use, like the Black Beauty.

Almost all parts are in fact made in-house, which testifies to the company's commitment to quality. Many of the models run on ETA movements, but Damasko also assembles its own caliber, the A35, which allows for a manufacturing depth of ninety percent. Parts made in the small factory include plates, bridges, pinions, balance, spring barrel, and rotors. Despite the strong focus on research, development, and use of new materials and processes, the watches produced manage to stay in the affordable range.

Damasko GmbH
Unterheising 17c
93092 Barbing
Germany

Tel.:
+49-9401-80481

E-mail:
sales@damasko-watches.com

Website:
www.damasko-watches.com

Founded:
1994

Number of employees:
30

Distribution:
U.S. Sales
Island Watch
273 Walt Whitman Road, Suite 217
11746 Huntington Station, NY
631-470-0762
sales@longislandwatch.com

Price range:
$1,000 to $4,000

DS 30 Green

Movement: automatic, ETA Caliber 2824-2; ø 25.6 mm, height 4.6 mm; 25 jewels; 28,800 vph; shock-resistant and amagnetic according to the German Industrial Norm (DIN); 38-hour power reserve
Functions: hours, minutes, sweep seconds; date
Case: stainless steel (submarine steel), ø 39 mm, height 9.95 mm; sapphire crystal; screw-in crown; water-resistant to 20 atm
Band: calfskin, buckle
Price: $971
Variations: leather strap with double stitching ($1,008); rubber strap ($986)

DS 30 Yellow

Movement: automatic, ETA Caliber 2824-2; ø 25.6 mm, height 4.6 mm; 25 jewels; 28,800 vph; shock-resistant and amagnetic according to the German Industrial Norm (DIN); 38-hour power reserve
Functions: hours, minutes, sweep seconds; date
Case: stainless steel (submarine steel), ø 39 mm, height 9.95 mm; sapphire crystal; screw-in crown; water-resistant to 20 atm
Band: calfskin, buckle
Price: $971
Variations: leather strap with double stitching ($1,008); rubber strap ($986)

DS 30 Blue

Movement: automatic, ETA Caliber 2824-2; ø 25.6 mm, height 4.6 mm; 25 jewels; 28,800 vph; shock-resistant and amagnetic according to the German Industrial Norm (DIN); 38-hour power reserve
Functions: hours, minutes, sweep seconds; date
Case: stainless steel (submarine steel), ø 39 mm, height 9.95 mm; sapphire crystal; screw-in crown; water-resistant to 20 atm
Band: calfskin, buckle
Price: $971
Variations: leather strap with double stitching ($1,008); rubber strap ($986)

DSub1

Movement: automatic, ETA Caliber 2824-2; ø 25.6 mm, height 4.6 mm; 25 jewels; 28,800 vph; shock-resistant and amagnetic according to the German Industrial Norm (DIN); 38-hour power reserve
Functions: hours, minutes, sweep seconds; date
Case: stainless steel (submarine steel), ø 43 mm, height 12.9 mm; unidirectional bezel with 0-60 scale; sapphire crystal; screw-in crown; water-resistant to 30 atm
Band: calfskin with rubber covering, buckle
Price: $1,560
Variations: rubber strap ($1,560)

DSub2

Movement: automatic, ETA Caliber 2824-2; ø 25.6 mm, height 4.6 mm; 25 jewels; 28,800 vph; shock-resistant and amagnetic according to the German Industrial Norm (DIN); 38-hour power reserve
Functions: hours, minutes, sweep seconds; date
Case: stainless steel (submarine steel), ø 43 mm, height 12.6 mm; unidirectional bezel with 0-60 scale; sapphire crystal; screw-in crown; water-resistant to 30 atm
Band: rubber, folding clasp
Price: $1,560
Variations: leather strap and buckle ($1,560)

DSub3

Movement: automatic, ETA Caliber 2824-2; ø 25.6 mm, height 4.6 mm; 25 jewels; 28,800 vph; shock-resistant and amagnetic according to the German Industrial Norm (DIN); 38-hour power reserve
Functions: hours, minutes, sweep seconds; date
Case: stainless steel (submarine steel), ø 43 mm, height 12.6 mm; unidirectional bezel with 0-60 scale; sapphire crystal; screw-in crown; water-resistant to 30 atm
Band: calfskin with rubber covering, buckle
Price: $1,560
Variations: leather strap ($1,521)

DC 80 LHV Black

Movement: automatic, Damasko Caliber C51-1 (base ETA 7750); ø 30.4 mm, height 7.9 mm; 27 jewels; 28,800 vph; shock-resistant and amagnetic according to the German Industrial Norm (DIN); 50-hour power reserve
Functions: hours, minutes; chronograph
Case: ice-hardened stainless steel with black coating, ø 42 mm, height 13.9 mm; bidirectional bezel, with 0-60 scale; sapphire crystal; screw-in crown; water-resistant to 10 atm
Band: calfskin, buckle
Price: $2,619
Variations: rubber strap ($2,657)

DC 82

Movement: automatic, Damasko Caliber C51-2 (base ETA 7750); ø 30.4 mm, height 7.9 mm; 27 jewels; 28,800 vph; central seconds and minute counters; shock-resistant and amagnetic according to the German Industrial Norm (DIN); 50-hour power reserve
Functions: hours, minutes; chronograph; date
Case: ice-hardened stainless steel, ø 42 mm, height 13.9 mm; bidirectional bezel, with 0-60 scale; sapphire crystal; screw-in crown; water-resistant to 10 atm
Band: stainless steel, folding clasp
Price: $3,300
Variations: calfskin strap and buckle ($3,372); rubber strap and buckle ($3,410)

DC 86 Green

Movement: automatic, Damasko Caliber C51-6 (base ETA 7750); ø 30.4 mm, height 7.9 mm; 27 jewels; 28,800 vph; central seconds and minute counters; shock-resistant and amagnetic according to the German Industrial Norm (DIN); 50-hour power reserve
Functions: hours, minutes, subsidiary seconds; additional 24-hour display (2nd time zone); chronograph; date
Case: ice-hardened stainless steel, ø 42 mm, height 14.4 mm; bidirectional bezel, with 0-12 scale; sapphire crystal; screw-in crown; water-resistant to 10 atm
Band: calfskin, buckle
Price: $3,372; **Variations:** stainless steel band ($3,966); rubber strap ($3,410)

DAVOSA

One of the more important brands occupying the lower segment of the market is Davosa, which manufactures a range of pilot watches, quality divers (with helium valve), dress watches, and ladies' watches, all at very affordable prices. The brand has even come out with an apnea training watch that cleverly comes out of its case. The company uses solid Swiss movements, which it occasionally modifies for its own designs, or it experiments with special coatings like the "gun" PVD coating on the latest Argonautics, which is dark green. The most recent series is dedicated to Isaac Newton. Among these dressy in a sporty sort of way timepieces, one finds a limited edition automatic chronograph with a moon phase, at under $2,400.

To create a broad portfolio requires experience, and that is something Davosa has in spades. The company was founded in 1891. Back then, farmer Abel Frédéric Hasler spent the long winter months in Tramelan, in Switzerland's Jura mountains, making silver pocket watch cases. Later, two of his brothers ventured out to the city of Geneva and opened a watch factory. The third brother also opted to engage with the watch industry and moved to Biel. The entire next generation of Haslers went into watchmaking as well.

The name Hasler & Co. appeared on the occasional package mailed in Switzerland or overseas. Playing the role of unassuming private-label watchmakers, the Haslers remained in the background and let their customers in Europe and the United States run away with the show. It wasn't until after World War II that brothers Paul and David Hasler dared produce their own timepieces.

The long experience with watchmaking and watches culminated in 1987 with the brothers developing their own line of watches under the brand name Davosa. The Haslers then signed a partnership with the German distributor Bohle. In Germany, mechanical watches were experiencing a boom, so the brand was able to evolve quickly. In 2000, Corinna Bohle took over as manager of strategic development. Davosa now reaches well beyond Switzerland's borders and has become an integral part of the world of mechanical watches.

DAVOSA Swiss
Bohle GmbH
Bunsenstrasse 1a
32052 Herford
Germany

Tel.:
+49 (0)5221 9942400

E-mail:
info@davosa.com

Website:
www.davosa.com

Founded:
1881

U.S. distributor:
Davosa U.S.A
11256 Brandywine Lake Way
Boynton Beach, FL 33473
877-DAVOSA1
info@davosa-usa.com
www.davosa-usa.com

Most important collections/price range:
Apnea Diver, Argonautic, Classic, Gentleman, Military, Newton, Pilot, Ternos, Titanium / $600 to $2,400

Newton Pilot Moonphase Chronograph Limited Edition

Reference number: 161.586.55
Movement: automatic, ETA Caliber 7751; ø 30 mm, height 7.9 mm; 25 jewels; 28,800 vph; 42-hour power reserve
Functions: hours, minutes, subsidiary seconds; additional 24-hour display; chronograph; full calendar with date, weekday, month, moon phase
Case: stainless steel, ø 44 mm, height 14 mm; sapphire crystal; transparent case back; water-resistant to 5 atm
Band: calfskin, buckle
Price: $2,398

Newton Pilot Day-Date

Reference number: 161.585.45
Movement: automatic, ETA Caliber 2834-2; ø 29.4 mm, height 5.05 mm; 25 jewels; 28,800 vph; 38-hour power reserve
Functions: hours, minutes, sweep seconds; date, weekday
Case: stainless steel, ø 44 mm, height 11 mm; sapphire crystal; transparent case back; water-resistant to 5 atm
Band: calfskin, buckle
Price: $898

Argonautic Bronze TT

Reference number: 161.526.55
Movement: automatic, Sellita Caliber SW200-1; ø 25.6 mm, height 4.6 mm; 26 jewels; 28,800 vph; 38-hour power reserve
Functions: hours, minutes, sweep seconds; date
Case: stainless steel, ø 43 mm, height 13.5 mm; unidirectional bezel in bronze with 0-60 scale; sapphire crystal; screw-in crown, helium valve; water-resistant to 30 atm
Band: rubber, folding clasp
Price: $899

Argonautic BG

Reference number: 161.522.02
Movement: automatic, Sellita Caliber SW200-1; ø 25.6 mm, height 4.6 mm; 26 jewels; 28,800 vph; 38-hour power reserve
Functions: hours, minutes, sweep seconds; date
Case: stainless steel, ø 42.5 mm, height 13.5 mm; unidirectional bezel with ceramic insert, 0-60 scale; sapphire crystal; screw-in crown; helium valve; water-resistant to 30 atm
Band: stainless steel, folding clasp, with safety lock and extension link
Price: $798
Variations: various colors

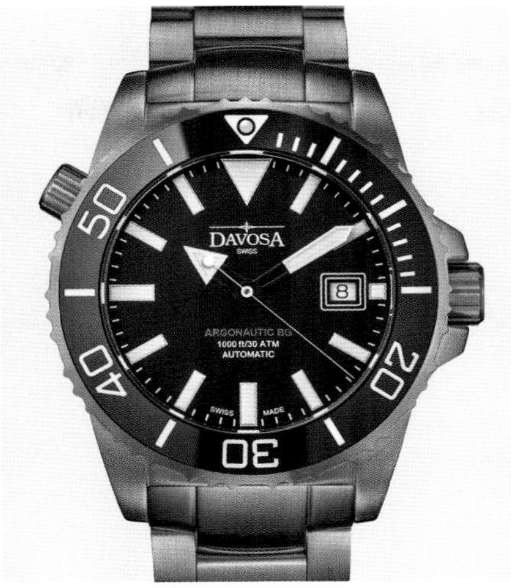

Argonautic Gun BG

Reference number: 161.523.50
Movement: automatic, Sellita Caliber SW200-1; ø 25.6 mm, height 4.6 mm; 26 jewels; 28,800 vph; 38-hour power reserve
Functions: hours, minutes, sweep seconds; date
Case: stainless steel with gray PVD, ø 43 mm, height 13.5 mm; unidirectional bezel with ceramic insert, with 0-60 scale; sapphire crystal; screw-in crown, helium valve; water-resistant to 30 atm
Band: stainless steel with gray PVD, folding clasp, with safety lock and extension link
Price: $849

Ternos Medium

Reference number: 166.195.10
Movement: automatic, Sellita Caliber SW200-1; ø 25.6 mm, height 4.6 mm; 26 jewels; 28,800 vph; 38-hour power reserve
Functions: hours, minutes, sweep seconds; date
Case: stainless steel, ø 36.5 mm, height 11.8 mm; unidirectional bezel with ceramic insert, with 0-60 scale; sapphire crystal; screw-in crown; water-resistant to 20 atm
Band: stainless steel, folding clasp, with safety lock and extension link
Price: $798

Ternos Professional GMT Black&White Limited Edition

Reference number: 161.571.15
Movement: automatic, Sellita Caliber SW330-1; ø 25.6 mm, height 4.1 mm; 25 jewels; 28,800 vph; 42-hour power reserve
Functions: hours, minutes, sweep seconds; additional 24-hour display (2nd time zone); date
Case: stainless steel, ø 42 mm, height 15.5 mm; unidirectional bezel with ceramic insert, with 0-24 scale; sapphire crystal; screw-in crown; water-resistant to 20 atm
Band: stainless steel, folding clasp, with safety lock and extension link
Remarks: comes with additional nylon strap
Price: $1,348

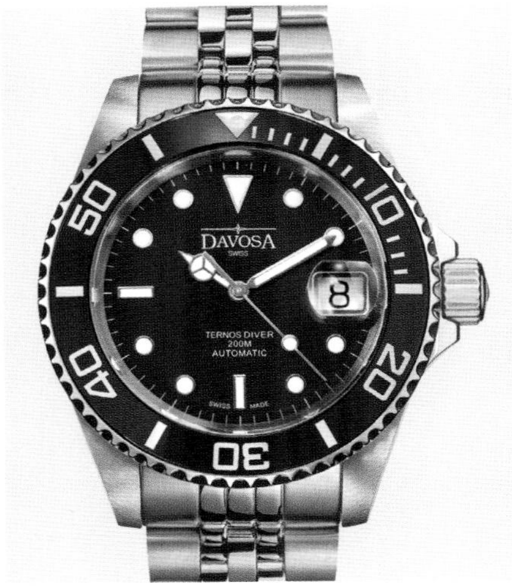

Ternos Ceramic

Reference number: 161.555.07
Movement: automatic, Sellita Caliber SW200-1; ø 25.6 mm, height 4.6 mm; 26 jewels; 28,800 vph; 38-hour power reserve
Functions: hours, minutes, sweep seconds; date
Case: stainless steel, ø 40 mm, height 12.5 mm; unidirectional bezel with ceramic insert, with 0-60 scale; sapphire crystal; screw-in crown; water-resistant to 20 atm
Band: stainless steel, folding clasp, with safety lock and extension link
Price: $798

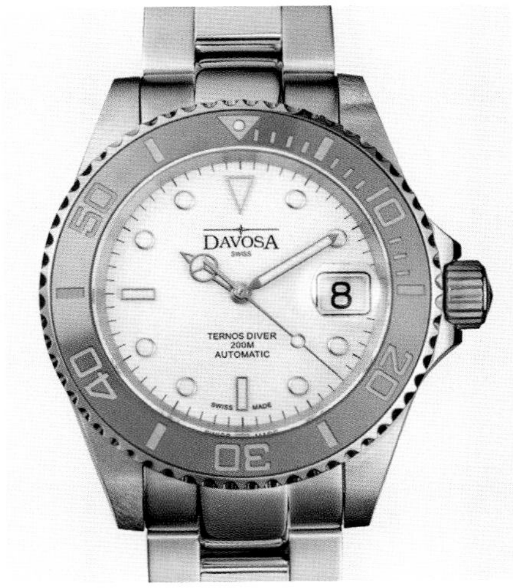

Ternos Ceramic

Reference number: 161.555.63
Movement: automatic, Sellita Caliber SW200-1; ø 25.6 mm, height 4.6 mm; 26 jewels; 28,800 vph; 38-hour power reserve
Functions: hours, minutes, sweep seconds; date
Case: stainless steel, ø 40 mm, height 12.5 mm; unilateral bezel with rose gold PVD and ceramic insert, with 0-60 scale; sapphire crystal; screw-in crown; water-resistant to 20 atm
Band: stainless steel with rose gold PVD on central links, folding clasp, with safety lock and extension link
Price: $879

DE BETHUNE

De Bethune SA
Granges Jaccard 6
CH-1454 La Chaux L'Auberson
Switzerland

Tel.:
+41-24-454-2281

Fax:
+41-24-454-2317

E-mail:
info@debethune.ch

Website:
www.debethune.ch

Founded:
2002

Number of employees:
30

Annual production:
150

Distribution:
For all inquiries from the U.S., contact the company directly.

De Bethune was named after an eighteenth-century French navy captain from an old aristocratic family, the Chevalier De Béthune, who did extensive research into watch and clockmaking and whose name is associated with a particularly clever escapement. Similarly, Denis Flageollet had had many years of experience in the research, conception, and implementation of prestigious timepieces. So he and David Zanetta, a well-known consultant for a number of high-end watch brands, founded their own company in 2002 in what used to be the village pub and turned it into a stunning factory. The modern CNC machinery, combined with an outstanding team of watchmakers and R&D specialists, allowed the company to rapidly produce prototypes and make small movement series with great dispatch. In order to become even more independent of suppliers, the little factory produced its own cases, dials, and hands.

A financial crisis occasioned by the rise of the Swiss franc led to a number of changes, including the departure of Zanetta. De Bethune reduced its output, but stuck to its focus on innovation. Among others, the company developed a manually wound caliber with a power reserve of up to eight days, a self-regulating double barrel, a balance wheel in titanium and platinum that allows for an ideal inertia/mass ratio, a balance spring with a patented De Bethune end curve, and a triple "parachute" shock-absorbing system. It also boasts the lightest and one of the fastest silicon/titanium tourbillons on the market. Another project was the use of a flying magnet to regulate the escape wheel of the "Résonique" escapement without touching it. Most recently, De Bethune designed a chronograph clutch that gives the totalizing counters more independence. It has been built into the DB29 Tourbillon Maxichrono.

De Bethune watches are esthetically compelling, thanks to the use of simple color schemes, mirror-polished titanium, and discreet microlight engraving. The "delta" on many of the dials is natural decoration, explains Flageollet: "The triangle is essential to holding the gearwheel pivots, so why not turn them into a natural ogival arch?"

DB28XP

Reference number: DB28XPTIS1
Movement: manually wound, De Bethune Caliber DB 2115v6; ø 30 mm; 29 jewels; 28,800 vph; self-regulating double spring barrel, titanium balance optimized for temperature fluctuations and air penetration; triple parachute shock absorber; open dial on balance; 144-hour power reserve
Functions: hours, minutes
Case: microlight mirror-polished titanium, ø 43 mm, height 7.2 mm; floating lugs; sapphire crystal; transparent case back with blued titanium ring; water-resistant to 3 atm
Band: reptile skin, titanium buckle
Remarks: titanium dial with microlight decoration
Price: $83,500

DB28XP Starry Sky

Reference number: DB28XPTIS3V2
Movement: manually wound, De Bethune Caliber DB 2115v7; ø 30 mm; 27 jewels; 28,800 vph; self-regulating double spring barrel, titanium balance optimized for temperature fluctuations and air penetration; open dial to show balance; 144-hour power reserve
Functions: hours, minutes
Case: microlight mirror-polished titanium, ø 43 mm, height 7.2 mm; floating lugs; sapphire crystal; transparent case back; water-resistant to 3 atm
Band: reptile skin, titanium buckle
Remarks: titanium dial with microlight decoration
Price: $83,500

DB28XP Tourbillon

Reference number: DB28XPTTIS1
Movement: manually wound, De Bethune Caliber DB 2009v4; ø 30 mm; 33 jewels; 36,000 vph; self-regulating double spring barrel, titanium balance, silicon escape wheel, optimized for temperature fluctuations and air penetration; open dial to show balance; 30-second tourbillon; 120-hour power reserve
Functions: hours, minutes, 30-second indicator on tourbillon cage
Case: mirror-polished titanium, ø 43 mm, height 8.1 mm; floating lugs; sapphire crystal; solid case back with position of planets on November 19, 2011, when De Bethune won the Aiguille d'Or; water-resistant to 3 atm; **Band:** reptile skin, titanium buckle
Price: $208,000; limited to 10 pieces

DB28 Steel Wheels Sapphire Tourbillon

Reference number: DB28SWTTIS1
Movement: manually wound, De Bethune Caliber DB 2019V5; ø 30 mm; 33 jewels; 36,000 vph; self-regulating double spring barrel, titanium balance, silicon escape wheel, optimized for temperature fluctuations and air penetration; open dial to show balance; 30-second tourbillon; 120-hour power reserve
Functions: hours, minutes
Case: titanium, ø 43 mm, height 9.8 mm; floating lugs; sapphire crystal; transparent case back; water-resistant to 3 atm
Band: reptile skin, buckle
Remarks: blued titanium minute hands
Price: $225,000; limited to 10 pieces

DB21 Maxichrono Réédition

Reference number: DB21RE
Movement: manually wound, De Bethune Caliber DB 2030; ø 30 mm; 51 jewels; 36,000 vph; self-regulating double spring barrel, titanium balance, silicon escape wheel, optimized for temperature fluctuations and air penetration; monopusher chronograph function; 120-hour power reserve
Functions: hours, minutes, sweep seconds; central chronograph with 24-hour, 60-minute, and 60-second counters
Case: titanium, ø 44.4 mm, height 12 mm; floating lugs; sapphire crystal; transparent case back; water-resistant to 3 atm; **Band:** reptile skin, titanium buckle
Remarks: 3-dimensional dial for readability
Price: $180,000; limited to 10 pieces

DB28 Digitale

Reference number: DB28DN / S
Movement: manually wound, De Bethune Caliber DB 2115v7; ø 30 mm; 27 jewels; 28,800 vph; self-regulating double spring barrel, titanium balance optimized for temperature fluctuations and air penetration; open dial to show balance; 144-hour power reserve; **Functions:** hours (jumping), minutes on disk; central moon phase
Case: polished titanium, ø 43 mm, height 7.2 mm; floating lugs; sapphire crystal; transparent case back; water-resistant to 3 atm
Band: reptile skin, titanium buckle
Remarks: palladium and blued titanium moon surrounded by blued titanium with gray-gold stars
Price: $113,500

DB28 Yellow Tones

Reference number: DB28YT
Movement: manually wound, De Bethune Caliber DB DB2114; ø 30 mm; 32 jewels; 28,800 vph; self-regulating double spring barrel, titanium balance, silicon escape wheel; barrel bridges with côtes de Bethune decoration; 120-hour power reserve
Functions: hours, minutes; spherical moon phase with one lunar day tolerance every 1,112 years; power reserve indicator
Case: titanium, ø 42.6 mm, height 9.3 mm; floating lugs; sapphire crystal; transparent case back; water-resistant to 3 atm; **Band:** reptile skin, titanium buckle
Remarks: flame-browned hands and moon phase bezel; polished titanium markers
Price: $110,000; limited to 25 pieces

Kind of Blue Tourbillon

Reference number: DB28TBMW
Movement: manually wound, De Bethune Caliber DB2115V4; ø 30 mm; 39 jewels; 36,000 vph; self-regulating double spring barrel, titanium balance, silicon escape wheel, optimized for temperature fluctuations and air penetration; open dial to show balance; finely finished movement, côtes de Bethune on bridges; 30-second tourbillon; 120-hour power reserve
Functions: hours, minutes, 30-second display on tourbillon cage; power reserve indicator on movement side
Case: polished titanium, ø 42.6 mm, height 9.8 mm; floating lugs; sapphire crystal; transparent case back; water-resistant to 3 atm
Band: reptile skin, blued titanium buckle
Price: $242,000; limited to 5 pieces

DB25 Starry Varius Chronomètre Tourbillon

Reference number: DB25STTIS3
Movement: manually wound, De Bethune Caliber DB2109V4; ø 30 mm; 43 jewels; 36,000 vph; self-regulating double spring barrel, titanium balance, silicon escape wheel, optimized for temperature fluctuations and air penetration; finely finished movement; 30-second tourbillon; 96-hour power reserve
Functions: hours, minutes; spherical moon phase
Case: titanium, ø 42.6 mm, height 10.3 mm; sapphire crystal; transparent case back
Band: reptile skin, buckle
Remarks: Milky Way pattern on dial by laser
Price: $226,000; limited to 10 pieces

DEEP BLUE

Deep Blue Watches
1716 Coney Island Avenue
Suite 3r
Brooklyn, NY 11230

Tel.:
718-484-7717

Website:
www.deepbluewatches.com

E-mail:
info@deepbluewatches.com

Founded:
2007

Number of employees:
70

Distribution:
Retail

Most important collections/price range:
Master 1000, Diver 1000, Defender / $300 to $500; Pro Sea Diver / $500 to $900; Daynight / $600 to $1,000; Alpha, Marine, Ocean / $700 to $1,500; Blue Water / $600 to $1,400

As far as anyone can tell, the fish do not care what you are wearing on your wrist. For the diver, it has to be accurate, genuinely water-resistant, and readable in less-than-ideal conditions. Those are the basics—or should be—of any real diver's watch. The rest is in the eye of the beholder. And it seems that New York–based Deep Blue does not wander too far off home plate, as it were. Founder Stan Betesh launched his company with the idea of providing divers with an array of tough watches that do the job and have the look and feel of a professional-quality diver's watch at a fraction of what you might expect to pay.

Little did he know in 2007—that is, more than a decade ago—that his watches would achieve cult status among divers. Deep Blue watches are accurate, robust, and ready for life in the open and underwater. There's no need to hide them in a safe, and getting banged up a little does them no harm—it's called patina, and it gives these timepieces the look and feel of a real tool watch . . . which is what they are.

The collection includes all sorts of models for every type of diving. The power is supplied by Miyota or ETA calibers, occasionally quartz movements. Some have special features like ceramic bezels; some are water-resistant to as much as 3,000 meters, like the Depthmaster, whose dimensions (ø 49 mm, height 19.5) and weight (300 g) will certainly contribute to the speed of the diver's descent.

For its tenth anniversary, the brand launched the Master 2000 Diver, which offers the buyer a variety of dial colors, from black to bright orange. Lots of care is given to lighting the dial, with generous application of Superluminova and the occasional use of autoluminescent tritium tubes, which may well attract some interesting fish. The second commemorative watch features this special technology: the Daynight Recon T-100 Tritium Diver 1 in a 45-mm stainless steel case with a ceramic 120-click unidirectional rotating bezel.

Daynight Recon Tritium T-100 GMT Swiss Automatic

Reference number: DNRECONGMTT100
Movement: automatic, ETA Caliber 2893-2; ø 25.6 mm, height 4.6 mm; 25 jewels; 28,800 vph
Functions: hours, minutes, sweep seconds; date, 2nd time zone
Case: stainless steel, ø 45 mm, height 16.5 mm; unidirectional bezel with 0-120 scale; transparent case back; sapphire crystal; water-resistant to 50 atm
Band: stainless steel bracelet with wetsuit extension
Remarks: blue wave dial with tritium gas–filled tube illumination on hands and hour markers
Price: $1,449
Variations: black dial

Daynight Recon Tritium Valjoux T100

Reference number: DNT100DVR7750
Movement: automatic, ETA Valjoux 7750; ø 30 mm, height 7.9 mm; 25 jewels; 28,800 vph
Functions: hours, minutes, subsidiary seconds; chronograph; weekday, date
Case: stainless steel, ø 45 mm, height 16.5 mm; screw-down case back; screw-in crown; unidirectional bezel with 0-120 scale: sapphire crystal; water-resistant to 50 atm
Band: stainless steel bracelet
Remarks: tritium gas–filled tube illumination on hands and hour markers
Price: $1,999
Variations: blue or white dial

Daynight Rescue Tritium T-100

Reference number: DNRESCURGMTT100
Movement: automatic, ETA Caliber 2893-2; ø 25.6 mm, height 4.6 mm; 25 jewels; 28,800 vph
Functions: hours, minutes, sweep seconds; 2nd time zone; date
Case: stainless steel, ø 45 mm, height 16.5 mm; unidirectional bezel with 0-120 scale; transparent case back; sapphire crystal; water-resistant to 50 atm
Band: stainless steel bracelet with wetsuit extension
Remarks: tritium gas–filled tube illumination on hands and hour markers
Price: $1,449
Variations: black dial

Delma Watch Limited
Solothurnstrasse 47
2543 Lengnau
Switzerland

Tel.:
+41 32 654 22 11

E-mail:
info@delma.ch

Website:
www.delma.ch

Founded:
1924

Number of employees:
15

Annual production:
25,000 watches

Distribution:
Contact headquarters in Switzerland.

Most important collections/price range:
Racing and Diver collections / up to $3,000

DELMA

Industries all have their major players and their minor ones. The major brands attract the attention thanks, oftentimes, to lots of clamorous advertising plus name recognition. In the watch business, as in many others, there are smaller, less noisy brands that also produce quality watches.

Delma began as one of four brands produced by a company founded in 1924 by two brothers, Alfred and Adolf Gilomen. For several decades, they manufactured a number of different models, from classic pocket watches and dress watches to a fine chronograph marketed under the name Midland, in 1946, which made a bit of a splash.

Following the death of Adolf Gilomen in 1966, the brand was sold to a man named Ulrich Wütrich. He decided to streamline the brand to a single name, Delma, and focus production on diver's watches, without, however, losing the customers in search of a nice watch that could be used every day. In 1969, they came out with the Periscope, an automatic diver's. It established a new style for the brand, one it has remained faithful to ever since. A few years later, it released the Shell Star, a professional diver's watch.

Today, the company is run by Wütrich's son-in-law Fred Leibundgut and grandson Andreas Leibundgut. The brand still produces casual watches, but its claim to fame is still its diver's. The Periscope and Shell Star have been revived with a modernized look and more pertinent technology. And in 2017, a new line, the Oceanmaster line, was launched, with the Antarctica model coming out in 2020; it was actually tested on the Sixth Continent by adventurer Nick Moloney and features a compass. In 2011, they put out the Blue Shark I, which could survive a 3,000-meter (9,900-foot) plunge. To prove they could improve even on that, in 2019 Delma came out with the Blue Shark III, which can go to 4,000 meters. It has a 6.8-millimeter sapphire crystal, and a thick steel back, so you may not survive the plunge, but the watch will.

Oceanmaster Antarctica

Reference number: 41701.670.6.049
Movement: automatic, ETA Caliber 2824; ø 25.6 mm, height 4.6 mm; 25 jewels; 28,800 vph; custom rotor; 38-hour power reserve
Functions: hours, minutes, sweep seconds; date
Case: stainless steel case, crown, and pushers, ø 44 mm at bezel, height 13.8 mm; unidirectional bezel; points of sail on dial, tactical planner and compass; Antarctica map on back; water-resistant to 50 atm
Band: stainless steel, folding clasp
Price: $1,450
Variations: black dial

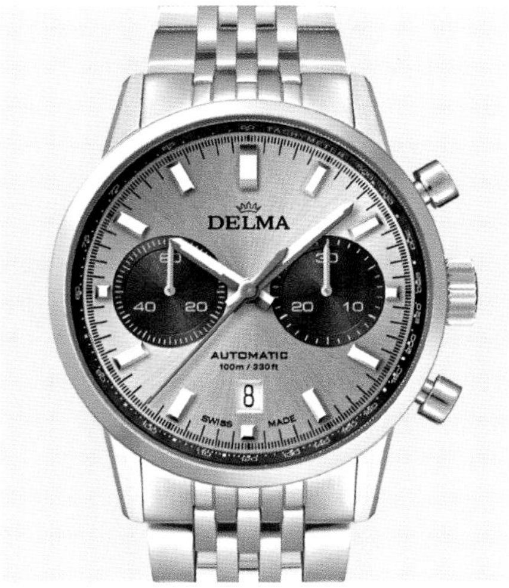

Continental

Reference number: 41701.702.6.061
Movement: automatic, Sellita Caliber SW510; ø 30 mm, height 7.9 mm; 27 jewels; 28,800 vph; 48-hour power reserve
Functions: hours, minutes, subsidiary seconds; chronograph; date
Case: stainless steel, ø 42 mm at bezel, height 13 mm; screw-down crown; sapphire crystal; transparent case back; water-resistant to 10 atm
Band: stainless steel, folding clasp
Price: $2,850
Variations: with black, blue, green; yellow gold bezel and bicolor bracelet ($2,950)

Blue Shark III

Reference number: 54701.700.6.044
Movement: automatic, ETA Caliber 2824-2; ø 25.6 mm, height 4.6 mm; 25 jewels; 28,800 vph; decorated rotor; 38-hour power reserve
Functions: hours, minutes, seconds; date
Case: stainless steel, ø 47 mm, height 18.5 mm; sapphire crystal; unidirectional bezel with DLC coating; screw-down crown and case back; water-resistant to 400 atm (4,000 m)
Band: stainless steel, folding clasp
Price: $2,290; limited to 500 pieces
Variations: stainless steel bezel ($2,190)

DETROIT WATCH COMPANY

Detroit Watch Company, LLC
P.O. Box 60
Birmingham, MI 48012

Tel:
248-321-5601

E-mail:
info@detroitwatchco.com

Founded:
2013

Number of employees:
3

Annual production:
500 watches

Distribution:
direct sales only

Most important collections/price range:
M1 Woodward Moonphase, 1701 Pontchartrain GMT, 1701 L'Horloge; B24 Liberator / $998 to $2,650

Founders Patrick Ayoub and Amy Ayoub launched Detroit Watch Company in 2013 with the first and only mechanical timepieces designed and assembled in Detroit, Michigan. Patrick, a car designer, and Amy, an interior designer, share a passion for original design and timepieces and have worked hard to develop their brand, which draws inspiration from, and celebrates, the city of "Détroit."

Detroit means a lot of things to different people, and because the history of the people and places have shaped the city, Detroit's stories are also part of the Detroit Watch Company's collective story, which deserves to be told. Their introductory timepiece, the 1701, for instance, commemorates Antoine de la Mothe Cadillac, Knight of St. Louis, who, with his company of colonists, arrived at Détroit on July 24, 1701. On that day, under the patronage of Louis XIV and protected by the flag of France, the city of Détroit, then called Fort Pontchartrain, was founded. These watches, while modern and chic, do recall the fairly clear-cut lines of an old church clock clock (*horloge*).

People phoning Detroit will understand why the company came out with a watch named 313 (see *Wristwatch Annual* 2020). It's the area code of the city that brought not only cars, but also Motown (*motor* + *town*) music to the world. Needless to say, the dial looks like an old-fashioned phone dial. Now the company has decided to include a few more of the U.S. area codes for good measure. And where did those cars ride and race informally? On Woodward Avenue, the first mile of concrete highway in the USA, where carriages once rolled. It's the name for a collection of sporty chronographs.

The Detroit Watch Company timepieces are beautifully designed and hand-assembled in-house, and may be purchased directly through the Detroit Watch Company website.

M1 Woodward Sport Chrono

Reference number: DWC M1W-SC
Movement: automatic, ETA Caliber 7751; ø 30 mm, height 7.9 mm; 25 jewels; 28,800 vph; 48-hour power reserve
Functions: hours, minutes, subsidiary seconds; chronograph; date, day, month, moon phase
Case: stainless steel, ø 42 mm, height 14.5 mm; sapphire crystal; screw-in crown; transparent case back with engraving; water resistant to 5 atm
Band: calfskin, folding clasp
Price: $1,895
Variations: blue, white, and black, with subsidiary dial at 9 o'clock

1701 L'Horloge

Reference number: DWC 1701HDG-S1
Movement: automatic or manual, Sellita SW200, ø 25.6 mm, height 4.6 mm; 26 jewels, date calendar, 28,800 vph, 38-hour power reserve
Functions: hours, minutes, subsidiary seconds; date
Case: stainless steel, ø 39 mm, height 11.5 mm; sapphire crystal; screw-down case back with engraving; water resistant to 5 atm
Band: calfskin, buckle
Price: $998
Variations: dark gray dial

Pontchartrain Moonphase

Reference number: PCT-Moon-Chrono
Movement: automatic, ETA Caliber 7751; ø 30 mm, height 7.90 mm; 25 jewels; 28,800 vph; 48-hour power reserve
Functions: hour, minute, subsidiary second; chronograph; day, month, moon phase with rapid correction
Case: stainless steel, ø 42 mm, height 14.5 mm; sapphire crystal; screw-in crown; transparent case back; water resistant to 5 atm
Band: calfskin, folding clasp
Price: $2,550

Montres DOXA SA
Rue de Zurich 23A
P.O. Box 6031
2500 Bienne 6, Switzerland

Tel.:
+41 32 344 42 72

E-mail:
contact@doxawatches.com

Website:
doxawatches.com

Founded:
1889

Number of employees:
35

Distribution:
Retail and direct sales
For the USA:
+1 520 369 2872
contact.usa@doxawatches.com

Most important collection/price range:
Doxa Sub dive watch collection / $950 to $4,900

DOXA

Watch aficionados who have visited the world-famous museum in Le Locle will know that the little castle in which it is housed once belonged to Georges Ducommun, the founder of Doxa. The *manufacture* was launched as a backyard operation in 1889 and originally produced pocket watches. Quality products and good salesmanship quickly put Doxa on the map, but the company's real game-changer came in 1967 with the uncompromising SUB 300, a heavy, bold diver's watch. It featured a unidirectional bezel with the official U.S. dive table engraved on it. The bright orange dial might seem quite ostentatious, but, in fact, it offers the best legibility under water. It also marked the beginning of a trend for colorful dials.

Doxa made a number of attractive, sportive watches, like the Ultraspeed and the Régulateur, but its claim to fame these days rests on its wide range of diver's watches. Their popularity was boosted early on by the commercialization of diving in the 1970s. Thriller writer Clive Cussler, chairman and founder of the National Underwater and Marine Agency (NUMA), even chose a Doxa as gear for his action hero Dirk Pitt.

The enduring vintage trend has shaped the recent development of the brand. Focus is on fewer lines with greater variations. The SUB 200s come in a wide variety of iterations and colors. The new (2020) SUB 300 Carbon Aqua Lung US Divers is another revived and improved watch created in a collaboration with Aqua Lung, the company that essentially launched scuba diving with the creation of a demand regulator in 1943. The carbon case is light and robust and a good background for the non-compression dive table—devised originally by the U.S. Navy— made up of an orange depth scale on the outer bezel and an inner scale for the dive timing.

SUB 200 T.GRAPH Professional

Reference number: 805.10.351.21
Movement: manually wound, Valjoux 7734; ø 31 mm, height 6.65 mm; 17 jewels; 18,000 vph; 45-hour power reserve
Functions: hours, minutes, subsidiary seconds; chronograph, 12-hour and 30-minute counters, chronograph; date
Case: stainless steel, ø 46 × 43 mm, height 15 mm; unidirectional bezel with engraved decompression scale; sapphire crystal; screw-in crown; screw-down case back with sailboat engraving; water-resistant to 20 atm
Band: rubber, folding clasp with wetsuit extension
Price: $4,900; limited to 300 pieces

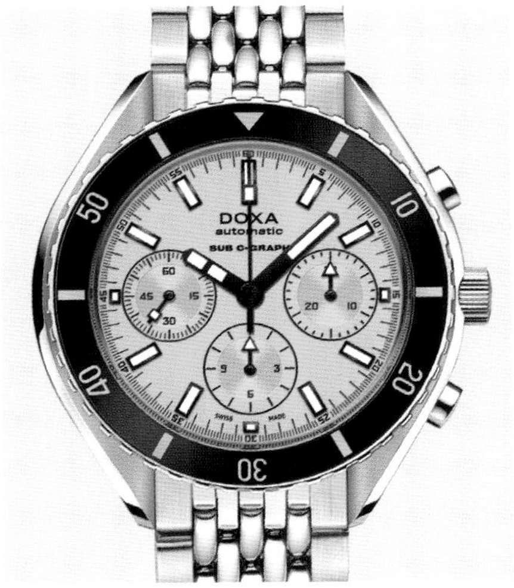

SUB 200 C-Graph Divingstar

Reference number: 798.10.361.10
Movement: automatic, SW 510; ø 25.6 mm, height 4.6 mm; 25 jewels; 28,800 vph; 48-hour power reserve
Functions: hours, minutes, subsidiary seconds; chronograph; date
Case: stainless steel, ø 45 × 49 mm, height 17.25 mm; unidirectional bezel with 0-60 scale; sapphire crystal; screw-in crown; water-resistant to 20 atm
Band: stainless steel, folding clasp with extension link
Price: $2,790
Variations: different color dials (turquoise, black, navy, orange, silver); with rubber strap

SUB 300 Carbon Aqua Lung US Divers

Reference number: 822.70.101AQL.20
Movement: automatic, ETA Caliber 2824-2; ø 25.6 mm, height 4.6 mm; 25 jewels; 28,800 vph; COSC-certified chronometer; 42-hour power reserve
Functions: hours, minutes, sweep seconds; date
Case: carbon, ø 42.5 × 45 mm, height 13.4 mm; unidirectional bezel with depth and time scales; sapphire crystal; screw-in crown; water-resistant to 30 atm
Remarks: forged carbon dial
Band: rubber, folding clasp
Price: $4,790; limited to 300 pieces

EBERHARD & CO.

Eberhard & Co.
73, Ave. Léopold-Robert
CH-2300 La Chaux-de-Fonds
Switzerland

Tel.:
+41-32-342-5141

E-mail:
info@eberhard1887.com

Website:
www.eberhard1887.com

Founded:
1887

Distribution:
Contact main office for information on U.S. distribution.

Most important collections:
Chrono 4; 8 Jours; Tazio Nuvolari; Extra-fort; Gilda; Scafograf

Chronographs weren't always the main focus of the Eberhard & Co. brand. In 1887, Georges-Emile Eberhard rented a workshop in La Chaux-de-Fonds to produce a small series of pocket watches, but it was the unstoppable advancement of the automotive industry that gave the young company its inevitable direction. By the 1920s, Eberhard was producing timekeepers for the first auto races. In Italy, Eberhard & Co. functioned well into the 1930s as the official timekeeper for all important events relating to motor sports. And the Italian air force later commissioned some split-second chronographs from the company, one of which went for 56,000 euros at auction.

Eberhard & Co. is still doing well, thanks to the late Massimo Monti. In the 1990s, he associated the brand with legendary racer Tazio Nuvolari. The company dedicated a chronograph collection to Nuvolari and sponsored the annual Gran Premio Nuvolari vintage car rally in his hometown of Mantua.

With the launch of its four-counter chronograph, this most Italian of Swiss watchmakers underscored its expertise and ambitions where short time/sports time measurement is concerned. Indeed, Eberhard & Co.'s Chrono 4 chronograph, featuring four little counters all in a row, has brought new life to the chronograph in general. CEO Mario Peserico has continued to develop it, putting out versions with new colors and slightly altered looks.

The brand is pure vintage, so it will come as no surprise that it regularly reissues and updates some of its older, popular models, like the two-totalizer Contograph chrono from the 1960s, which originally allowed the user to calculate phone units exactly (*conto* = bill). In 2016, it relaunched the venerable 1950s Scafograph. The latest resurrection: the Caliber EB 140, a beautifully simple, 28,800-vph movement that can be admired through the case back of its 1887 Hand-Wound model.

1887 Hand-Wound

Reference number: 21028
Movement: manually wound, Eberhard Caliber EB 140; ø 31.6 mm; 18 jewels; 28,800 vph; finely finished movement; 40-hour power reserve
Functions: hours, minutes, sweep seconds; date
Case: stainless steel, ø 41.8 mm, height 9.6 mm; sapphire crystal; transparent case back; water-resistant to 3 atm
Band: Jacquard satin, buckle
Price: $3,750
Variations: reptile skin band

Extra-fort Grande Taille Roue à Colonnes

Reference number: 31955
Movement: automatic, ETA Caliber 2894-2; ø 28.6 mm, height 6.3 mm; 42 jewels; 28,800 vph; column-wheel control of chronograph functions; 42-hour power reserve
Functions: hours, minutes, subsidiary seconds; chronograph; date
Case: stainless steel, ø 41 mm, height 13.9 mm; sapphire crystal; screw-in crown; water-resistant to 5 atm
Band: reptile skin, buckle
Price: $4,530
Variations: folding clasp

Scafograf GMT

Reference number: 41038 CAD
Movement: automatic, ETA Caliber 2893-2; ø 25.6 mm, height 4.1 mm; 21 jewels; 28,800 vph; 42-hour power reserve
Functions: hours, minutes, sweep seconds; additional 24-hour display (2nd time zone); date
Case: stainless steel, ø 43 mm, height 11.8 mm; bidirectional bezel with ceramic insert and 0-24 scale; sapphire crystal; screw-in crown; water-resistant to 10 atm
Band: stainless steel, folding clasp
Price: $4,400
Variations: blue dial; rubber strap

Nuvolari Legend

Reference number: 31138
Movement: automatic, ETA Caliber 7750; ø 30 mm, height 7.9 mm; 25 jewels; 28,800 vph; 42-hour power reserve
Functions: hours, minutes; chronograph
Case: stainless steel, ø 43 mm, height 13.5 mm; sapphire crystal; transparent case back; screw-in crown; water-resistant to 3 atm
Band: calfskin, buckle
Remarks: stylized gold Alfa Romeo on rotor
Price: $5,150
Variations: 39.5-mm case

Traversetolo in Black

Reference number: 21116
Movement: manually wound, ETA Caliber 6498; ø 36.6 mm, height 4.5 mm; 17 jewels; 21,600 vph; 38-hour power reserve
Functions: hours, minutes, subsidiary seconds
Case: stainless steel, ø 43 mm, height 10.7 mm; sapphire crystal; water-resistant to 5 atm
Band: calfskin, buckle
Price: $2,300
Variations: folding clasp; transparent case back ($2,700)

Chrono 4 130

Reference number: 31129 CP
Movement: automatic, Eberhard Caliber EB 251-12 1/2 (base ETA 2894-2); ø 33 mm, height 7.5 mm; 53 jewels; 28,800 vph; 4 counters in a row
Functions: hours, minutes, subsidiary seconds; additional 24-hour display; chronograph; date
Case: stainless steel, ø 42 mm, height 13.3 mm; sapphire crystal; screw-in crown; water-resistant to 5 atm
Band: reptile skin, buckle
Price: $6,150
Variations: various dials

Scafograf 300 MCMLIX

Reference number: 41034V.7 CU
Movement: automatic, ETA Caliber 2824-2; ø 25.6 mm, height 4.6 mm; 25 jewels; 28,800 vph; 42-hour power reserve
Functions: hours, minutes, sweep seconds; date
Case: stainless steel, ø 43 mm, height 12.6 mm; unidirectional bezel with ceramic insert, with 0-60 scale; sapphire crystal; screw-in crown, helium valve; water-resistant to 30 atm
Band: rubber, buckle
Remarks: inspired from a 1959 model
Price: $3,080
Variations: folding clasp

Chrono 4 Grande Taille

Reference number: 31052 CU
Movement: automatic, Eberhard Caliber EB 250-C4 (base ETA 2894-2); ø 33 mm, height 7.5 mm; 53 jewels; 28,800 vph; 4 counters in a row
Functions: hours, minutes, subsidiary seconds; additional 24-hour display; chronograph; date
Case: stainless steel, ø 43 mm, height 13.32 mm; sapphire crystal; screw-in crown; water-resistant to 5 atm
Band: rubber, folding clasp
Price: $6,730

8 Jours Grande Taille

Reference number: 21027 CP
Movement: manually wound, Eberhard Caliber EB 896 (base ETA 7001); ø 34 mm, height 5 mm; 25 jewels; 21,600 vph; 2 spring barrels, 192-hour power reserve
Functions: hours, minutes, subsidiary seconds; power reserve indicator
Case: stainless steel, ø 41 mm, height 10.85 mm; sapphire crystal; transparent case back; water-resistant to 3 atm
Band: reptile skin, buckle
Price: $4,950
Variations: white dial

ERNST BENZ

Ernst Benz, the man himself, was an accomplished Swiss inventor and engineer by trade who worked in numerous technologies. He was first known for his BenzMicro factory producing timepiece and industrial jewels for watch movement manufacturers and his legendary namesake BenzMicro turntable styluses. As a passionate aviator and engineer, he developed aircraft instruments, including altimeters, timing devices for military applications, and the Benz Micro aircraft gauge, which became a standard in many small aircraft. Ernst soon realized the need for a large-format, stable, reliable, and readable wristwatch that would be ideal for personal use in small aircraft and gliders' cockpits. Making ultimately readable watches was the next step.

He produced the first Great Circle ChronoScope for his own use and then gradually slipped into making timepieces based on the demands he received. Size and clarity were determining factors—his clean, vintage-inspired dials and 47-mm diameters—as well as reliability, which was guaranteed by the no-nonsense Valjoux 7750. The approval of fellow pilots led him to increase production.

In 2002, the company's now-signature model, the ChronoLunar, created with the participation of Leonid Khankin, made a splash in the watch world. Three years later, Ernst asked the Khankins, a watchmaking family with two generations of experience in complicated horology, to take the company's helm. Leonid, who has spent a lifetime in the business's hands-on side, expanded the brand geographically while creating exciting new models and collaborations for which the brand is now known. The ChronoScope, ChronoLunar, and Chronosport models were updated and received many versions, along with the development of new models, including the ChronoFlite GMT, the WorldTimer, and the ChronoDiver, inspired by Ernst's aviation instrument production.

Influenced by the history of horology and the spirit of travel, Khankin uses the broad dial of these distinct timepieces as a platform for adding design elements to passionately tell the story of the founder, the company, and watchmaking.

Ernst Benz
7 Route de Crassier
CH-1262 Eysins
Switzerland

E-mail:
info@ernstbenz.com

Website:
www.ernstbenz.com

Founded:
early 1960s

U.S. distributor:
Ernst Benz North America
177 S. Old Woodward
Birmingham, MI 48009
248-203-2323

Most important collections:
ChronoLunar, ChronoScope, ChronoSport, ChronoDiver, ChronoFlite

ChronoLunar Officer DLC

Reference number: GC10383
Movement: automatic, Valjoux Caliber 7750; ø 30 mm, height 7.9 mm; 25 jewels; 28,800 vph
Functions: hours, minutes, subsidiary seconds; day, date; chronograph
Case: stainless steel with black DLC, ø 47 mm, height 16 mm; sapphire crystal; screw-down transparent case back; double O-ring sealed crown; water-resistant to 5 atm
Band: reptile skin, buckle
Price: $8,175
Variations: 44-mm case ($7,575)

ChronoScope Traditional

Reference number: GC10112
Movement: automatic, Valjoux Caliber 7750; ø 30 mm, height 7.9 mm; 25 jewels; 28,800 vph
Functions: hours, minutes, subsidiary seconds; day, date; chronograph with hours, minutes, sweep seconds
Case: stainless steel, ø 47 mm, height 16 mm; sapphire crystal; screw-down transparent case back; double O-ring sealed crown; water-resistant to 5 atm
Band: reptile skin, buckle
Price: $5,425
Variations: 44-mm case ($4,825); 40-mm case ($4,475)

ChronoScope Traditional DLC

Reference number: GC10119-DLC
Movement: automatic, Valjoux Caliber 7750; ø 30 mm, height 7.9 mm; 25 jewels; 28,800 vph
Functions: hours, minutes, subsidiary seconds; day, date; chronograph with hours, minutes, sweep seconds
Case: stainless steel with black DLC, ø 47 mm, height 16 mm; sapphire crystal; screw-down transparent case back; double O-ring sealed crown; water-resistant to 5 atm
Band: buffalo skin, buckle
Price: $5,925
Variations: 44-mm case ($5,325)

ChronoLunar Traditional

Reference number: GC10311
Movement: automatic, Valjoux Caliber 7750; ø 30 mm, height 7.9 mm; 25 jewels; 28,800 vph
Functions: hours, minutes, subsidiary seconds; day, date; chronograph with hours, minutes, sweep seconds
Case: stainless steel, ø 47 mm, height 16 mm; sapphire crystal; screw-down transparent case back; double O-ring sealed crown; water-resistant to 5 atm
Band: reptile skin, buckle
Price: $7,275
Variations: 44-mm case ($6,675); 40-mm case ($6,375)

ChronoLunar Officer

Reference number: GC10382
Movement: automatic, Valjoux Caliber 7750; ø 30 mm, height 7.9 mm; 25 jewels; 28,800 vph
Functions: hours, minutes, subsidiary seconds; day, date; chronograph with hours, minutes, sweep seconds
Case: stainless steel, ø 47 mm, height 16 mm; sapphire crystal; screw-down transparent case back; double O-ring sealed crown; water-resistant to 5 atm
Band: reptile skin, buckle
Price: $7,675
Variations: 44-mm case ($7,075)

ChronoLunar Officer

Reference number: GC10381
Movement: automatic, Valjoux Caliber 7750; ø 30 mm, height 7.9 mm; 25 jewels; 28,800 vph
Functions: hours, minutes, subsidiary seconds; day, date; chronograph
Case: stainless steel, ø 47 mm, height 16 mm; sapphire crystal; screw-down transparent case back; double O-ring sealed crown; water-resistant to 5 atm
Band: reptile skin, buckle
Price: $7,675
Variations: 44-mm case ($7,075)

ChronoSport Traditional

Reference number: GC10218
Movement: automatic, Valjoux Caliber 7750; ø 30 mm, height 7.9 mm; 25 jewels; 28,800 vph
Functions: hours, minutes, subsidiary seconds; day, date; chronograph with hours, minutes, sweep seconds
Case: stainless steel, ø 47 mm, height 14 mm; sapphire crystal; screw-down transparent case back; double O-ring sealed crown; water-resistant to 5 atm
Band: reptile skin, buckle
Price: $3,475
Variations: 44-mm case ($2,875); 40-mm case ($2,575)

ChronoFlite World Timer

Reference number: GC10851_GENEVE
Movement: automatic, ETA Caliber 2893-2A; ø 25.6 mm, height 4.1 mm; 21 jewels; 28,800 vph
Functions: hours, minutes, sweep seconds; day; world time; 2nd time zone
Case: stainless steel, ø 47 mm, height 21.1 mm; sapphire crystal; screw-down transparent case back; double O-ring sealed crown; water-resistant to 5 atm
Band: reptile skin, buckle
Price: $5,275

ChronoDiver Instrument

Reference number: GC10721
Movement: automatic, Valjoux Caliber 7750; ø 30 mm, height 7.9 mm; 25 jewels; 28,800 vph
Functions: hours, minutes, subsidiary seconds; day, date; chronograph with hours, minutes, sweep seconds
Case: stainless steel, ø 47 mm, height 15.8 mm; unidirectionally rotating bezel with 60-minute divisions; sapphire crystal; screw-down transparent case back; screwed-in-crown; water-resistant to 20 atm
Band: reptile skin, buckle
Price: $5,825

FABERGÉ

Peter Carl Fabergé (1846–1920), son of a St. Petersburg jeweler of French Protestant stock and supplier to the Romanovs, is a legend. In 1885, he was commissioned by Tsar Alexander III to produce a special Easter egg for the tsarina. He did so, employing the best craftspeople of the time, and in the process catapulted himself into the good graces of the Romanovs. This also meant exile when the Bolsheviks took over in 1918. His sons set up a jewelry and restoration business in Paris.

After being sold several times during the twentieth century, the name Fabergé finally ended up being owned by Pallinghurst, a holding company with investments in mining that include the famous Gemfields, a specialist in colored stones.

In 2013, Fabergé decided to launch a new portfolio of watches. Utilizing colored stones and platinum was a foregone conclusion. Victor Mayer, a former licensee, took on the enamel guilloché dials of the Fabergé Flirt core collection, which received a Vaucher movement. For the men's watch, Renaud & Papi produced a subtly modern flying tourbillon with a geometrically openworked dial. But the pièce de résistance, the Lady Compliquée, was assigned to Jean-Marc Wiederrecht of Agenhor, who created a movement driving a retrograde peacock's tail (Peacock) or a wave of frost (Winter) to display the minutes, while the hours circle the dial in the opposite direction. It won a prize at the prestigious Grand Prix d'Horlogerie de Genève.

Sourcing quality continues to pay up for Fabergé with a new crop of outstanding watches, like the iteration of the Visionnaire DTZ, which features an almost invisible rotor oscillating just on the edge of the dial and a second time zone under a magnifying glass in the middle. The Visionnaire Chronograph has the three chrono hands stacked atop each other in the middle of the dial and required an entirely new module from Agenhor. The new model, Dynamique, has been primped with restive orange touches. Meanwhile, the Lady Libertine collection continues to grow, with fascinating gem layouts. As for the Flirt line, it offers all sorts of bright or staid colors, with or without diamonds, depending on how much the wearer wants to attract attention . . .

Fabergé
1 Cathedral Piazza
London, SW1E 5BP
United Kingdom

Tel.:
+44-20-7518-7297

E-mail:
information@faberge.com

Website:
www.faberge.com

Founded:
1842, current watch department relaunched 2013

Annual production:
approx. 350 watches

U.S. distributor:
Contact: sales@faberge.com

Most important collections:
Flirt; Summer in Provence; Compliquée; Visionnaire (DTZ & Chronograph); Altruist; Dalliance

Compliquée Peacock Ruby

Movement: manually wound, Caliber AGH6901 exclusive for Fabergé; ø 32.7 mm, height 3.58 mm; 38 jewels; 21,600 vph; 50-hour power reserve
Functions: hours (on disk at crown), minutes (retrograde)
Case: platinum, 38 mm, height 12.90 mm; 54 diamonds on bezel; transparent back; sapphire crystal; water-resistant to 3 atm
Band: reptile skin, platinum buckle
Remarks: after the 1908 Fabergé Peacock Egg; dial set with rubies and diamonds, hand-engraved peacock on dial
Price: $89,000
Variations: Lady Compliquée Peacock Emerald, Lady Compliquée Peacock Black Sapphire

Compliquée Peacock

Movement: manually wound, Caliber AGH6901 exclusive for Fabergé; ø 32.7 mm, height 3.58 mm; 38 jewels; 21,600 vph; 50-hour power reserve
Functions: hours (on disk at crown), minutes (retrograde)
Case: platinum, 38 mm, height 12.90 mm; 54 diamonds on bezel; transparent back; sapphire crystal; water-resistant to 3 atm
Band: reptile skin, platinum buckle
Remarks: after the 1908 Fabergé Peacock Egg; dial set with diamonds, tourmalines, and tsavorites, hand-engraved peacock on dial
Price: $89,000
Variations: Compliquée Peacock Ruby, Compliquée Peacock Black Sapphire

Peacock Black

Movement: manually wound, Caliber AGH 6901 exclusive for Fabergé; ø 32.7 mm, height 3.58 mm; 38 jewels; 21,600 vph; 50-hour power reserve
Functions: hours (on disk at crown), minutes (retrograde)
Case: white gold, 38 mm; transparent back; sapphire crystal; water-resistant to 3 atm
Band: reptile skin, white gold buckle
Remarks: black lacquer dial, black painted mother-of-pearl hour ring
Price: $34,500

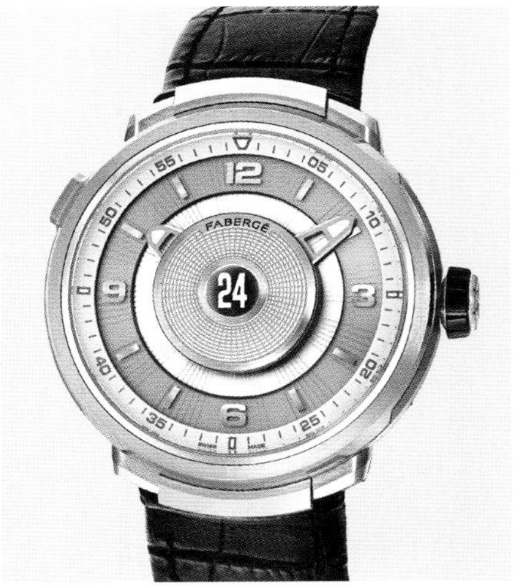

Visionnaire DTZ

Movement: automatic, Caliber AGH 6924 exclusive for Fabergé; ø 34.8, height 8.3 mm; 30 jewels; 21,600 vph; 50-hour power reserve; mainplate, bridges with côtes de Genève
Functions: hours, minutes, central dual time zone (24-hour indication)
Case: rose gold and titanium, ø 43 mm; sapphire crystal; transparent case back; water-resistant to 5 atm
Remarks: mysterious rotor with blue coloring on dial side and TC3 luminescent coating
Band: reptile skin, rose gold and titanium folding clasp
Price: $29,500
Variations: white gold and titanium ($29,500)

Visionnaire Chronograph Ceramic

Movement: automatic, Caliber AGH 6361; ø 34.40, height 7.17 mm; 67 jewels; 21,600 vph; 60-hour power reserve; mainplate, bridges with côtes de Genève
Functions: hours, minutes; central chronograph
Case: black ceramic and dark gray DLC treated titanium, ø 43 mm, height 14.34 mm; sapphire crystal; transparent case back; water-resistant to 5 atm
Remarks: black dial with mysterious rotor on dial side; TC1 luminescent coating
Band: reptile skin, folding clasp
Price: $34,500
Variations: rose gold and titanium with opaline dial ($39,500); ceramic ($40,000)

Visionnaire Chronograph Rose Gold

Movement: automatic, Caliber AGH 6361; ø 34.40, height 7.17 mm; 67 jewels; 21,600 vph; 60-hour power reserve; mainplate, bridges with côtes de Genève
Functions: hours, minutes; central chronograph
Case: rose gold and titanium, ø 43 mm, height 14.34 mm; sapphire crystal; transparent case back; water-resistant to 5 atm
Remarks: black dial with mysterious rotor on dial side; TC1 luminescent coating
Band: reptile skin, folding clasp
Price: $45,000
Variations: rose gold and titanium with opaline dial ($39,500)

Fabergé Lady Libertine I

Movement: manually wound, Caliber AGH 6911 exclusive for Fabergé; ø 30 mm, height 3.2 mm; 15 jewels; 21,600 vph; 50-hour power reserve; bridges with côtes de Genève
Functions: hours, minutes
Case: rose gold, 36 mm; sapphire crystal; transparent case back; bezel set with diamonds; water-resistant to 1 atm
Remarks: circular central space with representation of terrain in Zambia where emeralds for dial are mined; stylized arrowheads to point to hours and minutes
Band: reptile skin, rose gold buckle
Price: on request

Flirt

Movement: automatic, Vaucher Caliber 3000; ø 23.3 mm, height 3.9 mm; 28 jewels; 28,800 vph; white gold rotor; 50-hour power reserve
Functions: hours, minutes
Case: white gold, ø 36 mm; transparent case back; sapphire crystal; water resistant to 3 atm
Remarks: yellow lacquered middle ring
Band: reptile skin, buckle
Price: $14,000
Variations: various dial colors, set with diamonds

Fabergé Lady Libertine II

Movement: manually wound, Caliber AGH 6911 exclusive for Fabergé; ø 30 mm, height 3.2 mm; 15 jewels; 21,600 vph; 50-hour power reserve; bridges with côtes de Genève
Functions: hours, minutes
Case: white gold, ø 36 mm; sapphire crystal; transparent case back; bezel set with diamonds; water-resistant to 1 atm
Remarks: stylized arrowheads to point to hours and minutes
Band: reptile skin, white gold buckle
Price: on request

F.P. JOURNE

Born in Marseilles in 1957, François-Paul Journe might have become something else had he concentrated in school. He was kicked out and went to Paris, where he completed watchmaking school before going to work for his watchmaking uncle. And he has never looked back. By the age of twenty he had made his first tourbillon and soon was producing watches for connoisseurs.

He then moved to Switzerland, where he started out with handmade creations for a limited clientele and developed the most creative and complicated timekeepers for other brands before taking the plunge and founding his own in the heart of Geneva. The timepieces he basically single-handedly and certainly single-mindedly—hence his tagline *invenit et fecit*—conceives and produces are of such extreme complexity that it is no wonder they leave his workshop in relatively small quantities. Journe has won numerous top awards, some several times over. He particularly values the Prix de la Fondation de la Vocation Bleustein-Blanchet, since it came from his peers.

The family of Journe watches is divided into four collections: the automatic Octa collection, with classic complications; the lineSport, focusing on contemporary sportive esthetics; and the Elégante collection, an electromechanical watch providing 8 to 18 years of autonomy, depending on whether it is in daily use or in sleeping mode. The fourth is the Souveraine, featuring a minute repeater, a constant force tourbillon with dead-beat seconds, and a unique Chronomètre à Résonance with two escapements beating in resonance and providing chronometer precise timekeeping, especially in its most recent version, where it is equipped with a remontoir system to even out the mainspring's torque.

François-Paul Journe continues to develop new and fascinating ideas for his watches, like using tritalyt, a special surface treatment for titanium to improve the metal's ruggedness. Their fascination, though, lies in the combination of modernity, complexity, and order.

Montres Journe SA
17 rue de l'Arquebuse
CH-1204 Geneva
Switzerland

Tel.:
+41-22-322-09-09

E-mail:
info@fpjourne.com

Website:
www.fpjourne.com

Founded:
1999

Number of employees:
135

Annual production:
850–900 watches

U.S. distributor:
Montres Journe America
Epic Hotel
270 Biscayne Boulevard Way
Miami, FL 33131
305-572-9802
america@fpjourne.com

Most important collections:
Souveraine, Octa, lineSport, Elégante
(Prices are in Swiss francs. Use daily exchange rate for calculations.)

Chronomètre à Résonance Calibre 1520

Movement: manually wound, F.P. Journe Caliber 1520 in rose gold; ø 34.6 mm, height 6.9 mm; 40 jewels; 21,600 vph; unique concept of 2 escapements mutually influencing and stabilizing each other through acoustic resonance; 2 constant force mechanisms; zero reset; 42-hour power reserve
Functions: hours, minutes, subsidiary seconds; 2nd time zone; power reserve indicator
Case: red gold, ø 40 mm, height 11 mm; sapphire crystal; transparent case back
Band: reptile skin, platinum buckle
Price: CHF 109,300
Variations: platinum (CHF 113,100); comes in 42-mm case

Quantième Perpétuel

Movement: automatic, F.P. Journe Caliber 1300.3 in 6N gold; ø 33.0 mm, height 5.20 mm; 46 jewels; 21,600 vph; 160-hour power reserve
Functions: hours, minutes; indicates day, date, month in windows; leap year; power reserve
Case: platinum, ø 40 or 42 mm, height 11.0 mm; sapphire crystal; transparent case back
Band: leather bracelet and folding clasp
Price: CHF 73,500
Variations: 6N gold (CHF 69,600)

Chronographe Rattrapante

Movement: manually wound, F.P. Journe Caliber 1518 in rose gold; ø 33.6 mm, height 6.80 mm; 29 jewels; 21,600 vph; chronograph, rattrapante; rose gold plate and bridges; 80-hour power reserve without chronograph
Functions: hours, minutes, seconds; chronograph, rattrapante, large date
Case: platinum, ø 44 mm, height 12.10 mm; sapphire crystal; transparent case back; water-resistant to 3 atm
Remarks: silver guilloché dial
Band: platinum, folding clasp
Price: CHF 114,200
Variations: 6N gold (CHF 84,100) titanium (CHF 62,500)

Elégante 48 mm

Movement: electromechanical, F.P. Journe Caliber 1210; 28.5 × 28.3 mm, height 3.13 mm; 18 jewels; quartz frequency 32,768 Hz; autonomy: daily use up to 10 years, 18 years in standby mode
Functions: hours, minutes, subsidiary seconds; motion detector with inertia weight at 4:30
Case: titalyt, 48 × 40 mm, height 7.95 mm; sapphire crystal; transparent case back
Band: rubber, folding clasp
Remarks: goes into standby mode after 35 minutes without motion, microprocessor keeps time, restarts automatically, sets time when watch put back on; comes with straps in colored rubber
Price: CHF 11,500
Variations: in 48 mm: titanium or titalyt set with diamonds (CHF 24,400); various strap colors

Elégante 40 mm Diamonds

Movement: electromechanical, F.P. Journe Caliber 1210; 28.5 × 28.3 mm, height 3.13 mm; 18 jewels; quartz frequency 32,768 Hz; autonomy: daily use up to10 years, 18 years in standby mode
Functions: hours, minutes, subsidiary seconds; motion detector with inertia weight at 4:30
Case: titalyt, 40 × 35 mm, height 7.35 mm; set with 222 diamonds; sapphire crystal; transparent case back
Band: rubber, folding clasp
Remarks: goes into standby mode after 35 minutes without motion, microprocessor keeps time, restarts automatically, sets time when watch put back on; comes with straps in colored rubber
Price: CHF 20,800

Automatique Réserve

Movement: automatic, F.P. Journe Caliber 1300.3 in aluminum alloy; ø 30.8 mm, height 5.70 mm; 40 jewels; 21,600 vph; 160-hour power reserve
Functions: hours, minutes; large date, day/night indicator, small seconds
Case: titanium, ø 44 mm, height 11.6 mm; sapphire crystal; transparent case back
Band: titanium bracelet and folding clasp
Price: CHF 38,800
Variations: 6N gold (CHF 60,400) or platinum (CHF 90,500)

Centigraphe

Movement: automatic, F.P. Journe Caliber 1300.3 in aluminum alloy; ø 34.4 mm, height 5.60 mm; 50 jewels; 21,600 vph; 80-hour power reserve (without chronograph)
Functions: hours, minutes; 1-second, 20-second, and 10-minute chronograph;subsidiary dials at 10, 2, and 6 o'clock
Case: titanium, ø 44 mm, height 11 mm; sapphire crystal; transparent case back
Band: titanium bracelet and folding clasp
Price: CHF 60,400
Variations: 6N gold (CHF 81,900) or platinum (CHF 112,100)

Chronomètre Souverain

Movement: manually wound, F.P. Journe Caliber 1304 in rose gold; ø 30.4 mm, height 4 mm; 22 jewels; 21,600 vph; 2 parallel barrel springs; finely finished movement; 56-hour power reserve (without chronograph)
Functions: hours, minutes, sweep seconds
Case: 6N gold, ø 40 mm, height 8.6 mm; sapphire crystal; transparent case back; water-resistant to 3 atm
Band: leather, folding clasp
Price: CHF 32,400
Variations: in platinum (CHF 36,200)

Tourbillon Souverain

Movement: manually wound, F.P. Journe Caliber 1519 in rose gold; ø 34.6 mm, height 10.86 mm; 32 jewels; 21,600 vph; vertical tourbillon with constant force; balance with variable inertia; 80-hour power reserve; rose gold plate and bridges
Functions: hours, minutes, subsidiary dead-beat seconds; power reserve indicator
Case: platinum, ø 42 mm, height 13.6 mm; sapphire crystal; transparent case back
Remarks: 6N gold guilloché dial made from gold bridges
Band: calfskin, folding clasp
Price: CHF 247,800
Variations: 6N gold (CHF 243,900)

FRANCK MULLER

Francesco "Franck" Muller has been considered one of the great creative minds in the industry ever since he designed and built his first tourbillon watch back in 1986. In fact, he never ceased amazing his colleagues and competition ever since, with his astounding timepieces that combined complications in a new and imaginative manner.

But a while ago the "master of complications" stepped away from the daily business of the brand, leaving space for the person who had paved young Muller's way to fame, Vartan Sirmakes. It was Sirmakes, previously a specialist in watch cases, who had contributed to the development of the double-domed, tonneau-shaped Cintrée Curvex case, with its elegant, 1920s retro look. The complications never stop, either. Franck Muller created the Gigatourbillons, which are 20 millimeters across, and the Revolution series has a tourbillon that rises toward the crystal.

Even a brand that prides itself on a traditional look must make some concessions to modern esthetics. The more recent Vanguards and pieces like the Skafander reveal an edginess that generates attractive tensions in that traditional Art-Deco tonneau-shaped case that is so typical of the brand.

Muller and Sirmakes founded the Franck Muller Group Watchland in 1997. The Group now holds the majority interest in thirteen other companies, eight of which are watch brands. During the 2009 economic crisis, the company downsized somewhat, but it was only a glitch in an otherwise well-planned-out strategy to focus on developing complicated watches, like the Vanguard series, which has gone through numerous iterations, including being skeletonized. The far-reaching synergies within the Group mean that the success of the leader is indeed trickling laterally to the other participants, like Barthelay, Backes & Strauss, ECW, Martin Braun, Pierre Kunz, Rodolphe, Smalto Timepieces, and Roberto Cavalli by Franck Muller.

Groupe Franck Muller Watchland SA
22, route de Malagny
CH-1294 Genthod
Switzerland

Tel.:
+41-22-959-88-88

E-mail:
contact@franckmuller.ch

Website:
www.franckmuller.com

Founded:
1991

Number of employees:
approx. 500 (estimated)

U.S. distributor:
Franck Muller USA, Inc.
207 W. 25th Street, 8th Floor
New York, NY 10001
212-463-8898
www.franckmuller.com

Most important collections:
Giga Tourbillon, Aeternitas, Revolution, Evolution 3-1, Vanguard, Cintrée Curvex

Vanguard Seven Days

Reference number: V 45 S6 SQT (NR) 5N
Movement: manually wound, FM Caliber 1740-VS; ø 37.05 mm, height 6 mm; 21 jewels; 18,000 vph; skeletonized movement; 2 skeletonized spring barrels; finely finished movement; 168-hour power reserve
Functions: hours, minutes, subsidiary seconds; power reserve indicator
Case: rose gold, 44 × 53.7 mm, height 12.7 mm; sapphire crystal; transparent case back; water-resistant to 3 atm
Band: reptile skin, buckle
Price: $43,800

Vanguard Gravity Yachting Skeleton

Reference number: V 45 T GR CS SQT YACHT (BL) 5N
Movement: manually wound, FM Caliber CS-03; 38.4 × 39.6 mm, height 9.1 mm; 24 jewels; 18,000 vph; 1-minute tourbillon, skeletonized movement; 120-hour power reserve
Functions: hours, minutes
Case: rose gold, 44 × 53.7 mm, height 12.65 mm; sapphire crystal; transparent case back; water-resistant to 3 atm
Band: rubber, with textile layer, buckle
Price: $141,600
Variations: stainless steel ($131,600); white gold ($141,600)

Vanguard Yachting Anchor Skeleton

Reference number: V 45 S6 SQT ANCRE YACHT (BL) 5N
Movement: manually wound, FM Caliber 1740-VS; 37.05 × 40.2 mm, height 6 mm; 21 jewels; 18,000 vph; inverted and skeletonized movement; 168-hour power reserve
Functions: hours, minutes, subsidiary seconds; power reserve indicator, fine adjustment
Case: rose gold, 44 × 53.7 mm, height 12.65 mm; sapphire crystal; transparent case back; rose gold crown; water-resistant to 3 atm
Band: textile, buckle
Price: $45,400; **Variations:** stainless steel ($37,400); white gold ($45,400)

Vanguard Crazy Hours

Reference number: V 45 CH BR (BL)
Movement: automatic, FM Caliber 2800 CH; ø 25.6 mm, height 5.6 mm; 27 jewels; 28,800 vph; mechanism for jumping hours with "crazy" hour sequence of hour markers; 42-hour power reserve
Functions: hours (jumping), minutes, sweep seconds
Case: stainless steel, 44 × 53.7 mm, height 13.7 mm; sapphire crystal; transparent case back; water-resistant to 3 atm
Band: reptile skin, buckle
Price: stainless steel ($16,200); white gold ($26,200)

Vanguard Chronograph

Reference number: V 45 CC GD SQT (NR)
Movement: automatic, FM Caliber 7002-GGDTC3; ø 30 mm, height 9.9 mm; 33 jewels; 28,800 vph; finely finished movement; 46-hour power reserve
Functions: hours, minutes, subsidiary seconds; chronograph; large date
Case: rose gold, 44 × 53.7 mm, height 15.1 mm; sapphire crystal; transparent case back; water-resistant to 3 atm
Band: reptile skin, buckle
Price: stainless steel ($22,200); white gold ($32,300); rose gold ($32,300)

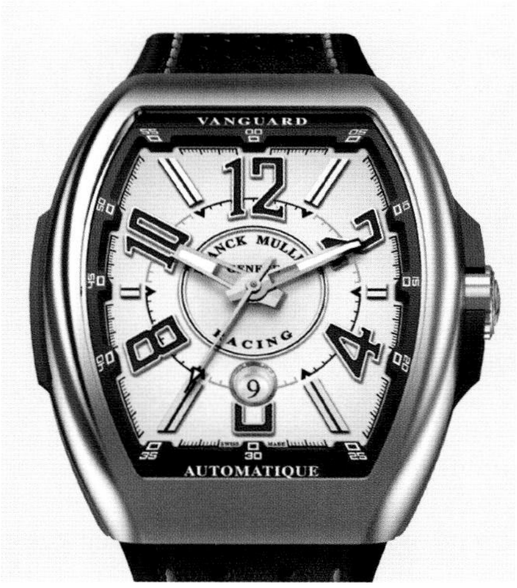

Vanguard Racing

Reference number: V 45 SC DT RACING (NR) AC
Movement: automatic, FM Caliber 2800-DT; ø 25.6 mm; height 3.6 mm; 21 jewels; 28,800 vph; 42-hour power reserve
Functions: hours, minutes, sweep seconds; date
Case: stainless steel, 44 × 53.7 mm, height 12.7 mm; sapphire crystal; transparent case back; water-resistant to 3 atm
Band: calfskin, buckle
Price: $9,200
Variations: rose gold ($18,800)

Skafander

Reference number: SKF 46 DV SC DT AC BR (AC)
Movement: automatic, FM Caliber 2800-SK; ø 31.5 mm, height 5.47 mm; 24 jewels; 28,800 vph; 42-hour power reserve
Functions: hours, minutes, sweep seconds
Case: stainless steel, 46 × 57 mm, height 15.6 mm; crown-activated scale ring, 0-60 scale, pushers with locking system to avoid accidental activation; sapphire crystal; screw-in crown; water-resistant to 10 atm
Band: rubber, buckle
Price: $14,800

Skafander Chronograph

Reference number: SKF 46 DV CC DT
Movement: automatic, FM Caliber 2800-SK-CC; ø 31.5 mm, height 5.44 mm; 37 jewels; 28,800 vph; 42-hour power reserve
Functions: hours, minutes, subsidiary seconds; chronograph; date
Case: titanium with black PVD coating, 46 × 57 mm, height 15.6 mm; crown-activated scale ring, 0-60 scale, pushers with locking system to avoid accidental activation; sapphire crystal; screw-in crown; water-resistant to 10 atm
Band: rubber, buckle
Price: $22,800
Variations: stainless steel ($22,800); rose gold ($33,800)

Vanguard Lady Crazy Hours

Reference number: V 32 CH COL DRM (BC) 5N
Movement: automatic, FM Caliber 2038-CH; ø 20.6 mm, height 3.9 mm; 18 jewels; 28,800 vph; 40-hour power reserve
Functions: hours, minutes, sweep seconds
Case: rose gold, 32 × 42.3 mm, height 9.9 mm; sapphire crystal; transparent case back; water-resistant to 3 atm
Band: reptile skin, buckle
Price: on request

FRÉDÉRIQUE CONSTANT

Peter and Aletta Stas, the Dutch couple who founded Frédérique Constant, have always sought to make high-end watches for consumers without deep pockets. So high-end, in fact, that in 2004 they went public with their first movement produced entirely in-house and equipped with silicon components. The company now has twenty-nine calibers to choose from.

The brand was founded in the late 1980s and named for Aletta's great-grandmother Frédérique Schreiner and Peter's great-grandfather Constant Stas. The couple parlayed affordable watches into a modern four-floor factory in Geneva's industrial Plan-les-Ouates, with ample room for manufacturing, administrative offices, conference rooms, a fitness area, and a cafeteria. Being in touch with the zeitgeist remained a key strategy, which generated the Horological Smartwatch, for example, equipped with a quartz movement and a mobile phone connection.

In 2016, Frédérique Constant and sister brand Alpina were sold to the Japanese brand Citizen. The move will increase the brand's presence on the market, with capacity scheduled to increase to 250,000 timepieces in the coming years. The existing production building was expanded in 2019 by an annex almost doubling the size of the workspace. Production workshops, research and development, and quality control were brought together on the first floor of the new building so that work processes and logistics could be optimally coordinated. The second floor houses functional offices for administration, sales, and marketing. In the future, visitors will be able to visit Frédérique Constant's "Manufacture Experience," which will be set up on the ground floor and will offer visitors insights into the brand's history and how watches are designed and made.

Frédérique Constant SA
Chemin du Champ des Filles 32
CH-1228 Plan-les-Ouates (Geneva)
Switzerland

Tel.:
+41-22-860-0440

E-mail:
info@frederique-constant.com

Website:
www.frederique-constant.com

Founded:
1988

Number of employees:
100

Annual production:
approx. 130,000 watches

U.S. distributor:
Alpina Frederique Constant USA
350 5th Avenue, 29th Floor
New York, NY 10118
646-438-8124
lmellor@usa.frederique-constant.com

Most important collections/price range:
Tourbillon Perpetual Calendar Manufacture/ from approx. $21,995 to $32,995; Hybrid Manufacture / from approx. $3,695 to $3,895; Worldtimer Manufacture / from approx. $4,195 to 4,395; Vintage Rally Healey Chronograph / from approx. $2,795 to $3,095; Ladies' Automatic Double Heart Beat / from approx. $1,995

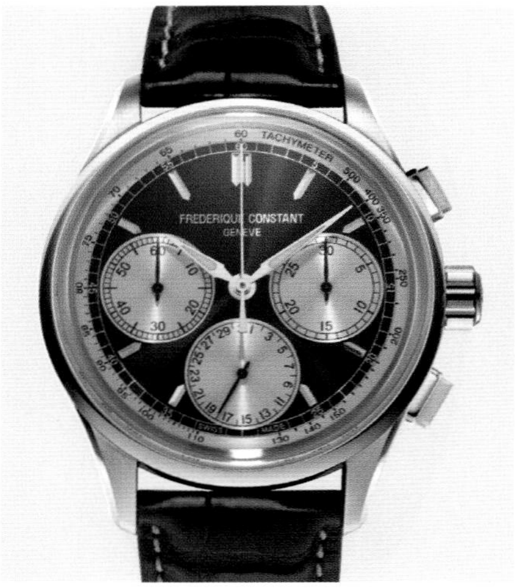

Flyback Chronograph Manufacture

Reference number: FC-760NS4H6
Movement: automatic, Caliber FC-760; ø 30 mm, height 7.9 mm; 32 jewels; 28,800 vph; finely finished with côtes de Genève; 42-hour power reserve
Functions: hours, minutes, subsidiary seconds; flyback chronograph; date
Case: stainless steel, ø 42 mm, height 14.45 mm; sapphire crystal; transparent case back; water-resistant to 5 atm
Band: reptile skin, folding clasp
Price: $4,295

Classic Worldtimer Manufacture

Reference number: FC-718NRWM4H9
Movement: automatic, Caliber FC-718; ø 30 mm, height 6.2 mm; 26 jewels; 28,800 vph; 42-hour power reserve
Functions: hours, minutes, sweep seconds; world time display (2nd time zone); date
Case: rose gold, ø 42 mm, height 12.4 mm; crown-activated inner bezel with 0-24 scale and reference cities; transparent case back; water-resistant to 3 atm
Band: reptile skin, folding clasp
Price: $15,995

Highlife Perpetual Calendar

Reference number: FC-775N4NH6B
Movement: automatic, Caliber FC-775; ø 30 mm, height 6.2 mm; 26 jewels; 28,800 vph; 38-hour power reserve
Functions: hours, minutes; perpetual calendar with date, weekday, month, moon phase, leap year
Case: stainless steel, ø 41 mm, height 12.15 mm; sapphire crystal; transparent case back; water-resistant to 5 atm
Band: stainless steel, folding clasp
Price: $9,295

Highlife Heart Beat

Reference number: FC-310B4NH6B
Movement: automatic, Caliber FC-310 (base Sellita SW200-1); ø 25.6 mm, height 4.6 mm; 26 jewels; 28,800 vph; partially skeletonize mainplate under escapement; 38-hour power reserve
Functions: hours, minutes, sweep seconds
Case: stainless steel, ø 41 mm, height 11.15 mm; sapphire crystal; water-resistant to 5 atm
Band: stainless steel, folding clasp
Remarks: dial with opening
Price: $1,995

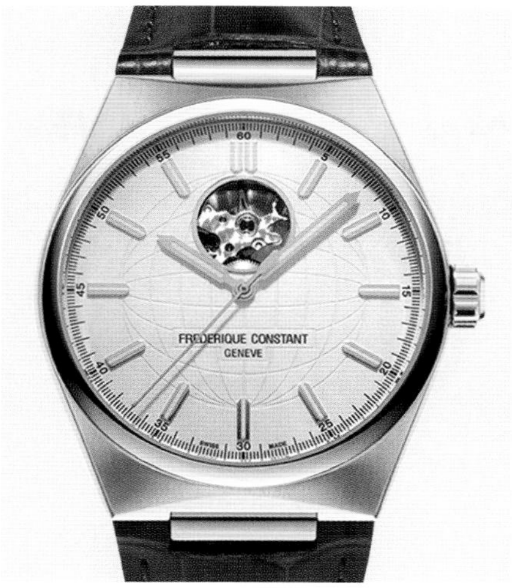

Highlife Heart Beat

Reference number: FC-310V4NH4
Movement: automatic, Caliber FC-310 (base Sellita SW200-1); ø 25.6 mm, height 4.6 mm; 26 jewels; 28,800 vph; partially skeletonized mainplate under escapement; 38-hour power reserve
Functions: hours, minutes, sweep seconds
Case: rose gold–plated stainless steel, ø 41 mm, height 11.15 mm; sapphire crystal; water-resistant to 5 atm
Band: calfskin, buckle
Remarks: dial with opening
Price: $2,195

Highlife Automatic COSC

Reference number: FC-303S4NH6
Movement: automatic, Caliber FC-303 (base Sellita SW200-1); ø 25.6 mm, height 4.6 mm; 26 jewels; 28,800 vph; 38-hour power reserve; COSC-certified chronometer
Functions: hours, minutes, sweep seconds; date
Case: stainless steel, ø 41 mm, height 11.15 mm; sapphire crystal; transparent case back; water-resistant to 5 atm
Band: calfskin, buckle
Price: $1,895

Runabout Chronograph

Reference number: FC-392RMS5B6
Movement: automatic, Caliber FC-392 (base Sellita SW500); ø 30 mm, height 7.9 mm; 26 jewels; 28,800 vph; 38-hour power reserve
Functions: hours, minutes, subsidiary seconds; chronograph; date
Case: stainless steel, ø 42 mm, height 14.45 mm; sapphire crystal; transparent case back; water-resistant to 5 atm
Band: calfskin, folding clasp
Price: $2,895; limited to 2,888 pieces

Vintage Rally

Reference number: FC-303HVBR5B4
Movement: automatic, Caliber FC-303 (base Sellita SW200-1); ø 25.6 mm, height 4.6 mm; 26 jewels; 28,800 vph; 38-hour power reserve
Functions: hours, minutes, sweep seconds; date
Case: rose gold–plated stainless steel, ø 40 mm, height 12 mm; sapphire crystal; transparent case back; water-resistant to 5 atm
Band: calfskin, buckle
Price: $1,895; limited to 2,888 pieces

Vintage Rally Chronograph

Reference number: FC-397HNR5B6
Movement: automatic, Caliber FC-397 (base Sellita SW500); ø 30 mm, height 7.9 mm; 25 jewels; 28,800 vph; 46-hour power reserve
Functions: hours, minutes, subsidiary seconds; chronograph
Case: stainless steel, ø 42 mm, height 14.45 mm; sapphire crystal; transparent case back; water-resistant to 5 atm
Band: calfskin, buckle
Price: $2,795; limited to 99 pieces

Smartwatch Gents Vitality

Reference number: FC-287N5B6B
Movement: quartz, with additional smartphone functionality
Functions: hours, minutes; digital display, activity and sleep tracker, heart frequency sensor, smartphone notification
Case: stainless steel, ø 42 mm, height 8.5 mm; sapphire crystal; water-resistant to 5 atm
Band: stainless steel, folding clasp
Price: $1,095

Yacht Timer GMT

Reference number: FC-350NT4H6
Movement: automatic, Caliber FC-350; ø 26 mm, height 6.1 mm; 26 jewels; 28,800 vph; 38-hour power reserve
Functions: hours, minutes, sweep seconds; additional 24-hour display (2nd time zone); date
Case: stainless steel, ø 42 mm, height 12.16 mm; sapphire crystal; transparent case back; water-resistant to 5 atm
Band: calfskin, folding clasp
Price: $1,995
Variations: stainless steel bracelet

Yacht Timer Regatta Countdown

Reference number: FC-380GT4H6B
Movement: automatic, Caliber FC-380; ø 30 mm, height 6.2 mm; 26 jewels; 28,800 vph; 46-hour power reserve
Functions: hours, minutes; regatta countdown (5-minute counter)
Case: stainless steel, ø 42 mm, height 14.1 mm; sapphire crystal; transparent case back; water-resistant to 10 atm
Band: stainless steel, folding clasp
Price: $4,195
Variations: calfskin strap

Caliber FC-760

Automatic; single spring barrel, 42-hour power reserve
Functions: hours, minutes, subsidiary seconds; flyback chronograph; date
Diameter: 30 mm
Height: 7.9 mm
Jewels: 32
Frequency: 28,800 vph
Hairspring: flat hairspring
Shock protection: Incabloc
Remarks: 233 parts, flyback module 96 parts

Caliber FC-718

Automatic; single spring barrel, 42-hour power reserve
Functions: hours, minutes, sweep seconds; 2nd time zone (world time display); date
Diameter: 30 mm
Height: 6.2 mm
Jewels: 26
Frequency: 28,800 vph
Hairspring: flat hairspring with fine adjustment
Shock protection: Incabloc
Remarks: crown-controlled functions

Caliber FC-775

Automatic; single spring barrel, 38-hour power reserve
Functions: hours, minutes; perpetual calendar with date, weekday, month, moon phase, leap year
Diameter: 30.5 mm
Height: 6.67 mm
Jewels: 26
Frequency: 28,800 vph
Hairspring: flat hairspring with fine adjustment
Shock protection: Incabloc II
Remarks: 191 parts

Garrick Watchmakers
Unit 2, Fletcher Way, Norwich, Norfolk
NR3 3ST
England

Tel.:
+44 (0)1603 327272

E-mail:
info@garrick.co.uk

Website:
www.garrick.co.uk

Founded:
2013

Employees:
9

Annual production:
50 watches maximum

Distribution:
direct sales

Most important collections/price range:
Regulator and S2 / £2,500 to £30,000
Prices only in pounds sterling

GARRICK WATCHMAKERS

Britain has contributed enormously to the development of watchmaking, so it's hardly astonishing to find that the country is home to a growing number of brands vying on the international markets. Garrick Watchmakers is one of them. It was founded in 2013 in Devon by David Brailsford together with Simon Michlmayr, one of the top English watchmakers. The aim of these two men was to revive the old tradition of English watchmaking and to achieve the greatest possible vertical integration in the construction of their watches.

Wherever possible, Garrick either manufactures in its own workshop in Norwich in Norfolk or purchases from English suppliers. The company goes so far as to make its own hands. The dials, too, are also printed in-house. Even cases are produced in England. In the beginning Garrick had to go new ways and regain the necessary knowledge together with English precision mechanics.

While the first models were still based on a Unitas caliber, the Portsmouth was presented in 2016, the first of what are now four of the company's own *manufacture* calibers. Each of these calibers has in common a self-developed "Trinity" balance made of a nonmagnetic alloy, Sircumet, and boasts a free-sprung balance: To adjust the rate, the balance wheel is equipped with rim screws. The hairspring's position can be changed as well. The dials are also mostly elaborately designed. In addition to genuine enamel dials, Garrick specializes in guilloché and finely engraved dials.

Garrick Watchmakers build no more than 50 watches every year. Thanks to its vertical manufacturing and the fact that each Garrick is built to order, Garrick can in fact build watches according to the wishes of its customers, including unique pieces, if need be.

S3

Movement: manually wound, Garrick Caliber UT-G04; ø 36 mm, height 4.5 mm; 19 jewels; 18,000 vph; "Trinity" balance with free-sprung hairspring, hand-matted, rhodium-plated, beveled parts; screw-mounted, hand-polished chatons; 48-hour power reserve
Functions: hours, minutes, subsidiary seconds; power reserve indicator
Case: stainless steel, ø 42 mm, height 14 mm; sapphire crystal; transparent case back; water-resistant to 3 atm
Band: reptile skin, buckle
Remarks: blued chapter ring with inserted scale elements
Price: £28,995 (plus taxes)

S2

Movement: manually wound, Garrick Caliber UT-G03; ø 36 mm, height 4.5 mm; 19 jewels; 18,000 vph; "Trinity" balance with free-sprung hairspring, hand-matted, rhodium-plated, beveled parts; screw-mounted, hand-polished chatons; 48-hour power reserve
Functions: hours, minutes, sweep seconds
Case: stainless steel, ø 42 mm, height 13 mm; sapphire crystal; transparent case back; water-resistant to 3 atm
Band: reptile skin, buckle
Remarks: silver dial with guilloché, applied blued chapter ring
Price: £14,985 (plus taxes)

S2

Movement: manually wound, Garrick Caliber SM001; ø 36 mm, height 4.5 mm; 19 jewels; 18,000 vph; screw balance; inverted movement construction with visible escapement on dial side; 48-hour power reserve
Functions: hours and minutes (off-center), subsidiary seconds
Case: stainless steel, ø 42 mm, height 14 mm; sapphire crystal; water-resistant to 3 atm
Band: calfskin, buckle
Remarks: finely structured metal dial, applied chapter rings
Price: £6,995 (plus taxes)

GIRARD-PERREGAUX

When Girard-Perregaux CEO Luigi ("Gino") Macaluso died in 2010, the former minority partner of Sowind Group, PPR (Pinault, Printemps, Redoute), increased its equity stake to 51 percent. It was Macaluso, however, who had established Girard-Perregaux as a major player in the high-end mechanical watch segment. The company's development team production department has played a key role in the success, with their innovative ideas and ability to implement them. The Constant Escapement, a new concept that stores energy by buckling an ultrathin silicon blade and then releasing the energy to the balance wheel, is one such concept.

In 2015, Antonio Calce (of Eterna and Corum fame) became the company CEO and launched a freshening-up program, which included its marketing strategies. Like many brands in the Era of Vintage, Girard-Perregaux has been revisiting its past milestones. The company turned the much coveted Laureato from 1975 into a flagship of sorts, beginning in 2016. Something in the octagonal bezel on the round base epitomizes our contemporary sportive-elegant style, especially with the integrated bracelets. The recently renovated and updated *manufacture* in La Chaux-de-Fonds has been putting out a number of remarkable creations, notably the Laureato Absolute Rock in "carbon glass," a new material made by pressing glass fiber into carbon composite at a high temperature. It is light and ensures water resistance, and it has a special look, with flashing blue accents. Next to this leading product, Girard-Perregaux has continued expanding its Bridges collection, featuring the three straight bridges that are so iconic they've become the company's logo. In the Quasar light, these three structural elements are made of sapphire crystal and add to the transparency of the skeletonized timepiece.

Finally, the 1966 collection has grown by a number of simple, attractive models for everyday use, such as the Orion, with a deep-blue aventurine dial.

Girard-Perregaux
1, Place Girardet
CH-2300 La Chaux-de-Fonds
Switzerland

Tel.:
+41-32-911-3333

Website:
www.girard-perregaux.com

Founded:
1791

Number of employees:
280

Annual production:
approx. 12,000 watches

U.S. distributor:
Girard-Perregaux
Tradema of America, Inc.
7900 Glades Road, Suite 200
Boca Raton, FL 33434
833-GPWATCH
www.girard-perregaux.com

Most important collections/price range:
Laureato / Vintage 1945 / approx. $7,500 to $625,000; ww.tc / $12,300 to $23,800; GP 1966 / $7,500 to $291,000

Laureato 42mm Automatic

Reference number: 81010-11-431-11A
Movement: automatic, GP Caliber 01800-0013; ø 30 mm, height 3.97 mm; 28 jewels; 28,800 vph; 54-hour power reserve
Functions: hours, minutes, sweep seconds; date
Case: stainless steel, ø 42 mm, height 10.88 mm; sapphire crystal; transparent case back; water-resistant to 10 atm
Band: stainless steel, double folding clasp
Price: $11,600
Variations: silver or black dial; reptile skin band ($10,800); titanium/rose gold with reptile skin band ($16,000)

Laureato 42mm Automatic

Reference number: 81010-11-634-11A
Movement: automatic, GP Caliber 01800-0013; ø 30 mm, height 3.97 mm; 28 jewels; 28,800 vph; 54-hour power reserve
Functions: hours, minutes, sweep seconds; date
Case: stainless steel, ø 42 mm, height 10.88 mm; sapphire crystal; transparent case back; water-resistant to 10 atm
Band: stainless steel, double folding clasp
Price: $11,600
Variations: silver or blue dial; reptile skin band ($10,800); titanium/rose gold with reptile skin band ($16,000)

La Laureato Chronograph 42mm

Reference number: 81020-11-131-11A
Movement: automatic, GP Caliber 03300-0137/0138/0141; ø 25.95 mm, height 6.5 mm; 63 jewels; 28,800 vph; 46-hour power reserve
Functions: hours, minutes, subsidiary seconds; chronograph; date
Case: stainless steel, ø 42 mm, height 12.01 mm; sapphire crystal; water-resistant to 10 atm
Band: stainless steel, triple folding clasp
Price: $15,000
Variations: reptile skin strap ($14,200)

Laureato Chronograph 42mm

Reference number: 81020-11-431-11A
Movement: automatic, GP Caliber 03300-0137/0138/0141; ø 25.95 mm, height 6.5 mm; 63 jewels; 28,800 vph; 46-hour power reserve
Functions: hours, minutes, subsidiary seconds; chronograph; date
Case: stainless steel, ø 42 mm, height 11.9 mm; sapphire crystal; water-resistant to 10 atm
Band: stainless steel, triple folding clasp
Price: $15,000
Variations: reptile skin strap ($14,200)

Laureato Absolute Chronograph 44mm

Reference number: 81060-21-491-FH6A
Movement: automatic, GP Caliber 03300-1058; ø 25.95 mm, height 6.5 mm; 63 jewels; 28,800 vph; 46-hour power reserve
Functions: hours, minutes, subsidiary seconds; chronograph; date
Case: titanium with black PVD coating, ø 44 mm, height 14.65 mm; sapphire crystal; transparent case back; water-resistant to 30 atm
Band: rubber, triple folding clasp
Price: $12,900

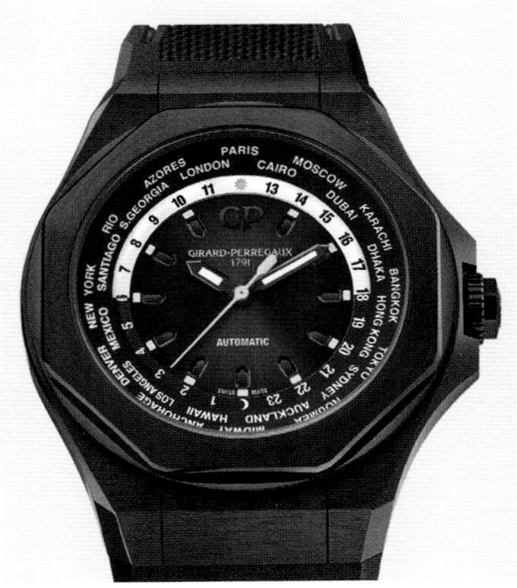

Laureato Absolute WW.TC

Reference number: 81065-21-491-FH6A
Movement: automatic, GP Caliber 03300-1056; ø 25.95 mm, height 5.73 mm; 32 jewels; 28,800 vph; 46-hour power reserve
Functions: hours, minutes, sweep seconds; world time display, day/night indicator (2nd time zone)
Case: titanium with black PVD, ø 44 mm, height 14.65 mm; crown-activated inner ring with reference cities; sapphire crystal; water-resistant to 30 atm
Band: rubber, double folding clasp
Price: $13,900

Laureato Absolute Rock

Reference number: 81060-36-691-FH6A
Movement: automatic, GP Caliber 03300-1058; ø 25.95 mm, height 6.5 mm; 63 jewels; 28,800 vph; 46-hour power reserve
Functions: hours, minutes, subsidiary seconds; chronograph; date
Case: composite material (carbon glass), ø 44 mm, height 14.65 mm; sapphire crystal; transparent case back; water-resistant to 5 atm
Band: rubber, double folding clasp
Price: $15,900; limited to 100 pieces

Laureato Absolute Light

Reference number: 81071-43-231-FB6A
Movement: automatic, GP Caliber 01800-1143; ø 30 mm, height 4.16 mm; 25 jewels; 28,800 vph; completely skeletonized movement with NAC coating; 54-hour power reserve
Functions: hours, minutes, subsidiary seconds
Case: sapphire crystal and titanium, ø 44 mm, height 11.56 mm; sapphire crystal; transparent case back; water-resistant to 3 atm
Band: rubber, folding clasp
Price: $84,700; limited to 88 pieces

Quasar Light

Reference number: 99295-43-001-BA6A
Movement: automatic, GP Caliber 09400-1128; ø 36 mm, height 9.54 mm; 27 jewels; 21,600 vph; 1-minute tourbillon under 3 sapphire crystal bridges; platinum microrotor; balance with variable inertia and golden regulating screws, hairspring with Phillips end curve; completely skeletonized movement; 60-hour power reserve
Functions: hours, minutes, subsidiary seconds (on tourbillon cage)
Case: ø 46 mm, height 15.25 mm; sapphire crystal; transparent case back; water-resistant to 3 atm
Band: textile, double folding clasp
Price: $294,000; limited to 18 pieces

Neo Bridges 45mm "Earth-to-Sky" Edition

Reference number: 84000-21-632-BH6A
Movement: automatic, GP Caliber 08400-0002; ø 32 mm, height 5.45 mm; 29 jewels; 21,600 vph; symmetrical skeleton construction; NAC-coated mainplate, PVD-coated bridges; microrotor; 54-hour power reserve
Functions: hours, minutes
Case: titanium with black DLC coating, ø 45 mm, height 12.18 mm; sapphire crystal; transparent case back; water-resistant to 3 atm
Band: reptile skin with rubber overlay, triple folding clasp
Price: $26,800

GP 1966 40mm

Reference number: 49555-11-131-BB60
Movement: automatic, GP Caliber 03300-0130; ø 25.6 mm, height 3.36 mm; 27 jewels; 28,800 vph; 46-hour power reserve
Functions: hours, minutes, sweep seconds; date
Case: stainless steel, ø 40 mm, height 8.9 mm; sapphire crystal; transparent case back; water-resistant to 3 atm
Band: reptile skin, buckle
Price: $7,900
Variations: various dials

GP 1966 Blue Moon

Reference number: 49545-11-432-BH6A
Movement: automatic, GP Caliber 03300-0115; ø 25.6 mm, height 4.8 mm; 27 jewels; 28,800 vph; 46-hour power reserve
Functions: hours, minutes, sweep seconds; date, moon phase
Case: stainless steel with black PVD, ø 40 mm; sapphire crystal; transparent case back; water-resistant to 3 atm
Band: reptile skin, buckle
Price: $9,600

1966 Orion

Reference number: 49555-11-435-BB4A
Movement: automatic, GP Caliber 03300-0132; ø 25.6 mm, height 3.36 mm; 27 jewels; 28,800 vph; 46-hour power reserve
Functions: hours, minutes, sweep seconds; date
Case: stainless steel, ø 40 mm, height 9.4 mm; sapphire crystal; transparent case back; water-resistant to 3 atm
Band: reptile skin, buckle
Remarks: model from Orion trilogy with vaulted aventurine dial
Price: $8,700

1966 Orion

Reference number: 49555-11-631-BB6D
Movement: automatic, GP Caliber 03300-0132; ø 25.6 mm, height 3.36 mm; 27 jewels; 28,800 vph; 46-hour power reserve
Functions: hours, minutes, sweep seconds; date
Case: stainless steel with black DLC, ø 40 mm, height 9.4 mm; sapphire crystal; transparent case back; water-resistant to 3 atm
Band: reptile skin, buckle
Remarks: model from Orion trilogy with vaulted aventurine dial
Price: $9,400

1966 Orion

Reference number: 49555-52-431-BB4A
Movement: automatic, GP Caliber 03300-0132; ø 25.6 mm, height 3.36 mm; 27 jewels; 28,800 vph; 46-hour power reserve
Functions: hours, minutes, sweep seconds; date
Case: rose gold, ø 40 mm, height 9.4 mm; sapphire crystal; transparent case back; water-resistant to 3 atm
Band: reptile skin, buckle
Remarks: model from Orion trilogy with vaulted aventurine dial
Price: $17,800

Caliber GP01800-0008

Automatic; single spring barrel, 54-hour power reserve
Functions: hours, minutes, sweep seconds; date
Diameter: 30 mm
Height: 3.97 mm
Jewels: 28
Frequency: 28,800 vph

Caliber GP3300

Automatic; rotor with ceramic ball bearings, stop-seconds mechanism; single spring barrel, 46-hour power reserve
Functions: hours, minutes, sweep seconds or subsidiary seconds at 9 o'clock; date
Diameter: 25.6 mm
Height: 3.2 mm
Jewels: 27
Balance: glucydur
Frequency: 28,800 vph
Balance spring: flat hairspring, fine adjustment
Shock protection: Kif
Remarks: 185 parts

Caliber GP09400-01035

Automatic; 1-minute tourbillon, bidirectional winding rotor; symmetrical skeleton construction with 3 bridges made of PVD-coated titanium; single spring barrel, 60-hour power reserve
Functions: hours, minutes
Diameter: 36 mm
Height: 9.54 mm
Jewels: 27
Balance: screw balance
Frequency: 21,600 vph
Remarks: modern version of tourbillon under 3 gold bridges; 260 parts

Caliber GP08400-0002

Automatic; symmetrical skeleton construction with 2 bridges; microrotor; single spring barrel, 54-hour power reserve
Functions: hours, minutes
Diameter: 32 mm
Height: 5.45 mm
Jewels: 29
Frequency: 21,600 vph
Remarks: NAC-coated platinum, titanium bridges with black PVD coating; 208 parts

Caliber GP09320-1098

Manually wound; 1-minute tourbillon; symmetrical skeleton construction with 2 bridges; single spring barrel, 60-hour power reserve
Functions: hours, minutes (off-center); sky map (with zodiac display) and 24-hour display (2nd time zone) as sculptural globe
Diameter: 37.85 mm
Height: 13.1 mm
Jewels: 52
Balance: screw balance
Frequency: 21,600 vph
Remarks: 362 parts

Caliber GP09400-1128

Automatic; 1-minute tourbillon under 3 sapphire bridges; ruthenium microrotor and spring barrel; completely skeletonized movement; single spring barrel, 60-hour power reserve
Functions: hours, minutes, subsidiary seconds (on tourbillon cage)
Diameter: 36 mm
Height: 9.54 mm
Jewels: 27
Balance: screw balance
Frequency: 21,600 vph
Hairspring: with Phillips end curve

GLASHÜTTE ORIGINAL

Is there a little nostalgia creeping into the designers at Glashütte Original? Or is it just understated ecstasy for older looks? The retro touches that started appearing again a few years ago with the Sixties Square Tourbillon are still in vogue as the company delves into its own past for inspiration, such as the use of a special silver treatment on dials.

Glashütte Original *manufacture* roots go back to the mid-nineteenth century, though the name itself came later. The company, which had a sterling reputation for precision watches, became subsumed in the VEB Glashütter Uhrenbetriebe, a group of Glashütte watchmakers and suppliers who were collectivized as part of the former East German system. After reunification, the company took up its old moniker of Glashütte Original, and in 1995, the *manufacture* released an entirely new collection. Later, it purchased Union Glashütte. In 2000, the Swiss Swatch Group acquired the whole company and invested in expanding the production space at Glashütte Original headquarters. The company decided to separate out Union Glashütte, whose models are not distributed in the USA, by the way.

Manufacturing depth has reached 95 percent. All movements are designed by a team of experienced in-house engineers, while the components they comprise, such as plates, screws, pinions, wheels, levers, spring barrels, balance wheels, and tourbillon cages, are manufactured in the upgraded production areas. These parts are lavishly finished by hand before assembly by a group of talented watchmakers. Even dials are in-house. Among the highlights of its catalogue are the Senator Chronometer, which boasts second and minute hands that automatically jump to zero when the crown is pulled, allowing for extremely accurate time setting; and the Spezialist, a diver's watch that is modeled on a design from 1969, which was developed especially for frogmen and sports divers and is not only precise but particularly resistant to shocks.

Glashütter Uhrenbetrieb GmbH
Altenberger Strasse 1
D-01768 Glashütte
Germany

Tel.:
+49-350-53-46-0

E-mail:
info@glashuette-original.com

Website:
www.glashuette-original.com

Founded:
1990 registration of the Glashütter Uhrenbetrieb GmbH; Glashütte Original brand name registered in 1994

U.S. distributor:
Glashütte Original
The Swatch Group (U.S.), Inc.
1200 Harbor Boulevard
Weehawken, NJ 07087
201-271-1400

Most important collections/price range:
Senator, Pano, Spezialist, Vintage, Ladies / $4,900 to $152,300

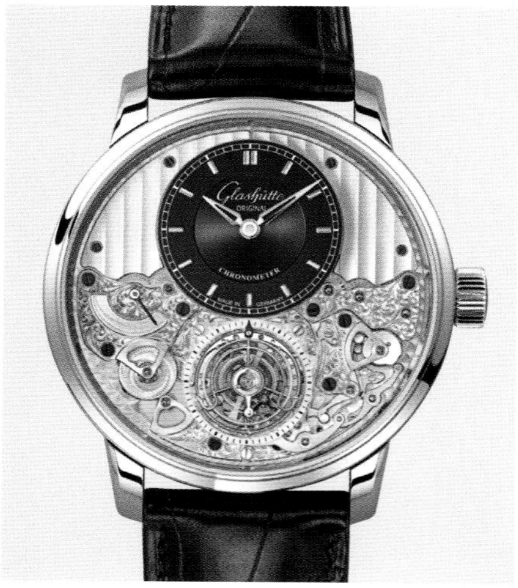

Senator Chronometer Tourbillon—Limited Edition

Reference number: 1-58-05-01-03-30
Movement: manually wound, Glashütte Original Caliber 58-05; ø 36.6 mm, height 8.48 mm; 85 jewels; 21,600 vph; flying 1-minute tourbillon, silicon hairspring, screw balance with 18 weighted screws, swan-neck fine adjustment; hand-engraved balance cock, finely finished movement; 70-hour power reserve; DIN-certified chronometer
Functions: hours, minutes (off-center), subsidiary seconds (on tourbillon cage); power reserve indicator
Case: platinum, ø 42 mm, height 12 mm; sapphire crystal; transparent case back; water-resistant to 5 atm
Band: reptile skin, folding clasp
Price: $152,300; limited to 25 pieces

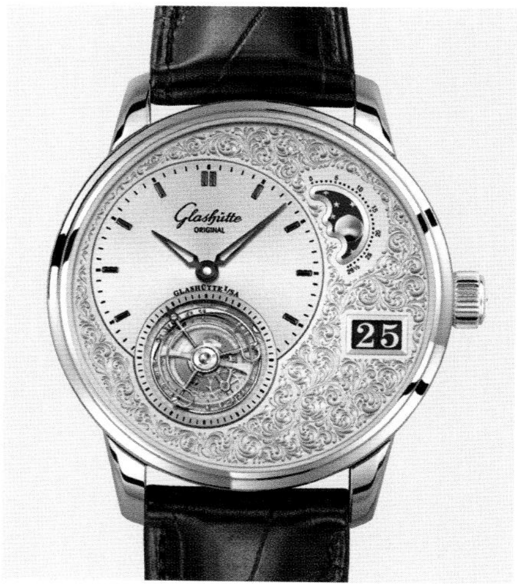

PanoLunarTourbillon—Limited Edition

Reference number: 1-93-12-01-03-30
Movement: automatic, Glashütte Original Caliber 93-12; ø 32.2 mm, height 7.65 mm; 48 jewels; 21,600 vph; flying 1-minute tourbillon, screw balance with 18 weighted screws, 2 diamond capstones, hand-engraved mainplate, skeletonized rotor with gold oscillating mass; 48-hour power reserve
Functions: hours, minutes (off-center), subsidiary seconds (on tourbillon cage); panorama date, moon phase
Case: platinum, ø 40 mm, height 13.1 mm; sapphire crystal; transparent case back; water-resistant to 5 atm
Band: reptile skin, folding clasp
Remarks: hand-engraved and silver-plated dial
Price: $132,000; limited to 25 pieces

Senator Cosmopolite

Reference number: 1-89-02-05-02-70
Movement: automatic, Glashütte Original Caliber 89-02; ø 39.2 mm, height 8 mm; 63 jewels; 28,800 vph; Glashütte three-quarter plate, balance with 4 regulating screws, swan-neck fine adjustment; 72-hour power reserve
Functions: hours, minutes, subsidiary seconds; additional 12-hour display (2nd time zone), world time display with 35 time zones, day/night indicator, power reserve indicator; panorama date
Case: stainless steel, ø 44 mm, height 14 mm; sapphire crystal; transparent case back; water-resistant to 5 atm; **Band:** stainless steel, folding clasp
Price: $22,700; **Variations:** reptile skin strap ($21,500); pink gold ($37,100); white gold ($38,600)

Senator Chronometer—Limited Edition

Reference number: 1-58-03-01-04-30
Movement: manually wound, Glashütte Original Caliber 58-03; ø 35 mm, height 6.47 mm; 58 jewels; 28,800 vph; Glashütte three-quarter plate, crown-activated second reset for precise setting of minutes hand; 18 weighted screws, swan-neck fine regulation; 44-hour power reserve; DIN certified chronometer
Functions: hours, minutes, subsidiary seconds; day/night indicator, power reserve indicator; panorama date
Case: white gold, ø 42 mm, height 12.47 mm; sapphire crystal; transparent case back; water-resistant to 5 atm; **Band:** reptile skin, folding clasp
Remarks: silver-plated gold dial
Price: $30,000; limited to 25 pieces

Senator Excellence Perpetual Calendar

Reference number: 1-36-02-02-05-30
Movement: automatic, GO Caliber 36-02; ø 32.2 mm, height 7.35 mm; 49 jewels; 28,800 vph; silicon hairspring, screw balance, swan-neck fine adjustment, skeletonized rotor with gold oscillating mass, finely finished movement; 100-hour power reserve
Functions: hours, minutes, sweep seconds; perpetual calendar with panorama date, weekday, month, moon phase, leap year
Case: red gold, ø 42 mm, height 12.8 mm; sapphire crystal; transparent case back; water-resistant to 5 atm
Band: reptile skin, folding clasp
Price: $32,800; **Variations:** buckle ($31,000); stainless steel ($20,100)

Senator Excellence Panorama Date Moonphase

Reference number: 1-36-04-01-02-30
Movement: automatic, Glashütte Original Caliber 36-04; ø 32.2 mm, height 6.7 mm; 43 jewels; 28,800 vph; silicon hairspring, screw balance with 4 regulator screws, swan-neck fine adjustment, skeletonized rotor with gold oscillating mass, finely finished movement; 100-hour power reserve
Functions: hours, minutes, sweep seconds; panorama date, moon phase
Case: stainless steel, ø 42 mm, height 12.2 mm; sapphire crystal; transparent case back; water-resistant to 5 atm; **Band:** reptile skin, folding clasp
Price: $10,700
Variations: pink gold ($21,400)

Senator Excellence Panorama Date

Reference number: 1-36-03-03-02-31
Movement: automatic, Glashütte Original Caliber 36-03; ø 32.2 mm, height 6.7 mm; 41 jewels; 28,800 vph; silicon hairspring, screw balance with 4 regulator screws, swan-neck fine adjustment, skeletonized rotor with gold oscillating mass; 100-hour power reserve
Functions: hours, minutes, sweep seconds; panorama date
Case: stainless steel, ø 42 mm, height 12.2 mm; sapphire crystal; transparent case back; water-resistant to 5 atm; **Band:** reptile skin, folding clasp
Price: $9,700; **Variations:** buckle ($9,400); blue or white dial ($9,700)

PanoMaticLunar

Reference number: 1-90-02-11-35-30
Movement: automatic, Glashütte Original Caliber 90-02; ø 32.6 mm, height 7 mm; 47 jewels; 28,800 vph; screw balance with 18 weighted screws, duplex swan-neck fine adjustment, skeletonized rotor with gold oscillating mass, finely finished movement; 42-hour power reserve
Functions: hours, minutes (off-center), subsidiary seconds; panorama date, moon phase
Case: red gold, ø 40 mm, height 12.7 mm; sapphire crystal; transparent case back; water-resistant to 5 atm
Band: reptile skin, folding clasp
Price: $20,500
Variations: buckle ($18,700); silver or black dial ($20,500); stainless steel ($9,900)

PanoReserve

Reference number: 1-65-01-22-12-04
Movement: manually wound, Glashütte Original Caliber 65-01; ø 32.2 mm, height 6.1 mm; 48 jewels; 28,800 vph; Glashütte three-quarter plate with ribbing, screw balance with 18 weighted screws, double swan-neck fine adjustment, screw-mounted gold chatons, hand-engraved balance bridge and second cock; 42-hour power reserve
Functions: hours, minutes (off-center), subsidiary seconds; power reserve indicator; panorama date
Case: stainless steel, ø 40 mm, height 11.7 mm; sapphire crystal; transparent case back; water-resistant to 5 atm; **Band:** reptile skin, folding clasp
Price: $9,900
Variations: stainless steel band ($11,100); blue or gray dial ($9,900); pink gold ($20,500)

SeaQ Panorama Date

Reference number: 1-36-13-02-81-70
Movement: automatic, Glashütte Original Caliber 36-13; ø 32.2 mm, height 6.7 mm; 39 jewels; 28,800 vph; silicon hairspring, balance with 4 regulating screws, swan-neck regulating spring, skeletonized rotor; 100-hour power reserve
Functions: hours, minutes, sweep seconds; panorama date
Case: stainless steel, ø 43.2 mm, height 15.65 mm; unidirectional bezel with ceramic insert, with 0-60 scale; sapphire crystal; transparent case back; screw-in crown; water-resistant to 30 atm
Band: stainless steel, folding clasp
Price: $12,400
Variations: rubber or textile strap ($14,800)

SeaQ Panorama Date

Reference number: 1-36-13-04-91-34
Movement: automatic, Glashütte Original Caliber 36-13; ø 32.2 mm, height 6.7 mm; 39 jewels; 28,800 vph; silicon hairspring, balance with 4 regulating screws, swan-neck regulating spring, skeletonized rotor with gold oscillating mass, finely finished movement; 100-hour power reserve
Functions: hours, minutes, sweep seconds; panorama date
Case: stainless steel, ø 43.2 mm, height 15.65 mm; unidirectional bezel in pink gold with ceramic insert, with 0-60 scale; sapphire crystal; transparent case back; screw-in pink gold crown; water-resistant to 30 atm; **Band:** textile, folding clasp
Price: $14,800; **Variations:** rubber strap

Seventies Chronograph Panorama Date

Reference number: 1-37-02-01-02-70
Movement: automatic, Glashütte Original Caliber 37-02; ø 31.6 mm, height 8 mm; 65 jewels; 28,800 vph; balance with 4 regulating screws, swan-neck fine adjustment; skeletonized rotor with gold oscillating mass, finely finished movement; 70-hour power reserve
Functions: hours, minutes, subsidiary seconds; power reserve indicator; flyback chronograph; panorama date
Case: stainless steel, 40 × 40 mm, height 13.5 mm; sapphire crystal; transparent case back; screw-in crown; water-resistant to 10 atm
Band: stainless steel, folding clasp
Price: $12,400
Variations: rubber or synthetic strap ($11,500)

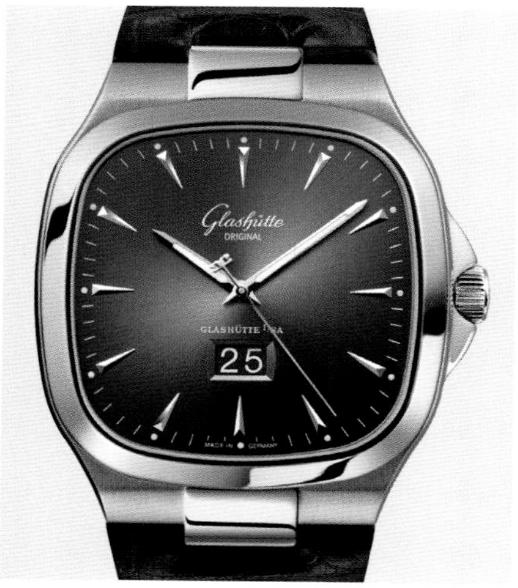

Seventies Panorama Date

Reference number: 2-39-47-13-12-04
Movement: automatic, Glashütte Original Caliber 39-47; ø 30.95 mm, height 5.9 mm; 39 jewels; 28,800 vph; swan-neck fine adjustment, Glashütte three-quarter plate with ribbing, skeletonized rotor with gold oscillating mass, finely finished movement; 40-hour power reserve
Functions: hours, minutes, sweep seconds; panorama date
Case: stainless steel, 40 × 40 mm, height 11.5 mm; sapphire crystal; transparent case back; screw-in crown; water-resistant to 10 atm
Band: reptile skin, folding clasp
Price: $8,700; **Variations:** gray or silver dial; rubber strap; stainless steel band ($9,900)

Sixties Chronograph Annual Edition 2020

Reference number: 1-39-34-04-22-04
Movement: automatic, Glashütte Original Caliber 39-34; ø 30.04 mm, height 7.2 mm; 51 jewels; 28,800 vph; swan-neck fine adjustment, skeletonized rotor with gold oscillating weight, finely finished movement; 40-hour power reserve
Functions: hours, minutes, subsidiary seconds; chronograph
Case: stainless steel, ø 42 mm, height 12.4 mm; sapphire crystal; transparent case back; water-resistant to 3 atm
Band: calfskin, buckle
Price: $8,300

Lady Serenade

Reference number: 1-39-22-09-16-04
Movement: automatic, Glashütte Original Caliber 39-22; ø 26 mm, height 4.3 mm; 25 jewels; 28,800 vph; swan-neck fine adjustment, Glashütte three-quarter plate with ribbing, skeletonized rotor with heavy metal oscillating weight; finely finished movement; 40-hour power reserve
Functions: hours, minutes, sweep seconds; date
Case: stainless steel, ø 36 mm, height 10.2 mm; rose gold bezel, set with 52 diamonds; sapphire crystal; transparent case back; rose gold crown with diamond; water-resistant to 5 atm
Band: reptile skin, folding clasp
Remarks: mother-of-pearl dial
Price: $14,100; **Variations:** buckle ($13,700); various dials, case materials, and straps

Caliber 36

Automatic; single spring barrel, 100-hour power reserve
Functions: hours, minutes, sweep seconds
Diameter: 32.2 mm; **Height:** 4.45 mm
Jewels: 27
Balance: screw balance with 4 regulating screws
Frequency: 28,800 vph
Balance spring: silicon, swan-neck spring to regulate rate symmetry; **Shock protection:** Incabloc
Remarks: very finely finished movement, three-quarter plate with Glashütte stripe finish, skeletonized rotor with gold oscillating mass
Related caliber: 36-02 (perpetual calendar), 36-03 (panorama date), 36-04 (panorama date and moon phase)

Caliber 37

Automatic; single spring barrel, 70-hour power reserve
Functions: hours, minutes, subsidiary seconds; power reserve indicator; flyback chronograph; panorama date
Diameter: 31.6 mm; **Height:** 8 mm
Jewels: 65; **Balance:** screw balance with 4 gold regulating screws
Frequency: 28,800 vph
Balance spring: flat hairspring, swan-neck spring to regulate rate symmetry
Remarks: finely finished movement, beveled edges, polished steel parts, blued screws, three-quarter plate with Glashütte stripe finish, skeletonized rotor with 21-kt gold oscillating mass

Caliber 39

Automatic; single spring barrel, 40-hour power reserve
Functions: hours, minutes, sweep seconds (base caliber)
Diameter: 26.2 mm; **Height:** 4.3 mm
Jewels: 25; **Balance:** glucydur
Frequency: 28,800 vph
Balance spring: flat hairspring, swan-neck fine adjustment
Shock protection: Incabloc
Related Caliber: 39-55 (GMT, 40 jewels), 38-52 (automatic, 25 jewels), 39-50 (perpetual calendar, 48 jewels), 38-41/39-42 (panorama date, 44 jewels), 39-31 (chronograph, 51 jewels), 39-21/39-22 (date, 25 jewels)

Caliber 58-03

Manually wound; 2nd reset when crown is pulled allowing precise setting of minutes hand; single spring barrel, 44-hour power reserve; DIN-certified chronometer
Functions: hours, minutes, subsidiary seconds; day/night indicator, power reserve indicator with planetary drive; panorama date
Diameter: 35 mm; **Height:** 6.5 mm
Jewels: 58
Balance: screw balance with 18 weighted screws
Frequency: 28,800 vph
Balance spring: flat hairspring, swan-neck fine adjustment
Remarks: beveled edges, polished steel parts, screw-mounted gold chatons, three-quarter plate with Glashütte stripe finish, hand-engraved balance cock

Caliber 58-05

Manually wound; flying 1-minute tourbillon; single spring barrel, 70-hour power reserve
Functions: hours, minutes (off-center), subsidiary seconds (on tourbillon cage); power reserve indicator
Diameter: 36.6 mm
Height: 8.48 mm
Jewels: 85
Balance: screw balance with 18 weighted screws
Frequency: 21,600 vph
Balance spring: silicon
Remarks: finely finished movement, beveled edges, polished steel parts, three-quarter plate with Glashütte stripe finish, blued screws, ratchet wheel with double sunburst brushing, hand-polished structural parts

Caliber 61

Manually wound; single spring barrel, 42-hour power reserve
Functions: hours, minutes (off-center), subsidiary seconds; flyback chronograph; panorama date
Diameter: 32.2 mm
Height: 7.2 mm
Jewels: 41
Balance: screw balance with 18 weighted screws
Frequency: 28,800 vph
Balance spring: flat hairspring, swan-neck fine adjustment
Remarks: finely finished movement, beveled edges, polished steel parts, screw-mounted gold chatons, blued screws, bridges and balance cock with Glashütte stripe finish, hand-engraved balance cock

Caliber 65

Manually wound; single spring barrel, 42-hour power reserve
Functions: hours, minutes (off-center), subsidiary seconds; power reserve indicator; panorama date
Diameter: 32.2 mm
Height: 6.1 mm
Jewels: 48
Balance: screw balance with 18 weighted screws
Frequency: 28,800 vph
Balance spring: flat hairspring, duplex swan-neck fine adjustment for rate symmetry
Shock protection: Incabloc
Remarks: finely finished movement, three-quarter plate with Glashütte stripe finish, hand-engraved balance bridge

Caliber 89-02

Automatic; single spring barrel, 72-hour power reserve
Functions: hours, minutes, subsidiary seconds; 2nd time zone, world time with 37 time zones, day/night indicator, power reserve indicator; panorama date
Diameter: 39.2 mm; **Height:** 8 mm
Jewels: 63; **Balance:** screw balance with 4 gold regulating screws
Frequency: 28,800 vph
Balance spring: flat hairspring, duplex swan-neck fine adjustment for rate symmetry
Shock protection: Incabloc
Remarks: winding gears with double sun brushing, three-quarter plate with Glashütte stripe finish, hand-engraved balance bridge

Caliber 90

Automatic; single spring barrel, 42-hour power reserve
Functions: hours, minutes (off-center), subsidiary seconds; panorama date, moon phase
Diameter: 32.6 mm
Height: 5.4 mm
Jewels: 28
Balance: screw balance with 18 weighted screws
Frequency: 28,800 vph
Balance spring: flat hairspring, duplex swan-neck fine adjustment for rate symmetry
Shock protection: Incabloc
Remarks: eccentric, skeletonized, 21-kt gold oscillating weight, hand-engraved balance bridge

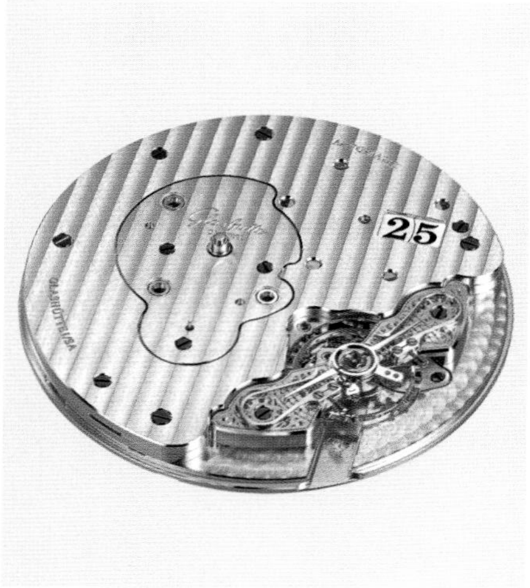

Caliber 91-02

Automatic; inverted movement with rate regulator on dial side; single spring barrel, 42-hour power reserve
Functions: hours, minutes (off-center), subsidiary seconds; panorama date
Diameter: 38.2 mm
Height: 7.1 mm
Jewels: 49
Balance: screw balance with 18 weighted screws
Frequency: 28,800 vph
Balance spring: flat hairspring, duplex swan-neck fine adjustment for rate symmetry
Shock protection: Incabloc
Remarks: finely finished movement, three-quarter plate with Glashütte stripe finish

Caliber 93-02

Automatic; flying tourbillon, single spring barrel, 48-hour power reserve
Functions: hours, minutes (off-center), subsidiary seconds (on tourbillon cage); panorama date, moon phase
Diameter: 32.2 mm
Height: 7.65 mm
Jewels: 48, plus 2 diamond endstones
Balance: screw balance with 18 weighted screws in rotating frame
Frequency: 21,600 vph
Balance spring: flat hairspring
Remarks: finely finished movement, off-center skeletonized rotor, with 21-kt gold oscillating mass

Caliber 96-01

Automatic; twin spring barrel, bidirectional winding in 2 speeds via stepped reduction gear; 42-hour power reserve
Functions: hours, minutes (off-center), subsidiary seconds; 2-digit counter (pusher-controlled, forward and backward); flyback chronograph; panorama date
Diameter: 32.2 mm
Height: 8.9 mm
Jewels: 72
Balance: screw balance with 18 weighted screws
Frequency: 28,800 vph
Balance spring: flat hairspring, swan-neck fine adjustment
Remarks: separate wheel bridges for winding and chronograph, finely finished movement

Graham
Boulevard des Eplatures 38
CH-2300 La Chaux-de-Fonds
Switzerland

Tel.:
+41-32-910-9888

E-mail:
info@graham1695.com

Website:
www.graham1695.com

Founded:
1995

Number of employees:
approx. 30

Annual production:
5,000–7,000 watches

U.S. distributor:
Graham Watchmakers
169 East Flagler Street, Suite 932
Miami, FL 33131
305-890-6409
m.leemon@graham1695.com

Most important collections:
Geo.Graham, Chronofighter, Silverstone, Swordfish

GRAHAM

In the mid-1990s, unusual creations gave an old English name in watchmaking a brand-new life. In the eighteenth century, George Graham perfected the cylinder escapement and the dead-beat escapement as well as inventing the chronograph. For these contributions and more, Graham certainly earned the right to be considered one of the big wheels in watchmaking history.

Despite his merits in the development of precision timekeeping, it was the mechanism he invented to measure short times—the chronograph—that became the trademark of his wristwatch company. To this day, the fundamental principle of the chronograph hasn't changed at all: A second set of hands can be engaged to or disengaged from the constant flow of energy of the movement. Given the British Masters' aim to honor this English inventor, it is certainly no surprise that the Graham collection includes quite a number of fascinating chronograph variations.

In 2000, the company released the Chronofighter, with its striking thumb-controlled lever mechanism—a modern twist on a function designed for World War II British fighter pilots, who couldn't activate the crown button of their flight chronographs with their thick gloves on. To enhance the retro look and feel, the brand decided to release several models bearing famous World War II pinups. The company has also started a special series to "give back," as it were. Made of a special carbon, this U.S. Navy SEAL Chronofighter also features a special camo look designed to help hide soldiers from satellite cameras. A part of the sales of these watches will go to the nonprofit Navy SEAL Foundation.

The attraction of the brand remains in the muscle watch–sportive look, which it seems to have relinquished in part for a sober-sportive look in the Swordfish line. In recent years, Graham has also added comparatively conventionally designed watches to its collection. For lovers of special pieces, there are the models of the Geo.Graham series. It was the name used by the brilliant watchmaker-inventor.

Chronofighter Vintage Ltd. Bear Edition

Reference number: 2CVAS.B32A
Movement: automatic, Graham Caliber G1745; ø 30 mm, height 8 mm; 25 jewels; 28,800 vph; 48-hour power reserve
Functions: hours, minutes; chronograph; date, weekday
Case: stainless steel, ø 44 mm; sapphire crystal; transparent case back; crown and pusher with finger lever on left side; water-resistant to 10 atm
Band: calfskin, buckle
Price: $6,450; limited to 100 pieces

Chronofighter Grand Vintage Ltd. Swiss Edition

Reference number: 2CVDS.W01A
Movement: automatic, Graham Caliber G1747; ø 30 mm, height 8 mm; 25 jewels; 28,800 vph; 48-hour power reserve
Functions: hours, minutes, subsidiary seconds; chronograph; date
Case: stainless steel, ø 47 mm; sapphire crystal; transparent case back; crown and pusher with finger lever on left side; water-resistant to 10 atm
Band: calfskin, buckle
Price: $7,950; limited to 50 pieces

Chronofighter Vintage Pulsometer Ltd. Edition

Reference number: 2CVAS.U14A
Movement: automatic, Graham Caliber G1718; ø 30 mm, height 8 mm; 25 jewels; 28,800 vph; 48-hour power reserve
Functions: hours, minutes, subsidiary seconds; chronograph; date, weekday
Case: stainless steel, ø 44 mm; sapphire crystal; transparent case back; crown and pusher with finger lever on left side; water-resistant to 10 atm
Band: calfskin, buckle
Remarks: pulsometer scale on dial
Price: $5,250; limited to 250 pieces

GRAND SEIKO

In 2017, Shinji Hattori, president of the Seiko Watch Company, announced that the Grand Seiko line had become a separate *manufacture* brand. In the years since, these watches have developed their own identity.

One must say, however, that this separate path had been taking shape for a while already. The Grand Seiko watches always existed in a segment of their own and had become something of a focus for collectors. For the brand's fiftieth anniversary in 2010, the Grand Seiko collection was given a host of new models and started being sold in the European market.

What makes the Grand Seiko collection special is the "Spring Drive" technology, a technology invented by a Seiko engineer that took twenty-eight years to perfect and, according to the company, six hundred prototypes. Essentially, it consists of a complex combination of mostly mechanical parts with a small but crucial electronic regulating element to tame the energy from the mainspring. These watches also boast some classical mechanical hijinks, such as the "Hi-Beat" balance with 36,000 vibrations per hour. The basic platform for all movements is the 9S mechanical caliber, introduced in 1998. It has been continuously improved over time, notably with the use of a special alloy called SPRON, used for the mainspring and the hairspring. Grand Seiko also draws on micromechanical systems (MEMS) technology to make parts boasting tolerances of a thousandth of a millimeter. It's no surprise that classic watch fans have welcomed the Grand Seikos into their midst. The range of models has been widened with a number of sportive divers' watches that are giving established Swiss brands some stiff competition when it comes to price and amenities.

Seiko Holdings
Ginza, Chuo, Tokyo
Japan

Website:
www.grand-seiko.com

Founded:
1881

Number of employees:
90,000 (for the entire holding)

U.S. distributor:
Grand Seiko Corporation of America
1111 MacArthur Boulevard
Mahwah, NJ 07430
201-529-5730
info@grand-seiko.us.com
www.grand-seiko.us.com

Most important collections/price range:
Elegance, Sport, Heritage / approx. $5,000 to $59,000

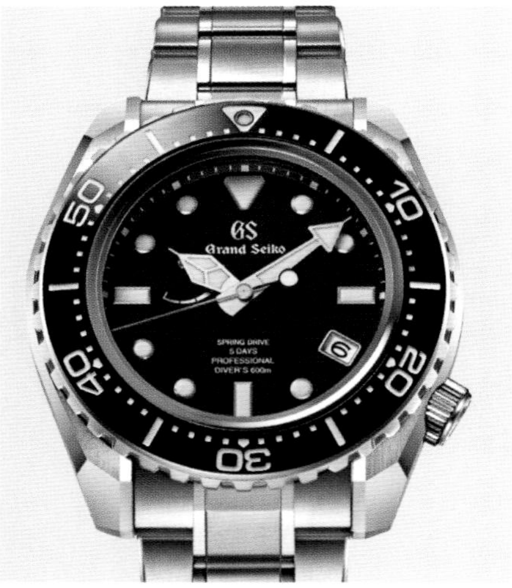

Spring Drive Professional Diver's 600M 60th Anniversary

Reference number: SLGA001
Movement: automatic, Grand Seiko Caliber 9RA5; ø 34 mm, height 5 mm; 38 jewels; electromagnetic Tri-Synchro Regulator escapement system with sliding wheel; amagnetic to 4800 A/m; 120-hour power reserve
Functions: hours, minutes, sweep seconds; power reserve indicator; date
Case: titanium (with hard coating), ø 46.9 mm, height 16 mm; unidirectional bezel with 0-60 scale; sapphire crystal; screw-in crown; water-resistant to 60 atm
Band: titanium (with hard coating), folding clasp, with safety catch and extension link
Price: $11,100; limited to 700 pieces

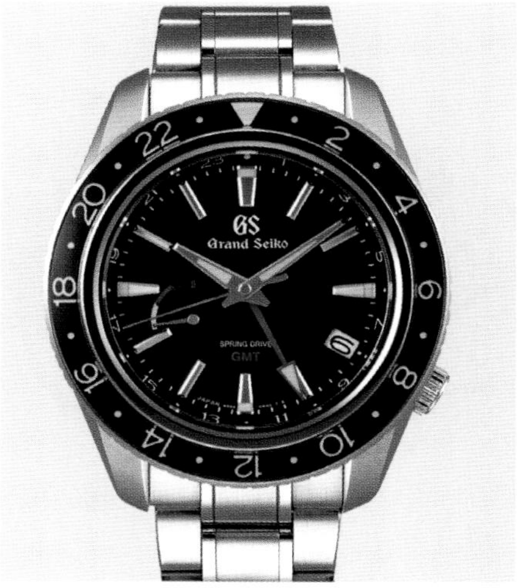

Sport Spring Drive GMT

Reference number: SBGE201
Movement: automatic, Grand Seiko Caliber 9R66; ø 30 mm; 30 jewels; electromagnetic Tri-Synchro regulator escapement system with sliding wheel; amagnetic to 4800 A/m; 72-hour power reserve
Functions: hours, minutes, sweep seconds; additional 24-hour display (2nd time zone), power reserve indicator; date
Case: stainless steel, ø 43.5 mm, height 14.5 mm; unidirectional bezel with 24-hr division; sapphire crystal; screw-in crown; water-resistant to 20 atm
Band: stainless steel, folding clasp
Price: $5,800

Sport Quartz 60th Anniversary Limited Edition

Reference number: SBGP015
Movement: quartz, Grand Seiko Caliber 9F85; twin pulse control motor, amagnetic to 16,000 A/m
Functions: hours, minutes, sweep seconds; date
Case: stainless steel, ø 40 mm, height 12.4 mm; ceramic bezel; sapphire crystal; screw-in crown; water-resistant to 20 atm
Band: stainless steel, folding clasp
Price: $3,800; limited to 2,000 pieces

Heritage Hi-Beat 36,000 60th Anniversary Limited Edition

Reference number: SBGH281
Movement: automatic, Grand Seiko Caliber 9S85; ø 28.4 mm, height 4.1 mm; 37 jewels; 36,000 vph; amagnetic to 4,800 A/m; 55-hour power reserve
Functions: hours, minutes, sweep seconds; date
Case: stainless steel, ø 40 mm, height 13.3 mm; sapphire crystal; transparent case back; screw-in crown; water-resistant to 10 atm
Band: stainless steel, folding clasp
Price: $6,300; limited to 1,500 pieces

Heritage Quartz GMT

Reference number: SBGN013
Movement: quartz, Grand Seiko Caliber 9F86; twin pulse control motor, amagnetic to 16,000 A/m
Functions: hours, minutes, sweep seconds; additional 24-hour display (2nd time zone); date
Case: stainless steel, ø 40 mm, height 12.2 mm; sapphire crystal; water-resistant to 10 atm
Band: stainless steel, folding clasp
Price: $3,000

Heritage Spring Drive "Snowflake"

Reference number: SBGA211
Movement: automatic, Grand Seiko Caliber 9R65; ø 30 mm, height 5.1 mm; 30 jewels; electromagnetic Tri-Synchro regulator escapement system with sliding wheel; amagnetic to 4,800 A/m; 72-hour power reserve
Functions: hours, minutes, sweep seconds; power reserve indicator; date
Case: titanium (with hard coating), ø 41 mm, height 12.5 mm; sapphire crystal; transparent case back; screw-in crown; water-resistant to 10 atm
Band: titanium (with hard coating), folding clasp
Price: $5,800

Elegance with Manual Winding 60th Anniversary Limited Editon

Reference number: SBGW264
Movement: manually wound, Grand Seiko Caliber 9S64; ø 28.4 mm; 24 jewels; 28,800 vph; amagnetic to 4,800 A/m; 72-hour power reserve
Functions: hours, minutes, sweep seconds
Case: pink gold, ø 39 mm, height 11.8 mm; sapphire crystal; transparent case back; water-resistant to 3 atm
Band: reptile skin, folding clasp
Price: $24,000; limited to 120 pieces

Elegance Spring Drive

Reference number: SBGA407
Movement: automatic, Grand Seiko Caliber 9R65; ø 30 mm, height 5.1 mm; 30 jewels; electromagnetic Tri-Synchro regulator escapement system with sliding wheel; amagnetic to 4800 A/m; 72-hour power reserve
Functions: hours, minutes, sweep seconds; power reserve indicator; date
Case: stainless steel, ø 40.2 mm, height 12.8 mm; sapphire crystal; transparent case back; screw-in crown; water-resistant to 10 atm
Band: reptile skin, folding clasp
Price: $5,800

Elegance Ladies' Automatic 60th Anniversary Limited Edition

Reference number: STGK015
Movement: automatic, Grand Seiko Caliber 9S27; ø 19.4 mm, height 4.5 mm; 35 jewels; 28,800 vph; amagnetic to 4,800 A/m; 50-hour power reserve
Functions: hours, minutes, sweep seconds; date
Case: stainless steel, ø 27.8 mm, height 11.2 mm; bezel set with 56 diamonds; sapphire crystal; transparent case back; water-resistant to 10 atm
Band: stainless steel, folding clasp
Remarks: mother-of-pearl dial set with 11 diamonds
Price: $9,500; limited to 300 pieces

GREUBEL FORSEY

In 2004, when Alsatian Robert Greubel and Englishman Stephen Forsey presented a new movement at Baselworld, eyes snapped open: Their watch featured not one, but *two* tourbillon carriages working at a 30° incline. In their design, Forsey and Greubel not only took up the basic Abraham-Louis Breguet idea of canceling out the deviations of the balance by the continuous rotation of the tourbillon cage, but they went further, creating a quadruple tourbillon.

In 2010, Greubel Forsey moved into new facilities at a renovated farmhouse between Le Locle and La Chaux-de-Fonds and a brand-new modern building. After capturing an Aiguille D'Or for the magical Double Tourbillon 30° and the Grand Prix d'Horlogerie in Geneva, these two masters of technically extreme watchmaking snatched up the top prize at the International Chronometry Competition in Le Locle for the Double Tourbillon 30° tourbillon.

Greubel and Forsey continue to stun the watch community with some spectacular pieces, like the Quadruple Tourbillon Secret, which shows the complex play of the tourbillons through the case back, and the Greubel Forsey GMT with the names of world cities and a huge floating globe. Their first Art Piece came out in 2013, a most natural collaboration with British miniaturist Willard Wigan, who can sculpt the head of a pin. In 2019, their Art Piece paid homage to their own double tourbillon inclined at 30°. And the QP à Equation not only does all that a full calendar is supposed to do, but it also offers sun time on the movement side.

Meanwhile, Greubel and Forsey continue to push for tiny increments in chronometric precision. Two inclined oscillators might have seemed the ultimate. But four tourbillons connected to a spherical differential, each aimed at canceling gravity, could eke out one more second of precision.

Greubel Forsey SA
Eplatures-Grise 16
CH-2301 La Chaux-de-Fonds
Switzerland

Tel.:
+41-32-925-4545

E-mail:
info@greubelforsey.com
press@greubelforsey.com

Website:
www.greubelforsey.com

Founded:
2004

Number of employees:
approx. 100

Annual production:
approx. 100 watches

U.S. distributor:
Time Art Distribution
550 Fifth Avenue
New York, NY 10036
212-221-8041
info@timeartdistribution.com

Remarks:
Prices given only in Swiss francs (before taxes).
Use daily exchange rate for conversion.

QP à Équation

Reference number: P556
Movement: manually wound, GF Caliber GF07; ø 36.4 mm, height 9.6 mm; 75 jewels; 21,600 vph; 24-second tourbillon inclined at 25°, balance with variable inertia; 2 flying spring barrels, 72-hour power reserve
Functions: hours, minutes, subsidiary seconds; additional 24-hour display (2nd time zone), day/night indicator, power reserve indicator, function indicator; perpetual calendar with large date, weekday, month, leap year; time equation and year (4 digits) on back
Case: pink gold, ø 43.5 mm, height 16 mm; sapphire crystal; transparent case back; water-resistant to 3 atm
Band: reptile skin, folding clasp
Price: CHF 670,000

Art Piece Edition Historique

Reference number: P381
Movement: manually wound, GF Caliber; ø 36.4 mm, height 12.37 mm; 50 jewels; 21,600 vph; 4-minute outer tourbillon, 1-minute inner tourbillon inclined at 30°, balance with variable inertia, Phillips end curve, 2 spring barrels, finely finished movement decorated with microengraved writing; 72-hour power reserve
Functions: hours, minutes (off-center, disk display and indices), subsidiary seconds; power reserve indicator
Case: platinum, ø 44 mm, height 15.95 mm; sapphire crystal; transparent case back; water-resistant to 3 atm; **Band:** reptile skin, folding clasp
Remarks: third "Art Piece" as homage to the double 30° tourbillon
Price: CHF 550,000; limited to 11 pieces

Balancier Contemporain

Reference number: P180
Movement: manually wound, GF Caliber; ø 32.4 mm, height 9.2 mm; 33 jewels; 21,600 vph; balance with variable inertia, Phillips end curve, 2 spring barrels, finely finished movement with microengraving; 72-hour power reserve
Functions: hours, minutes (off-center), subsidiary seconds; power reserve indicator
Case: white gold, ø 39.6 mm, height 12.21 mm; sapphire crystal; transparent case back; water-resistant to 3 atm
Band: reptile skin, buckle
Price: CHF 195,000; limited to 33 pieces

In 1944, the Hellion was the name of one of many experimental weapons systems designed to clear beaches at arm's length ahead of the amphibious landings. In the end, the weapons systems proved ineffective, but the name Hellion came to describe the spirit of the pilots who flew missions over the Pacific and the people that built the foundation of the UDT/SEALs. Pilots such as John Glenn of the VMF-218 "Hellions". The kind of people who threw themselves at a heavily defended beach dressed as if on a snorkeling holiday with the subtle addition of towing 40 lbs of explosives. The kind of person that hands a hotel manager today's equivalent of $50,000 in back pay towards a V-J Day party for his teammates and asks only to be notified once the tab ran out; ending the party...12 days later it turns out.

It's from this tradition we drew the name for the second variant of the Mk II Cruxible, the Cruxible-Hellion. Starting with the specifications laid out by the US Navy air arm and combat swimmers, the Mk II Cruxible-Hellion would have exceeded either set of requirements.

Life, Liberty, and the Pursuit.

MIIK

Built for the Pursuit

For additional information and to order direct visit: **www.mkiiwatches.com**

HABRING²

Fine mechanical works of art are created with smaller and larger complications in a small workshop in Austria's Völkermarkt, where the name Habring² stands for Maria Kristina Habring and her husband, Richard. "You get two for one," he jokes. The couple's first watch labeled with their own name came out in 2004: a simple three-handed watch based on a refined and unostentatiously decorated ETA pocket watch movement, the Unitas 6498-1. In connoisseur circles the news spread like wildfire that exceptional quality down to the smallest detail was hidden behind its inconspicuous specifications.

Since then, they have put their efforts into a wide range of products, notably their movements, like the Caliber A09, which is available in both a manual and a bidirectionally wound automatic version. All the little details that differentiate this caliber are either especially commissioned or are made in-house. Its sporty version drives a pilot's watch. Also more or less in-house are the components of Habring²'s Seconde Foudroyante, with the foudroyante mechanism fed by a separate spring barrel.

For the twentieth anniversary of the IWC double chronograph, Habring² built a limited, improved edition. The movement, based on the ETA 7750 "Valjoux," was conceived in 1991/1992 with an additional module between the chronograph and automatic winder. Suffice to say, the five-member team's technical sophistication is remarkable. They do not shy away from modern materials like silicon, or technologies, or ion etching. But they also keep their feet on the ground, using classic materials like steel. And whatever they can't do in-house, they will purchase to ensure quality, like the perpetual calendar module that goes into the brand's flagship model, the Perpetual Doppel.

Habring Uhrentechnik OG
Hauptplatz 16
A-9100 Völkermarkt
Austria

Tel.:
+43-4232-51-300

E-mail:
info@habring.com

Website:
www.habring2.com

Founded:
1997

Number of employees:
3

Annual production:
200 watches

U.S. retailers:
Martin Pulli (USA-East)
215-508-4610
www.martinpulli.com
Passion Fine Jewelry (USA-West)
858-794-8000
www.passionfinejewelry.com

Most important collections/price range:
Felix / from $5,200; Jumping Second / from $6,400; Doppel 3 / from $8,750; Chrono COS / from $8,100

Perpetual Doppel

Reference number: Perpetual Doppel
Movement: manually wound, Habring Caliber A11P; ø 30 mm, height 8.7 mm; 27 jewels; 28,800 vph; tangential screw fine adjustment, amagnetic escapement with Carl Haas hairspring, monopusher for chronograph functions, finely finished movement; 48-hour power reserve
Functions: hours, minutes, subsidiary seconds; split-second chronograph; perpetual calendar with date, weekday, month, moon phase, leap year
Case: stainless steel, ø 43 mm, height 12 mm; sapphire crystal; transparent case back; water-resistant to 3 atm; **Band:** calfskin, buckle
Price: $24,300
Variations: various dials

Perpetual Doppel

Reference number: Perpetual Doppel
Movement: manually wound, Habring Caliber A11P; ø 30 mm, height 8.7 mm; 27 jewels; 28,800 vph; tangential screw fine adjustment, amagnetic escapement with Carl Haas hairspring, monopusher for chronograph functions, finely finished movement; 48-hour power reserve
Functions: hours, minutes, subsidiary seconds; split-second chronograph; perpetual calendar with date, weekday, month, moon phase, leap year
Case: stainless steel, ø 43 mm, height 12 mm; sapphire crystal; transparent case back; water-resistant to 3 atm; **Band:** calfskin, buckle
Price: $24,300
Variations: various dials

Doppel Felix

Reference number: Doppel Felix
Movement: manually wound, Habring Caliber A11R; ø 30 mm, height 8.4 mm; 27 jewels; 28,800 vph; Triovis fine adjustment; 48-hour power reserve
Functions: hours, minutes, subsidiary seconds; flyback chronograph
Case: stainless steel, ø 42 mm, height 13 mm; sapphire crystal; transparent case back; water-resistant to 5 atm
Band: calfskin, buckle
Price: $8,750
Variations: various dials; with date function ($9,300)

Doppel-Felix

Reference number: Doppel Felix
Movement: manually wound, Habring Caliber A11R; ø 30 mm, height 8.4 mm; 25 jewels; 28,800 vph; Triovis fine adjustment; 48-hour power reserve
Functions: hours, minutes, subsidiary seconds; flying chronograph
Case: stainless steel, ø 42 mm, height 13 mm; sapphire crystal; transparent case back; water-resistant to 5 atm
Band: calfskin, buckle
Price: $9,150
Variations: various dials; with date function ($9,740)

COS Felix Date

Reference number: COS Felix Date
Movement: automatic, Habring Caliber A11COSD; ø 30 mm, height 7.9 mm; 29 jewels; 28,800 vph; Triovis fine adjustment of chronograph functions by turning the crown ("Crown Operation System")
Functions: hours, minutes, subsidiary seconds; chronograph; date
Case: stainless steel, ø 42 mm, height 13 mm; sapphire crystal; transparent case back; water-resistant to 5 atm
Band: calfskin, buckle
Price: $9,000
Variations: manually-wound movement

Chrono-Felix

Reference number: Chrono Felix
Movement: automatic, Habring Caliber A11C-H1; ø 30 mm, height 6.5 mm; 25 jewels; 28,800 vph; tangential screw fine adjustment, amagnetic escapement with Carl Haas balance hairspring; monopusher control of chronograph functions; 48-hour power reserve
Functions: hours, minutes, subsidiary seconds; chronograph
Case: stainless steel, ø 42 mm, height 11 mm; sapphire crystal; transparent case back; water-resistant to 5 atm
Band: calfskin, buckle
Price: $7,350
Variations: various dials

Chrono-Felix

Reference number: Chrono Felix
Movement: automatic, Habring Caliber A11C-H1; ø 30 mm, height 6.5 mm; 25 jewels; 28,800 vph; tangential screw fine adjustment, amagnetic escapement with Carl Haas balance hairspring; monopusher control of chronograph functions; 48-hour power reserve
Functions: hours, minutes, subsidiary seconds; chronograph
Case: stainless steel, ø 42 mm, height 11 mm; sapphire crystal; transparent case back; water-resistant to 5 atm
Band: calfskin, buckle
Price: $7,350
Variations: various dials

Time Date Felix

Reference number: Time Date Felix
Movement: manually wound, Habring Caliber A11MD; ø 30 mm, height 4.2 mm; 18 jewels; 28,800 vph; Triovis fine adjustment, finely finished movement; 48-hour power reserve
Functions: hours, minutes, subsidiary seconds; date
Case: stainless steel, ø 38.5 mm, height 13 mm; sapphire crystal; transparent case back; water-resistant to 5 atm
Band: textile, buckle
Price: $6,550
Variations: automatic movement ($7,000)

Foudroyante Felix Date

Reference number: Foudroyante Felix
Movement: manually wound, Habring Caliber A11MFD; ø 30 mm, height 7.9 mm; 23 jewels; 28,800 vph; tangential screw fine adjustment, amagnetic escapement with Carl Haas balance hairspring, finely finished movement; 48-hour power reserve
Functions: hours, minutes, sweep seconds (jumping); foudroyante display of 1/8th of a second ("seconde foudroyante"); date
Case: stainless steel, ø 42 mm, height 13 mm; sapphire crystal; transparent case back; water-resistant to 5 atm; **Band:** calfskin, buckle
Price: $8,300
Variations: automatic movement ($8,650)

HAGER

Keeping it simple and smart is a Hager specialty. The company, owned and operated by American service veteran Pierre "Pete" Brown, is named after the town where the company was started in 2009. The business model was equally streamlined: create high-quality and affordable automatic watches accessible to those who have never experienced the joy of owning a mechanical watch. The look: rugged and refined, for individuals with a bit of adventure in their bones.

The timepieces are designed by Brown and his small team in Hagerstown. All the cues are there for the watch connoisseur: the brushed and polished cases with beveled edges, two-tiered stadium dial, with brass markers and hands outlined in black and coated with Superluminova, domed sapphire crystal, 120-click ceramic bezels and 24-click GMT ceramic bezels also enhanced with Superluminova. The cases are rated a sportive 20 atm, meaning they are good for more than just washing the dishes. Inside them beats one of a variety of automatic winding Swiss and Japanese mechanical movements that are both installed and regulated in the USA. The latest is the Atelier 1, a Swiss-American collaboration, which fits into the Commando 10th Anniversary watch, a tough diver with a straightforward, practical look. At any rate, the spirit of elegant adventure is in each of the collections. Even the BroadArrow, with its uncluttered dial, has a dynamic look and feel.

Brown is well aware of the foibles of the watch industry, one major complaint being customer service. His personal boast since launching the company is that Hager Watch has never charged a customer for a repair yet, even when it's clear that the customer is at fault. "We aren't just selling watches," says Brown, "we are selling the experience of owning a luxury timepiece. That's not to say that at some point we will have to reverse this because of overall costs, but it's been a hallmark of our brand and it builds brand loyalty."

Hager Watches
36 South Potomac Street
Suite 204
Hagerstown, MD 21740

Tel.:
240-232-2172

E-mail:
info@hagerwatches.com

Website:
www.hagerwatches.com

Founded:
2009

Number of employees:
2

Annual production:
1,000–1,500 watches

Most important collections/price range:
Commando, GMT Aquamariner, U2 / $550 to $1,050

Commando 10th Anniversary

Reference number: 25517
Movement: automatic, Atelier Caliber 1; ø 25.6 mm, height 4.6 mm; 22 jewels; 28,800 vph; 44-hour power reserve
Functions: hours, minutes, sweep seconds; date
Case: stainless steel, ø 40 mm, height 13 mm; screw-in crown; unidirectional bezel with black ceramic insert; sapphire crystal; screw-down sapphire case back with logo; water-resistant to 30 atm
Band: stainless steel with 2-button clasp and 2-button slidelock extension system
Price: $950
Variations: stainless steel with black or ceramic insert ($950)

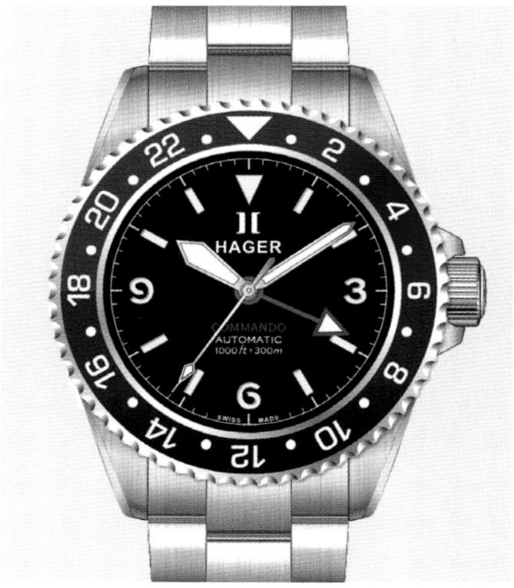

GMT Traveler Red/Blue Insert

Reference number: 16738
Movement: automatic, Soprod C125; ø 25.6 mm, height 5.67 mm; 25 jewels; 28,800 vph; 40-hour power reserve
Functions: hours, minutes, sweep seconds; date; 2nd time zone
Case: stainless steel, ø 40 mm, height 13 mm; screw-in crown; unidirectional bezel with black ceramic insert; sapphire crystal; screw-down sapphire case back with logo; water-resistant to 30 atm
Band: stainless steel with 2-button clasp and 2-button slidelock extension system
Price: $1,050
Variations: stainless steel with black or blue or black and blue ceramic insert ($1,050)

BroadArrow

Reference number: D0529G
Movement: automatic, Soprod C125; ø 25.6 mm, height 5.67 mm; 25 jewels; 28,800 vph; 40-hour power reserve
Functions: hours, minutes, seconds; sweep 2nd time zone
Case: stainless steel, ø 42 mm, height 10.5 mm; sapphire crystal; screw-down case back; water-resistant to 20 atm
Band: stainless steel, stitching, folding clasp with slidelock extension
Price: $1,050
Variations: stainless steel with seconds at 6 o'clock ($800) and 3-hand ($950)

Hamilton International Ltd.
Mattenstrasse 149
CH-2503 Biel/Bienne
Switzerland

Tel.:
+41-32-343-4004

E-mail:
info@hamiltonwatch.com

Website:
www.hamiltonwatch.com
shop.hamiltonwatch.com

Founded:
1892

U.S. distributor:
Hamilton
Swatch Group (US), Inc.
703 Waterford Way, Suite 450
Miami, FL 33126
800-234-8463
Hamilton.US@swatchgroup.com

Price range:
between approx. $500 and $2,500

HAMILTON

The Hamilton Watch Co. was founded in 1892 in Lancaster, Pennsylvania, and, within a very brief period, grew into one of the world's largest *manufactures*. Around the turn of the twentieth century, every second railway employee in the United States was carrying a Hamilton watch in his pocket, not only to make sure the trains were running punctually, but also to assist in coordinating them and organizing schedules. And during World War II, the American army officers' kits included a service Hamilton.

Hamilton is the sole survivor of the large U.S. watchmakers—though only as a brand within the Swiss Swatch Group. At one time, Hamilton had itself owned a piece of the Swiss watchmaking industry in the form of the Büren brand in the 1960s and 1970s. As part of a joint venture with Heuer-Leonidas, Breitling, and Dubois Dépraz, Hamilton-Büren also made a significant contribution to the development of the automatic chronograph. Just prior in its history, the tuning fork watch pioneer was all the rage when it took the new movement technology and housed it in a modern case created by renowned industrial designer Richard Arbib. The triangular Ventura hit the watch-world ground running in 1957, in what was truly a frenzy of innovation that benefited the brand especially in the U.S. market. The American spirit of freedom and belief in progress this model embodies, something evoked in Hamilton's current marketing, are taken quite seriously by its designers—even those working in Biel, Switzerland. Today's collections are more inspired from adventure and aviator watches. The brand also continues to focus on revamped remakes of its classics, like the PSR, which boldly and loudly whoops up the glorious days of the digital watch.

Jazzmaster Skeleton

Reference number: H42505510
Movement: automatic, Hamilton Caliber H-10-S (base ETA C07.631); ø 25.6 mm, height 4.6 mm; 25 jewels; 21,600 vph; partly skeletonized movement; 80-hour power reserve
Functions: hours, minutes, sweep seconds
Case: stainless steel with rose gold PVC, ø 40 mm; sapphire crystal; transparent case back; water-resistant to 5 atm
Band: calfskin, buckle
Price: $1,345

Jazzmaster

Reference number: H42535640
Movement: automatic, Hamilton Caliber H-10 (base ETA C07.611); ø 25.6 mm, height 4.6 mm; 25 jewels; 21,600 vph; 80-hour power reserve
Functions: hours, minutes, sweep seconds
Case: stainless steel, ø 40 mm; sapphire crystal; transparent case back; water-resistant to 5 atm
Band: calfskin, buckle
Price: $895

PSR

Reference number: H52414130
Movement: quartz
Functions: hours, minutes
Case: stainless steel, 40.8 × 34.7 mm; sapphire crystal; water-resistant to 10 atm
Band: stainless steel, folding clasp
Price: $745

HANHART

The reputation of this rather special company really goes back to the twenties and thirties. At the time, the brand manufactured affordable and robust stopwatches, pocket watches, and chronograph wristwatches. These core timepieces were what the fans of instrument watches wanted, and so they were thrilled as the company slowly abandoned its quartz dabbling of the eighties and reset its sights on the brand's rich and honorable tradition. A new collection was in the wings, raising expectations of great things to come. Support by the shareholding Gaydoul Group provided the financial backbone to get things moving.

Hanhart managed to rebuild a name for itself with a foot in Switzerland and the other in Germany, but it began to drift after the 2009 recession. Following bankruptcy, the company reorganized under the name Hanhart 1882 GmbH and moved everything to its German hometown. It has also returned to its stylistic roots: The characteristic red start/stop pusher graces the new collections, even on the bi-compax chronos of the Racemasters, which come with a smooth bezel. Pilots' chronographs have never lost any of their charm, either, and Hanhart was already making them in the 1930s, notably the Caliber 41 and the Tachy Tele, with asymmetrical pushers and the typical red pusher. These timepieces have to survive extreme conditions, like shocks and severe temperature fluctuations. Hanhart's long tradition and expertise with flyers' chronographs struck a chord with the Austrian Army. It ordered a special edition of the Primus series decorated with the coat of arms of the Austrian Air Force on the dial and certified by the military.

Hanhart 1882 GmbH
Hauptstrasse 33
D-78148 Gütenbach
Germany

Tel.:
+49-7723-93-44-0

E-mail:
info@hanhart.com

Website:
www.hanhart.com

Founded:
1882 in Diessenhofen, Switzerland;
in Germany since 1902

Number of employees:
22

Annual production:
approx. 1,000 chronographs and 30,000 stopwatches

U.S. distributor:
WatchBuys
888-333-4895
www.watchbuys.com

Most important collections/price range:
Mechanical stopwatches / from approx. $600; Pioneer / from approx. $1,070; Primus / from approx. $2,300

Primus Nautic Pilot Bronze

Reference number: 740.170
Movement: automatic, modified Sellita Caliber SW510; ø 30 mm, height 7.9 mm; 27 jewels; 28,800 vph; 48-hour power reserve
Functions: hours, minutes, subsidiary seconds; chronograph; date
Case: stainless steel with bronze PVD, ø 44 mm, height 15 mm; sapphire crystal; transparent case back; screw-in crown; water-resistant to 10 atm
Band: textile with calfskin layer, folding clasp
Remarks: movable lugs
Price: $3,350; limited to 300 pieces

S 105 OE GMT

Reference number: 751.511
Movement: automatic, ETA Caliber 2893-2 or Sellita SW330-1; ø 25.6 mm, height 4.1 mm; 25 or 26 jewels; 28,800 vph; 38-hour power reserve
Functions: hours, minutes, sweep seconds; additional 24-hour display (2nd time zone); date
Case: stainless steel with black PVD, ø 40 mm, height 12 mm; sapphire crystal; water-resistant to 10 atm
Band: calfskin, buckle
Price: $1,570; limited to 105 pieces

Pioneer Mk II Reversed Panda

Reference number: 716.210
Movement: automatic, Caliber HAN3703 (base ETA Caliber 7753); ø 30 mm, height 7.9 mm; 27 jewels; 28,800 vph; 42-hour power reserve
Functions: hours, minutes, subsidiary seconds; chronograph
Case: stainless steel, ø 40 mm, height 15 mm; bidirectional bezel with reference markings; sapphire crystal; water-resistant to 10 atm
Band: calfskin, buckle
Price: $2,280

Hautlence
Rue Numa-Droz 150
CH-2300 La Chaux-de-Fonds
Switzerland

Tel.:
+41-32-924-00-60

E-mail:
info@hautlence.com

Website:
www.hautlence.com

Founded:
2004

Number of employees:
10

Annual production:
150 watches

U.S. distributor:
Westime
8569 Westime Sunset Boulevard
West Hollywood, CA 90069
310-289-0808
info@westime.com
www.westime.com

Most important collections:
Concepts d'Exception, Atelier, Signature

HAUTLENCE

Time can be read in so many ways. Back in 2004, after spending years in the Swiss watch industry, Guillaume Tetu and Renaud de Retz decided that their idea for tracking it was new and unique. They were not watchmakers, but they knew whom to bring on board for the genesis of Hautlence, an anagram of Neuchâtel, the town where their small company is located. And soon, the first HL model was produced: a fairly large, rectangular timepiece with the ratios of a television set and a lively and visible mechanical life. All good things in watchmaking being small, the big innovation was a "connecting rod," as Tetu calls it, to propel the hour disk. When the retrograde minute hand reaches the end of its arc, it triggers the rod, which advances the hour.

Having survived the Great Recession, Hautlence persisted, and thinned down, without de Retz. The watches evolved, developing shape and character. For the HLq, the movement was reengineered for a round case. Instead of a tourbillon, Hautlence has found a way to have the whole escapement rotate four times a day.

In 2012, Hautlence became the first member of the brand-new MELB Holding, headed by Georges-Henri Meylan (formerly of Audemars Piguet) and former Breguet CFO Bill Muirhead. The experience and contacts of these two horological powerhouses have energized the brand. The Atelier and Signature series were streamlined and given a little more structure. The stark industrial look is now tempered with daubs of color, but prices have been lowered by the use of trusty Soprod engines in some models. Then, in 2014, the brand acquired former French soccer star Eric Canton, an art collector as well and an edgy personality, as an ambassador, which goes along well with the chic-steampunkish look and the brand's will to be different, come what may. Under a new CEO, Sandro Reginelli, Hautlence found its deeply technical roots again, bringing out the incredible Sphere in 2019, as well as the boldly punk Punk.

HL2.3 Punk

Movement: automatic, in-house caliber HL2.0 mobile bridge-type caliber; 37.8 × 33.2 mm, height 12.35 mm; 18,000 vph; 92 jewels; côtes de Genève, components decorated and finished by hand; 45-hour power reserve
Functions: hours, retrograde minutes; power reserve indicator
Case: titanium with black PVD, 50 × 42 × 17.8 mm; 84 steel studs (1.75–5.75 mm); rose gold crown and case back screws; 3D beveled sapphire crystals; water-resistant to 3 atm
Band: reptile skin, folding clasp
Price: $220,000; limited to 28 pieces

HL Vagabonde Tourbillon 01

Movement: automatic HTL 405-1 based on H. Moser & Cie HMC 804 automatic caliber; ø 32.00 mm; 21,600 vph; 35 jewels; 1-minute tourbillon; bidirectional rotor; côtes de Genève, decorated and finished by hand, stain-brushed bridges with blue PVD; 72-hour power reserve
Functions: skeleton hours split over two levels
Case: pink gold, ø 46 × 39 mm, height 12 mm; beveled sapphire crystal; transparent case back; water-resistant to 3 atm
Band: rubber-lined reptile skin, folding clasp
Price: $79,000

HL Sphere

Movement: manually wound, HTL 501-1; ø 32.00 mm, height 5.5 mm; 38 jewels; 21,600 vph; components decorated and finished by hand; 72-hour power reserve
Functions: hour, retrograde minutes
Case: satin-finished and polished white gold, 46 × 39 mm, height 12 mm, with 3.75-mm dome; polished white gold crown; transparent case back; water-resistant to 3 atm
Band: reptile skin, folding clasp
Remarks: spherical hour, with braked retrograde minute system
Price: $99,000

HERMÈS

La Montre Hermès
Erlenstrasse 31A
CH-2555 Brügg
Switzerland

Tel.:
+41-32-366-7100

E-mail:
info@montre-hermes.ch

Website:
www.hermes.ch

Founded:
1978

Number of employees:
150

U.S. distributor:
Hermès of Paris, Inc.
55 East 59th Street
New York, NY 10022
800-441-4488
www.hermes.com

Most important collections/price range:
Arceau, Cape Cod, Clipper, Dressage, Faubourg, Heure H, Klikti, Kelly, Medor, Slim / $2,400 to $500,000

Thierry Hermès's timing was just right. When he founded his saddlery in Paris in 1837, France's middle class was booming and spending money on beautiful things and activities like horseback riding. Hermès became a household name and a symbol of good taste—not too flashy, not trendy, useful. The advent of the automobile gave rise to luggage, bags, headgear, and soon Hermès, still in family hands today, diversified its range of products—foulards, fashion, porcelain, glass, perfume, and gold jewelry are active parts of its portfolio.

Watches were a natural, especially with the advent of the wristwatch in the years prior to World War I. Hermès even had a timepiece that could be worn on a belt. But some time passed before the company engaged in "real" watchmaking. In 1978, La Montre Hermès opened its watch manufactory in Biel.

Rather than just produce fluffy lifestyle timepieces, Hermès has gone to the trouble to get an in-depth grip on the business. "Our philosophy is all about the quality of time," says Laurent Dordet, who took over as CEO from Luc Perramond in March 2015. "It's about imagination; we want people to dream." "Poetic complications" is what allowed the company to navigate between classy but plain watches and muscular tool timepieces bristling with complications. On the one hand there was the esthetics: the lively leaning numerals of the Arceau series or the bridoon recalling the company's equine roots at 12 o'clock for holding the strap. The Cape Cod and Nantucket series recall some of the grand old days of Art Deco, with streamlined forms and orderly dials. As for in-house complications, they are produced in collaboration with external designers, notably Jean-Marc Wiederrecht and his company, Agenhor. In the Slim line, one finds a thin perpetual calendar with modern numerals that raise it above the standard retro watch. The clever "Temps Suspendu" lets the wearer stop time for a moment. There are also fascinating moon phase displays, or charming countdowns that will add a little romantic pizzazz to the last hour before a rendezvous.

Arceau "L'Heure de la lune"

Reference number: MO-AR1.890.435/MM41
Movement: automatic, Hermès Caliber H1837 with "L'heure de la lune" module; ø 38 mm, height 7.9 mm; 42 jewels; 28,800 vph; finely finished movement; 42-hour power reserve
Functions: hours, minutes (off-center); date, double phase (for northern and southern hemispheres)
Case: white gold, ø 43 mm, sapphire crystal; transparent case back; water-resistant to 3 atm
Band: reptile skin, folding clasp
Remarks: meteorite dial with photorealistic moon disks; rotating disks act as moon phase displays
Price: $33,200; **Variations:** black Sahara meteorite dial ($54,000, limited to 36 pieces); with meteorites from Mars (price on request, limited to 2 pieces)

Slim d'Hermès GMT

Reference number: MO-AR1.890.435/MM41
Movement: automatic, Hermès Caliber H1950 with GMT module; ø 33.6 mm, height 4 mm; 38 jewels; 21,600 vph; microrotor; 42-hour power reserve
Functions: hours, minutes; additional 12-hour display (2nd time zone), day/night indicator; date
Case: rose gold, ø 39.5 mm, height 9.48 mm; sapphire crystal; transparent case back; water-resistant to 3 atm
Band: reptile skin, buckle
Price: $7,300

Arceau Squelette

Reference number: MO-AR2.710.330/MM89
Movement: automatic, ETA Caliber 2892-A2; ø 25.6 mm, height 3.6 mm; 21 jewels; 28,800 vph; fully skeletonized movement; 42-hour power reserve
Functions: hours, minutes
Case: stainless steel, ø 40 mm; sapphire crystal; transparent case back; water-resistant to 3 atm
Band: reptile skin, buckle
Remarks: sapphire crystal dial
Price: $8,600

Arceau Le Temps Suspendu

Reference number: AR8.910.220/MM41
Movement: automatic, ETA Caliber 2892 (modified); ø 26 mm, height 5.6 mm; 28,800 vph; hands can be parked at 12:30, then started again at current time with pusher; double spring barrel; 42-hour power reserve
Functions: hours, minutes; date (retrograde)
Case: stainless steel, ø 43 mm; sapphire crystal; transparent case back; water-resistant to 3 atm
Band: reptile skin, folding clasp
Price: $22,400
Variations: rose gold ($45,900)

Slim d'Hermès L'Heure Impatiente

Reference number: CA4.870.220/MM7K
Movement: automatic, Hermès Caliber H1912 (base with "L'heure impatiente" module); ø 31.96 mm, height 5.9 mm; 36 jewels; 28,800 vph; mainplate and bridges with snail and côtes de Genève decoration; 50-hour power reserve
Functions: hours, minutes; "Heure impatiente" alarm with 60-minute countdown
Case: rose gold, ø 40.5 mm, height 10.67 mm; sapphire crystal; transparent case back; water-resistant to 3 atm
Band: reptile skin, buckle
Price: $39,900

Carré H

Reference number: T12.710.230/VB343
Movement: automatic, Hermès Caliber H1912; ø 23.3 mm, height 3.7 mm; 28 jewels; 28,800 vph; 50-hour power reserve
Functions: hours, minutes, sweep seconds
Case: stainless steel, 38 × 38 mm, height 10 mm; sapphire crystal; transparent case back; water-resistant to 3 atm
Band: calfskin, buckle
Price: $7,350

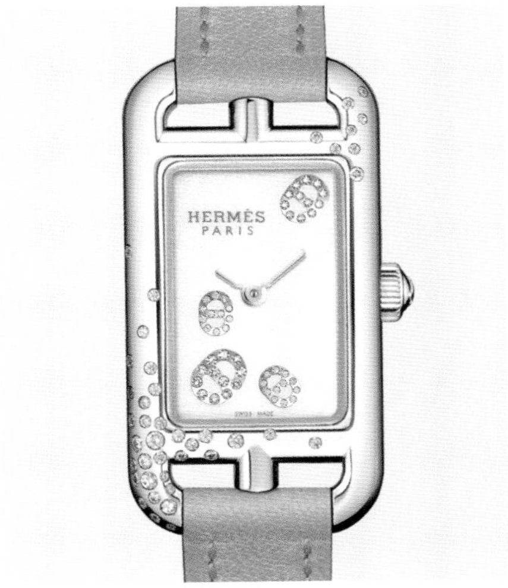

Nantucket Jeté de Chaîne d'Ancre

Reference number: MO-NA2.131.221/SW9D
Movement: quartz
Functions: hours, minutes
Case: stainless steel, set with 41 diamonds, 17 × 23 mm, height 6 mm; sapphire crystal
Band: calfskin, buckle
Remarks: dial set with 48 diamonds
Price: $6,025
Variations: reptile skin strap

Cape Cod Chaîne d'Ancre

Reference number: MO-CC2.710.220/SWS47-I
Movement: quartz
Functions: hours, minutes, sweep seconds; date
Case: stainless steel, 29 × 29 mm, height 8 mm; sapphire crystal; water-resistant to 3 atm
Band: calfskin, buckle
Price: $2,950
Variations: rose-colored dial and strap ($2,950)

Galop d'Hermès

Reference number: GA1.270.221/ZZ95
Movement: quartz
Functions: hours, minutes
Case: pink gold, 26 × 40.8 mm, height 7 mm; sapphire crystal; water-resistant to 3 atm
Band: reptile skin, buckle
Price: $9,725
Variations: with diamonds ($15,750)

H. MOSER & CIE.

H. Moser & Cie. has been making a name for itself in the industry as a serious watchmaker, though not averse to flashes of humor, like the Swiss Mad (sic) Watch made of Vacherin Mont d'Or cheese it presented in 2017 (the cheese for the case is mixed with a hardening resin). And there's the Swiss Alp watch, made to look like an Apple Watch, but with all the essential Moser codes: streamlined design, top-notch technical implementation.

The company was originally founded in Le Locle in 1825 by one Heinrich Moser (1805–1874), from Schaffhausen, at the tender age of twenty-one. Soon after, he moved to Saint Petersburg, Russia, where ambitious watchmakers were enjoying a good market. In 1828, H. Moser & Cie. was brought to life—a brand resuscitated in modern times by a group of investors and watch experts together with Moser's great-grandson, Roger Nicholas Balsiger.

With the support of a host of Swiss and German specialists, the company returned to quality fundamentals. Its claim to fame is movements that contain a separate, removable escapement module supporting the pallet lever, escape wheel, and balance. The latter is fitted with the Straumann spring, made by Precision Engineering, another one of the Moser Group companies.

This small company has considerable technical know-how, which is probably what attracted MELB Holding, owners of Hautlence, and now majority owners of H. Moser shares. Under a new CEO, the brand redefined its style: understatement, soft tones, and subtle technicity. The three core collections, Endeavour, Venturer, and Pioneer, feature "clean" dials in solid colors, including the blackest black, called Vantablack. The month hand on the Endeavour is a mere arrowhead in the center of the dial that points to the hours, which double as the months. The minimalism extends to watches that would otherwise clamor for more complexity. The 2020 Streamliner Chronograph uses the Agenhor mechanism, as a basis to drive sweep second and minute hands inside a very flowing case, thus avoiding crowding by subsidiary dials. Another symbiotic cooperation, with MB&F, produced the Cylindrical Tourbillon, lateral-cycling of MB&F's remarkable Flying T.

H. Moser & Cie.
Rundbuckstrasse 10
CH-8212 Neuhausen am Rheinfall
Switzerland

Tel.:
+41-52-674-0050

E-mail:
info@h-moser.com

Website:
www.h-moser.com

Founded:
1828

Number of employees:
60

Annual production:
approx. 1,500 watches

U.S. distributor:
Horology Works LLC
11 Flagg Road
West Hartford, CT 06117
860-986-9676
mmargolis@horologyworks.com

Most important collections/price range:
Endeavour / approx. $17,200 to $110,000; Pioneer / approx. $11,900 to $49,900; Swiss Alp Watch / approx. $21,900 to $650,000; Venturer / approx. $19,500 to $100,000

Streamliner Flyback Chronograph Automatic Funky Blue

Reference number: 6902–1201
Movement: automatic, Moser Caliber HMC 902 (developed by Agenhor); ø 34.4 mm, height 7.3 mm; 55 jewels; 21,600 vph; column-wheel control of chronograph functions; horizontal clutch with friction wheel to prevent chronograph hand's jump on starting chrono; inverted movement with winding rotor under dial; double spring barrel; 54-hour power reserve
Functions: hours, minutes; flyback chronograph
Case: stainless steel, ø 42.3 mm, height 14.2 mm; sapphire crystal; transparent case back; water-resistant to 12 atm
Band: stainless steel, triple folding clasp
Price: $43,900

Endeavour Cylindrical Tourbillon H. Moser × MB&F

Reference number: 1810–1200
Movement: automatic, Moser Caliber HMC 810; ø 32 mm, height 5.5 mm; 29 jewels; 21,600 vph; flying 1-minute tourbillon with cylindrical hairspring; skeletonized bridges, oscillating weight in pink gold; 72-hour power reserve
Functions: hours, minutes
Case: stainless steel, ø 42 mm, height 19.5 mm; sapphire crystal; transparent case back
Band: reptile skin, folding clasp
Remarks: H. Moser & Cie. and MB&F collaboration
Price: $79,900; limited to 15 pieces

Endeavour Centre Seconds Diamonds Concept

Reference number: 1200–1208
Movement: automatic, Moser Caliber HMC 200; ø 32 mm, height 5.5 mm; 27 jewels; 21,600 vph; escapement with Straumann hairspring; 72-hour power reserve
Functions: hours, minutes, sweep seconds
Case: stainless steel, ø 38 mm, height 10.3 mm; bezel set with 60 diamonds; sapphire crystal; transparent case back
Band: reptile skin, buckle
Price: $15,900

Endeavour Tourbillon Concept Vantablack

Reference number: 1804–0212
Movement: automatic, Moser Caliber HMC 804; ø 32 mm, height 5.5 mm; 21,600 vph; interchangeable escapement with flying 1-minute tourbillon, Straumann double hairspring, skeletonized bridges with black PVD, oscillating mass in pink gold; 72-hour power reserve
Case: white gold, ø 42 mm, height 11.6 mm; sapphire crystal; transparent case back
Band: reptile skin, folding clasp
Price: $75,000; limited to 50 pieces

Venturer Vantablack Black Hands

Reference number: 2327–0222
Movement: manually wound, Moser Caliber HMC 327; ø 32 mm, height 4.5 mm; 29 jewels; 18,000 vph; interchangeable escapement with Straumann hairspring; 72-hour power reserve
Functions: hours, minutes; power reserve indicator (on movement side)
Case: white gold, ø 39 mm, height 11.9 mm; sapphire crystal; transparent case back
Band: reptile skin, buckle
Price: $26,500

Heritage Centre Seconds Funky Blue

Reference number: 8200–1201
Movement: automatic, Moser Caliber HMC 200; ø 32 mm, height 5.5 mm; 27 jewels; 21,600 vph; escapement with Straumann hairspring; 72-hour power reserve
Functions: hours, minutes, sweep seconds
Case: stainless steel, ø 42 mm, height 11.1 mm; sapphire crystal; transparent case back
Band: antelope leather, buckle
Price: $13,900

Caliber HMC 341

Manually wound; exchangeable escapement with beveled wheels, hardened gold pallet fork and escapement wheel; screw-mounted gold chatons; double spring barrel, 168-hour power reserve
Functions: hours, minutes, subsidiary seconds; power reserve indicator; perpetual calendar with large date and small sweep month hand, leap year (dial side)
Diameter: 34 mm; **Height:** 5.8 mm
Jewels: 28
Balance: glucydur with white gold screws
Frequency: 18,000 vph
Balance spring: Straumann with Breguet end curve
Shock protection: Incabloc
Remarks: double-pull crown mechanism for easy switching of crown position

Caliber HMC 902

Automatic; column-wheel control of chronograph functions; horizontal clutch with friction wheel to avoid intermeshing of gears and to minimize accidental jumps when chronograph is activated; inverted movement with tungsten winding rotor under the dial; tungsten oscillating weight; double spring barrel; 54-hour power reserve
Functions: hours, minutes; flyback chronograph
Diameter: 34.4 mm
Height: 7.3 mm
Jewels: 55
Frequency: 21,600 vph
Remarks: developed by Agenhor; 434 parts

Caliber HMC 200

Automatic; double spring barrel, 72-hour power reserve
Functions: hours, minutes, sweep seconds
Diameter: 32 mm
Height: 5.5 mm
Jewels: 27
Frequency: 21,600 vph
Hairspring: Straumann

HUBLOT

Ever since Hublot moved into a new, modern, spacious factory building in Nyon, near Geneva, the brand has evolved with stunning speed. The growth has been such that Hublot has built a second factory, which is even bigger than the first. The ground-breaking ceremony took place on March 3, 2014, and the man holding the spade was then Hublot chairman Jean-Claude Biver, who now also heads LVMH Group's Watch Division.

Hublot grew and continues to grow thanks to a combination of innovative watchmaking and vigorous communication. It was together with current CEO Ricardo Guadalupe that Biver developed the idea of fusing different and at times incompatible materials in a watch: carbon composite and gold, ceramic and steel, denim and diamonds. In 2011, the brand introduced the first scratchproof precious metal, an alloy of gold and ceramic named "Magic Gold." In 2014, Hublot came out with a watch whose dial is made of osmium, one of the world's rarest metals. Using a new patented process, Hublot has also implemented a unique concept of cutting wafer-thin bits of glass that are set in the open spaces of a skeletonized movement plate.

The "art of fusion" tagline drove the brand into all sorts of technical and scientific partnerships and created a buzz that is ongoing, apparently, regardless of the economic environment. Hublot's concept is based on the idea of "being the first, different and unique." To achieve that goal, it has associated its name with major sports events and brands.

The current trend in the industry is to integrate bracelets, an idea that was already floated, even implemented, in the 1970s. And even though Hublot did not exist back then, the new Big Bang Integral does have the feeling of déjà vu. But oddly, a careful look reveals the strap to be a veritable bracelet rather than a strap made of rubber, silicone, patent leather, Kevlar, or denim. The links are polished in the same way the cases of these watches are and so the Big Bangs look as if they had always come on bracelets. That, however, is not the case.

Hublot SA
Chemin de la Vuarpillière 33
CH-1260 Nyon
Switzerland

Tel.:
+41-22-990-9000

E-mail:
info@hublot.ch

Website:
www.hublot.com

Founded:
1980

Number of employees:
approx. 700

Annual production:
approx. 50,000 watches

U.S. distributor:
Hublot of America, Inc.
100 N. Biscayne Blvd., Suite 1900
Miami, FL 33132
786-405-8677

Most important collections/price range:
Big Bang / $11,000 to $1,053,000; Classic Fusion / $5,200 to $474,000; Manufacture Piece (MP) / $82,000 to $579,000

Big Bang Integral Titanium

Reference number: 451.NX.1170.NX
Movement: automatic, Caliber HUB 1280 "Unico 2"; ø 30 mm, height 6.75 mm; 43 jewels; 28,800 vph; mainplate and bridges with gray coating; 72-hour power reserve
Functions: hours, minutes, subsidiary seconds; flyback chronograph; date
Case: titanium, ø 42 mm, height 13.45 mm; bezel mounted with 6 titanium screws; sapphire crystal; transparent case back; water-resistant to 10 atm
Band: titanium, folding clasp
Price: $20,900
Variations: rose gold ($52,500); ceramic ($23,100)

Big Bang Integral King Gold

Reference number: 451.OX.1180.OX
Movement: automatic, Caliber HUB 1280 "Unico 2"; ø 30 mm, height 6.75 mm; 43 jewels; 28,800 vph; mainplate and bridges with gray coating; 72-hour power reserve
Functions: hours, minutes, subsidiary seconds; flyback chronograph; date
Case: rose gold, ø 42 mm, height 13.45 mm; mounted to case with 6 titanium screws; sapphire crystal; transparent case back; water-resistant to 10 atm
Band: rose gold, folding clasp
Price: $52,500
Variations: titanium ($20,900); ceramic ($23,100)

Big Bang Integral All Black

Reference number: 451.CX.1140.CX
Movement: automatic, Caliber HUB 1280 "Unico 2"; ø 30 mm, height 6.75 mm; 43 jewels; 28,800 vph; mainplate and bridges with gray coating; 72-hour power reserve
Functions: hours, minutes, subsidiary seconds; flyback chronograph; date
Case: ceramic, ø 42 mm, height 13.45 mm; mounted to case with 6 titanium screws; sapphire crystal; transparent case back; water-resistant to 10 atm
Band: ceramic, folding clasp
Price: $23,100; limited to 500 pieces
Variations: rose gold ($52,500); titanium ($20,900)

Big Bang MP-11 Red Ceramic

Reference number: 911.CF.0113.RX
Movement: manually wound, Caliber HUB 9011; ø 34 mm, height 10.95 mm; 39 jewels; 28,800 vph; 7 spring barrels stacked at right angle to movement axes, energy redirected via bevel gears; black coating on bridges; 336-hour power reserve
Functions: hours, minutes (off-center); power reserve indicator
Case: ceramic, ø 45 mm, height 14.4 mm; bezel mounted to case with 6 titanium screws; sapphire crystal; transparent case back; water-resistant to 3 atm
Band: rubber, folding clasp
Price: $86,000; limited to 100 pieces

Big Bang MP-11 Green Saxem

Reference number: 911. JG.0129.RX
Movement: manually wound, Caliber HUB 9011; ø 34 mm, height 10.95 mm; 39 jewels; 28,800 vph; 7 spring barrels stacked at right angle to movement axes, energy redirected via bevel gears; black coating on bridges; 336-hour power reserve
Functions: hours, minutes (off-center); power reserve indicator
Case: composite material ("Saxem"), ø 45 mm, height 14.4 mm; mounted to case with 6 titanium screws; sapphire crystal; transparent case back; water-resistant to 3 atm
Band: rubber, folding clasp
Price: $127,000; limited to 20 pieces

Big Bang Meca-10 Black Magic

Reference number: 414.CI.1123.RX
Movement: manually wound, Caliber HUB 1201; ø 34.8 mm, height 6.8 mm; 24 jewels; 21,600 vph; 240-hour power reserve
Functions: hours, minutes, subsidiary seconds; power reserve indicator
Case: ceramic, ø 45 mm, height 15.95 mm; mounted to case with 6 titanium screws; sapphire crystal; transparent case back; water-resistant to 10 atm
Band: rubber, folding clasp
Price: $27,300

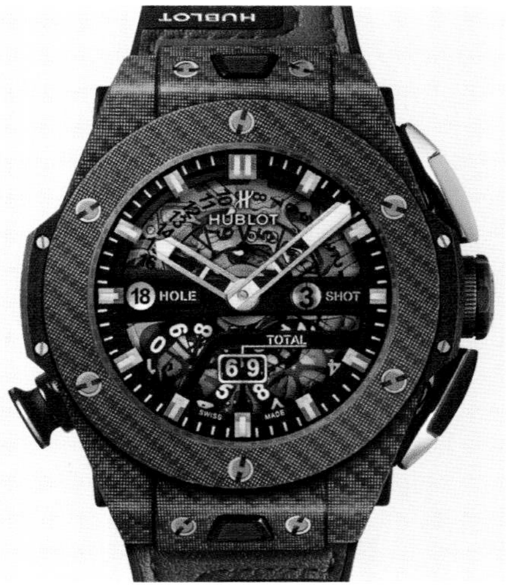

Big Bang Unico Golf Green Carbon

Reference number: 416.YG.5220.VR
Movement: automatic, Caliber HUB 1580 "Unico"; ø 34 mm, height 10.4 mm; 43 jewels; 28,800 vph; 72-hour power reserve
Functions: hours, minutes; mechanical golf counter per hole, total strokes, and hole number
Case: carbon fiber and Texalium, ø 45 mm, height 18.1 mm; bezel mounted to case with 6 titanium screws; sapphire crystal; transparent case back; water-resistant to 10 atm
Band: rubber, with calfskin layer, folding clasp
Price: $32,500; limited to 100 pieces

Big Bang Unico Full Magic Gold

Reference number: 441.MX.1138.RX
Movement: automatic, Caliber HUB 1280 "Unico 2"; ø 30 mm, height 6.75 mm; 43 jewels; 28,800 vph; mainplate and bridges with gray coating; 72-hour power reserve
Functions: hours, minutes, subsidiary seconds; flyback chronograph; date
Case: composite of yellow gold and ceramic ("Magic Gold"), ø 42 mm, height 14.5 mm; bezel mounted to case with 6 titanium screws; sapphire crystal; transparent case back; water-resistant to 10 atm
Band: rubber, folding clasp
Price: $34,600

Big Bang Unico Sang Bleu II Titanium Blue Pavé

Reference number: 418.NX.5107.RX.1604.MXM20
Movement: automatic, Caliber HUB 1240.MXM "Unico"; ø 34 mm, height 8.05 mm; 38 jewels; 28,800 vph; 72-hour power reserve
Functions: hours, minutes, subsidiary seconds (disk display with index corners); chronograph; date
Case: titanium, set with 172 diamonds, ø 45 mm, height 16.5 mm; bezel set with 48 diamonds and mounted to case with 6 titanium screws; sapphire crystal; transparent case back; water-resistant to 10 atm
Band: rubber, folding clasp
Price: $44,100

Classic Fusion Ferrari GT Titanium

Reference number: 526.NX.0124.VR
Movement: automatic, Caliber HUB 1281 "Unico 2"; ø 30 mm, height 6.75 mm; 43 jewels; 28,800 vph; mainplate and bridges with gray coating; 72-hour power reserve
Functions: hours, minutes, subsidiary seconds; flyback chronograph; date
Case: titanium, ø 45 mm, height 13.15 mm; bezel mounted to case with 4 titanium screws; sapphire crystal; transparent case back; water-resistant to 10 atm
Band: rubber, folding clasp
Price: $22,000; limited to 1,000 pieces

Classic Fusion Orlinski King Gold Alternative Pavé

Reference number: 550.OS.1800.RX.1804.ORL19
Movement: automatic, Caliber HUB 1100 (base Sellita SW300); ø 25.6 mm, height 3.6 mm; 25 jewels; 28,800 vph; personalized Hublot rotor; 42-hour power reserve
Functions: hours, minutes, sweep seconds
Case: rose gold, set with 112 diamonds, ø 40 mm, height 11.1 mm; bezel set with 54 diamonds, mounted to case with 6 titanium screws; sapphire crystal; transparent case back; water-resistant to 5 atm
Band: rubber, folding clasp
Price: $29,400

Classic Fusion King Gold Full Pavé

Reference number: 510.OX.9000.OX.3704
Movement: automatic, Caliber HUB 1112 (base Sellita SW300); ø 25.6 mm, height 3.6 mm; 25 jewels; 28,800 vph; personalized Hublot rotor; 42-hour power reserve
Functions: hours, minutes, sweep seconds; date
Case: rose gold, set with 100 diamonds, ø 45 mm, height 10.95 mm; bezel set with 126 diamonds, mounted to case with 6 titanium screws; sapphire crystal; transparent case back; water-resistant to 5 atm
Band: rose gold, set with 1,248 diamonds, folding clasp
Price: $120,000

Classic Fusion Gold Crystal Firmament

Reference number: 511.CX.0660.LR
Movement: automatic, Caliber HUB 1112 (base Sellita SW300); ø 25.6 mm, height 3.6 mm; 25 jewels; 28,800 vph; personalized Hublot rotor; 42-hour power reserve
Functions: hours, minutes, sweep seconds
Case: ceramic, ø 45 mm, height 10.95 mm; mounted to case with 6 titanium screws; sapphire crystal; transparent case back; water-resistant to 5 atm
Band: rubber, with reptile skin insert, folding clasp
Remarks: dial decorated with unique gold crystals
Price: $21,100

Classic Fusion Chronograph Chelsea Football Club

Reference number: 521.EX.7179.RX.CFC19
Movement: automatic, Caliber HUB 1143; ø 30 mm, height 6.9 mm; 59 jewels; 28,800 vph; 42-hour power reserve
Functions: hours, minutes, subsidiary seconds; chronograph; date
Case: ceramic, ø 45 mm, height 13.05 mm; mounted to case with 6 titanium screws; sapphire crystal; transparent case back; water-resistant to 5 atm
Band: rubber, buckle
Remarks: special edition for Chelsea Football Club
Price: $14,100; limited to 100 pieces

Big Bang One Click Sang Bleu King Gold Pink Diamonds

Reference number: 465.OS.89P8.VR.1204.MXM20
Movement: automatic, Caliber HUB 1710 (base Zenith Elite 670); ø 26.2 mm, height 3.7 mm; 27 jewels; 28,800 vph; 50-hour power reserve
Functions: hours, minutes, sweep seconds (disk display with index corners)
Case: rose gold, ø 39 mm, height 12.55 mm; bezel set with 48 diamonds, mounted to case with 6 titanium screws; sapphire crystal; transparent case back; water-resistant to 10 atm
Band: rubber with calfskin layer, folding clasp
Price: $29,400; limited to 100 pieces

Spirit of Big Bang King Gold Rainbow

Reference number: 641.OX.0110.LR.0999
Movement: automatic, Caliber HUB 4700 (base Zenith El Primero); ø 30 mm, height 6.6 mm; 31 jewels; 36,000 vph; 50-hour power reserve
Functions: hours, minutes, subsidiary seconds; chronograph; date
Case: rose gold, set with 166 precious stones, 42 × 51 mm, height 14.1 mm; bezel set with 54 precious stones, mounted to case with 6 titanium screws; sapphire crystal; transparent case back; water-resistant to 10 atm
Band: rubber, with reptile skin layer, folding clasp
Remarks: flange set with 89 precious stones
Price: $93,700

Spirit of Big Bang Meca-10 Titanium

Reference number: 614.NX.1170.RX
Movement: manually wound, Caliber HUB 1233; 31.25 × 32.9 mm, height 6.8 mm; 26 jewels; 21,600 vph; skeletonized movement; 240-hour power reserve
Functions: hours, minutes, subsidiary seconds; power reserve indicator
Case: titanium, 39 × 45 mm, height 14.45 mm; bezel mounted to case with 6 titanium screws; sapphire crystal; transparent case back; water-resistant to 5 atm
Band: rubber, folding clasp
Price: $23,100
Variations: rose gold ($44,100); black ceramic ($27,300)

Big Bang Unico Yellow Sapphire

Reference number: 441.JY.4909.RT
Movement: automatic, Caliber HUB 1280 "Unico 2"; ø 30 mm, height 6.75 mm; 43 jewels; 28,800 vph; mainplate and bridges with gray coating; 72-hour power reserve
Functions: hours, minutes, subsidiary seconds; flyback chronograph; date
Case: sapphire crystal, ø 42 mm, height 14.5 mm; mounted to case with 6 titanium screws; sapphire crystal; transparent case back; water-resistant to 5 atm
Band: rubber, folding clasp
Price: $95,000; limited to 100 pieces

Caliber HUB 1240

Automatic; column-wheel control of chronograph functions; silicon pallet lever and escapement, removable escapement; double-pawl automatic winding (Pellaton system), winding rotor on ceramic ball bearings; single barrel spring, 70-hour power reserve
Functions: hours, minutes, subsidiary seconds; flyback chronograph; date
Diameter: 30.4 mm; **Height:** 8.05 mm
Jewels: 38
Balance: glucydur
Frequency: 28,800 vph
Hairspring: flat spring with fine regulation
Shock protection: Incabloc
Remarks: 330 parts

Caliber HUB 1201

Manually wound skeletonized movement; silicon pallet lever and escape wheel; double mainspring barrel, 240-hour power reserve
Functions: hours, minutes, subsidiary seconds; power reserve indicator; date
Diameter: 34.80 mm
Height: 6.8 mm
Jewels: 24
Balance: CuBe
Frequency: 21,600 vph
Balance spring: flat hairspring with fine adjustment
Shock protection: Incabloc
Remarks: 223 parts

Caliber HUB 1280

Automatic; column-wheel control of chronograph functions; silicon pallet lever and escapement, removable escapement; double-pawl automatic winding (Pellaton system), winding rotor with ceramic ball bearing; single spring barrel, 72-hour power reserve
Functions: hours, minutes, subsidiary seconds; flyback chronograph; date
Diameter: 30 mm; **Height:** 6.75 mm
Jewels: 43
Balance: glucydur
Frequency: 28,800 vph
Balance spring: flat hairspring with fine adjustment
Shock protection: Incabloc
Remarks: 354 parts

ITAY NOY

Our relationship to precious objects is complex and ultimately reveals as much about ourselves as about the object. Furthermore, the relationship we build up with precious objects is special. Itay Noy's watches, each unique in its look and feel, seem made to foster this conversation and, in many ways, keep it going. Noy, who hails from and lives in Israel, has been producing watches that immediately fire up the imagination.

His journey began with the City Squares model, which shows time on the backdrop of a map of the owner's favorite or native city. In 2013, Noy showcased a square watch run on a Technotime automatic movement with a face-like dial that changes with the movement of the hands, a tongue-in-cheek reminder of our daily communication with our phones and the meaning of the frame.

Exploring this intimacy between the watch and the owner is an endless source of inspiration for Noy, a jeweler by trade who, with time, as it were, has begun reaching into the engineer's magic box—including working on a bespoke movement with a Swiss firm. In 2016, he created the Chrono Gears, which essentially runs on a large, invisible circular gear that drives a.m. and p.m. indicators and more. A year later, Time Tone, another "dynamic dial," to use his term, gave the owner the choice of a colored hour disk that only he or she would know, while the minute hand does its work in the center of the dial. The Full Month shows the date or the moon appearing through a circle of digits carved into the dial. The 2019 object is a subtle reminder that hours are almost irrelevant, but every minute counts: ReOrder has the hours digitally flashing on a sandwich dial, haphazardly it would seem. . . . In 2020, he returned to the map idea with Night Flight, replicating cities from around the world on the dial using lacquer and gold. Turn the watch around and you are looking out an airplane window at the movement.

ITAY NOY
19 Mazal Arieh
Old Jaffa
Israel

Tel. (for customer questions):
+97235247380

E-mail (for customer questions):
studio@itay-noy.com

Website:
www.itay-noy.com

Founded:
2000

Number of employees:
4

Annual production:
150

U.S distribution:
Please contact Studio ITAY NOY for information.
www.itay-noy.com

Most important collections/price range:
ReOrder, Full Month, Chrono Gears, Part Time, Night Flight / $2,400 to $16,800

Night Flight Jerusalem

Reference number: NF.Jerusalem
Movement: manually wound skeleton 6497-1; ø 36.6 mm, height 4.5 mm; 17 jewels; 18,000 vph; 38-hour power reserve
Functions: hours, minutes, subsidiary seconds
Case: stainless steel with black PVD, ø 44 mm, height 12 mm; sapphire crystal dome; transparent case back; water-resistant to 5 atm
Dial: layers of lacquer combined with gold
Band: calfskin, double folding clasp
Price: $16,800
Variations: different world cities

Rally

Reference number: RALLY.BPVD
Movement: manually wound skeleton 6498-1; ø 36.6 mm, height 4.5 mm; 17 jewels; 21,600 vph; 38-hour power reserve
Functions: hours, minutes, subsidiary seconds
Case: stainless steel with black PVD, ø 44 mm, height 12 mm; sapphire crystal dome; transparent case back; water-resistant to 5 atm
Band: calfskin, double folding clasp
Price: $5,150; limited to 99 numbered pieces
Variations: stainless steel

Fractal

Reference number: FRAC.N1
Movement: Caliber IN.VmF5400, automatic extra-thin microrotor; 30 mm, height 3 mm; 29 jewels; 21,600 vph; 48-hour power reserve
Functions: hours, minutes, sweep seconds
Case: stainless steel with black PVD, 40 mm × 44 mm, height 6.24 mm; sapphire crystal box; transparent case back; water-resistant to 5 atm
Band: calfskin, double folding clasp
Price: $11,800; unique piece
Variations: 8 different fractals

ReOrder

Reference number: REORDER.BL
Movement: manually wound IN.IP13; ø 36.6 mm, height 5.5 mm; 20 jewels; 21,600 vph; 42-hour power reserve
Functions: dynamic dial with 12 digit-shaped windows indicating hours, minutes, and central seconds
Case: stainless steel, ø 44 mm, height 12 mm; sapphire crystal dome; transparent case back; water-resistant to 5 atm
Band: calfskin, double folding clasp
Price: $6,800; limited and numbered edition of 24 pieces
Variations: blue, white, and gold-plated

Full Month—Moon

Movements: automatic, Caliber IN.VMF5400; ø 30 mm, height 3 mm; 29 jewels; 21,600 vph; extra-thin microrotor; 48-hour power reserve
Functions: hours, minutes, sweep seconds; full date window
Case: stainless steel, 40 mm × 44 mm, height 7.44 mm; sapphire crystal; transparent case back; water-resistant to 5 atm
Band: calfskin, double folding clasp
Remarks: date projected through digit-shaped slits in dial
Price: $11,800; limited and numbered edition of 18 pieces

Full Month

Reference number: FM-NUM.WT
Movements: automatic, Caliber IN.VMF5400; ø 30 mm, height 3 mm; 29 jewels; 21,600 vph; extra-thin microrotor; 48-hour power reserve
Functions: hours, minutes, sweep seconds; full date window
Case: stainless steel, 40 mm × 44 mm, height 6.44 mm; sapphire crystal box (+1.2 mm); sapphire crystal; transparent case back; water-resistant to 5 atm
Band: calfskin, double folding clasp
Remarks: date projected through digit-shaped slits in dial
Price: $9,800; limited and numbered edition of 18 pieces

Time Tone

Reference number: TT.BL
Movement: manually wound IN.IP13; ø 36.6 mm, height 5.5 mm; 20 jewels; 21,600 vph; 42-hour power reserve
Functions: hours with special disk display, minutes, seconds
Case: stainless steel, ø 44 mm, height 12 mm; sapphire crystal; transparent case back; water-resistant to 5 atm
Band: calfskin, double folding clasp
Remarks: dynamic dial with colored disks owner can choose as "secret" hour hand
Price: $5,800; limited and numbered edition of 24 pieces
Variations: blue or black

Celestial Time

Reference number: CT.W
Movement: manually wound IN.IP13; ø 36.6 mm, height 5.5 mm; 20 jewels; 21,600 vph; 42-hour power reserve
Functions: hours displayed as astrological sign, minutes, seconds
Case: stainless steel, ø 44 mm, height 12 mm; sapphire crystal dome; transparent case back; water-resistant to 5 atm
Band: calfskin, double folding clasp
Remarks: dynamic dial with zodiac signs owner can choose as "secret" hour hand
Price: $5,800; limited and numbered edition of 24 pieces
Variations: Western or Chinese zodiac signs

Chrono Gears

Reference number: CG.BK
Movement: manually wound IN.IP13; ø 36.6 mm, height 5.5 mm; 20 jewels; 21,600 vph; 42-hour power reserve
Functions: chronogear hand indicator for a.m./p.m., chronogear hand indicator for 8 time situations, central hours, minutes, seconds
Case: stainless steel, ø 44 mm, height 12 mm; sapphire crystal; transparent case back; water-resistant to 5 atm
Band: calfskin, double folding clasp
Price: $6,800; limited and numbered edition of 24 pieces
Variations: blue dial

Part Time

Reference number: PT-DN.BL
Movement: manually wound IN.DD&6498-1, ø 36.6 mm, height 5.2 mm; 17 jewels; 21,600 vph, 38-hour power reserve
Functions: hours from 6 a.m.–6 p.m., hours from 6 p.m.–6 a.m., analog hours, moon disk, sun disk, minutes, subsidiary seconds
Case: stainless steel, ø 41.6 mm × 44.6 mm, height 10.6 mm; sapphire crystal; transparent case back; water-resistant to 5 atm
Band: calfskin, double folding clasp
Price: $6,800; limited and numbered edition of 24 pieces
Variations: blue or black

DiaLOG

Reference number: DiaLOG.Num
Movement: manually wound, ETA Caliber 6498-1; ø 36.6 mm, height 4.5 mm; 17 jewels; 21,600 vph, 38-hour power reserve
Functions: hours, minutes, subsidiary seconds
Case: stainless steel, ø 41.6 mm × ø 44.6 mm, height 10 mm; sapphire crystal; screw-down case back; water-resistant to 50 m
Band: calfskin, double folding clasp
Price: $4,400; limited to 99 numbered pieces

X-Ray

Reference number: XRAY6498.INV
Movement: manually wound, ETA Caliber 6498-1; ø 36.6 mm, height 4.5 mm; 17 jewels; 21,600 vph; 38-hour power reserve
Functions: hours, minutes, subsidiary seconds
Case: stainless steel, ø 41.6 mm, height 10 mm; sapphire crystal; screw-down case back; water-resistant to 5 atm
Band: calfskin, double folding clasp
Price: $3,640; limited and numbered edition of 99 pieces
Variations: gold-plated dial ($3,900); brown leather strap

Open Mind

Reference number: OM-S
Movement: manually wound, ETA Caliber 6497-1; ø 36.6 mm, height 4.5 mm; 17 jewels; 21,600 vph; open-worked dial reveals escapement; 38-hour power reserve
Functions: hours, minutes, subsidiary seconds
Case: stainless steel, ø 44 mm, height 12 mm; sapphire crystal; transparent case back; water-resistant to 5 atm
Band: calfskin, double folding clasp
Price: $4,400; limited to 99 numbered pieces
Variations: blue or black dial; black or brown leather band

Identity Hebrew

Reference number: ID-HEB.BL
Movement: automatic, ETA Caliber 2824-2, ø 25.6 mm, height 4.6 mm; 25 jewels; 28,800 vph; 38-hour power reserve
Functions: hours, minutes, sweep seconds, quick-set date window
Case: stainless steel 316L, ø 42.4 mm, height 10 mm; sapphire crystal; screw-down case back; water-resistant to 50 m
Band: calfskin, folding clasp
Price: $2,800; limited and numbered edition of 99 pieces
Variations: black or brown leather band

Landscape

Reference number: LS.B
Movement: automatic, Caliber TT651-24H; ø 26.2 mm, height 5.25 mm; 21 jewels; 28,800 vph; 42-hour power reserve
Functions: hours, minutes, sweep seconds; quick-set big date window, 2nd time zone, 24-hour indicator disk, day/night indicator
Case: stainless steel, square 42.4 mm × 42.4 mm, height 11.6 mm; sapphire crystal; transparent case back; water-resistant to 5 atm
Band: calfskin, double folding clasp
Price: $5,800; limited and numbered edition of 24 pieces
Variations: cityscape view; rubber strap

International Watch Co.
Baumgartenstrasse 15
CH-8201 Schaffhausen
Switzerland

Tel.:
+41-52-635-6565

E-mail:
info@iwc.com

Website:
www.iwc.com

Founded:
1868

Number of employees:
approx. 750

U.S. distributor:
IWC North America
645 Fifth Avenue, 5th Floor
New York, NY 10022
800-432-9330

Most important collections/price range:
Da Vinci, Pilot's, Portuguese, Ingenieur, Aquatimer, Pallweber / approx. $4,000 to $260,000

IWC

It was an American who laid the cornerstone for an industrial watch factory in Schaffhausen—now environmentally state-of-the-art facilities. In 1868, Florentine Ariosto Jones, watchmaker and engineer from Boston, crossed the Atlantic to the then low-wage venue of Switzerland to open the International Watch Company Schaffhausen.

Jones was a talented designer as well, who had a significant influence on the development of watch movements. Soon, he gave IWC its own seal of approval, the Ingenieursmarke (Engineer's Brand), a standard it still maintains today. The company has never deviated from that course, in spite of many different owners. In 2000, it joined Richemont Group, and has since vastly expanded its range of timepieces and added a number of movements to drive them. There are the rugged and sportive Pilot and Big Pilot watches, the refined Da Vincis, elegant Portofinos, and complicated Portuguese. And then there is the unabashedly retro Pallweber series, which borrows from a pocket watch from the 1880s showing digital time.

IWC movements include the Jones caliber, named for the IWC founder, and the pocket watch caliber 89, introduced in 1946 as the creation of then technical director Albert Pellaton. Four years later, Pellaton created the first IWC automatic movement and, with it, a company monument.

For 2020, IWC decided to equip all the Portuguese models with in-house calibers. These include the automatic 52000 and 82000 caliber families, which use Pellaton or double-pawl winding mechanisms. The chronographs are driven by the 89000 and 69000 calibers, which ensure precise measuring of stop times. Even the lower-priced Portuguese timepieces now feature a transparent case back. The Portuguese Automatic 40 is unusually small (40-millimeter diameter) for an IWC, and puts the small seconds in a classic space, at 6 o'clock.

As for the Perpetual Calendar 42, it debuts this complication in a compact timepiece for the first time, the Caliber 82650. The recent pride and joy of the company, however, is the tidal indicator of the Portuguese Yacht Club Moon & Tide.

Portuguese Chronograph

Reference number: IW371604
Movement: automatic, IWC Caliber 69355; ø 30 mm, height 7.9 mm; 27 jewels; 28,800 vph; column-wheel control; movement with perlage and finely finished with côtes de Genève; 46-hour power reserve
Functions: hours, minutes, subsidiary seconds; chronograph
Case: stainless steel, ø 41 mm, height 13 mm; sapphire crystal; transparent case back; water-resistant to 3 atm
Band: reptile skin, folding clasp
Price: $7,950
Variations: various dials; pink gold ($17,800)

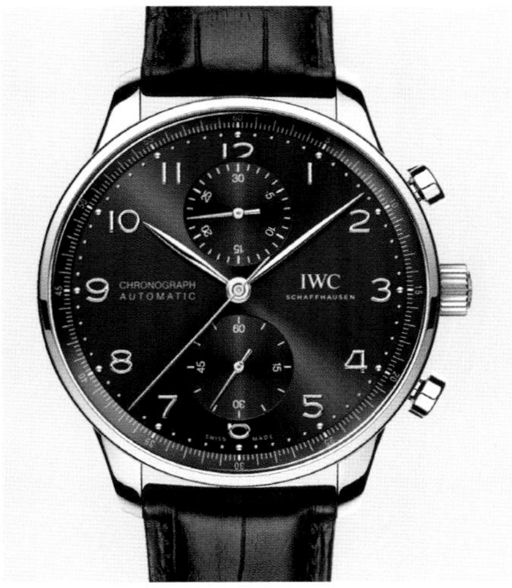

Portuguese Chronograph

Reference number: IW371615
Movement: automatic, IWC Caliber 69355; ø 30 mm, height 7.9 mm; 27 jewels; 28,800 vph; column-wheel control; movement with perlage and finely finished with côtes de Genève; 46-hour power reserve
Functions: hours, minutes, subsidiary seconds; chronograph
Case: stainless steel, ø 41 mm, height 13 mm; sapphire crystal; transparent case back; water-resistant to 3 atm
Band: reptile skin, folding clasp
Price: $7,950
Variations: various dials; pink gold ($17,800)

Portuguese Annual Calendar

Reference number: IW503502
Movement: automatic, IWC Caliber 52850; ø 37.8 mm, height 8.95 mm; 36 jewels; 28,800 vph; movement decorated with perlage and côtes de Genève; 168-hour power reserve
Functions: hours, minutes, subsidiary seconds; power reserve indicator; annual calendar with date, weekday, month
Case: stainless steel, ø 44.2 mm, height 14.9 mm; sapphire crystal; transparent case back; water-resistant to 3 atm
Band: reptile skin, folding clasp
Price: $20,900

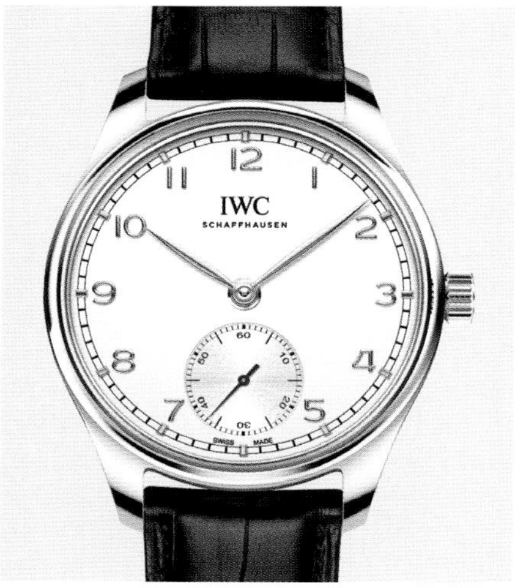

Portuguese Automatic 40

Reference number: IW358303
Movement: automatic, IWC Caliber 82200; ø 30 mm, height 6.6 mm; 31 jewels; 28,800 vph; Pellaton winding system; movement with perlage and finely finished with côtes de Genève; 60-hour power reserve
Functions: hours, minutes, subsidiary seconds
Case: stainless steel, ø 40.4 mm, height 12.3 mm; sapphire crystal; transparent case back; water-resistant to 3 atm
Band: reptile skin, folding clasp
Price: $12,700
Variations: pink gold ($16,900)

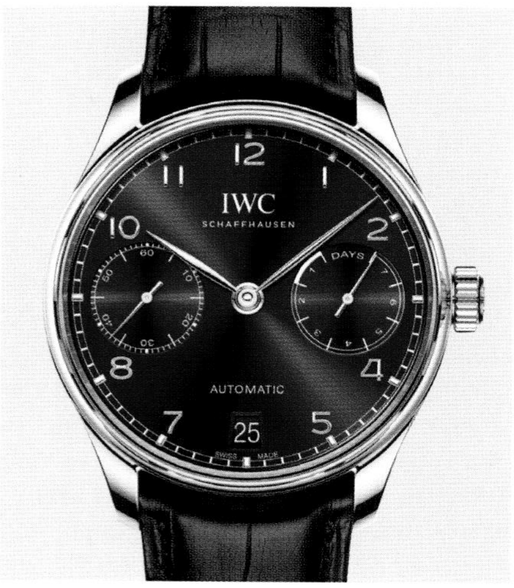

Portuguese Automatic

Reference number: IW500714
Movement: automatic, IWC Caliber 52010; ø 37.8 mm, height 7.5 mm; 31 jewels; 28,800 vph; Pellaton winding system; 168-hour power reserve
Functions: hours, minutes, subsidiary seconds; power reserve indicator; date
Case: stainless steel, ø 42.3 mm, height 14.1 mm; sapphire crystal; transparent case back; water-resistant to 3 atm
Band: reptile skin, folding clasp
Price: $12,700
Variations: various dial colors; pink gold ($23,900)

Portuguese Perpetual Calendar 42

Reference number: IW344202
Movement: automatic, IWC Caliber 82650; ø 30 mm, height 7.8 mm; 46 jewels; 28,800 vph; Pellaton winding system; rhodium-plated movement; 60-hour power reserve
Functions: hours, minutes, sweep seconds; perpetual calendar with date, weekday, month, moon phase
Case: pink gold, ø 42.4 mm, height 13.8 mm; sapphire crystal; transparent case back; water-resistant to 3 atm
Band: reptile skin, buckle
Price: $32,900
Variations: stainless steel ($22,900)

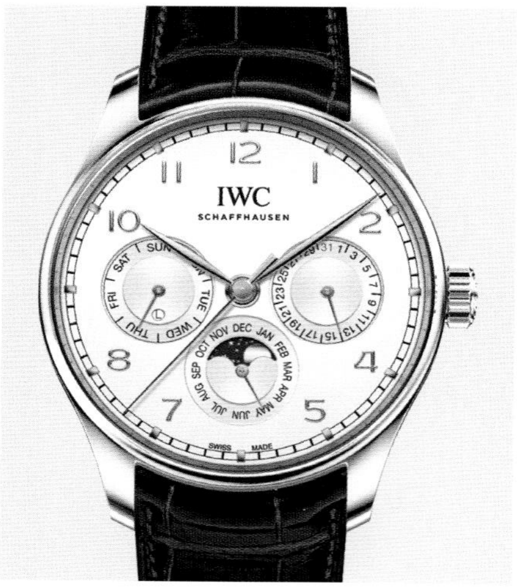

Portuguese Perpetual Calendar 42

Reference number: IW344203
Movement: automatic, IWC Caliber 82650; ø 30 mm, height 7.8 mm; 46 jewels; 28,800 vph; Pellaton winding system; rhodium-plated movement; 60-hour power reserve
Functions: hours, minutes, sweep seconds; perpetual calendar with date, weekday, month, moon phase
Case: stainless steel, ø 42.4 mm, height 13.8 mm; sapphire crystal; transparent case back; water-resistant to 3 atm
Band: reptile skin, folding clasp
Price: $22,900
Variations: pink gold ($32,900)

Ingenieur Chronograph

Reference number: IW380802
Movement: automatic, IWC Caliber 69375; ø 30 mm, height 7.9 mm; 33 jewels; 28,800 vph; column-wheel control; movement decorated with perlage and côtes de Genève; 46-hour power reserve
Functions: hours, minutes, subsidiary seconds; chronograph; date
Case: stainless steel, ø 42.3 mm, height 14.9 mm; sapphire crystal; transparent case back; screw-in crown; water-resistant to 12 atm
Band: stainless steel, folding clasp
Price: $7,950

Pilot's Watch Chronograph Edition "Antoine de Saint Exupéry"

Reference number: IW377713
Movement: automatic, IWC Caliber 79320 (base ETA 7750); ø 30 mm, height 7.9 mm; 25 jewels; 28,800 vph; movement with perlage and finely finished with côtes de Genève; 44-hour power reserve
Functions: hours, minutes, subsidiary seconds; chronograph; date, weekday
Case: stainless steel, ø 43 mm, height 15.4 mm; sapphire crystal; screw-in crown; water-resistant to 6 atm
Band: calfskin, buckle
Price: $5,500

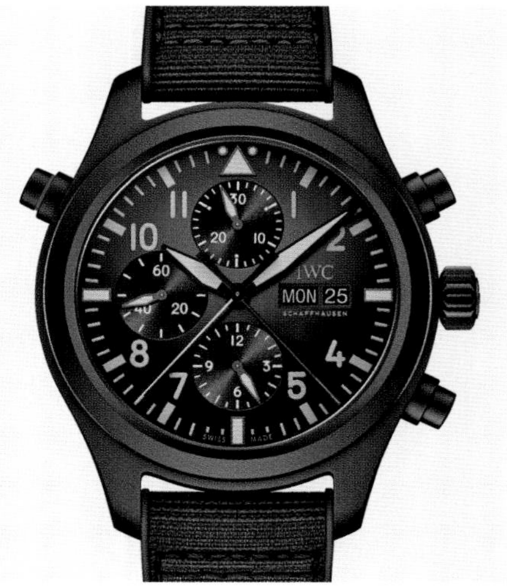

Pilot's Watch Double Chronograph Top Gun Ceratanium

Reference number: IW371815
Movement: automatic, IWC Caliber 79420 (base ETA 7750); ø 30 mm, height 7.9 mm; 29 jewels; 28,800 vph; amagnetic soft iron core; 44-hour power reserve
Functions: hours, minutes, subsidiary seconds; flyback chronograph; date, weekday
Case: special ceramic- and titanium-based alloy (Ceratanium), ø 44 mm, height 16.7 mm; sapphire crystal; screw-in crown; water-resistant to 6 atm
Band: rubber, with textile layer, buckle
Price: $14,600

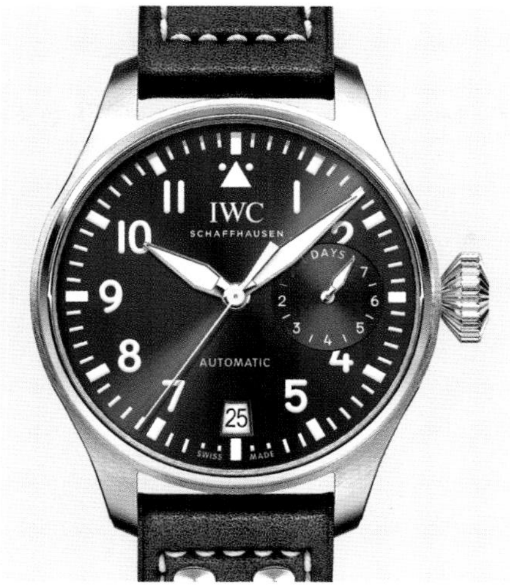

Big Pilot's Watch Edition "Le Petit Prince"

Reference number: IW501002
Movement: automatic, IWC Caliber 52110; ø 38.2 mm, height 7.6 mm; 31 jewels; 28,800 vph; 2 spring barrels; Pellaton winding system; amagnetic soft iron core; 168-hour power reserve
Functions: hours, minutes, sweep seconds; power reserve indicator; date
Case: stainless steel, ø 46.2 mm, height 15.5 mm; sapphire crystal; screw-in crown; water-resistant to 6 atm
Band: calfskin, folding clasp
Price: $12,900

Portuguese Yacht Club Chronograph

Reference number: IW390701
Movement: automatic, IWC Caliber 89361; ø 30 mm, height 7.5 mm; 38 jewels; 28,800 vph; column-wheel control of chronograph functions; 68-hour power reserve
Functions: hours, minutes, subsidiary seconds; flyback chronograph; date
Case: stainless steel, ø 44.6 mm, height 14.3 mm; sapphire crystal; transparent case back; screw-in crown; water-resistant to 6 atm
Band: stainless steel, folding clasp
Price: $13,100

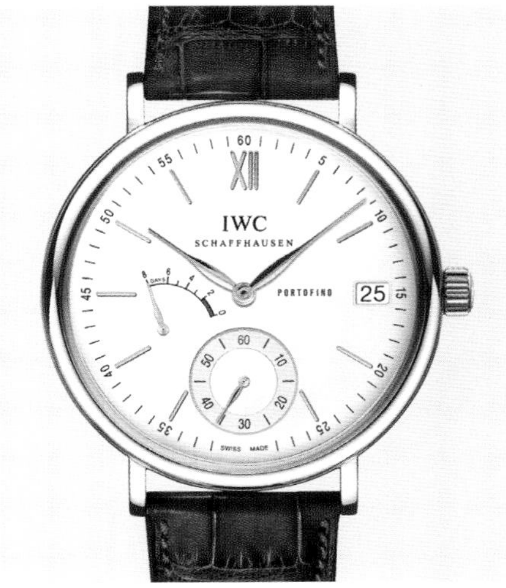

Portofino Hand-Wound Eight Days

Reference number: IW510103
Movement: manually wound, IWC Caliber 59210; ø 37.8 mm, height 5.8 mm; 30 jewels; 28,800 vph; Breguet hairspring; 192-hour power reserve
Functions: hours, minutes, subsidiary seconds; power reserve indicator; date
Case: stainless steel, ø 45 mm, height 11.7 mm; sapphire crystal; transparent case back; water-resistant to 3 atm
Band: reptile skin, buckle
Price: $9,900

Portofino Automatic 34

Reference number: IW357404
Movement: automatic, IWC Caliber 35100 (base Sellita SW200-1); ø 25.6 mm, height 4.6 mm; 25 jewels; 28,800 vph; movement with perlage and finely finished with côtes de Genève; 42-hour power reserve
Functions: hours, minutes, sweep seconds
Case: stainless steel, ø 34 mm, height 8.6 mm; sapphire crystal; water-resistant to 3 atm
Band: stainless steel Milanese mesh, folding clasp
Price: $6,200

Aquatimer Chronograph Edition "Expedition Charles Darwin"

Reference number: IW379503
Movement: automatic, IWC Caliber 89365; ø 30 mm, height 7.5 mm; 35 jewels; 28,800 vph; 68-hour power reserve
Functions: hours, minutes, subsidiary seconds; chronograph; date
Case: bronze, ø 44 mm, height 16.9 mm; crown-activated inner bezel with 0-60 scale; sapphire crystal; screw-in crown; water-resistant to 30 atm
Band: rubber, buckle
Price: $10,600

Caliber 82200

Automatic; double-pawl winding (Pellaton system); single spring barrel, 60-hour power reserve
Functions: hours, minutes, subsidiary seconds
Diameter: 30 mm
Height: 6.6 mm
Jewels: 31
Frequency: 28,800 vph
Hairspring: flat hairspring
Remarks: movement with perlage and finely finished with côtes de Genève

Caliber 69355

Automatic; column-wheel control of chronograph functions; single spring barrel, 46-hour power reserve
Functions: hours, minutes, subsidiary seconds; chronograph
Diameter: 30 mm
Height: 7.9 mm
Jewels: 27
Balance: glucydur
Frequency: 28,800 vph
Hairspring: flat hairspring
Remarks: movement with perlage and finely finished with côtes de Genève

Caliber 82650

Automatic; double-pawl winding (Pellaton system); single spring barrel, 60-hour power reserve
Functions: hours, minutes, sweep seconds; perpetual calendar with date, weekday, month, moon phase
Diameter: 30 mm
Height: 7.8 mm
Jewels: 46
Frequency: 28,800 vph
Hairspring: flat hairspring
Remarks: movement with perlage and finely finished with côtes de Genève; 326 parts

Caliber 52615

Automatic; double-pawl winding (Pellaton system) with ceramic wheels; double spring barrel, 168-hour power reserve
Functions: hours, minutes, subsidiary seconds; power reserve indicator; perpetual calendar with month, weekday, date, double moon phase (for northern and southern hemispheres), 4-digit year display
Diameter: 37.8 mm
Height: 9 mm
Jewels: 54
Balance: with variable inertia
Frequency: 28,800 vph
Hairspring: Breguet
Shock protection: Incabloc

Caliber 89361

Automatic; double-pawl winding (Pellaton system), column-wheel control of chronograph functions; single spring barrel, 68-hour power reserve
Base caliber: 89000
Functions: hours, minutes, subsidiary seconds; flyback chronograph; date
Diameter: 30 mm
Height: 7.46 mm
Jewels: 38
Balance: glucydur with variable inertia
Frequency: 28,800 vph
Hairspring: flat hairspring
Shock protection: Incabloc
Remarks: concentric chronograph totalizer for minutes and hours

Caliber 98295 "Jones"

Manually wound; single spring barrel, 46-hour power reserve
Base caliber: 98000
Functions: hours, minutes, subsidiary seconds
Diameter: 38.2 mm
Height: 5.3 mm
Jewels: 18
Balance: screw balance with fine adjustment cams
Frequency: 18,000 vph
Balance spring: Breguet
Shock protection: Incabloc
Remarks: exceptionally long regulator index; three-quarter plate of German silver, hand-engraved balance cock

Manufacture Jaeger-LeCoultre
Rue de la Golisse, 8
CH-1347 Le Sentier
Switzerland

Tel.:
+41-21-852-0202

E-mail:
info@jaeger-lecoultre.com

Website:
www.jaeger-lecoultre.com

Founded:
1833

Number of employees:
over 1,000

Annual production:
approx. 50,000 watches

U.S. distributor:
Jaeger-LeCoultre
645 Fifth Avenue
New York, NY 10022
800-JLC-TIME
www.jaeger-lecoultre.com

Most important collections/price range:
Atmos / starting at $6,600; Duomètre / starting at $39,100; Geophysic / starting at $9,100; Master / starting at $5,700; Polaris / starting at $6,600; Rendez-Vous / starting at $8,700; Reverso / starting at $4,150

JAEGER-LECOULTRE

The Jaeger-LeCoultre *manufacture* has had a long and tumultuous history. In 1833, Antoine LeCoultre opened his own workshop for the production of gearwheels. Having made his fortune, he then did what many other artisans did: In 1866, he had a large house built and brought together all the craftspeople needed to produce timepieces, from the watchmakers to the turners and polishers. He outfitted the workshop with the most modern machinery of the day, all powered by a steam engine. "La Grande Maison" was the first watch *manufacture* in the Vallée de Joux.

At the start of the twentieth century, the grandson of the company founder, Jacques-David LeCoultre, built slender, complicated watches for the Paris manufacturer Edmond Jaeger. The Frenchman was so impressed with these that, after a few years of fruitful cooperation, he engineered a merger of the two companies.

In the 1970s, the German VDO Group (later Mannesmann) took over the company and helped it weather the quartz crisis.

Thanks to its inclusion in the Richemont stable, Jaeger-LeCoultre continued to grow. A vast array of calibers (around 1,200), including minute repeaters, tourbillons, and other *grandes complications,* a lubricant-free movement, and more than 400 patents, tell their own story. Today, it is the largest employer in the Vallée de Joux—just as it was back in the 1860s. The most enduring collection produced by the brand is probably the Reverso, which can swivel around to show a second watch face on the back. Jaeger-LeCoultre boasts other iconic collections, like the Master, the Polaris, the Rendez-Vous, and the Atmos.

The brand has always managed to unify technical wizardry with a very fine sense of esthetics, which is expressed in many models illustrating the many métiers d'art from the watch world. The most recent stunner is a Master Grande Tradition Grande Complication offer in sidereal time combined with a minute repeater that rings on sapphire crystal gongs soldered to the sapphire crystal itself for a more penetrating sound.

Polaris Date

Reference number: 906 86 70
Movement: automatic, JLC Caliber 899A/1; ø 26 mm, height 4.6 mm; 32 jewels; 28,800 vph; 38-hour power reserve
Functions: hours, minutes, sweep seconds; date
Case: stainless steel, ø 42 mm, height 13.1 mm; crown-activated inner bezel with 0-60 scale; sapphire crystal; water-resistant to 20 atm
Band: rubber, double folding clasp
Price: $7,600; limited to 800 pieces

Polaris Chronograph

Reference number: 902 81 80
Movement: automatic, JLC Caliber 751H; ø 25.6 mm, height 5.7 mm; 37 jewels; 28,800 vph; skeletonized rotor; 65-hour power reserve
Functions: hours, minutes; chronograph
Case: stainless steel, ø 42 mm, height 11.9 mm; sapphire crystal; transparent case back; water-resistant to 10 atm
Band: stainless steel, double folding clasp
Price: $10,700
Variations: calfskin strap

Master Control Date

Reference number: 401 84 20
Movement: automatic, JLC Caliber 899AC; ø 26 mm, height 3.7 mm; 32 jewels; 28,800 vph; 70-hour power reserve
Functions: hours, minutes, sweep seconds; date
Case: stainless steel, ø 40 mm, height 8.78 mm; sapphire crystal; transparent case back; water-resistant to 5 atm
Band: calfskin, double folding clasp
Price: $6,700

Master Control Calendar

Reference number: 414 84 20
Movement: automatic, JLC Caliber 866AA; ø 26 mm, height 6.15 mm; 34 jewels; 28,800 vph; 70-hour power reserve
Functions: hours, minutes, subsidiary seconds; full calendar with date, weekday, month, moon phase
Case: stainless steel, ø 40 mm, height 10.95 mm; sapphire crystal; transparent case back; water-resistant to 5 atm
Band: calfskin, double folding clasp
Price: $11,000

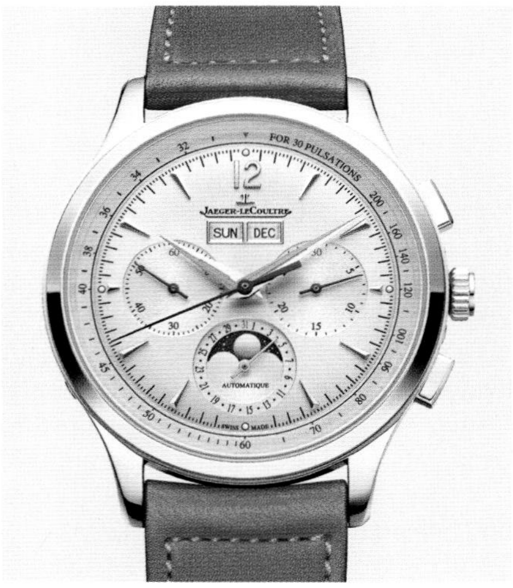

Master Control Chronograph Calendar

Reference number: 413 84 20
Movement: automatic, JLC Caliber 759; ø 25.6 mm; 41 jewels; 28,800 vph; column-wheel control of chronograph functions, gold rotor; 65-hour power reserve
Functions: hours, minutes, subsidiary seconds; chronograph; full calendar with date, weekday, month, moon phase
Case: stainless steel, ø 40 mm, height 12.05 mm; sapphire crystal; transparent case back; water-resistant to 5 atm
Band: calfskin, double folding clasp
Price: $11,600
Variations: rose gold

Master Control Memovox Timer

Reference number: 410 84 8J
Movement: automatic, JLC Caliber 956AA; ø 28 mm, height 7.47 mm; 24 jewels; 28,800 vph; 45-hour power reserve
Functions: hours, minutes, sweep seconds; alarm with additional display of time remaining toll alarm signal; date
Case: stainless steel, ø 40 mm, height 12.39 mm; crown-activated scale ring with 0-60 scale; sapphire crystal; transparent case back; water-resistant to 5 atm
Band: reptile skin, buckle
Price: $15,600; limited to 250 pieces

Master Grande Tradition Grande Complication

Reference number: 526 24 60
Movement: manually wound, JLC Caliber 945A; ø 34.7 mm, height 12.56 mm; 52 jewels; 28,800 vph; flying 1-minute tourbillon; 40-hour power reserve
Functions: hours, minutes; sidereal time (on rotating tourbillon cage) with reference to celestial vault; minute repeater with sapphire crystal gongs soldered to sapphire crystal
Case: pink gold, ø 45 mm, height 16.05 mm; sapphire crystal; water-resistant to 5 atm
Band: reptile skin, double folding clasp
Remarks: star chart on dial with night-sky constellation of northern hemisphere
Price: on request; limited to 8 pieces

Reverso Tribute Duoface

Reference number: 398 84 82
Movement: manually wound, JLC Caliber 854A/2; 17.2 × 22 mm, height 3.8 mm; 19 jewels; 21,600 vph; 42-hour power reserve
Functions: hours, minutes, subsidiary seconds; additional 24-hour display (2nd time zone, on movement side)
Case: stainless steel, 28.3 × 47 mm, height 10.3 mm; sapphire crystal; water-resistant to 3 atm
Band: calfskin, double folding clasp
Remarks: case can be turned and rotated 180°
Price: $11,000

Reverso Tribute Moon

Reference number: 395 84 20
Movement: manually wound, JLC Caliber 853A; 17.2 × 22 mm, height 5.15 mm; 19 jewels; 21,600 vph; 42-hour power reserve
Functions: hours, minutes; additional 12-hour display (2nd time zone) and day/night indicator on movement side; date, moon phase
Case: stainless steel, 29.9 × 49.4 mm, height 10.9 mm; sapphire crystal; water-resistant to 3 atm
Band: reptile skin, double folding clasp
Remarks: case can be turned and rotated 180°
Price: $13,600

Reverso Classic Medium Small Seconds

Reference number: 243 85 22
Movement: manually wound, JLC Caliber 822/2; 17.2 × 22 mm, height 5.15 mm; 19 jewels; 21,600 vph; 42-hour power reserve
Functions: hours, minutes, additional 12-hour display (2nd time zone), day/night indicator on movement side; date, moon phase
Case: stainless steel, 29.9 × 49.4 mm, height 7.5 mm; sapphire crystal; water-resistant to 3 atm
Band: reptile skin, double folding clasp
Remarks: case can be turned and rotated 180°
Price: $6,300

Master Ultra Thin Moon Enamel

Reference number: 136 35 E1
Movement: automatic, JLC Caliber 925/2; ø 26 mm, height 4.9 mm; 30 jewels; 28,800 vph; 70-hour power reserve
Functions: hours, minutes, sweep seconds; date, moon phase
Case: white gold, ø 39 mm, height 10.04 mm; sapphire crystal; transparent case back; water-resistant to 5 atm
Band: reptile skin, buckle
Remarks: enamel dial
Price: $35,800; limited to 100 pieces

Master Ultra Thin Perpetual Enamel

Reference number: 130 35 E1
Movement: automatic, JLC Caliber 868A/2; ø 26 mm, height 4.72 mm; 46 jewels; 28,800 vph; 70-hour power reserve
Functions: hours, minutes, sweep seconds; perpetual calendar with date, weekday, month, moon phase, 4-digit year display
Case: white gold, ø 39 mm, height 10.44 mm; sapphire crystal; transparent case back; water-resistant to 5 atm
Band: reptile skin, buckle
Remarks: enamel dial
Price: $88,500; limited to 100 pieces

Master Ultra Thin Tourbillon

Reference number: 168 24 10
Movement: automatic, JLC Caliber 978G; ø 30 mm, height 6.5 mm; 33 jewels; 28,800 vph; 1-minute tourbillon; 45-hour power reserve
Functions: hours, minutes, subsidiary seconds (on tourbillon cage)
Case: pink gold, ø 40 mm, height 10.77 mm; sapphire crystal; transparent case back; water-resistant to 5 atm
Band: reptile skin, double folding clasp
Price: $70,500

Master Ultra Thin Date

Reference number: 123 84 20
Movement: automatic, JLC Caliber 899/1; ø 26 mm, height 3.3 mm; 32 jewels; 28,800 vph; 38-hour power reserve
Functions: hours, minutes, sweep seconds; date
Case: stainless steel, ø 39 mm, height 7.8 mm; sapphire crystal; transparent case back; water-resistant to 5 atm
Band: reptile skin, double folding clasp
Price: $7,500

Master Ultra Thin Perpetual

Reference number: 130 84 70
Movement: automatic, JLC Caliber 868/1; ø 27.8 mm, height 4.72 mm; 46 jewels; 28,800 vph; 38-hour power reserve
Functions: hours, minutes, sweep seconds; perpetual calendar with date, weekday, month, moon phase, 4-digit year display
Case: stainless steel, ø 39 mm, height 9.2 mm; sapphire crystal; transparent case back; water-resistant to 5 atm
Band: reptile skin, double folding clasp
Price: $19,950

Caliber 956

Automatic; automatic winding for time and alarm mechanisms; single spring barrel, 45-hour power reserve
Functions: hours, minutes, sweep seconds; date; alarm
Diameter: 28 mm
Height: 7.45 mm
Jewels: 23
Balance: glucydur
Frequency: 28,800 vph
Balance spring: flat hairspring
Remarks: perlage on mainplate, bridges with côtes de Genève, element for sounding board

Caliber 899AC

Automatic; silicon escapement; gold rotor; single spring barrel, 70-hour power reserve
Functions: hours, minutes, sweep seconds; date
Diameter: 26 mm
Height: 3.7 mm
Jewels: 32
Frequency: 28,800 vph
Remarks: mainplate with perlage, bridges with côtes de Genève; 218 parts

Caliber 866AA

Automatic; silicon escapement; gold rotor; single spring barrel, 70-hour power reserve
Functions: hours, minutes, subsidiary seconds; full calendar with date, weekday, month, moon phase
Diameter: 26 mm
Height: 5.65 mm
Jewels: 34
Balance: glucydur
Frequency: 28,800 vph
Remarks: mainplate with perlage, bridges with côtes de Genève

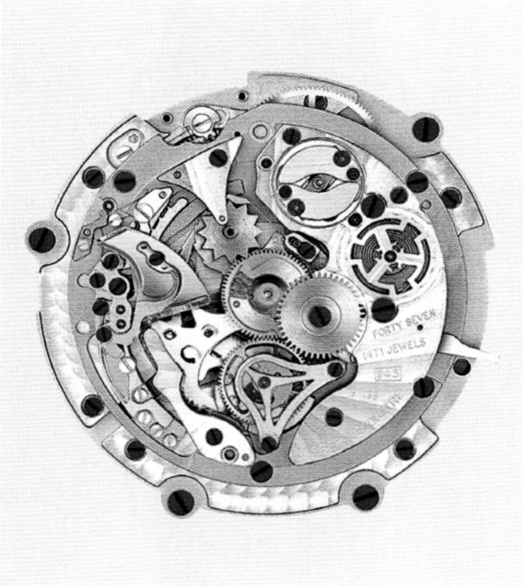

Caliber 945

Manually wound; silicon anchor with integrated pallets, flying tourbillon rotates with dial in 56 minutes (sidereal time, star time); single spring barrel, 48-hour power reserve
Functions: hours, minutes, quarter hour and minute repeater; perpetual calendar with date, month, celestial map with zodiac signs
Diameter: 34.7 mm
Height: 12.62 mm
Jewels: 49
Balance: screw balance
Frequency: 28,800 vph
Hairspring: flat hairspring
Remarks: repetition with "trebuchet" hammers to strengthen the impulses; 527 parts

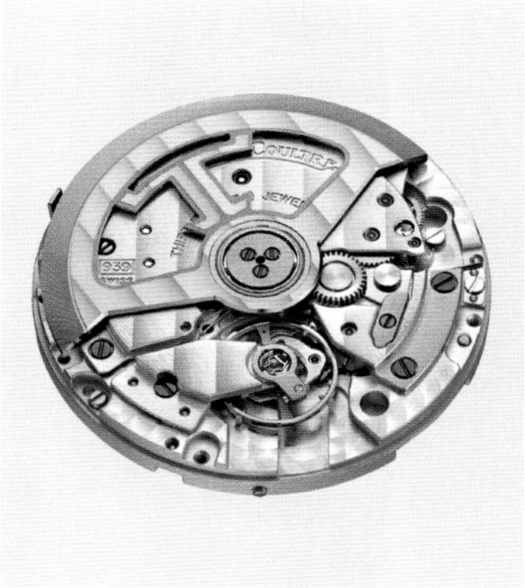

Caliber 939AA

Automatic; silicon escapement; gold rotor; single spring barrel, 70-hour power reserve
Functions: hours, minutes, sweep seconds; 2nd time zone; additional 12-hour display combined with world time; power reserve indicator; date
Diameter: 26 mm
Height: 4.9 mm
Jewels: 32
Frequency: 28,800 vph
Remarks: mainplate with perlage, bridges with côtes de Genève

Caliber 759

Automatic; silicon escapement, column-wheel control of chronograph functions, gold rotor; single spring barrel, 65-hour power reserve
Functions: hours, minutes, subsidiary seconds; chronograph; full calendar with date, weekday, month, moon phase
Diameter: 25.6 mm
Jewels: 41
Frequency: 28,800 vph

Caliber 854A/2

Manually wound; single spring barrel, 42-hour power reserve
Functions: hours, minutes, subsidiary seconds; additional 24-hour display (2nd time zone, on movement side)
Dimensions: 13 × 15.2 mm
Height: 3.8 mm
Jewels: 19
Balance: glucydur
Frequency: 21,600 vph
Hairspring: flat hairspring
Shock protection: Kif
Remarks: 160 parts

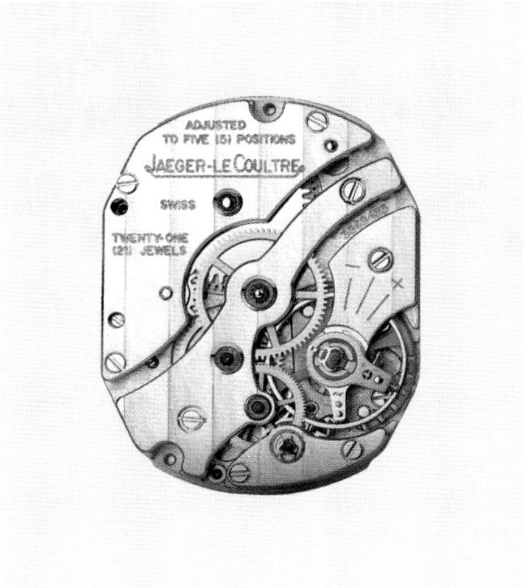

Caliber 822/2

Manually wound; single spring barrel, 42-hour power reserve
Functions: hours, minutes, subsidiary seconds
Dimensions: 17.2 × 22 mm
Height: 2.94 mm
Jewels: 19
Balance: screw balance
Frequency: 21,600 vph
Hairspring: flat hairspring

Caliber 925/2

Automatic; single spring barrel, 70-hour power reserve
Functions: hours, minutes, sweep seconds; date, moon phase
Diameter: 26 mm
Height: 4.9 mm
Jewels: 30
Frequency: 28,800 vph
Remarks: 245 parts

Caliber 978F

Automatic; 1-minute tourbillon; gold rotor; single spring barrel, 45-hour power reserve
Functions: hours, minutes, subsidiary seconds (on tourbillon cage); hand date (jumping from 15th to 16th of month)
Diameter: 30 mm
Height: 7.2 mm
Jewels: 33
Balance: glucydur with weighted screws
Frequency: 28,800 vph
Hairspring: Breguet hairspring
Shock protection: Kif
Remarks: mainplate with perlage, bridges with côtes de Genève; 302 parts

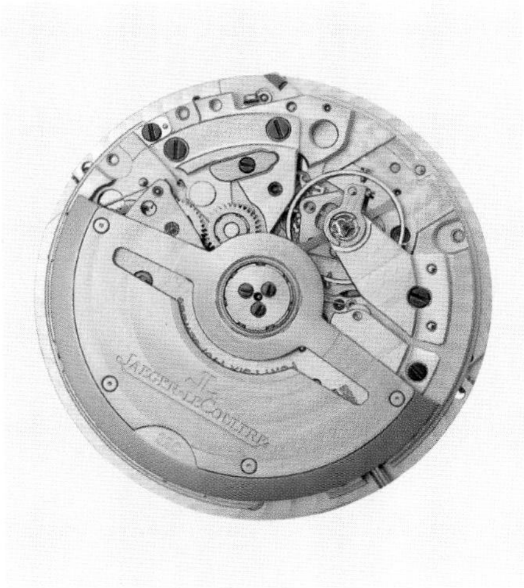

Caliber 868/A2

Automatic; single spring barrel, 70-hour power reserve
Functions: hours, minutes, sweep seconds; perpetual calendar with date, weekday, month, moon phase, 4-digit year display
Diameter: 26 mm
Height: 4.72 mm
Jewels: 46
Balance: glucydur
Frequency: 28,800 vph
Remarks: 332 parts

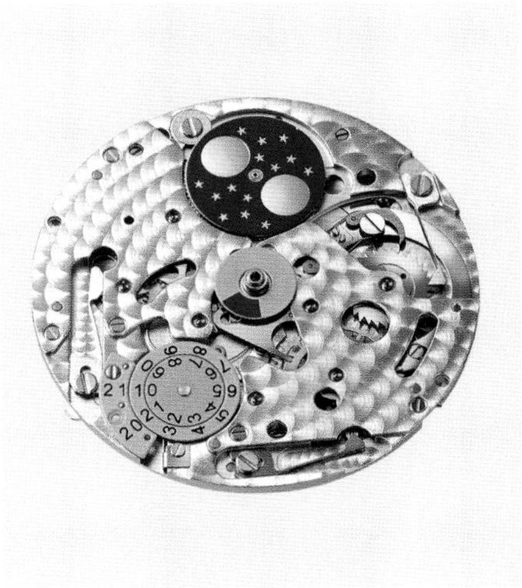

Caliber 868/1

Automatic; single spring barrel, 38-hour power reserve
Functions: hours, minutes, sweep seconds; perpetual calendar with date, weekday, month, moon phase, 4-digit year display
Diameter: 27.8 mm
Height: 4.72 mm
Jewels: 46
Balance: glucydur
Frequency: 28,800 vph
Remarks: 336 parts

JAQUET DROZ

Montres Jaquet Droz SA
CH-2300 La Chaux-de-Fonds
Switzerland

Tel.:
+41-32-924-2888

E-mail:
info@jaquet-droz.com

Website:
www.jaquet-droz.com

Founded:
1738

U.S. Distribution:
The Swatch Group (U.S.), Inc.
1200 Harbor Boulevard
Weehawken, NJ 07086
201-271-1400
www.swatchgroup.com

Most important collections:
Les Ateliers d'Art, Grande Seconde, Grande Seconde SW, Astrale Collection, Petite Heure Minute, Lady 8

Though this watch brand first gained real notice when it was bought by the Swatch Group in 2001, Jaquet Droz looks back on a long tradition. Pierre Jaquet-Droz (1721–1790) was actually supposed to be a pastor, but instead followed the call to become a mechanic and a watchmaker. In the mid-eighteenth century, he began to push the limits of micromechanics, and his enthusiasm for it quickly led him to work on watch mechanisms and more complicated movements, which he attempted to operate through purely mechanical means.

Jaquet-Droz became famous in Europe for his automatons. More than once, he had to answer to religious institutions, whose guardians of public morals suspected there might be some devil's work and witchcraft behind his mechanical children, scribes, and organists. He even designed prostheses. A small enterprise in La Chaux-de-Fonds still produces items of this applied art, proof that the name Jaquet-Droz is alive and well in the Jura mountains, and its watches combined with automatons continue to thrill collectors and enthusiasts alike.

The Swatch Group has developed an esthetically and technically sophisticated collection based on outstanding wristwatch movements from Le Brassus (the former Frédéric Piguet movement factory, now serving as the exclusive extended workbench for the top-of-the-line brands in the Swatch Group portfolio). In recent years, the classically beautiful watch dials have taken on a slightly modern look without losing any of their identity. The brand has also amazed the watch world with a number of beautiful and clever automatons for the wrist.

Grande Seconde "Skelet-One" Plasma Ceramic

Reference number: J003525542
Movement: automatic, Jaquet Droz Caliber 2663 SQ; ø 26.2 mm, height 3.8 mm; 30 jewels; 28,800 vph; double barrel spring, silicon anchor horns and hairspring; skeletonized movement, oscillating weight in pink gold; 68-hour power reserve
Functions: hours, minutes (off-center), subsidiary seconds
Case: plasma-treated ceramic, ø 41.5 mm, height 12.48 mm; sapphire crystal; transparent case back; water-resistant to 3 atm; **Band:** textile, folding clasp
Remarks: sapphire crystal dial
Price: $23,600

Grande Seconde Quantième Dark Blue Enamel

Reference number: J007023201
Movement: automatic, Jaquet Droz Caliber 2660Q2; ø 26.2 mm; 30 jewels; 28,800 vph; double barrel spring, silicon anchor horns and hairspring; oscillating weight in pink gold; 68-hour power reserve
Functions: hours, minutes (off-center), subsidiary seconds; date
Case: pink gold, ø 41 mm, height 12.1 mm; sapphire crystal; water-resistant to 3 atm
Band: reptile skin, buckle
Remarks: enamel dial
Price: $20,000

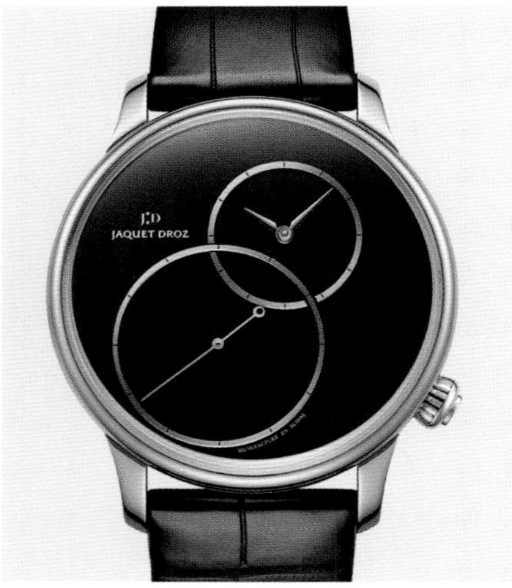

Grande Seconde Off-Centered Black Jade

Reference number: J006033275
Movement: automatic, Jaquet Droz Caliber 2663A.P; ø 26.2 mm, height 4.95 mm; 30 jewels; 28,800 vph; double barrel spring, silicon pallet horns and hairspring; 68-hour power reserve
Functions: hours, minutes (off-center), subsidiary seconds
Case: pink gold, ø 43 mm, height 12 mm; sapphire crystal; water-resistant to 3 atm
Band: reptile skin, buckle
Remarks: jade dial
Price: $25,900; limited to 88 pieces
Variations: opaline dial ($9,100)

Jörg Schauer
c/o Stowa GmbH & Co. KG
Gewerbepark 16
D-75331 Engelsbrand
Germany

Tel.:
+49-7082-942630

E-mail:
info@stowa.com

Website:
www.stowa.de

Founded:
1990

Number of employees:
25

Annual production:
approx. 500 watches

Distribution:
direct sales; online shop; please contact the address in Germany

JÖRG SCHAUER

Jörg Schauer's watches are first and foremost cool. The cases have been carefully worked; the look is planned to draw the eye. After all, he is a perfectionist and leaves nothing to chance. He works on every single case himself, polishing and performing his own brand of magic for as long as it takes to display his personal touch. This time-consuming process is one that Schauer believes is absolutely necessary. "I do this because I place a great deal of value on the fact that my cases are absolutely perfect," he explains. "I can do it better than anyone, and I would never let anyone else do it for me."

Schauer, a goldsmith by training, has been making watches since 1990. He began by doing one-off pieces in precious metals for collectors and then opened his business and simultaneously moved to stainless steel. His style is to produce functional, angular cases with visibly screwed-down bezels and straightforward dials in plain black or white. Forget finding any watch close to current trends in his collection; Schauer only builds timepieces that he genuinely likes.

Purchasing a Schauer is not that easy. He has chosen a strategy of genuine quality over quantity and produces only about 500 watches annually. This includes special watches like the One-Hand Durowe, running on a modified Unitas made by the movement manufacturer Durowe, which Schauer acquired in 2002. It has been revived as the One-Hand 44. His production structure is a vital part of his success and includes prototyping, movement modification, finishing, case production, dial painting, and printing—all done in Schauer's own workshop in Engelsbrand. Any support he needs from the outside he prefers to find among regional specialists.

One-Hand 44 Limited

Reference number: Einzeiger44limitiert
Movement: manually wound, modified ETA Caliber 6498; ø 36.6 mm, height 4.5 mm; 17 jewels; 18,000 vph; handmade gearwheel bridge; finely finished movement; 38-hour power reserve
Functions: hours (interim lines)
Case: stainless steel, ø 44 mm, height 10.6 mm; bezel fixed with 12 screws; sapphire crystal; transparent case back; water-resistant to 5 atm
Band: rubber, double folding clasp
Price: $2,646; limited to 100 pieces

Edition 10

Reference number: Ed10
Movement: automatic, ETA Caliber 7753; ø 30 mm, height 7.9 mm; 27 jewels; 28,800 vph; finished with ornamental stripes and blued screws, exclusive engraved "Schauer" rotor; 48-hour power reserve
Functions: hours, minutes, subsidiary seconds; chronograph
Case: stainless steel, ø 42 mm, height 15 mm; bezel fixed with 12 screws; sapphire crystal; transparent case back; water-resistant to 5 atm
Band: calfskin, double folding clasp
Price: $3,820
Variations: stainless steel bracelet ($4,110); reptile skin strap ($3,775); manually wound movement ($4,200)

Edition 12

Reference number: Ed12
Movement: automatic, ETA Caliber 7753; ø 30 mm, height 7.9 mm; 27 jewels; 28,800 vph; finished with ornamental stripes and blued screws, exclusive engraved "Schauer" rotor; 48-hour power reserve
Functions: hours, minutes, subsidiary seconds; chronograph
Case: stainless steel, ø 41 mm, height 15 mm; bezel fixed with 12 screws; sapphire crystal; transparent case back; water-resistant to 5 atm
Band: calfskin, double folding clasp
Price: $4,325
Variations: stainless steel bracelet ($4,725); reptile skin strap ($4,325); manually wound movement ($4,675)

JS WATCH CO.

JS Watch Co.
Hverfisgata 82B
101 Reykjavik
Iceland

Tel.:
+354-551-05-00

E-mail:
info@jswatch.com

Website:
www.jswatch.com

Founded:
2003

Number of employees:
5

Annual production:
500 pieces

Distribution:
Retail and direct sales
info@jswatch.com
+354-551-41-00

Most important collections/price range:
Collection 101, Frisland, Islandus, Sif N.A.R.T. / $1,650 to $11,860

When they weren't pillaging Europe and terrorizing populations from the British Isles to Russia, the Vikings were in fact a very hardworking and talented bunch, and when not roaming about, they tended their fields, their herds, their houses, and, as a number of exhibitions in the past twenty years have shown, made jewelry. Their work in this field is remarkable and fed their commercial supply chains, to use a modern term.

Iceland is where many descendants of the Norsemen live—a rugged and stark landscape, with over three hundred volcanoes and long winter nights. The ability to design and create fine jewelry lives on, and since 2003, the tiny country with a population of 330,000 has been producing watches as well, thanks to three friends, designer Grimkell Sigurþórsson, watchmaker Sigurður Gilbertsson, and Júlíus Heiðarsson.

Their first launch in 2005 of one hundred watches sold out within half a year, and so they persisted, using Swiss or German parts and movements (ETA, Sellita), but creating watches with some unique features paying tribute to their small but very creative country. The timepieces are inspired and named after an event, place, or year in Iceland or Icelandic history. "We made the Sif N.A.R.T., which was named for the first helicopter of Iceland's Coast Guard rescue teams and the North Atlantic Rescue Timer," says Sigurþórsson, now the Director of Design & Marketing of the tiny company. In 2018, when Iceland qualified for the Football World Cup, JS Watch Co. was ready with a limited series.

Other ways of tying their product to their country are the use of volcanic ash from the Eyjafjallajökull on the dial, or carving head letters (Höfðaletur) or Viking motifs into the case, as with the Frisland Goð Special Edition. The watches are otherwise very sober in style, classical and well balanced. They are worn by ordinary people, as well as some international stars who seem to appreciate the understatement radiated by this self-effacing brand

Vínland GMT

Reference number: Vin-41-3
Movement: automatic, Eterna Caliber 3914A, 30.0 mm, height 5.6 mm, 29 jewels; 28,800 vph; 65-hour power reserve
Function: small seconds counter, date display, GMT hand
Case: stainless steel, 0 41 mm, height 11.6 mm; sapphire crystal; transparent case back; water-resistant to 5 atm
Band: alligator, reptile skin, buckle
Price: $5,593
Variations: silver or black dial

Islandus 44 mm

Reference number: Isl-44-2
Movement: automatic, Soprod Caliber M100; 25.60 mm, height 3.60 mm; 25 jewels; 28,800 vph; 42-hour power reserve
Functions: central hours, minutes, subsidiary seconds; date
Case: stainless steel, 0 44 mm, height 11.5 mm; sapphire crystal; transparent case back; water-resistant to 5 atm
Band: ostrich and ostrich leg, buckle
Price: $2,244
Variations: black or white dials, roman numerals

World Cup MMXVIII Limited Edition

Reference number: Wor-43-1
Movement: automatic, Soprod Caliber M100; 25.60 mm, height 3.60 mm; 25 jewels; 28,800 vph; 42-hour power reserve
Functions: central hours, minutes, subsidiary seconds; date
Case: stainless steel, 0 43.3 mm, height 9.5 mm; sapphire crystal; transparent case back; water-resistant to 5 atm
Band: alligator, reptile skin, buckle
Price: $2,619
Variations: steel Milanese mesh bracelet, limited to 300 pieces

Uhrenfabrik Junghans
GmbH & Co. KG
Geisshaldenstrasse 49
D-78713 Schramberg

Tel.:
+49-742-218-0

E-mail:
info@junghans.de

Website:
www.junghans.de

Founded:
1861

Number of employees:
127

Annual production:
approx. 60,000 watches

U.S. distributor:
DKSH Luxury & Lifestyle North America Inc.
9-D Princess Road
Lawrenceville, NJ 08648
609-750-8800

Most important collections/price range:
Meister; Max Bill by Junghans; MEGA; Form / from approx. $395 to $2,500; special pieces up to $10,000

JUNGHANS

The town of Glashütte in Saxony was already a watchmaking name to be reckoned with when Erhard Junghans founded his factory in 1861 in Schramberg, a small town in the Black Forest. His son Arthur then developed it into a large-scale production site on the American industrial model. At the height of its success, the factory employed nearly three thousand men and women making nine thousand wall clocks and alarm clocks daily.

In the boom years after World War II, the company, with its logo featuring a star, produced mainly wristwatches. It went on to ring in modern times with its own solar and radio-controlled watches. Junghans was twice the official timekeeper at the Olympic Games, and for a long time it remained the largest chronometer maker in the world.

In 2009, Dr. Hans-Jochem Steim, a successful entrepreneur and political figure from Schramberg, purchased the company, which had gone bankrupt due to the shaky business practices of its previous owner. Thanks to heavy investments, the company was able to set up a new production and distribution schedule. Today, the brand boasts an extensive collection of high-quality wristwatches, ranging from genuine icons of design to major classics, all the way to sporty chronographs. In 2018, the company opened a watch- and clockmaking museum in the restored Terrassenbau, a century-old, terraced construction that allowed Junghans employees to work with strong natural lighting. A museum was installed in the building, devoted to company history and the history of the watch industry in the Black Forest. In the same year, Junghans came out with a brand-new radio-controlled movement, the Caliber J101, designed to mix high-tech with a classic look. To satisfy a broad market, Junghans manufactures quartz and mechanical watches, all in a sober Bauhaus idiom. The latest products include the Meister S, a sporty, masculine watch, and a series of watches that combine the radio-controlled Caliber J101 with the latest in solar technology, all packaged in the traditional Junghans look. A brand-new time signal enables rapid synchronization with a smartphone thanks to a specially developed app.

Meister Handaufzug Terrassenbau

Reference number: 027/3000.02
Movement: manually wound, Caliber J815.1 (base ETA 7001); ø 23.3 mm, height 2.5 mm; 17 jewels; 21,600 vph; rhodium-plated movement, blued screws, rotor with côtes de Genève; 42-hour power reserve
Functions: hours, minutes, subsidiary seconds
Case: stainless steel, ø 37.7 mm, height 7.3 mm; sapphire crystal; water-resistant to 5 atm
Band: reptile skin, buckle
Remarks: mineral glass case back with Junghans's terraced building as a motif
Price: $1,695; limited to 1,500 pieces

Meister Chronoscope Gold

Reference number: 027/9000.02
Movement: automatic, Caliber J880.1 (base ETA 7750 or Sellita SW500); ø 30 mm, height 7.9 mm; 25 jewels; 28,800 vph; rhodium-plated movement, blued screws, rotor with côtes de Genève; 48-hour power reserve
Functions: hours, minutes, subsidiary seconds; chronograph; date, weekday
Case: yellow gold, ø 40.7 mm, height 13.9 mm; sapphire crystal; transparent case back; water-resistant to 3 atm
Band: reptile skin, buckle
Price: $8,995
Variations: stainless steel ($2,045)

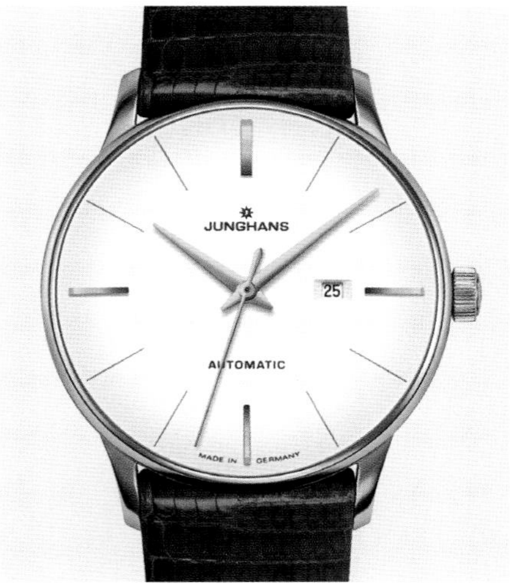

Meister Ladies' Automatic

Reference number: 027/7045.00
Movement: automatic, Caliber J840.1 (base ETA2671); ø 17.2 mm, height 4.8 mm; 25 jewels; 28,800 vph; rhodium-plated movement, blued screws, rotor with côtes de Genève; 38-hour power reserve
Functions: hours, minutes, subsidiary seconds; date
Case: stainless steel with rose gold PVD, ø 33.1 mm, height 13.9 mm; sapphire crystal; transparent case back; water-resistant to 3 atm
Band: reptile skin, buckle
Price: $1,495
Variations: stainless steel without PVD ($1,295); set with diamonds ($2,095)

Meister S Chronoscope

Reference number: 027/4025.01
Movement: automatic, Caliber J880.1 (base ETA 7750); ø 30 mm, height 7.9 mm; 25 jewels; 28,800 vph; rhodium-plated movement, blued screws, rotor with stripe finishing; 48-hour power reserve
Functions: hours, minutes, subsidiary seconds; chronograph; date, weekday
Case: stainless steel with black PVD, ø 45 mm, height 15.9 mm; sapphire crystal; screw-in crown; water-resistant to 20 atm
Band: rubber, with calfskin inserts, folding clasp
Price: $2,795; limited to 888 pieces

Meister S Chronoscope

Reference number: 027/4023.44
Movement: automatic, Caliber J880.1 (base ETA 7750); ø 30 mm, height 7.9 mm; 25 jewels; 28,800 vph; rhodium-plated movement, blued screws, rotor with stripe finishing; 48-hour power reserve
Functions: hours, minutes, subsidiary seconds; chronograph; date, weekday
Case: stainless steel, ø 45 mm, height 15.9 mm; sapphire crystal; screw-in crown; water-resistant to 20 atm
Band: stainless steel, double folding clasp
Price: $2,595
Variations: gray dial

Meister Pilot

Reference number: 027/3794.00
Movement: automatic, Caliber J880.4 (base ETA 2824-2 with Dubois Dépraz module); ø 30 mm, height 7.6 mm; 49 jewels; 28,800 vph; rhodium-plated movement, rotor with stripe finishing; 38-hour power reserve
Functions: hours, minutes, subsidiary seconds; chronograph
Case: stainless steel with DLC, ø 43.3 mm, height 14.4 mm; sapphire crystal; water-resistant to 10 atm
Band: calfskin, buckle
Price: $2,745
Variations: without DLC ($2,495)

Meister Calendar

Reference number: 027/4200.01
Movement: automatic, Caliber J800.3 (base ETA 2824-2 or Sellita SW200-1 with Dubois Dépraz module); ø 25.6 mm; 25 or 26 jewels; 28,800 vph; rhodium-plated movement, blued screws, rotor with stripe finishing; 42-hour power reserve
Functions: hours, minutes, sweep seconds; full calendar with date, weekday, month, moon phase
Case: stainless steel, ø 40.4 mm, height 12 mm; acrylic glass; transparent case back; water-resistant to 3 atm
Band: horse leather, buckle
Remarks: hardened Plexiglas with scratch-resistant coating
Price: $2,245
Variations: rose gold PVD ($2,195)

Meister MEGA Subsidiary Seconds

Reference number: 058/4901.00
Movement: quartz, multifrequency radio-controlled movement J101.66; radio-controlled time zone recognition and setting accurate to the second, app-based time-setting; "perpetual" date (also in quartz mode)
Functions: hours, minutes, subsidiary seconds; date
Case: stainless steel, ø 38.4 mm, height 9.6 mm; acrylic glass; transparent case back; water-resistant to 3 atm
Band: calfskin, buckle
Remarks: hardened Plexiglas with scratch-resistant coating
Price: $1,140; **Variations:** white dial and brown band or stainless steel band ($1,235)

Meister MEGA

Reference number: 058/4803.44
Movement: quartz, multifrequency radio-controlled movement J101.66; radio-controlled time zone recognition and setting accurate to the second, app-based time-setting; "perpetual" date (also in quartz mode)
Functions: hours, minutes, sweep seconds; date
Case: stainless steel, ø 38.4 mm, height 9.6 mm; sapphire crystal; transparent case back; water-resistant to 5 atm
Band: stainless steel, folding clasp
Price: $1,290
Variations: various straps and dials

Form A

Reference number: 027/4730.00
Movement: automatic, Caliber J800.2 (base ETA 2824-2 or Sellita SW200-1); ø 25.6 mm, height 4.6 mm; 25 or 26 jewels; 28,800 vph; 38-hour power reserve
Functions: hours, minutes, sweep seconds; date
Case: stainless steel, ø 39.3 mm, height 9.5 mm; sapphire crystal; transparent case back; water-resistant to 5 atm
Band: calfskin, buckle
Price: $995
Variations: various straps and dials; with quartz chronograph movement ($445)

Max Bill MEGA Solar

Reference number: 059/2022.48
Movement: quartz, multifrequency radio-controlled movement J101.85; radio-controlled time zone recognition and setting accurate to the second, app-based time-setting; "perpetual" date (also in quartz mode), solar charging
Functions: hours, minutes, sweep seconds; date
Case: titanium, ø 38 mm, height 9 mm; acrylic glass; water-resistant to 3 atm
Band: titanium Milanese mesh, folding clasp
Remarks: hardened Plexiglas with scratch-resistant coating
Price: $1,095
Variations: calfskin strap ($995)

Max Bill Chronoscope

Reference number: 027/4008.04
Movement: automatic, Caliber J880.2 (base ETA 7750); ø 30 mm, height 7.9 mm; 25 jewels; 28,800 vph; rhodium-plated movement, blued screws, rotor with stripe finishing; 48-hour power reserve
Functions: hours, minutes; chronograph; date, weekday
Case: stainless steel with black PVD, ø 40 mm, height 14.4 mm; acrylic glass; transparent case back; water-resistant to 3 atm
Band: calfskin, buckle
Remarks: hardened Plexiglas with scratch-resistant coating
Price: $2,095
Variations: various straps and dials

Form C

Reference number: 041/4771.00
Movement: quartz
Functions: hours, minutes, subsidiary seconds; chronograph; date
Case: stainless steel, ø 40 mm, height 10.5 mm; sapphire crystal; water-resistant to 5 atm
Band: calfskin, buckle
Price: $545
Variations: with Arab numerals; black dial and stainless steel Milanese mesh bracelet ($640)

Max Bill Automatic Bauhaus

Reference number: 027/4009.02
Movement: automatic, Caliber J800.1 (base ETA 2824-2 or Sellita SW200-1); ø 25.6 mm, height 4.6 mm; 25 or 26 jewels; 28,800 vph; 38-hour power reserve
Functions: hours, minutes, sweep seconds; date
Case: stainless steel, ø 38 mm, height 10 mm; sapphire crystal; transparent case back; water-resistant to 3 atm
Band: calfskin, buckle
Remarks: mineral glass case back with Bauhaus motif
Price: $1,325

Max Bill Small Automatic

Reference number: 027/4006.04
Movement: automatic, Caliber J800.2 (base ETA 2824-2 or Sellita SW200-1); ø 25.6 mm, height 4.6 mm; 25 or 26 jewels; 28,800 vph; 38-hour power reserve
Functions: hours, minutes, sweep seconds; date
Case: stainless steel, ø 34 mm, height 10 mm; acrylic glass; water-resistant to 3 atm
Band: calfskin, buckle
Remarks: hardened Plexiglas with scratch-resistant coating
Price: $1,095
Variations: with 38-mm case; various straps and dials

KOBOLD

Like many others in the field, Michael Kobold had already developed an interest in the watch industry in childhood. As a young man, he found a mentor in Chronoswiss founder Gerd-Rüdiger Lang, who encouraged him to start his own brand. This he did in 1998—at the age of nineteen, while he was still a student at Carnegie Mellon University.

Today, Kobold Watch Company is situated in Pittsburgh, Pennsylvania, Berlin, Germany, and Kathmandu, Nepal. The company manufactures cases, movement components, dials, hands, and even straps. The brand's centerpiece is the Soarway collection and the fabled Soarway case, which was originally created in 1999 by explorer Ranulph Fiennes, master watchmaker and Chronoswiss founder Lang, as well as company founder Kobold, himself an avid mountain climber. And "adventure" also means muscle and tool watches, like the Phantom Black Ops chronograph or the Richard Byrd Tactical, watches that can stay on the wrist even when exposed to the harshest elements. "We make tough, rugged watches and so the case plays a more important role than the movement," says Kobold. "So for now, we're concentrating on making the toughest cases possible. One day, we'll tackle making in-house movements." The Soarway collection includes several novelties, such as the Soarway Transglobe, a watch with a second time zone that displays minutes as well as hours. Kobold's love of the Himalayas has driven his commitment to the people of Nepal. His company produces leather accessories and straps there and uses the operation to offer marginalized women vocational training. In 2015, he launched the Soarway Foundation/Engage Nepal to help Nepal in the event of earthquakes. The conjuring of adventure caught up with Kobold. A few weeks later the first of two devastating earthquakes struck. Less than five months later, the Indian government enacted a secret economic blockade against Nepal. Five years later, Michael Kobold and a new team are rebuilding his company and planning to release a two-hour-long documentary film about his work in Nepal.

Kobold Watch Company, LLC
1801 Parkway View Drive
Pittsburgh, PA 15205

Tel.:
1-877-SOARWAY

E-mail:
info@koboldwatch.com

Website:
koboldwatch.com

Founded:
1998

Number of employees:
8

Annual production:
maximum 2,500 watches

Distribution:
factory-direct, select retailers

Most important collection/price range:
Soarway / $2,650 to $35,000

Seal Ceramic James Gandolfini—Meteorite dial

Reference number: KD 842121C
Movement: automatic, ETA 2892-A2; ø 36 mm, height 3.6 mm; 21 jewels; 28,800 vph; 46-hour power reserve
Functions: hours, minutes, sweep seconds
Case: stainless steel, ø 44 mm, height 17.0 mm; unidirectional rotating bezel; sapphire crystal; screwed-down case back; water-resistant to 100 atm
Band: canvas, signed buckle
Price: $8,500; limited to 51 pieces
Variations: varied dials, including Mount Everest summit rock, malachite, turquoise

SMG-2

Reference number: KD 956853
Movement: automatic, Caliber ETA 2893-A2; ø 26.2 mm, height 6.1 mm; 21 jewels; 28,800 vph; 40-hour power reserve
Functions: hours, minutes, sweep seconds; 2nd time zone; date
Case: stainless steel, made in USA; ø 43 mm, height 12.75 mm; unidirectional bezel; soft iron core; antireflective sapphire crystal; screwed-down case back; screwed-in crown; water-resistant to 30 atm
Band: canvas, buckle
Price: $3,650

Intrepid

Reference number: KD 924453
Movement: automatic, ETA 2824; ø 25.6 mm, height 4.6 mm; 25 jewels; 28,800 vph; 38-hour power reserve; côtes de Genève, perlage, engraved and skeletonized gold-plated rotor
Functions: hours, minutes, subsidiary seconds; date, day; chronograph
Case: stainless steel, ø 43.5 mm, height 15 mm; unidirectional bezel with 60-minute divisions; screwed-in crown; sapphire crystal; screwed-down back; water-resistant to 10 atm
Band: calfskin, buckle
Price: $3,450

Kudoke Uhren
Tannenweg 5
D-15236 Frankfurt (Oder)
Germany

Tel.:
+49-335-280-0409

E-mail:
info@kudoke.eu

Website:
www.kudoke.eu

Founded:
2007

Number of employees:
1

Annual production:
30–50 watches

Distribution:
Contact the brand directly for information.

Price range:
approx. $4,500 to $11,500

KUDOKE

Stefan Kudoke, a watchmaker from Frankfurt/Oder, has made a name for himself as an extremely skilled and imaginative creator of timepieces. He apprenticed with two experienced watchmakers and graduated as the number one trainee in the state of Brandenburg. This earned him a stipend from a federal program promoting gifted individuals. He then moved on to one of the large *manufactures* in Glashütte, where he refined his skills in its workshop for complications and prototyping. At the age of twenty-two, with a master's diploma in his pocket, he decided to get an MBA and then devote himself to building his own company.

His guiding principle is individuality, and that is not possible to find in a serial product. So Kudoke began building unique pieces. By realizing the special wishes of customers, he manages to reflect each person's uniqueness in each watch. And he has produced some out-of-the-ordinary pieces, like the ExCentro 1 and 2, or more recently a watch with an octopus that seems to be climbing out of the case. Even his more minimalistic pieces, like the Kudoke 1 and 2 are deeply thought out. Their strength also lies in the subtle interplay of forms and colors, which won Kudoke the "Petite Aiguille" prize at the coveted Grand Prix d'Horlogerie Genève in November 2019 for the Kudoke 2.

His specialties include engraving and goldsmithing. Within his creations bridges may in fact be graceful bodies, or the fine skeletonizing of a plate fragment, a world of figures and garlands. His recent creations include a skull watch, done with characteristic care, and the minimalistic Kurt.

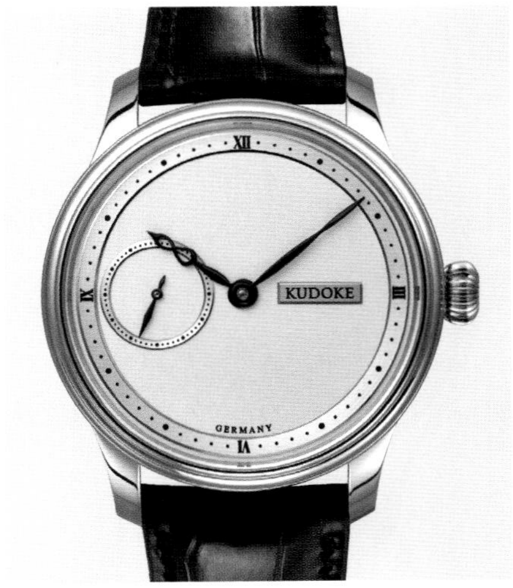

Kudoke 1

Movement: manually wound, Kudoke Caliber 1; ø 30 mm, height 4.3 mm; 18 jewels; 28,800 vph; hand-engraved and finished movement; 46-hour power reserve
Functions: hours, minutes, subsidiary seconds
Case: stainless steel, ø 39 mm, height 9.5 mm; sapphire crystal; transparent case back
Band: reptile skin, buckle
Price: $9,270

Kudoke 2

Movement: manually wound, Kudoke Caliber 1-Version 24h; ø 30 mm, height 5.05 mm; 18 jewels; 28,800 vph; hand-engraved and finished movement; 46-hour power reserve
Functions: hours, minutes; additional 24-hour display
Case: stainless steel, ø 39 mm, height 10.7 mm; sapphire crystal; transparent case back
Band: reptile skin, buckle
Remarks: hand-engraved celestial disk with 3-color galvanic treatment
Price: $8,870

KudOktopus

Movement: manually wound, modified ETA Caliber 6498; ø 36.6 mm, height 4.5 mm; 17 jewels; 18,000 vph; screw balance, polished anchor and escape wheel, hand-skeletonized movement, sculptural rendering of octopus in 3 galvanic colors; 46-hour power reserve
Functions: hours, minutes
Case: stainless steel, ø 42 mm, height 10.7 mm; sapphire crystal; transparent case back
Band: reptile skin, buckle
Price: $9,170

LAURENT FERRIER

A rock rolling along a riverbed or being buffeted by coastal surf will, over time, achieve a kind of perfect shape, streamlined, flowing, smooth. It will usually become a comfortable touchstone for the human hand—a fine pebble, or *galet* in French. And that is the name given to the watches made by Laurent Ferrier in Geneva, Switzerland. The name refers to the special look and feel of the cases, which are just one hallmark of this very unusual, yet classical, watch brand.

Laurent Ferrier is a real person, the offspring of a watchmaking family from the Canton of Neuchâtel, and a trained watchmaker. As a young man he had a passion for cars, too, and even raced seven times at the 24 Hours of Le Mans. In 2009, after thirty-five years of employment at Patek Philippe working on new movements, Ferrier decided he had been shaped enough by his industry. He gathered up his deep experience and founded his own enterprise. He was joined by his son, Christian Ferrier, a watchmaker in his own right, and fellow former race driver François Sérvanin.

One of the first watches was a tourbillon using a natural escapement with a double hairspring, ensuring greater accuracy (a technical idea going back to Breguet). The tourbillon is once again concealed on the movement side (as it used to be)—very intriguing and effective—keeping the dial free of clutter. Purists always praise the brand's minimal dials, the spear hands, and the drop markers. The case, smooth and sporty, is a redux of 1970s design.

The flagship Galet keeps evolving and being used to house different complications, like a second time zone. At the 2019 SIHH, Ferrier proudly presented a form watch inspired by a bridge construction, a timepiece that almost magically fits any wrist. And more recently, the brand has come out with a classic three-hander with a restrained green dial.

Laurent Ferrier
Route de Saint Julien 150
CH-1228 Plan-les-Ouates
Switzerland

Tel.:
+41-22-716-3388

E-mail:
info@laurentferrier.ch

Website:
laurentferrier.ch

Founded:
2010

Number of employees:
12

Annual production:
135

U.S. distributor:
Cellini Jewelers
430 Park Avenue
at 56th Street
New York, NY 10022
212.888.0505
800.CELLINI
Contact@CelliniJewelers.com

Most important collections/price range:
Variations of the Galet / from $40,000 to $345,000

Bridge One

Reference number: LCF 032.AC.E01
Movement: manually wound, Laurent Ferrier Caliber LF707.01; ø 22.20 mm × 30 mm, height 4.35 mm; 21,600 vph; 21 jewels; Swiss lever escapement, finely decorated bridges and mainplate; 80-hour power reserve
Functions: hours, minutes, subsidiary seconds
Case: stainless steel, ø 44 mm × 30 mm, height 10.70 mm; domed and tinted sapphire crystal; transparent case back; ball-shaped crown; water-resistant to 3 atm
Band: reptile skin, buckle or folding clasp
Remarks: case inspired from a bridge; grand-feu white enamel dial
Price: $42,000; **Variations:** slate-gray dial ($37,000)

Classic Origin Green

Reference number: LCF036.TI.G1G
Movement: manually wound, Laurent Ferrier Caliber LF116.01; ø 31.6 mm, height 4.35 mm; 21,600 vph; 21 jewels; Swiss lever escapement, finely decorated bridges and mainplate; semi-instantaneous calendar with correction forward or backward; 80-hour power reserve
Functions: hours, minutes, subsidiary seconds
Case: titanium, ø 40 mm, height 10.70 mm; ball-shaped crown; sapphire crystal front, transparent case back; water-resistant to 3 atm
Band: calfskin, buckle
Price: $31,000
Variations: white opaline dial

Galet Traveler

Reference number: LCF007
Movement: automatic, Laurent Ferrier Caliber LF230.02; ø 31.6 mm, height 5.8 mm; 21,600 vph; 44 jewels; gold off-center microrotor; natural lever escapement with double escape wheel; finely decorated bridges and mainplate; Besançon Observatory certified chronometer; 72-hour power reserve; **Functions:** hours, minutes, subsidiary seconds; 2nd time zone
Case: white gold, ø 41 mm, height 12.64 mm; ball-shaped crown; sapphire crystal, transparent case back; water-resistant to 10 atm
Band: reptile skin, folding clasp
Remarks: white opaline dial
Price: $61,500; limited to 12 pieces; **Variations:** black or navy blue opaline dial; Superluminova dial

Longines Watch Co.
Rue des Noyettes 8
CH-2610 St.-Imier
Switzerland

Tel.:
+41-32-942-5425

E-mail:
info@longines.com

Website:
www.longines.com

Founded:
1832

Number of employees:
worldwide approx. 2,000

U.S. distributor:
Longines
The Swatch Group (U.S.), Inc.
Longines Division
703 Waterford Way, Ste. 450
Miami, FL 33126
800-897-9477
www.longines.com

Most important collections/price range:
The Longines Master Collection, Longines DolceVita, Conquest V.H.P., HydroConquest, Heritage Collection / from approx. $1,000 to $6,500

LONGINES

The Longines winged hourglass logo is the world's oldest trademark, according to the World Intellectual Property Organization (WIPO). Since its founding in 1832, the brand has manufactured somewhere in the region of 35 million watches, making it one of the genuine heavyweights of the Swiss watch world. In 1983, Nicolas G. Hayek merged the two major Swiss watch manufacturing groups ASUAG and SIHH into what would later become the Swatch Group. Longines, the leading ASUAG brand, barely missed capturing the same position in the new concern; that honor went to Omega, the SIHH frontrunner. However, from a historical and technical point of view, this brand has what it takes to be at the helm of any group. Was it not Longines that equipped polar explorer Roald Amundsen and air pioneer Charles Lindbergh with their watches? It has also been the timekeeper at many Olympic Games and, since 2007, the official timekeeper for the French Open at Roland Garros. In fact, this brand is a major sponsor at many sports events, from riding to archery.

It is not surprising then to find that this venerable Jura company also has an impressive portfolio of in-house calibers in stock, from simple manual winders to complicated chronographs. This broad technological base has benefited the company. As a genuine "one-stop shop," the brand can supply the Swatch Group with anything from cheap, thin quartz watches to heavy gold chronographs and calendars with quadruple retrograde displays. Longines does have one particular specialty, besides elegant ladies' watches and modern sports watches, in that it often has the luxury of rebuilding the classics from its own long history.

HydroConquest

Reference number: L3.781.4.06.6
Movement: automatic, Longines Caliber L888 (base ETA A31.L01); ø 25.6 mm, height 3.85 mm; 21 jewels; 25,200 vph; 64-hour power reserve
Functions: hours, minutes, sweep seconds; date
Case: stainless steel, ø 41 mm, height 11.9 mm; unidirectional bezel with ceramic insert, with 0-60 scale; sapphire crystal; screw-in crown; water-resistant to 30 atm
Band: stainless steel, double folding clasp, with safety catch diving extension
Price: $1,600
Variations: various straps and dials

HydroConquest

Reference number: L3.782.4.06.9
Movement: automatic, Longines Caliber L888 (base ETA A31.L01); ø 25.6 mm, height 3.85 mm; 21 jewels; 25,200 vph; 64-hour power reserve
Functions: hours, minutes, sweep seconds; date
Case: stainless steel, ø 43 mm, height 11.9 mm; unidirectional bezel with ceramic insert, with 0-60 scale; sapphire crystal; screw-in crown; water-resistant to 30 atm
Band: rubber, double folding clasp, with safety lock
Price: $1,600
Variations: various straps and dials

HydroConquest

Reference number: L3.781.4.96.6
Movement: automatic, Longines Caliber L888 (base ETA A31.L01); ø 25.6 mm, height 3.85 mm; 21 jewels; 25,200 vph; 64-hour power reserve
Functions: hours, minutes, sweep seconds; date
Case: stainless steel, ø 41 mm, height 11.9 mm; unidirectional bezel with ceramic insert, with 0-60 scale; sapphire crystal; screw-in crown; water-resistant to 30 atm
Band: stainless steel, double folding clasp, with safety catch and diving extension
Price: $1,600
Variations: various straps and dials

HydroConquest

Reference number: L3.782.4.76.9
Movement: automatic, Longines Caliber L888 (base ETA A31.L01); ø 25.6 mm, height 3.85 mm; 21 jewels; 25,200 vph; 64-hour power reserve
Functions: hours, minutes, sweep seconds; date
Case: stainless steel, ø 43 mm, height 11.9 mm; unidirectional bezel with ceramic insert, with 0-60 scale; sapphire crystal; screw-in crown; water-resistant to 30 atm
Band: rubber, double folding clasp, with safety lock
Price: $1,600
Variations: various straps and dials

HydroConquest

Reference number: L3.784.4.56.9
Movement: automatic, Longines Caliber L888 (base ETA A31.L01); ø 25.6 mm, height 3.85 mm; 21 jewels; 25,200 vph; 64-hour power reserve
Functions: hours, minutes, sweep seconds; date
Case: ceramic, ø 43 mm, unidirectional bezel with ceramic insert, with 0-60 scale; sapphire crystal; screw-in crown; water-resistant to 30 atm
Band: rubber, double folding clasp, with safety lock and fine adjustment
Price: $3,725

Master Collection Automatic

Reference number: L2.793.4.78.3
Movement: automatic, Longines Caliber L888 (base ETA A31.L01); ø 25.6 mm, height 3.85 mm; 21 jewels; 25,200 vph; 64-hour power reserve
Functions: hours, minutes, sweep seconds; date
Case: stainless steel, ø 40 mm, height 9.8 mm; sapphire crystal; transparent case back; water-resistant to 3 atm
Band: reptile skin, triple folding clasp
Price: $2,150
Variations: rose gold ($5,900)

Master Collection Annual Calendar

Reference number: L2.920.4.92.6
Movement: automatic, Longines Caliber L897 (base ETA A31.L81); ø 25.6 mm, height 5.2 mm; 21 jewels; 25,200 vph; 64-hour power reserve
Functions: hours, minutes, sweep seconds; annual calendar with date, month
Case: stainless steel, ø 42 mm; sapphire crystal; transparent case back; water-resistant to 3 atm
Band: stainless steel, triple folding clasp
Price: $2,450

Master Collection Moonphase

Reference number: L2.673.4.92.0
Movement: automatic, Longines Caliber L687 (base ETA A08.L91); ø 30 mm, height 7.9 mm; 25 jewels; 28,800 vph; 54-hour power reserve
Functions: hours, minutes, subsidiary seconds; additional 24-hour display; chronograph; full calendar with date, weekday, month, moon phase
Case: stainless steel, ø 40 mm, height 14.3 mm; sapphire crystal; transparent case back; water-resistant to 3 atm
Band: reptile skin, triple folding clasp
Price: $3,325
Variations: stainless steel band ($3,325)

Master Collection Automatic

Reference number: L2.793.8.78.3
Movement: automatic, Longines Caliber L888 (base ETA A31.L01); ø 25.6 mm, height 3.85 mm; 21 jewels; 25,200 vph; 64-hour power reserve
Functions: hours, minutes, sweep seconds; date
Case: rose gold, ø 40 mm; sapphire crystal; transparent case back; water-resistant to 3 atm
Band: reptile skin, triple folding clasp
Price: $6,500

Master Collection Lady

Reference number: L2.257.8.87.3
Movement: automatic, Longines Caliber L592 (base ETA A20.L01); ø 19.4 mm, height 4.1 mm; 22 jewels; 28,800 vph; 40-hour power reserve
Functions: hours, minutes, sweep seconds; date
Case: rose gold, ø 29 mm, height 8.5 mm; sapphire crystal; water-resistant to 3 atm
Band: reptile skin, triple folding clasp
Remarks: mother-of-pearl dial set with 12 diamonds
Price: $4,250

Conquest Classic Lady

Reference number: L2.386.3.87.7
Movement: quartz
Functions: hours, minutes, sweep seconds; date
Case: stainless steel, ø 34 mm; bezel and crown with rose gold PVD; sapphire crystal; water-resistant to 5 atm
Band: stainless steel with rose gold PVD on central links, triple folding clasp
Remarks: mother-of-pearl dial set with 11 diamonds
Price: $1,475

Flagship Heritage

Reference number: L4.795.4.58.0
Movement: automatic, Longines Caliber L615 (base ETA 2895-2); ø 25.6 mm, height 4.35 mm; 27 jewels; 28,800 vph; 42-hour power reserve
Functions: hours, minutes, subsidiary seconds; date
Case: stainless steel, ø 38.5 mm, height 10.3 mm; sapphire crystal; water-resistant to 3 atm
Band: reptile skin, buckle
Price: $1,675

Heritage Classic

Reference number: L2.330.4.93.0
Movement: automatic, Longines Caliber L893 (base ETA A31.501); ø 25.6 mm, height 4.1 mm; 26 jewels; 25,200 vph; 64-hour power reserve
Functions: hours, minutes, subsidiary seconds
Case: stainless steel, ø 38.5 mm, height 11.65 mm; sapphire crystal; water-resistant to 3 atm
Band: calfskin, buckle
Price: $2,000

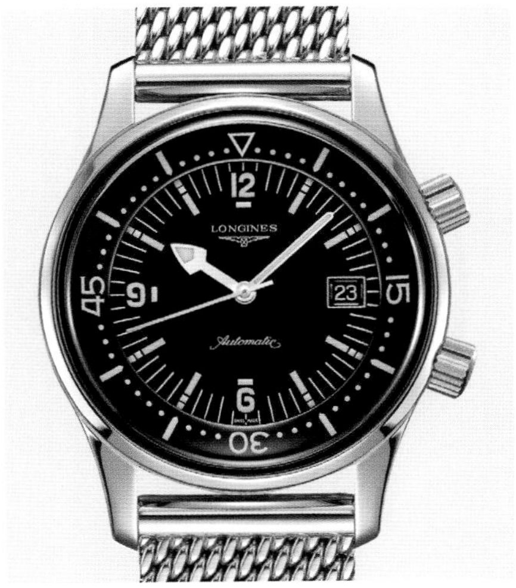

Legend Diver Watch

Reference number: L3.774.4.50.6
Movement: automatic, Longines Caliber L888 (base ETA A31.L01); ø 25.6 mm, height 3.85 mm; 21 jewels; 25,200 vph; 64-hour power reserve
Functions: hours, minutes, sweep seconds; date
Case: stainless steel, ø 42 mm, height 12.7 mm; crown-activated inner bezel with 0-60 scale; sapphire crystal; screw-in crown; water-resistant to 30 atm
Band: stainless steel Milanese mesh, triple folding clasp
Price: $2,400
Variations: black PVD ($2,700)

The Lindbergh Hour Angle Watch

Reference number: L2.678.4.11.0
Movement: automatic, Longines Caliber L699 (base ETA A07.L01); ø 36.6 mm, height 7.9 mm; 24 jewels; 28,800 vph; 46-hour power reserve
Functions: hours, minutes, sweep seconds, rotatable inner dial to synchronize second hand with radio time signals
Case: stainless steel, ø 47.5 mm, height 16.3 mm; bidirectional bezel with scale for time synchronization; sapphire crystal; water-resistant to 3 atm
Remarks: case back with hinged cover
Band: reptile skin, buckle
Price: $5,000

LOUIS ERARD

Louis Erard SA
Ouest 2
CH-2340 Le Noirmont
Switzerland

Tel.:
+41 32 957 65 30

E-mail:
info@louiserard.ch

Website:
www.louiserard.com

Founded:
1929

Number of employees:
15

Distribution:
Contact the company in Switzerland.

Most important collections/price range:
Excellence, Heritage, La Sportive / prices given subject to change

Once upon a time in the watchmaking workshops, there was a large clock that gave the minutes as the main time increment and the hours on a separate dial. This allowed the watchmakers to set and test the accuracy of the piece they were assembling. Over time, so-called regulator dials became popular with the public. It is said that train conductors preferred them because they needed accuracy to the minute.

Among the rare brands that have made regulator watches an important part of their output is Louis Erard. The company namesake (1893-1964), a watchmaker by trade, founded a watchmaking school in his native La Chauds-de-Fonds, and later a casing business for the thriving industry, and then a watchmaking company under his own name.

Erard's business acumen was as good as his technical skill. In the 1930s, he worked on the Valjoux 72 chronograph movement, and in 1956, his company received the right to manufacture movements. In fact, Louis Erard, the company, managed to weather the quartz crisis thanks to a careful modernization program in the 1970s launched by Erard's grandson.

The company changed hands in 1992, moved to Le Noirmont farther up the Jura mountains for a restructuring. In 2003, it was purchased again. The new CEO, Alain Spinedi, understood the need for a distinct look with affordable pricing. The regulator dial thus became the hallmark of the brand and one that well represents its origins in the hands-on, salt-of-the-earth world of watchmaking in the Jura Mountains.

Louis Erard has four distinct lines. The regulators are found under the heading Excellence. Classic tri-compax chronographs in fashionable colors are in the La Sportive line. And the Heritage line has timepieces for everyday use—elegant, not flashy. For those interested in some extra spice, Louis Erard has been collaborating with the likes of Vianney Halter and Alain Silberstein, and the results are well worth seeing.

Le Régulateur Louis Erard × Vianney Halter

Reference number: 85237AA51
Movement: automatic, Sellita SW266-1; ø 25.6 mm, height 5.6 mm; 31 jewels; 28,800 vph; carefully decorated with open-worked oscillating weight; 38-hour power reserve
Functions: hours, minutes, subsidiary seconds
Case: stainless steel, ø 42 mm, height 12.25 mm; sapphire crystal; transparent case back; water-resistant to 5 atm
Collaboration: watch developed in association with Vianney Halter; rapid change strap mechanism
Band: calfskin, buckle
Price: $3,850; limited to 178 pieces

Excellence Chrono Monopoussoir

Reference number: 74239AA01
Movement: automatic, Sellita SW500MPCa; ø 30 mm, height 7.9 mm; 25 jewels; 28,800 vph; monopusher chronograph movement; open-worked oscillating weight, 48-hour power reserve
Functions: hours, minutes, chronograph, 30-minute counter
Case: stainless steel, ø 43 mm, height 15.7 mm; sapphire crystal; transparent case back; water-resistant to 5 atm
Band: calfskin, buckle
Price: $3,850

La Sportive Limited Edition Bronze

Reference number: 78119BR19
Movement: automatic, ETA 7750 Valjoux; ø 30 mm, height 7.9 mm; 25 jewels; 28,800 vph, chronograph movement; open-worked oscillating weight, 48-hour power reserve
Functions: hours, minutes, subsidiary seconds; chronograph; date, weekday
Case: bronze with satin finish and high polish, ø 44 mm, height 15 mm; sapphire crystal; transparent case back; water-resistant to 5 atm
Band: calfskin, folding clasp
Price: $3,250; limited to 250 pieces
Variations: gray, green, brown, or blue dial; titanium case ($3,600)

Les Ateliers Louis Moinet SA
Rue du Temple 1
CH-2072 Saint-Blaise
Switzerland

Tel.:
+41-32-753-6814

E-mail:
info@louismoinet.com

Website:
www.louismoinet.com

Founded:
2005

U.S. distributor:
Fitzhenry Consulting
1029 Peachtree Parkway, #346
Peachtree City, GA 30269
561-212-6812
Don@fitzhenry.com

Most important collections:
Memoris, Sideralis, Tempograph Chrome, Spacewalker, Ultravox; numerous unique pieces

LOUIS MOINET

In the race to be the first to invent something new, Louis Moinet (1768–1853) emerged as a notable winner: In 2013, a *Compteur de tierces* from 1816 was shown to the public, a chronograph that counts one-sixtieth of a second with a frequency of 216,000 vph. It was proudly signed by Moinet. This professor at the Academy of Fine Arts in Paris and president of the Société Chronométrique was in fact one of the most inventive, multitalented men of his time. He worked with such eminent watchmakers as Breguet, Berthoud, Winnerl, Janvier, and Perrelet. Among his accomplishments is an extensive two-volume treatise on horology.

Following in such footsteps is hardly an easy task, but Jean-Marie Schaller and Micaela Bertolucci decided that their idiosyncratic creations were indeed imbued with the spirit of the great Frenchman. They work with a team of independent designers, watchmakers, movement specialists, and suppliers to produce the most unusual wristwatches filled with clever functions and surprising details. The Jules Verne chronographs have hinged levers, for example, and the second hand on the Tempograph changes direction every ten seconds.

Increasingly, this independent-minded brand is exploring the space-time continuum and the worlds of astronomy, space travel, and science fiction. Spacewalker pays tribute to the late Alexey Leonov, the first person to leave an orbiting capsule to take a little spacewalk. Ad Astra has planet earth revolving in the immensity of space, and a battle of spaceships on two tourbillons is the animation on the Space Revolution's dial.

Space Revolution

Reference number: LM-104.50.50
Movement: automatic, Louis Moinet Caliber LM104, ø 30.4 mm, height 6.7 mm; 56 jewels; 21,600 vph; double flying satellite tourbillons; 48-hour power reserve; côtes de Genève, circular-grained wheels, clous de Paris on rotor
Functions: hours, minutes, subsidiary seconds
Case: rose gold, ø 43.5 mm, height 14.8 mm; sapphire crystal; screw-in transparent back; water-resistant to 1 atm
Band: reptile skin, folding clasp
Remarks: animation of 2 spaceships doing battle 18 times an hour on the dial
Price: on request; limited to 8 watches

Spacewalker

Reference number: LM-62.50G.25
Movement: manually wound, Louis Moinet Caliber LM 48; ø 37.65 mm, height 10.33 mm; 20 jewels; 21,600 vph; 72-hour power reserve; "satellite" 13.59-mm tourbillon balanced by a diamond on the cage; rhodium-plated, satin-brushed mainplate, bridges with côtes de Genève; **Functions:** hours, minutes
Case: rose gold with engravings, ø 47.4 mm, height 16.9 mm; sapphire crystal; transparent case back; water-resistant to 5 atm
Remarks: tourbillon and rotating diamond represent spaceship of 1965 Voskhod-2 mission, when Alexey Leonov walked in space
Band: reptile skin, double folding clasp
Price: $229,000; limited to 12 pieces
Variations: without engravings ($199,000)

Ad Astra

Reference number: LM-56.50.50
Movement: automatic, Louis Moinet Caliber LM 56; ø 38.40 mm, height 8.34 mm; 2 jewels; 21,600 vph; sunburst côtes de Genève on rhodium-plated bridges; 38-hour power reserve
Functions: hours, minutes; hour repeater
Case: titanium, ø 46.5 mm, height 14.5 mm; sapphire crystal; transparent case back; water-resistant to 5 atm
Remarks: dial-side repeating mechanism
Band: reptile skin, folding clasp
Price: on request; limited to 8 pieces

LUMINOX

Lumondi Inc. (Luminox Watches)
27 W. 24th Street, Suite 804
New York, NY 10010

Tel.:
917-522-3600

E-mail:
info@luminoxusa.com

Website:
www.luminox.com
shop.luminox.com

Founded:
1989

Most important collections:
Navy SEAL 3500, Leatherback Sea, Turtle Giant, XCOR Aerospace

Watches, as the old industry axiom goes, are jewelry for men. And some men do like watches that express masculinity in no uncertain terms, or that feel like real tools, or that recall the cockpits of fast-moving vehicles. So when Barry Cohen came across the tiny tritium gas–filled luminescent tubes made by the Swiss company mb-microtech, he spotted an opportunity. Here was a way to give sports watches the kind of illumination that would make them dependable and practical time-givers at night. The radioactive tritium, which has a half-life of 12.32 years, makes a coating on the inside of the tubes glow for up to 25 years.

Cohen and his business partner Richard Timbo called their brand Luminox, derived from the Latin "light" and "night." They created a collection of rugged-looking sports timepieces that soon found a loyal following. In 1992 came the first big breakthrough, when a Luminox watch prevailed in a tough competition to become a mission watch for Navy SEALs. The brand now established a reputation, and soon other law enforcement agencies and organizations began ordering watches, notably F-117 Nighthawk and Stealth pilots.

As the brand grew and expanded beyond American borders, it continued developing its product. A new lightweight carbon compound case with a matte finish was developed that is insensitive to outside temperatures. The latest versions of this case can withstand dives of up to 300 meters. A special mineral crystal was also developed that is highly scratch resistant.

Luminox also partnered with the Swiss company Mondaine, famous for its Railroad Watch and the Helvetica, to manufacture watches in their premises in Switzerland. A new company, called Lumondi Inc., was founded to oversee the two brands after Mondaine purchased the 50 percent of remaining shares from Barry Cohen in November 2016.

Luminox watches are unabashedly muscular and outdoorsy. Wherever extreme sports or activities are being performed, that is where Luminox finds its fans. The Scott Cassell Deep Dive Automatic, for example, was made for explorer and deep-sea diver Scott Cassell as part of his "essential gear." The watches are run either on Swiss quartz or on mechanical movements.

Scott Cassell Deep Dive Automatic

Reference number: 1523
Movement: automatic, ETA Caliber 2826-2; ø 25.6 mm, height 6.2 mm; 25 jewels; 28,800 vph; 38-hour power reserve
Functions: hours, minutes, sweep seconds; large date
Case: stainless steel, ø 44 mm, height 17 mm; unidirectional bezel with blue aluminum ring, bezel locker at 3 o'clock; sapphire crystal with antireflective coating; helium release valve; stainless steel screw-in case back; water-resistant to 50 atm
Band: rubber strap, stainless steel buckle
Remarks: constant glow for up to 25 years in any light condition
Price: $2,000
Variations: black/yellow dial with black rubber strap

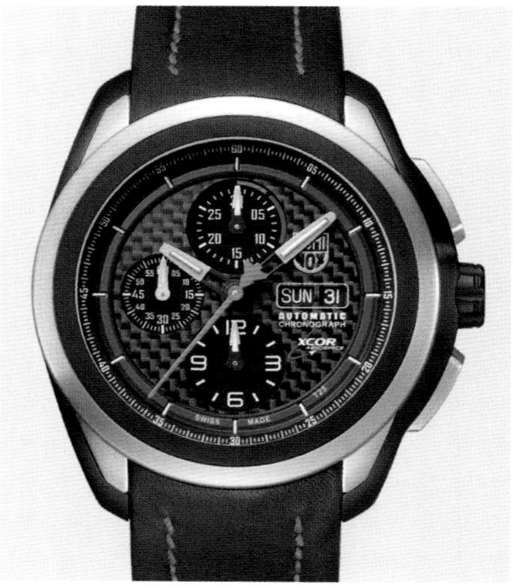

XCOR Aerospace Automatic Valjoux Chronograph

Reference number: 5261
Movement: automatic, ETA Caliber 7750 Valjoux; ø 30 mm, height 7.9; 25 jewels; 28,800 vph; 42-hour power reserve
Functions: hours, minutes, chronograph; date
Case: titanium and black PVD, ø 45.5 mm, height 18 mm; sapphire crystal; titanium screw-down case back; water-resistant to 20 atm
Band: calfskin, titanium buckle
Remarks: constant glow for up to 25 years in any light condition
Price: $3,000

F-117 Nighthawk

Reference number: 6422
Movement: quartz, Ronda Caliber 515; ø 26.2 mm, height 3 mm
Functions: hours, minutes; date; 2nd time zone
Case: stainless steel IP gun metal, ø 44 mm, height 12.6 mm; bidirectional bezel; sapphire crystal; water-resistant to 20 atm
Band: stainless steel and buckle with black PVD
Remark: constant glow for up to 25 years in any light condition
Price: $1,400
Variations: Kevlar strap with black stitching, black leather lining, and black PVD buckle

Manufacture Royale SA
ZI Le Day
CH-1337 Vallorbe
Switzerland

Tel.:
+41-21-843-01-01

E-mail:
info@manufacture-royale.com

Website:
www.manufacture-royale.com

Founded:
by Voltaire in 1770, revived in 2010

Number of employees:
5

Annual production:
150 watches

Distribution:
Retail and online

Most important collections/price range:
ADN Spirit / from $26,800; Androgyne / from $52,500; 1770 / from $30,500; Opera / $367,500

MANUFACTURE ROYALE

Originally, Manufacture Royale was the short-lived watch factory belonging to a genuinely interesting personality of the eighteenth century: François-Marie Arouet (1694–1778), or Voltaire, a brilliant playwright, historian, freewheeling philosopher, historian, and all-around thinker. He opposed slavery and the death penalty, for instance, and, thanks to his stunning wealth, could fire satirical barbs at the powers-that-be, from iniquitous aristocrats and crowned heads to a budding, conservative middle class. In Geneva, where he often found refuge from the French king, he went further: The local established bourgeoisie steadfastly refused to give political and economic rights to a class of craftsmen known as the *natifs*, whose origins were not local and who made up nearly half the population. In 1770, at his estate in neighboring Ferney-Voltaire (France), Voltaire opened a number of workshops for these discriminated people, including the "Manufacture Royale," which produced very respectable watches.

In 2010, four highly experienced and related watch executives, Gérard, David, and Alexis Gouten, and Marc Guten, decided to revive the brand. Their basic idea: high-end complications, affordable prices, *manufacture* movements assembled in-house.

The brand has gained lots of experience since its founding and the self-confidence to sally into more experimental realms, but without ever disturbing the fundamental classicism of the timepieces. The 1770 Haute Voltige series is definitely twenty-first century, with its second time zone cowering under the mysterious bridges that rise from the dial to hold the balance wheel over the dial. Strong colors and a bold design, with just hands and two tourbillons whirling at different speeds, give the Micromégas family a very noticeable look. As for the ADN, it cuts to the chase, literally, with extreme skeletonization, but inside a redesigned, somewhat softer Androgyne case.

ADN Spirit Steel & Forged Carbon Bronze

Reference number: ADN46.04CS04.MC
Movement: manually wound, Caliber MR10; ø 32.6 mm, height 7.40 mm; 21 jewels, 48-hour power reserve, 28,800 vph; CVD-coated plates and bridges
Functions: hours, minutes, small seconds
Case: DLC-coated stainless steel and forged carbon, ø 46 mm, height 12.35 mm; sapphire crystal, screw-down transparent sapphire case back; water-resistant to 3 atm
Band: Nebur Tec strap, triple folding clasp
Price: $31,400; limited edition of 28 pieces per model
Variations: stainless steel ($26,800)

Micromegas Titanium Bespoke

Reference number: 1770MM45.08.D.K
Movement: automatic, MR04 Caliber; ø 36 mm, height 8.7 mm; 26 jewels; 1-minute flying tourbillon (28,800 vph) and 6-second tourbillon (21,600 vph), both with silicon escapement wheel and levers; 40-hour power reserve
Functions: hours (off-center), minutes
Case: titanium, ø 45 mm, height 11.8 mm; transparent case back; water resistant to 3 atm
Band: reptile skin, titanium buckle
Price: $189,000
Variations: different color patterns

Androgyne Rose Gold Bespoke

Reference number: AN43.08P08.LB
Movement: manually wound, MR02 Caliber; 17 jewels; ø 30.9 mm, height 6.26 mm; 21,600 vph; 1-minute tourbillon; 108-hour power reserve
Functions: hours, minutes
Case: rose gold, ø 43 mm, height 10.20 mm; sapphire crystal; water resistant to 3 atm
Remarks: skeletonized bridges in different colors
Band: reptile skin, buckle
Price: $72,500

MAURICE LACROIX

Maurice Lacroix SA
Rüschlistrasse 6
CH-2502 Biel/Bienne
Switzerland

Tel.:
+41-44-209-1111

E-mail:
info@mauricelacroix.com

Website:
www.mauricelacroix.com

Founded:
1975

Number of employees:
about 250 worldwide

Annual production:
approx. 90,000 watches

U.S. distributor:
DKSH Luxury & Lifestyle North America Inc.
9-D Princess Road
Lawrenceville, NJ 08648
609-750-8800

Most important collections/price range:
Aikon / $890 to $2,900; Les Classiques / $950 to $4,300; Eliros / $690 to $1,390; Fiaba (ladies') / $980 to $2,900; Pontos / $1,750 to $7,900; Masterpiece *manufacture* models / $6,800 to $14,900

The roots of the brand Maurice Lacroix run deep, all the way to the late nineteenth century, in fact. The name Maurice Lacroix, however was chosen in 1975 and carried the brand to respectable international success. In 2011, DKSH (Diethelm Keller & Siber-Hegner), a Swiss holding company, which specializes in international market expansions, became the majority shareholder. This has ensured Maurice Lacroix a strong position in all major markets, with flagship stores and its own boutiques.

Nevertheless, the heart of the company remains the production facilities in the highlands of the Jura, in Saignelégier and Montfaucon, where the brand built La Manufacture des Franches-Montagnes SA (MFM) outfitted with state-of-the-art technology for the production of very specific individual parts and movement components.

The watchmaker can thank the clever interpretations of "classic" pocket watch characteristics for its steep ascent in the 1990s. Since then, the *manufacture* has redesigned the complete collection, banning every lick of Breguet-like bliss from its watch designs. In the upper segment, *manufacture* models such as the chronograph and the retrograde variations on Unitas calibers set the tone. In the lower segment, modern "little" complications outfitted with module movements based on ETA and Sellita are the kings. The brand is mainly associated with the hypnotically turning square wheel, the "roue carrée." The idea was used for the latest ladies' watch, the Power of Love, which has three turning hearts forming the word "love" at regular intervals. And in 2020, it released it's Embrace, with two rotating and meshing hearts on the dial, one of which gives the seconds.

Maurice Lacroix's drive to freshen up its look has earned the brand a great deal of recognition in past years, notably eleven Red Dot awards.

Masterpiece Moon Retrograde

Reference number: MP6608-SS001-110-1
Movement: automatic, Caliber ML 292; ø 36.6 mm; 36 jewels; 28,800 vph; finely finished movement; 36-hour power reserve
Functions: hours, minutes, subsidiary seconds; date, weekday (retrograde), moon phase
Case: stainless steel, ø 43 mm, height 15 mm; sapphire crystal; transparent case back; water-resistant to 10 atm
Band: reptile skin, folding clasp
Price: $5,000

Masterpiece Embrace

Reference number: MP6068-SS001-160-1
Movement: automatic, Caliber ML 258; ø 34 mm, height 8.6 mm; 37 jewels; 28,800 vph; finely finished movement; 36-hour power reserve
Functions: hours, minutes, subsidiary seconds (heart-shaped, meshing disk displays); date (retrograde, with answers instead of numbers)
Case: stainless steel, ø 40 mm, height 14 mm; sapphire crystal; transparent case back; water-resistant to 10 atm
Band: calfskin, folding clasp
Price: $6,990

Masterpiece Gravity

Reference number: MP6118-SS001-434-1
Movement: automatic, Caliber ML 230; ø 37.2 mm, height 9.05 mm; 35 jewels; 18,000 vph; inverted movement construction with escapement on dial; silicon pallet lever and pallet fork; 48-hour power reserve
Functions: hours, minutes (off-center), subsidiary seconds
Case: stainless steel, ø 43 mm, height 16.2 mm; sapphire crystal; transparent case back; water-resistant to 5 atm
Band: reptile skin, folding clasp
Price: $13,900
Variations: various cases and dials

Aikon Mercury

Reference number: AI6088-SS002-030-1
Movement: automatic, Caliber ML 225; ø 36.6 mm, height 8.9 mm; 54 jewels; 28,800 vph; skeletonized and finely finished movement; bridges with black PVD coating; 38-hour power reserve
Functions: hours, minutes, subsidiary seconds
Case: stainless steel, ø 44 mm, height 14 mm; sapphire crystal; water-resistant to 10 atm
Band: stainless steel, double folding clasp
Remarks: when changing position, the 2 hands shift to the "12" position; when watch is horizontal, they tell time again
Price: $7,690

Aikon Skeleton Chronograph

Reference number: AI6098-SS001-090-1
Movement: automatic, Caliber ML 206 (base ETA 7753); ø 30 mm, height 7.9 mm; 25 jewels; 28,800 vph; skeletonized and finely finished movement; 48-hour power reserve
Functions: hours, minutes, subsidiary seconds; chronograph
Case: stainless steel, ø 44 mm, height 15.1 mm; sapphire crystal; transparent case back; water-resistant to 20 atm
Band: calfskin, folding clasp
Remarks: skeletonized dial
Price: $6,990

Aikon Skeleton Manufacture

Reference number: AI6028-SS001-030-1
Movement: automatic, Caliber ML 234; ø 36.6 mm, height 8.7 mm; 34 jewels; 18,000 vph; completely skeletonized movement; 52-hour power reserve
Functions: hours, minutes, subsidiary seconds
Case: stainless steel, ø 45 mm, height 13 mm; sapphire crystal; transparent case back; screw-in crown; water-resistant to 10 atm
Band: reptile skin, double folding clasp
Price: $5,890

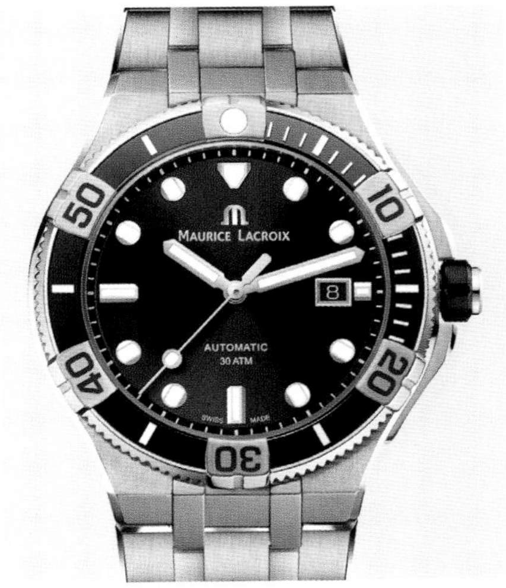

Aikon Venturer

Reference number: AI6058-SS001-330-1
Movement: automatic, Sellita Caliber SW200-1; ø 25.6 mm, height 4.6 mm; 26 jewels; 28,800 vph; 38-hour power reserve
Functions: hours, minutes, sweep seconds; date
Case: stainless steel, ø 43 mm, height 11.6 mm; unidirectional bezel with ceramic insert, 0-60 scale; sapphire crystal; screw-in crown; water-resistant to 30 atm
Band: rubber, folding clasp
Price: $1,890
Variations: various dial colors; rubber strap ($1,890)

Aikon Venturer Bronze

Reference number: AI6058-BZR01-630-1
Movement: automatic, Caliber ML 115 (base Sellita SW200-1); ø 25.6 mm, height 4.6 mm; 26 jewels; 28,800 vph; 38-hour power reserve
Functions: hours, minutes, sweep seconds; date
Case: bronze, ø 43 mm, height 12 mm; unidirectional bezel with ceramic insert, with 0-60 scale; sapphire crystal; screw-in crown; water-resistant to 30 atm
Band: rubber, buckle
Remarks: comes with additional calfskin strap
Price: $2,490; limited to 500 pieces

Aikon Venturer Bicolor

Reference number: AI6058-SY013-430-1
Movement: automatic, Caliber ML 115 (base Sellita SW200-1); ø 25.6 mm, height 4.6 mm; 26 jewels; 28,800 vph; 38-hour power reserve
Functions: hours, minutes, sweep seconds; date
Case: stainless steel, ø 43 mm, height 12 mm; unidirectional bezel with ceramic insert and yellow gold PVD, 0-60 scale; sapphire crystal; screw-in crown, with yellow gold PVD; water-resistant to 30 atm
Band: stainless steel with yellow gold PVD on central links, double folding clasp
Price: $2,690

Aikon Automatic

Reference number: AI6007-SS002-330-1
Movement: automatic, Caliber ML 115 (base Sellita SW200-1); ø 25.6 mm, height 4.6 mm; 26 jewels; 28,800 vph; 38-hour power reserve
Functions: hours, minutes, sweep seconds; date
Case: stainless steel, ø 39 mm, height 11 mm; sapphire crystal; transparent case back; screw-in crown; water-resistant to 20 atm
Band: stainless steel, double folding clasp
Price: $1,990
Variations: calfskin strap ($1,890)

Aikon Date Quartz

Reference number: AI1008-PVB21-330-1
Movement: quartz
Functions: hours, minutes, sweep seconds; date
Case: stainless steel, ø 42 mm, height 9 mm; bezel with black PVD; sapphire crystal; water-resistant to 10 atm
Band: calfskin, double folding clasp
Price: $980

Eliros Chronograph

Reference number: EL1098-SS001-114-1
Movement: quartz
Functions: hours, minutes, subsidiary seconds; chronograph; date
Case: stainless steel, ø 40 mm, height 10 mm; sapphire crystal; water-resistant to 5 atm
Band: calfskin, buckle
Price: $890

Aikon Automatic Date 35mm

Reference number: AI6006-PVY13-450-1
Movement: automatic, Caliber ML 115 (base Sellita SW200-1); ø 25.6 mm, height 4.6 mm; 26 jewels; 28,800 vph; 38-hour power reserve
Functions: hours, minutes, sweep seconds; date
Case: stainless steel, ø 35 mm, height 11 mm; sapphire crystal; transparent case back; screw-in crown, with yellow-gold PVD; water-resistant to 20 atm
Band: stainless steel with yellow gold PVD on central links, double folding clasp
Remarks: dial set with 8 diamonds
Price: $1,990

Aikon Automatic Date 35mm

Reference number: AI6006-PVY11-170-1
Movement: automatic, Caliber ML 115 (base Sellita SW200-1); ø 25.6 mm, height 4.6 mm; 26 jewels; 28,800 vph; 38-hour power reserve
Functions: hours, minutes, sweep seconds; date
Case: stainless steel, ø 35 mm, height 11 mm; sapphire crystal; transparent case back; screw-in crown; water-resistant to 20 atm
Band: calfskin, double folding clasp
Remarks: mother-of-pearl dial set with 8 diamonds
Price: $990

Fiaba Moonphase

Reference number: FA1084-SS002-170-1
Movement: quartz
Functions: hours, minutes, sweep seconds; date, moon phase
Case: stainless steel, ø 32 mm, height 9.89 mm; sapphire crystal; water-resistant to 3 atm
Band: stainless steel, double folding clasp
Price: $1,290

MB&F
Boulevard Helvétique 22
Case postale 3466
CH-1211 Geneva 3
Switzerland

Tel.:
+41-22-786-3618

E-mail:
info@mbandf.com

Website:
www.mbandf.com

Founded:
2005

Number of employees:
26

Annual production:
approx. 220 watches

U.S. distributors:
Westime Los Angeles and Miami
310-470-1388 (Los Angeles)
786-347-5353 (Miami)
info@westime.com
Provident Jewelry, Florida
561-747-4449; nick@providentjewelry.com
Stephen Silver, Redwood City (California)
650-325-9500; www.shsilver.com
Cellini, New York
212-888-0505; contact@cellinijewelers.com

Most important collections/price range:
Horological Machines / from $63,000; Legacy Machines / from $64,000

MB&F

In the world of alternative time-tellers, there is one prophet: Maximilian Büsser. After breaking away from brand constraints at Harry Winston, where he launched the Opus line, Büsser founded MB&F (that is, and friends) with the mission of setting creators free. He acts as initiator and coordinator. His Horological Machines are developed and realized in cooperation with highly specialized watchmakers, inventors, and designers in an "idea collective" creating unheard-of mechanical timepieces of great inventiveness, complication, and exclusivity. The composition of this collective varies as much as each machine. Number 5 ("On the Road Again") is an homage to the 1970s, when streamlining rather than brawn represented true strength. The display in the lateral window is reflected by a prism. The "top" of the watch opens to let in light to charge the Superluminova numerals on the disks. As for the Space Pirate, Number 6, it is a talking piece that makes a genial nod to sci-fi moviemakers, and all the talk was real: The model won a coveted Red Dot "Best of the Best" award in 2015. Contrasting sharply with the modern productions are the Legacy Machines, which reach into horological history and reinterpret past mechanical feats.

The spirit of Büsser is always present in each new watch. Perhaps the most intimate Legacy Machine, though, is the Flying T, dedicated to the women in his life (notably his late mother, who never saw it finished): a central tourbillon, an inclined lateral dial only the wearer can see, all under a vaulted sapphire crystal, and available, too, on a sea of diamonds. It is vented freely in the M.A.D. Gallery in Geneva, where "mechanical art objects" on display are beautiful, intriguing, technically impeccable, and sometimes perfectly useless. They have their own muse and serve as worthy companions to the sci-fi-inspired table clocks that MB&F produces with L'épée 1938.

Legacy Machine Thunderdome

Reference number: 06.PL.BL
Movement: manually wound, MB&F Caliber Thunderdome (base developed by Eric Coudray and Kari Voutilainen); 63 jewels; 21,600 vph; tourbillon with 3 axes on different levels with different rotating speeds (8, 12, and 20 seconds); 3 spring barrels, 45-hour power reserve
Functions: hours, minutes, on inclined dial; power reserve indicator (on back)
Case: platinum, ø 44 mm, height 22.2 mm; sapphire crystal; transparent case back
Band: reptile skin, folding clasp
Price: $298,000; limited to 33 pieces

HM7 Platinum Red

Reference number: 70.PBL.B
Movement: automatic, MB&F Caliber HM7; ø 31.4 mm, height 17.45 mm; 35 jewels; 18,000 vph; flying 1-minute tourbillon, 3D vertical architecture, titanium and platinum rotor; 72-hour power reserve
Functions: hours, minutes (on spherical aluminum/titanium disks)
Case: platinum, ø 53.8 mm, height 21.3 mm; unidirectional sapphire crystal bezel with 0-60 scale; sapphire crystal; transparent case back; screw-in crown for winding and time-setting; water-resistant to 5 atm
Band: rubber, folding clasp
Price: $108,000; limited to 25 pieces

Legacy Machine FlyingT

Reference number: 05.RL.BG
Movement: automatic, MB&F Caliber LM FlyingT; 30 jewels; central, flying 1-minute tourbillon; double spring barrel; dial inclined at 50°; 100-hour power reserve
Functions: hours, minutes
Case: red gold, with diamonds, 38 × 20 mm; sapphire crystal; transparent case back; separate winding crowns for winding and time setting; water-resistant to 3 atm
Band: reptile skin, buckle
Price: $115,000; limited to 18 pieces

MEISTERSINGER

MeisterSinger GmbH & Co. KG
Hafenweg 46
D-48155 Münster
Germany

Tel.:
+49-251-133-4860

E-mail:
info@meistersinger.de

Website:
www.meistersinger.de

Founded:
2001

Number of employees:
13

Annual production:
approx. 10,000 watches

U.S. distributor:
Duber Time
1920 Dr. MLK Jr. Street North
Suite #D
St. Petersburg, FL 33704
727-202-3262
damir@meistersingertime.com

Price range:
from approx. $995 to $5,900

The moving hands of a watch have different functions. The seconds hand is essentially there to tell that the watch is working, and the hour hand is essentially a slower minute hand, so the two can be pressed into service for a single function, thereby making space on the dial for the eye to wander. MeisterSinger made this into a core design concept and in 2014 presented a portfolio of exclusively one-hand watches.

Founder Martin Brassler launched his little collection of stylistically neat dials at the beginning of the new millennium. Looking at these ultimately simplified dials does tempt one to classify the one-hand watch as an archetype. The single hand simply cannot be reduced any further, and the 144 minutes for 12 hours around the dial do have a normative function of sorts. In a frenetic era when free time has become so rare, these watches slow things down a little. In one model, the hour jumps very precisely in a window under 12 o'clock—hence its Italian name *Salthora*, or "jumping hour."

Minimalism, however, does not mean less dynamism. Brassler always has some exciting idea, like the fun Metris, or the rigorously elegant Lunascope moon phase. The Vintago is a vintage lookalike, with a disk display of the date at 3 o'clock. The Black Line, for its part, pays homage to the color black and its potential depths.

The 2020 collection is an extension of this idea. The Astroscope combines a day and date function with a look at heavenly bodies, and proves that an astronomical watch doesn't need lots of complicated displays. A classic watch from "Age of Streamlining," the Neo, now comes with a pointer date. And the Perigraph, an old-time favorite, has returned to the portfolio with contrasting colors and a brushed steel case.

Design, product planning, service, and management all happen in Münster, Germany. The watches, however, are Swiss made, with ETA and Sellita movements. The Circularis is the brand's first model with an in-house movement, a manually wound caliber with two barrel springs developed in collaboration with the Swiss firm Synergies Horlogères.

Astroscope

Reference number: AS902B
Movement: automatic, Sellita Caliber SW220-1; ø 25.6 mm, height 5.1 mm; 26 jewels; 28,800 vph; 38-hour power reserve
Functions: hours (each scale line indicates 5 minutes); date, weekday
Case: stainless steel, ø 40 mm, height 10.5 mm; sapphire crystal; transparent case back; water-resistant to 5 atm
Band: calfskin, buckle
Remarks: weekdays represented by the moon, Mars, Mercury, Jupiter, Venus, Saturn, and the sun; white dot indicator seems to jump around dial randomly
Price: $2,295

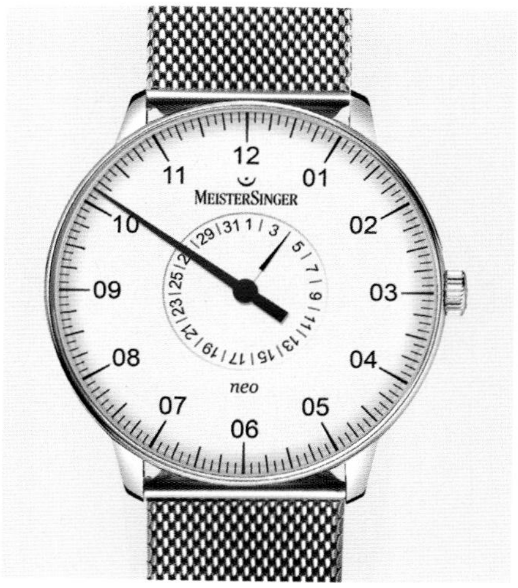

Neo Pointer Date

Reference number: NED917
Movement: automatic, Sellita Caliber SW221-1; ø 25.6 mm, height 5.5 mm; 25 jewels; 28,800 vph; 38-hour power reserve
Functions: hours (each scale line indicates 5 minutes); date
Case: stainless steel, ø 36 mm, height 9.7 mm; hardened acryl glass; water-resistant to 3 atm
Band: stainless steel Milanese mesh, folding clasp
Price: $1,495
Variations: blue dial

Perigraph Bronze

Reference number: AM1007BR
Movement: automatic, Sellita Caliber SW200-1; ø 25.6 mm, height 4.6 mm; 26 jewels; 28,800 vph; 38-hour power reserve
Functions: hours (each scale line indicates 5 minutes); date
Case: bronze, ø 43 mm, height 11.5 mm; sapphire crystal; transparent case back; water-resistant to 5 atm
Band: calfskin, buckle
Price: $2,495
Variations: stainless steel ($2,295); stainless steel with black PVD ($1,999)

Metris Bronze

Reference number: ME917BR
Movement: automatic, Sellita Caliber SW200-1; ø 25.6 mm, height 4.6 mm; 26 jewels; 28,800 vph; 38-hour power reserve
Functions: hours (each scale line indicates 5 minutes); date
Case: bronze, ø 38 mm, height 11.1 mm; sapphire crystal; transparent case back; water-resistant to 20 atm
Band: calfskin, buckle
Price: $2,295

Urban Day Date

Reference number: URDD902
Movement: automatic, Miyota Caliber 8285; ø 29.2 mm, height 5.94 mm; 21 jewels; 21,600 vph; 42-hour power reserve
Functions: hours (each scale line indicates 5 minutes); date, weekday
Case: stainless steel, ø 40 mm, height 13.25 mm; sapphire crystal; transparent case back; water-resistant to 5 atm
Band: textile, buckle
Remarks: comes with additional calfskin strap
Price: $1,195
Variations: various dial colors

Pangaea Date

Reference number: PMD907D
Movement: automatic, Sellita Caliber SW200-1; ø 25.6 mm, height 4.6 mm; 26 jewels; 28,800 vph; 38-hour power reserve
Functions: hours (each scale line indicates 5 minutes); date
Case: stainless steel, ø 40 mm, height 11.25 mm; sapphire crystal; transparent case back; water-resistant to 5 atm
Band: calfskin, buckle
Price: $2,145

Lunascope

Reference number: LS901
Movement: automatic, Sellita Caliber SW220-1 with MeisterSinger module; ø 25.6 mm, height 5.05 mm; 26 jewels; 28,800 vph; 38-hour power reserve
Functions: hours (each scale line indicates 5 minutes); date, moon phase
Case: stainless steel, ø 40 mm, height 12 mm; sapphire crystal; transparent case back; water-resistant to 5 atm
Band: calfskin, buckle
Price: $3,845

Perigraph

Reference number: AM10Z17S
Movement: automatic, Sellita Caliber SW200-1; ø 25.6 mm, height 4.6 mm; 26 jewels; 28,800 vph; with côtes de Genève; 38-hour power reserve
Functions: hours (each scale line indicates 5 minutes); date
Case: stainless steel, ø 43 mm, height 11.5 mm; sapphire crystal; transparent case back; water-resistant to 5 atm
Band: horse leather, buckle
Price: $1,995
Variations: black or ivory-colored dial

N° 01 40 mm

Reference number: DM317
Movement: manually wound, Sellita Caliber SW210; ø 25.6 mm, height 3.4 mm; 19 jewels; 28,800 vph; 42-hour power reserve
Functions: hours (each scale line indicates 5 minutes)
Case: stainless steel, ø 40 mm, height 11.5 mm; sapphire crystal; transparent case back; water-resistant to 5 atm
Band: calfskin, buckle
Price: $1,695
Variations: various dial colors

MIDO

Among the legacies of World War I was the popularization of the wristwatch, which had freed up soldiers' and aviators' hands to fight and steer, respectively, and permitted artillery officers to coordinate barrages. And, not surprisingly, this led to a kind of re-industrialization of the watch industry. Among the earliest companies to appear on the scene was Mido, which was founded on November 11, 1918—Armistice Day—by Georges Schaeren in Solothurn, Switzerland. The name means "I measure" in Spanish.

At first, the brand produced colorful and imaginative watches that were well suited to the Roaring Twenties. But in the 1930s Mido began making more serious, robust, sportive timepieces better suited for everyday use. For the watch fan of today, water resistance and self-winding are normal. Mido, however, was already offering this functionality in the 1930s with the introduction of the Multifort, which really put the company on the map. This Swiss manufacturer was equally innovative with its movements. It developed a number of very practical novelties like the Radiotime model (1939) and the Multicenterchrono (1941), which today have become genuine collectors' items.

In 1971 the Schaeren family sold the company to the General Watch Co. Ltd., a holding company belonging to ASUAG, which, in turn became the SMH and, ultimately, Swatch Group. Mido continues to produce mostly mechanical watches with about one-quarter of its production devoted to quartz movements. In 1998, Mido decided to revive some of its older watchmaking values. The Multifort, Commander, Battalion, and Baroncelli collections are each in their own way expressions of that mission. Nothing in-your-face, just affordable timepieces with the basic hallmarks of a good Swiss watch, like côtes de Genève on the rotors and, in some cases, even COSC certification. In the meantime, the brand has extended its sales potential to about 2,700 retailers in seventy countries.

Mido SA
Chemin des Tourelles 17
CH-2400 Le Locle
Switzerland

Tel.:
+41 32 933 35 11

Website:
www.midowatches.com

Founded:
1918

Number of employees:
50 (estimated)

Annual production:
over 100,000

U.S. distributor:
Mido, division of The Swatch Group (U.S.) Inc.
703 Waterford Way, Suite 450
Miami, FL 33126
www.midowatches.com/us

Most important collections/price ranges:
Baroncelli / $460 to $1,450; Commander / $710 to $2,000; Multifort / $620 to $2,230; Ocean Star / $890 to $1,700

Ocean Star Tribute

Reference number: M026.830.11.041.00
Movement: automatic, Mido Caliber 80.621 (base ETA C07.621); ø 25.6 mm, height 5.22 mm; 25 jewels; 21,600 vph; rotor with côtes de Genève; 80-hour power reserve
Functions: hours, minutes, sweep seconds; date, weekday
Case: stainless steel, ø 40.5 mm, height 10.45 mm; unidirectional bezel with aluminum insert, with 0-60 scale; sapphire crystal; screw-in crown; water-resistant to 20 atm
Band: stainless steel, folding clasp, with extension link
Remarks: comes with additional textile strap
Price: $1,150

Commander Gradient

Reference number: M021.407.37.411.00
Movement: automatic, Mido Caliber 80.611 (base ETA C07.611); ø 25.6 mm, height 4.74 mm; 25 jewels; 21,600 vph; partially skeletonized dial; rotor with côtes de Genève; 80-hour power reserve
Functions: hours, minutes, sweep seconds; date
Case: stainless steel with black PVD, ø 40 mm, height 10.84 mm; sapphire crystal; transparent case back; water-resistant to 5 atm
Band: textile, buckle
Remarks: transparent dial
Price: $960

Multifort Chronometer

Reference number: M038.431.37.051.00
Movement: automatic, Mido Caliber 80.821 COSC (base ETA C07.821); ø 25.6 mm, height 5.22 mm; 25 jewels; 21,600 vph; silicon hairspring; rotor with côtes de Genève; 80-hour power reserve; COSC-certified chronometer
Functions: hours, minutes, sweep seconds; date, weekday
Case: stainless steel with black PVD, ø 42 mm, height 11.99 mm; sapphire crystal; transparent case back; water-resistant to 10 atm
Band: rubber, with textile insert, buckle
Price: $1,380

Minase
Company representation
H-Development Sarl
Ch. du Long-Champ 99
CH-2504 Biel-Bienne
Switzerland

Tel.:
+41-79 901 30 35

E-mail:
info@h-development.ch

Website:
www.minasewatches.ch
www.h-development.ch

Founded:
2005

Distribution:
Contact the representation in Switzerland

Annual production:
approx. 500 pieces

Most important collections/price range:
Five Windows, Horizon, Divido; $3,800 to $5,000; special editions

MINASE

Successful companies frequently like to build a monument to their achievements. It might be a real structure, like the Chrysler Building in New York, or something more ephemeral, like an arts endowment. In 2005, Kyowa, a toolmaking enterprise founded in Japan in 1963, paid homage to its own skills in working on watch components by founding a watch brand. Its logo, appearing at 12 o'clock on some models, was inspired from a step drill.

Minase Watches was named after a small village some 250 miles north of Tokyo that was absorbed in that same year 2005 into the neighboring city of Yazuma. Until recently, it produced no more than five hundred watches a year for the Japanese market, but lately it has begun widening its marketing horizons.

The brand has three basic collections, each of which expresses the company's dedication to hand-finishing. The Five Windows—with a subcollection called the Seven Windows—features many sapphire crystals integrated into these models' cases. They give the beholder an in-depth view of the complex case-in-case structure, the intricate dial, and the mechanism inside. The date aperture is oversized, emphasizing the feeling of spaciousness on the dial. The Horizon timepieces are sportive, with an elegantly curved sapphire crystal covering an arched dial on a tonneau case, harmoniously weaving together different geometrical shapes. The Divido is far more classical, with a round dial in a slightly angular case. The dial is decorated with a dimpled pattern and a large date aperture at 3 o'clock.

The physical appearance of a product in Japan is of utmost importance because it suggests extreme care at all levels of design and production. Minase watches are all made according to this *monozukuri* philosophy, which essentially means excellent manufacturing practices. One technique used is *sallaz,* or block polishing, which gives a particularly sparkling polish. Even the stainless steel bracelets have been inspired by complex Japanese wooden puzzles.

Five Windows

Reference number: VM03-M03SB
Movement: automatic, Caliber ETA 2824 (customized by Minase); ø 25.6 mm, height 4.6 mm; 25 jewels; 28,800 vph; case-in-case design, hand-polishing and perlage on bridges and plates; 38-hour power reserve
Functions: hours, minutes, sweep seconds; date in large aperture at 4 o'clock
Case: stainless steel, ø 38 × 46.5 mm, height 14 mm; sapphire crystal; transparent case back; water-resistant to 5 atm; **Band:** stainless steel, folding clasp
Remarks: special *sallaz* mirror polishing on case; bracelet inspired by traditional Japanese wood puzzles
Price: $4,950; **Variations:** midsize case (32 × 40.3 mm, height 11.6 mm); in palladium or rose or yellow gold; different color dials; reptile skin or leather strap; prices on request; special editions in gold

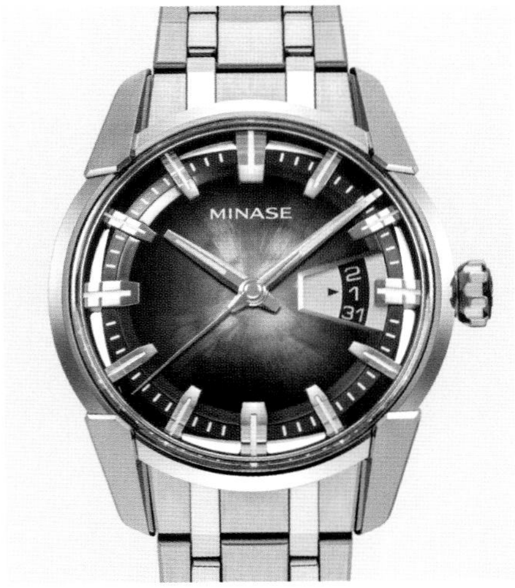

Divido

Reference number: VM04-M01SB
Movement: automatic, Caliber ETA 2824 (customized by Minase); ø 25.6 mm, height 4.6 mm; 25 jewels; 28,800 vph; 38-hour power reserve
Functions: hours (hand-cut into rotating dial), minutes
Case: stainless steel, ø 40.5 × 40.5 mm, height 12 mm; sapphire crystal; transparent case back; water-resistant to 3 atm
Band: stainless steel, folding clasp
Price: $4,980
Variations: blue, white, or black dials; rubber strap ($3,900)

Horizon

Reference number: VM02-MO1SB
Movement: automatic, Caliber ETA 2824 (customized by Minase); ø 25.6 mm, height 4.6 mm; 25 jewels; 28,800 vph; ø 40 mm, height 4.5 mm; 17 jewels; 28,800 vph; 38-hour power reserve
Functions: hours, minutes
Case: stainless steel with black PVD, ø 51 × 38 mm, height 11.5 mm; sapphire crystal; transparent case back; water-resistant to 5 atm
Band: leather, buckle
Price: $4,820
Variations: case with rose gold or black PVD, rubber strap ($3,680)

MING

Horologer Ming Sdn Bhd
B-3A-3, Sunway Palazzio
1 Jalan Sri Hartamas 3
50480 Kuala Lumpur
Malaysia

E-mail:
hello@ming.watch

Website:
ming.watch

Founded:
2017

Number of employees:
5

Annual production:
500–1,000 watches

Distribution:
online, direct sales

Most important collections:
19.01, 19.02, 17.06
Note: All dollar prices are indicative, since the watches are priced in Swiss francs.

It takes a certain courage to launch a new watch brand in a crowded market that is subject to emotional swings. Ming, however, is no ordinary brand. It is a cooperative enterprise made up of six watchmaking enthusiasts from around the world. Leading the team is Ming Thein, a well-known photographer, designer, corporate strategist, and watch fan. He hails from Malaysia. Added up, the Ming team computes to a total of eighty solid years' experience collecting watches of all sorts, from vintage pieces to avant-garde works of kinetic art, from robust ground-level timepieces to custom-made products in the six-figure range.

Each of their purchases always gave them a genuine feeling of value and happiness. The mission of the six brand founders was therefore to reconnect with that feeling of emotional excitement that comes from discovering an authentic diamond in the rough. Their strategy was to create a series of watches that are conscientiously finished and stand out thanks to some subtle details in the finishing and the design. These are not flashy pieces, but rather subtle seducers by dint of the details, like the carefully worked lugs or the modified ETA 7001 caliber, turning a fairly square assembly into a delicate and colorful ballet of gearwheels and bridges. They also wanted their timepieces to be accessible to a large circle of collectors—in other words, affordable. The company is clear about one thing: They are not a classical *manufacture*. Rather, they cooperate with partners that are compatible with the brand's esthetic goals and price points. Most of these partners work with major established Swiss brands. All Ming watches are assembled, adjusted, and tested in Switzerland. The final quality control is then done in Kuala Lumpur by Ming Thein in person. "Ming is our way to share our cooperative's experience with other fans," he says, "people who would like to discover real horology above and beyond well-known labels and logos, and regardless whether they are experienced collectors or have just discovered their passion for watches."

19.02 Worldtimer

Reference number: 19.02
Movement: automatic, Ming Caliber ASE220.1 (Schwarz Etienne base); ø 30.4 mm, height 5.55 mm; 34 jewels; 21,600 vph; microrotor; partially skeletonized movement, galvanized movement bridges; 70-hour power reserve
Functions: hours, minutes; world time display (2nd time zone)
Case: titanium, ø 39 mm, height 11.2 mm; sapphire crystal; transparent case back; water-resistant to 5 atm
Band: calfskin, buckle
Remarks: dyed central sapphire crystal, front sapphire crystal with engraved markings
Price: starting at $12,000

27.01 Ultra Thin

Reference number: 27.01
Movement: manually wound, Ming Caliber 7001.M1 (base ETA 7001 "Peseux," modified); ø 25.3 mm, height 2.5 mm; 17 jewels; 21,600 vph; partially skeletonized movement, galvanized movement bridges, with black chromed bridges; 42-hour power reserve
Functions: hours, minutes
Case: stainless steel, ø 38 mm, height 6.9 mm; sapphire crystal; transparent case back; water-resistant to 5 atm
Band: calfskin, buckle
Remarks: brushed sandwich dial
Price: $4,300

18.01 H41

Reference number: 18.01
Movement: automatic, ETA Caliber 2824-2; ø 25.6 mm, height 4.6 mm; 25 jewels; 28,800 vph; modified (2 crown positions), regulated in 5 positions; 42-hour power reserve
Functions: hours, minutes, sweep seconds
Case: titanium, ø 40 mm, height 12.9 mm; unidirectional bezel; sapphire crystal; water-resistant to 100 atm
Band: titanium, folding clasp
Remarks: sapphire dial with integrated luminous indices made of HyCeram
Price: $3,650
Variations: rubber strap; case completely coated in DLC

Mk II Corporation
303 W. Lancaster Avenue, #283
Wayne, PA 19087

E-mail:
info@mkiiwatches.com

Website:
www.mkiiwatches.com

Founded:
2002

Number of employees:
3

Annual production:
800 watches

Distribution:
direct sales and select retail

Most important collections/price range:
Ready-to-Wear Collection / $500 to $995;
Bencrafted Collection / $1,000 to $2,000

MK II

If vintage and unserviceable watches had their say, they would probably be naturally attracted to Mk II for the name alone, which is a military designation for the second generation of equipment. The company, which was founded by watch enthusiast and maker Bill Yao in 2002, not only puts retired designs back into service, but also modernizes and customizes them. Before the screwed-down crown, diving watches were not nearly as reliably sealed, for example. And some beautiful old pieces were made with plated brass cases or featured Bakelite components, which are either easily damaged or have aged poorly. The company substitutes not only proven modern materials, but also modern manufacturing methods and techniques to ensure a better outcome.

These are material issues that the team at Mk II handles with great care. They will not, metaphorically speaking, airbrush a Model-T. As genuine watch lovers themselves, they make sure that the final design is in the spirit of the watch itself, which still leaves a great deal of leeway for many iterations, given a sufficient number of parts. In the company's output, vintage style and modern functionality are key. The watches are assembled by hand at the company's workshop in Pennsylvania—and subjected to a rigorous regime of testing. The components are individually inspected, the cases tested at least three times for water resistance, and at the end the whole watch is regulated in six positions. Looking to the future, Mk II aspires to carry its clean vintage style into the development of what it hopes will be future classics of its own.

Paradive

Reference number: CD04.1-1002N
Movement: automatic (hack setting), Seiko Caliber SII NE15; ø 27.40 mm, height 5.32 mm; 24 jewels; 21,600 vph; 50-hour power reserve; rotor decorated with côtes de Genève
Functions: hours, minutes, sweep seconds, date
Case: stainless steel, ø 41.2 mm, height 15.50 mm; 120-click unidirectional bezel; high domed sapphire crystal with antireflective coating; screw-down case back; screw-in crown; water-resistant to 20 atm
Band: nylon
Price: $895
Variations: without date, dive bezel

Hawkinge AGL

Reference Number: CG05-3001N
Movement: automatic (hack setting), Seiko Caliber SII NE15 (made in Japan); ø 27.40 mm, height 5.32 mm; 24 jewels; 21,600 vph; 50-hour power reserve; rotor decorated with côtes de Genève
Functions: hours, minutes, sweep seconds
Case: stainless steel; ø 37.80 mm, height 12.75 mm; domed sapphire crystal with antireflective coating; screw-down case back; screw-in crown; water-resistant to 10 atm
Band: nylon
Price: $595
Variations: leather strap

Cruxible

Reference Number: CG06-2001N
Movement: automatic (hack setting), Seiko Caliber SII NE15 (made in Japan); ø 27.40 mm, height 5.32 mm; 24 jewels; 21,600 vph; 50-hour power reserve; rotor decorated with côtes de Genève
Functions: hours, minutes, sweep seconds
Case: stainless steel, ø 39 mm, height 13.55 mm; domed sapphire crystal with antireflective coating; screw-down case back; screw-in crown; water-resistant to 10 atm
Band: nylon
Price: $649
Variations: with date, leather strap

MONDAINE

On February 23, 1983, Switzerland's Migros supermarket chain presented its annual report to the business press. In addition to the reams of paper, each reporter present received a watch. The day after, all the papers in Switzerland were talking not about groceries but rather about the birth of the M-Watch, the *Volksuhr,* the "people's watch." It was a week before the coming-out of Swatch . . .

Few have ever realized that the "M" stood not for Migros but for Mondaine Watch, a company founded in the early fifties by Erwin Bernheim, who parlayed a side job dealing in watches into a sizable company carrying several brands. The Migros cooperation was a major coup. But then Bernheim, now joined by his sons Ronnie and André, decided to make something quintessentially Swiss. After some intense brainstorming, they locked onto the Swiss Railways (SBB) clock, originally designed by the Bauhaus engineer Hans Hilfiker (1901–1993).

Like its model, which hangs in every Swiss railway station, this watch features a simple dial with the characteristic red second hand with its round end, recalling the stationmaster's signaling pan. It became a sensation and has appeared in dozens of iterations, including wall clocks and dashboard watches. A special series was even made that replicates the characteristic 58.5-second journey of the second hand that travelers always see. Before hitting the 12, the second hand pauses to let all clocks in Swiss railway stations be synchronized.

In 2014, the two brothers, co-CEOs since their father's death, came out with a new Swiss icon: the Helvetica, the first watch to pay tribute to a font. It is in some ways a contradiction, a watch that attracts attention by being as unobtrusive as possible. Helvetica's only character with a serif, the number 1, was cleverly worked into the lugs. When the brand decided to come out with a chic smartwatch, the Helvetica line, with its restrained look, was the obvious choice.

Mondaine Watch Ltd.
Etzelstrasse 27
CH-8808 Pfäffikon SZ
Switzerland

Tel.:
+41-58 666 88 00

E-mail:
info@mondaine.com

Website:
www.mondaine.com

Founded:
1951

Number of employees
120

Distributor:
Mondaine USA
Lumondi Inc.
27 W. 24th St., Suite 700B
New York, NY 10010
www.mondaine-usa.com
917-522-3421

Most important collections/price range:
Quartz and mechanical versions of the Swiss Railways Watch and Helvetica / $195 to $1,150

Helvetica Hybrid Smartwatch Black

Reference number: mh1b2s20rb
Movement: connected quartz movement MOMT285-2
Functions: hours, minutes, subsidiary seconds; date, automatic calendar; world time, 24 time zones; date; sleep tracking; motion alert; alarm; notification of mails and messaging
Case: black-plated stainless steel, ø 44 mm, height 13 mm; sapphire crystal; water-resistant to 3 atm
Band: rubber, buckle
Remarks: needs Android 4.4 or iOS 8 or higher for compatibility with MMT-365 smartwatch app
Price: $950
Variations: different dials and case materials

Swiss Railways Watch Evo Big Automatic

Reference number: A132.30348.11SBB
Movement: automatic, Sellita Caliber SW2120-1; ø 25.6 mm, height 5.6 mm; 25 jewels; 28,800 vph; 38-hour power reserve
Functions: hours, minutes, sweep seconds; day, date
Case: stainless steel, ø 40 mm, height 10 mm; hardened mineral glass; transparent case back; water-resistant to 10 atm
Band: leather, buckle
Price: $650
Variations: different diameters and dials; quartz

Helvetica Hand Winder

Reference number: MH1.R3610.LG
Movement: manually wound, Sellita Caliber SW210-1; ø 25.6 mm, height 3.35 mm; 19 jewels; 28,800 vph; 50-hour power reserve
Functions: hours, minutes, sweep seconds; date
Case: stainless steel, ø 40 mm, height 8 mm; sapphire crystal; water-resistant to 3 atm
Band: leather, buckle
Price: $1,150

Montblanc Montre SA
10, chemin des Tourelles
CH-2400 Le Locle
Switzerland

Tel.:
+41-32-933-8888

E-mail:
service@montblanc.com

Website:
www.montblanc.com

Founded:
1997 (1906 in Hamburg)

Number of employees:
worldwide approx. 3,000

U.S. distributor:
Montblanc North America
645 Fifth Avenue, 7th Floor
New York, NY 10022
800-995-4810
www.montblanc.com

Most important collections:
Heritage Chronométrie, Heritage Spirit, Meisterstück, Star, Nicolas Rieussec, 4810, TimeWalker, Collection Villeret, 1858 Collection

MONTBLANC

It was with great skill and cleverness that Nicolas Rieussec (1781–1866) used the invention of a special chronograph—the "Time Writer," a device that released droplets of ink onto a rotating sheet of paper—to make a name for himself. Montblanc, once famous only for its exclusive writing implements, borrowed that name on its way to becoming a distinguished watch brand. Within a few years, it had created an impressive range of chronographs driven by in-house calibers: from simple automatic stopwatches to flagship pieces with two independent spring barrels for time and "time-writing."

The Richemont Group, owner of Montblanc, has placed great trust in its "daughter" company, having put the little *manufacture* Minerva, which it purchased at the beginning of 2007, at the disposal of Montblanc. Minerva, which was founded in Villeret in 1858, was already building keyless pocket watches in the 1880s, and by the early twentieth century was producing monopusher chronographs with a reputation for precision. Today, the Minerva Institute serves as a kind of think tank for the future, a place where young watchmakers can absorb the old traditions and skills, as well as the wealth of experience and mind-set of the masters.

Montblanc is continuing the Minerva tradition today with four leading collections. The 1858 and the Heritage clearly look back to the company's genomes, with quotations from the 1920s and 1930s, like those salmon-colored dials. The Star Legacy and the TimeWalker lines allow Montblanc to explore some more complex complications packaged in more modern forms. And la Bohème, a name that suggests flights of romantic fancy, is the line dedicated essentially to women, or men who are not afraid of wearing more delicate beautiful objects.

1858 Geosphere

Reference number: 125567
Movement: automatic, Montblanc Caliber MB 29.25; 26 jewels; 28,800 vph; 42-hour power reserve
Functions: hours, minutes; additional 12-hour display (2nd time zone), synchronously counter-rotating world time indicators for northern and southern hemispheres; date
Case: titanium, ø 42 mm, height 12.8 mm; bezel with ceramic inlay; sapphire crystal; transparent case back; water-resistant to 10 atm
Band: titanium and steel, folding clasp
Price: $6,400
Variations: calfskin strap ($6,100); stainless steel (from $5,600)

1858 Split Second Chronograph

Reference number: 126006
Movement: manually wound, Caliber MB M16.31; ø 38.4 mm, height 8.13 mm; 25 jewels; 18,000 vph; 2 column wheels and sequential control of chronograph functions using a single crown pusher; flyback activation using a separate pusher on case; 50-hour power reserve
Functions: hours, minutes, subsidiary seconds; flyback chronograph
Case: titanium, ø 44 mm, height 14.55 mm; sapphire crystal; transparent case back
Band: reptile skin, buckle
Remarks: enamel dial
Price: $31,000; limited to 100 pieces

1858 Automatic

Reference number: 126758
Movement: automatic, Caliber MB 24.15 (base Sellita SW200-1); ø 25.6 mm, height 4.6 mm; 26 jewels; 28,800 vph; 38-hour power reserve
Functions: hours, minutes
Case: stainless steel, ø 40 mm, height 11 mm; bezel with ceramic insert; sapphire crystal; water-resistant to 10 atm
Band: calfskin, buckle
Price: $2,565

1858 Automatic Chronograph

Reference number: 126912
Movement: automatic, Caliber MB 25.13 (base ETA 7753); ø 30 mm, height 7.9 mm; 27 jewels; 28,800 vph; 48-hour power reserve
Functions: hours, minutes, subsidiary seconds; chronograph
Case: stainless steel, ø 42 mm, height 14.7 mm; bezel with ceramic insert; sapphire crystal; water-resistant to 10 atm
Band: calfskin, double folding clasp
Price: $4,800

1858 Automatic 24H

Reference number: 126007
Movement: automatic, Caliber MB 24.20; ø 25.6 mm; 25 jewels; 28,800 vph; 42-hour power reserve
Functions: 24 hours (each line on dial indicates 15 minutes)
Case: stainless steel, ø 42 mm, height 11.2 mm; bezel in bronze; sapphire crystal; water-resistant to 10 atm
Band: textile, buckle
Price: $3,030

Heritage Automatic

Reference number: 126464
Movement: automatic, Caliber MB 24.27 (base Sellita SW200-1); ø 25.6 mm, height 3.75 mm; 25 jewels; 28,800 vph; 42-hour power reserve
Functions: hours, minutes, sweep seconds
Case: yellow gold, ø 40 mm, height 11.65 mm; sapphire crystal; water-resistant to 5 atm
Band: reptile skin, buckle
Price: $9,860

Heritage Small Second LE 38

Reference number: 124781
Movement: manually wound, Caliber MB M62.00; ø 23.6 mm, height 3.9 mm; 20 jewels; 18,000 vph; swan-neck fine adjustment; finely finished movement; 50-hour power reserve
Functions: hours, minutes, subsidiary seconds
Case: stainless steel, ø 39 mm, height 9.45 mm; sapphire crystal; transparent case back; water-resistant to 5 atm
Band: reptile skin, triple folding clasp
Price: $18,100; limited to 38 pieces

Star Legacy Nicolas Rieussec Chronograph

Reference number: 126097
Movement: automatic, Caliber MB R200; ø 31 mm, height 8.46 mm; 40 jewels; 28,800 vph; 2 spring barrels; monopusher column-wheel control of chronograph functions; 72-hour power reserve
Functions: hours, minutes, subsidiary seconds; additional 12-hour display (2nd time zone), day/night indicator; chronograph; date
Case: rose gold, ø 44.8 mm, height 15.02 mm; sapphire crystal; transparent case back; water-resistant to 3 atm
Band: reptile skin, buckle
Price: $21,500
Variations: stainless steel ($8,640)

Star Legacy ExoTourbillon Slim

Reference number: 126469
Movement: automatic, Caliber MB M29.24; ø 30.6 mm, height 4.5 mm; 27 jewels; 21,600 vph; 1-minute tourbillon with external hairspring; screw balance; gold microrotor; 2 spring barrels; 48-hour power reserve
Functions: hours, minutes
Case: rose gold, ø 42 mm, height 10.29 mm; sapphire crystal; transparent case back; water-resistant to 5 atm
Band: reptile skin, buckle
Price: on request

Star Legacy Orbis Terrarum

Reference number: 126108
Movement: automatic, Caliber MB 29.20 (base Sellita SW300 with module); ø 25.6 mm, height 5.9 mm; 26 jewels; 28,800 vph; 42-hour power reserve
Functions: hours, minutes; world time display, day/night indicator (2nd time zone)
Case: stainless steel, ø 43 mm, height 13.84 mm; sapphire crystal; transparent case back; water-resistant to 5 atm
Band: reptile skin, triple folding clasp
Remarks: sapphire crystal dial, day/night disk over color continents
Price: $7,100

TimeWalker Manufacture Chronograph

Reference number: 119942
Movement: automatic, Montblanc Caliber MB 25.10; ø 30.15 mm, height 7.9 mm; 33 jewels; 28,800 vph; column-wheel control of chronograph functions, screw balance; 46-hour power reserve
Functions: hours, minutes, subsidiary seconds; chronograph; date
Case: stainless steel, ø 43 mm, height 15.2 mm; ceramic bezel; sapphire crystal; transparent case back; water-resistant to 10 atm
Band: calfskin, triple folding clasp
Price: $5,400
Variations: stainless steel bracelet ($5,700)

Bohème Date Automatic

Reference number: 119920
Movement: automatic, Montblanc Caliber MB 24.17 (base ETA 2824-2); ø 25.6 mm, height 4.6 mm; 25 jewels; 28,800 vph; 38-hour power reserve
Functions: hours, minutes, sweep seconds; date
Case: stainless steel, ø 34 mm, height 9.32 mm; sapphire crystal; 8 diamond indices; water-resistant to 3 atm
Band: stainless steel, folding clasp
Price: $3,305

Caliber MB R200

Automatic; monopusher column-wheel control, vertical chronograph clutch, stop-seconds mechanism; double spring barrel, 72-hour power reserve
Functions: hours, minutes, subsidiary seconds; additional 12-hour display (2nd time zone), chronograph; date
Diameter: 31 mm
Height: 8.46 mm
Jewels: 40
Balance: screw balance
Frequency: 28,800 vph
Balance spring: flat hairspring
Remarks: rhodium-plated mainplate with perlage, bridges with côtes de Genève

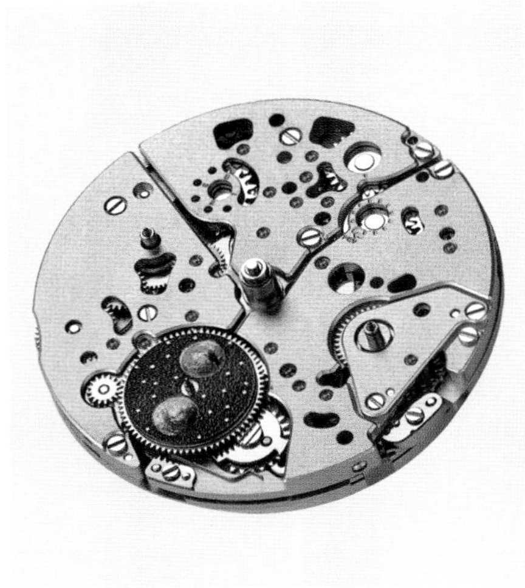

Caliber MB 29.22

Automatic; single spring barrel, 48-hour power reserve
Base caliber: Cartier 1904-PS MC
Functions: hours, minutes, sweep seconds; additional 12-hour display (2nd time zone); perpetual calendar with date, weekday, month, moon phase, leap year
Diameter: 28.2 mm
Height: 4.95 mm
Jewels: 77
Frequency: 28,800 vph
Balance spring: flat hairspring
Remarks: 378 parts

Caliber MB M16.31

Manually wound; monopusher for column-wheel control of chronograph functions, swan-neck fine adjustment; single spring barrel, 50-hour power reserve
Functions: hours, minutes, subsidiary seconds; split-second chronograph
Diameter: 38.4 mm
Height: 8.13 mm
Jewels: 22
Balance: screw balance with Breguet hairspring
Frequency: 18,000 vph
Balance spring: with Phillips end curve
Remarks: rhodium-plated mainplate with perlage, bridges with côtes de Genève, gold-plated wheelworks; 262 parts

MONTRES CHOISI

Montres Choisi
Rue des Draizes 5
CH-2000 Neuchâtel
Switzerland

Tel.:
+41-79-765-1466

E-mail:
askme@choisiwatch.com

Website:
www.choisiwatch.com

Founded:
1929

Number of employees:
4

Distribution:
Montres Choisi deals directly with customers.

Most important collections/price range:
1929 Collection / from $800; Heritage Collection / from $800

Sometimes even the most forward-thinking and -conceiving artists may feel, for whatever reason, the need to express their art in a more conventional style. One might think of Arnold Schoenberg transcribing Strauss waltzes. Similarly, watch brands engaging in some very creative, avant-garde watchmaking or, as some might call it, kinetic art, may feel the impulse to just make a watch with a wide appeal that can be worn every day without necessarily attracting undue attention. It was one reason why, in 2013, Azimuth (see page 76), according to its CEO, Chris Long, purchased a venerable Swiss brand that had sunk into obscurity.

Montres Choisi is a member of that coterie of companies that boosted the reputation of Swiss watchmaking during the twentieth century. It traces its roots to 1924, but became a full-fledged brand in 1929, manufacturing and distributing a host of attractive and fashionable watches. During World War II, it branched out into robust military timepieces that were purchased by both sides of the conflict. It managed to stay above water during the 1950s, but then went dormant.

When reviving the brand, the new owners decided to focus on two clear lines that are unabashedly vintage but include modern touches like brushed surfaces and a more honed look. This is particularly true for the 1929 line, whose cushion cases give it a timeless vintage demeanor, anywhere between the 1920s and early 1970s. Of note is the 2019 Diver, celebrating Choisi's ninetieth anniversary with its a minimalist bezel providing minute markers only for the last critical fifteen minutes of a dive.

Another noteworthy watch is the Docteurgraph, a chronograph with a pulsometer on a racy black dial and striking gold hands. The pushers for this left-handed watch are all on the left side of the case to avoid their pressing into the wearer's hand in the event he or she must perform CPR.

The second line is called Heritage and is distinguished by its round, 42-millimeter cases, and dials that are elegant and discrete. All watches run on robust ETA, Unitas, or vintage movements, like the FHF 96.

1929 GT FHF96

Movement: manually wound, FHF96; ø 25.6 mm, height 4.50 mm; 17 jewels; 18,000 vph; 48-hour power reserve
Functions: hours, minutes, seconds
Case: stainless steel, ø 44 mm, height 12.2 mm; water-resistant to 5 atm
Band: calfskin strap, folding clasp
Remarks: 1960s vintage movement
Price: $800

1929 Bienne

Movement: manually wound, FHF96; ø 25.6 mm, height 4.50 mm; 17 jewels; 18,000 vph; 48-hour power reserve
Functions: hours, minutes, seconds
Case: stainless steel, 44 mm, height 12.2 mm; water-resistant to 5 atm
Band: calfskin, folding clasp
Remarks: 1960s vintage movement
Price: $800

1929 Tachygraph

Movement: automatic, Valjoux 7750; ø 30 mm, height 7.9 mm; 29 jewels; 28,800 vph; 48-hour power reserve
Functions: hours, minutes, chronograph with minute totalizer; tachymeter
Case: stainless steel, 44 mm, height 16.5 mm; water-resistant to 5 atm
Band: calfskin, folding clasp
Price: $1,800

1929 Docteurgraph

Movement: automatic, Valjoux 7750; ø 30 mm, height 7.9 mm; 29 jewels; 28,800 vph; 48-hour power reserve
Functions: hours, minutes, chronograph with minute totalizer; 30-pulsation graph
Case: stainless steel, 44 mm, height 16.5 mm; water-resistant to 5 atm
Band: calfskin, folding clasp
Price: $1,800
Variations: beige dial

1929 Diver

Movement: manually wound, AS1950/51; ø 25.6 mm, height 4.50 mm; 17 jewels; 21,600 vph; 46-hour power reserve
Functions: hours, minutes, seconds
Case: stainless steel, ø 41 mm, height 12.5 mm; unidirectional bezel; water-resistant to 20 atm
Band: textile, folding clasp
Remarks: special 90th anniversary edition
Price: $900; limited to 90 pieces

Heritage Suisse

Movement: manually wound, ETA 6498-1; ø 36.6 mm, height 4.5 mm; 18,000 vph; with côtes de Genève and blued screws
Functions: hours, minutes, subsidiary seconds
Case: stainless steel, ø 42 mm, height 11.8 mm; transparent case back; water-resistant to 5 atm
Band: calfskin, folding clasp
Price: $950

Military Original

Movement: manually wound, Unitas 6498-1; ø 36.60 mm, height 4.50 mm; 17 jewels; 53-hour power reserve
Functions: hours, minutes, subsidiary seconds
Case: stainless steel, ø 42 mm, height 11.8 mm; water-resistant to 5 atm
Band: calfskin, folding clasp
Remarks: 1950s vintage movement
Price: $950

Heritage Tachygraph

Movement: automatic, Valjoux 7750; ø 30 mm, height 7.9 mm; 29 jewels; 28,800 vph; 48-hour power reserve
Functions: hours, minutes, chronograph, subsidiary seconds; tachymeter
Case: stainless steel, ø 42 mm, height 15.5 mm; water-resistant to 5 atm
Band: calfskin, folding clasp
Price: $1,800

Heritage Military 47

Movement: manually wound, ETA 6497-1; ø 36.60 mm, height 4.50 mm; 18,000 vph; with blued screws; 46-hour power reserve
Functions: hours, minutes, petite seconds
Case: stainless steel, ø 47 mm, height 11.9 mm; water-resistant to 3 atm, transparent case back
Band: calfskin, folding clasp
Remarks: available with silver dial
Price: $900

MÜHLE GLASHÜTTE

Mühle Glashütte GmbH
Nautische Instrumente und Feinmechanik
Altenberger Strasse 35
D-01768 Glashütte
Germany

Tel.:
+49-35053-3203-0

E-mail:
info@muehle-glashuette.de

Website:
www.muehle-glashutte.de

Founded:
first founding 1869; second founding 1993

Number of employees:
47

U.S. distributor:
Mühle Glashütte
Old Northeast Jewelers
1131 4th Street North
St. Petersburg, FL 33701
800-922-4377
www.muehle-glashuette.com

Most important collections/price range:
mechanical wristwatches / approx. $1,399 to $5,400

Family-run businesses are notoriously successful, especially if each generation is able to keep up with the tradition and yet manage the challenges that the mere fact of time bring. Rob. Mühle & Sohn has been doing just this for over 150 years. It started as a manufacturer of precision measuring instruments and managed to survive the ups and downs of German history. Originally, this was for the local watch industry and the German School of Watchmaking. By the early 1920s, the firm was supplying the automobile industry, making speedometers, automobile clocks, tachometers, and other measurement instruments.

As a supplier for the Wehrmacht, it drew Soviet bombers during World War II, and was then nationalized. After the fall of the Iron Curtain, Hans-Jürgen Mühle took the helm, followed, in 2007, by his son, Thilo Mühle.

The wristwatch line was launched as a sideline of sorts in mid-1994, but has now overtaken the nautical instruments for which Mühle was famous. Its collection comprises mechanical wristwatches at entry- and mid-level prices. For these, the company uses Swiss base movements that are equipped with such in-house developments as a patented woodpecker-neck regulation and the Mühle rotor. The modifications are so extensive that they have led to the calibers having their own names. The traditional line named "R. Mühle & Sohn," introduced in 2014, is equipped with the RMK 1 and RMK 2 calibers. And there are other, somewhat less nautically inspired timepieces, like the Lunova series or the 29ers, which are simply elegant in an unspectacular way.

29er Casual

Reference number: M1-25-72-NB
Movement: automatic, Sellita Caliber SW300-1; ø 25.6 mm, height 3.6 mm; 25 jewels; 28,800 vph; woodpecker-neck adjustment, Mühle rotor, carefully reworked with special Mühle finish; 42-hour power reserve
Functions: hours, minutes, sweep seconds; date
Case: stainless steel, ø 42.4 mm, height 9.35 mm; sapphire crystal; transparent case back; screw-in crown; water-resistant to 10 atm
Band: textile, buckle
Price: $1,999
Variations: calfskin strap ($1,999)

Terrasport IV Bronze

Reference number: M1-45-07-LB
Movement: automatic, Sellita Caliber SW200-1; ø 25.6 mm, height 4.6 mm; 26 jewels; 28,800 vph; woodpecker-neck adjustment, Mühle rotor, carefully reworked with special Mühle finish; 38-hour power reserve
Functions: hours, minutes, sweep seconds; date
Case: bronze, ø 42 mm, height 10.2 mm; sapphire crystal; transparent case back; screw-in crown; water-resistant to 10 atm
Band: calfskin, buckle
Price: $2,099; limited to 250 pieces
Variations: mocha-colored dial ($2,099; limited to 250 pieces)

Panova Gray

Reference number: M1-40-75-LB
Movement: automatic, Sellita Caliber SW200-1; ø 25.6 mm, height 4.6 mm; 26 jewels; 28,800 vph; woodpecker-neck adjustment, Mühle rotor, carefully reworked with special Mühle finish; 38-hour power reserve
Functions: hours, minutes, sweep seconds
Case: stainless steel, ø 40 mm, height 10.4 mm; sapphire crystal; screw-in crown; water-resistant to 10 atm
Band: calfskin, buckle
Price: $1,000
Variations: textile strap ($1,000)

S.A.R. Rescue-Timer

Reference number: M1-41-03-MB
Movement: automatic, Sellita Caliber SW200-1; ø 25.6 mm, height 4.6 mm; 26 jewels; 28,800 vph; woodpecker-neck adjustment, Mühle rotor, carefully reworked with special Mühle finish; 38-hour power reserve
Functions: hours, minutes, sweep seconds; date
Case: stainless steel, ø 42 mm, height 13.5 mm; bezel with rubber ring; sapphire crystal; screw-in crown; water-resistant to 100 atm
Band: stainless steel, folding clasp, with extension link
Price: $2,699
Variations: rubber strap ($2,599)

S.A.R. Flieger Chronograph

Reference number: M1-41-33-KB
Movement: automatic, Caliber MU 9413 (base Sellita SW500); ø 30 mm, height 7.9 mm; 25 jewels; 28,800 vph; woodpecker-neck adjustment, three-quarter plate, Mühle rotor, carefully reworked with special Mühle finish; 48-hour power reserve
Functions: hours, minutes, subsidiary seconds; chronograph; date
Case: stainless steel, ø 45 mm, height 16.2 mm; bidirectional bezel, with 0-60 scale; sapphire crystal; transparent case back; screw-in crown; water-resistant to 10 atm
Band: rubber, folding clasp, with extension link
Price: $4,699
Variations: stainless steel band ($4,799)

Seebataillon GMT

Reference number: M1-28-62-KB
Movement: automatic, Sellita Caliber SW330-1; ø 25.6 mm, height 4.1 mm; 21 jewels; 28,800 vph; woodpecker-neck adjustment, Mühle rotor, carefully reworked with special Mühle finish; 48-hour power reserve
Functions: hours, minutes, sweep seconds; additional 24-hour display (2nd time zone); date
Case: titanium, ø 45 mm, height 12.7 mm; bidirectional bezel, with 0-60 scale; sapphire crystal; transparent case back; screw-in crown; water-resistant to 30 atm
Band: rubber, folding clasp, with extension link
Price: $3,999

Teutonia Sport I

Reference number: M1-29-65-LB
Movement: automatic, Mühle Caliber MU 9419 (base Sellita SW510-1); ø 30 mm, height 7.9 mm; 25 jewels; 28,800 vph; woodpecker-neck adjustment, three-quarter plate, Mühle rotor, carefully reworked with special Mühle finish; 48-hour power reserve
Functions: hours, minutes, subsidiary seconds; chronograph; date
Case: stainless steel, ø 42.6 mm, height 15.5 mm; bidirectional bezel, with 0-60 scale; sapphire crystal; transparent case back; screw-in crown; water-resistant to 10 atm
Band: calfskin, buckle
Price: $3,899

Teutonia Sport II

Reference number: M1-29-73-NB
Movement: automatic, Sellita Caliber SW290-1; ø 25.6 mm, height 5.6 mm; 31 jewels; 28,800 vph; woodpecker-neck adjustment, Mühle rotor, carefully reworked with special Mühle finish; 38-hour power reserve
Functions: hours, minutes, subsidiary seconds; date
Case: stainless steel, ø 41.6 mm, height 12.8 mm; sapphire crystal; transparent case back; screw-in crown; water-resistant to 10 atm
Band: rubber, with leather layer, buckle
Price: $2,549

Teutonia II Chronograph

Reference number: M1-30-95-LB
Movement: automatic, Mühle Caliber MU 9413 (base Sellita SW500); ø 30 mm, height 7.9 mm; 25 jewels; 28,800 vph; woodpecker-neck adjustment, three-quarter plate, Mühle rotor, carefully reworked with special Mühle finish; 48-hour power reserve
Functions: hours, minutes, subsidiary seconds; chronograph; date, weekday
Case: stainless steel, ø 42 mm, height 15.5 mm; sapphire crystal; transparent case back; screw-in crown; water-resistant to 10 atm
Band: reptile skin, double folding clasp
Price: $4,599
Variations: stainless steel band ($4,799)

Lunova Chronograph

Reference number: M1-43-06-LB
Movement: automatic, Mühle Caliber MU 9413 (base Sellita SW500); ø 30 mm, height 7.9 mm; 25 jewels; 28,800 vph; woodpecker-neck adjustment, three-quarter plate, Mühle rotor, carefully reworked with special Mühle finish; 48-hour power reserve
Functions: hours, minutes, subsidiary seconds; chronograph; date, weekday
Case: stainless steel, ø 42.3 mm, height 14.2 mm; sapphire crystal; transparent case back; screw-in crown; water-resistant to 10 atm
Band: reptile skin, buckle
Price: $2,990

Lunova Day/Date

Reference number: M1-43-26-LB
Movement: automatic, Sellita Caliber SW220-1; ø 25.6 mm, height 5.05 mm; 26 jewels; 28,800 vph; woodpecker-neck adjustment, Mühle rotor, carefully reworked with special Mühle finish; 38-hour power reserve
Functions: hours, minutes, sweep seconds; date, weekday
Case: titanium, ø 42.3 mm, height 11 mm; sapphire crystal; transparent case back; screw-in crown; water-resistant to 10 atm
Band: reptile skin, buckle
Price: $2,349

29er Big

Reference number: M1-25-33-MB
Movement: automatic, Sellita Caliber SW200-1; ø 25.6 mm, height 4.6 mm; 26 jewels; 28,800 vph; woodpecker-neck adjustment, Mühle rotor, carefully reworked with special Mühle finish; 38-hour power reserve
Functions: hours, minutes, sweep seconds; date
Case: stainless steel, ø 42.4 mm, height 11.3 mm; sapphire crystal; transparent case back; screw-in crown; water-resistant to 10 atm
Band: stainless steel, folding clasp
Price: $2,199
Variations: calfskin strap ($2,099); rubber strap ($2,099)

29er Hand Date

Reference number: M1-25-32-NB
Movement: automatic, Sellita Caliber SW221-1; ø 25.6 mm, height 5.05 mm; 26 jewels; 28,800 vph; woodpecker-neck adjustment, Mühle rotor, carefully reworked with special Mühle finish; 38-hour power reserve
Functions: hours, minutes, sweep seconds; date
Case: stainless steel, ø 42.4 mm, height 12.2 mm; sapphire crystal; transparent case back; water-resistant to 10 atm
Band: textile, buckle
Price: $1,899
Variations: stainless steel band ($1,630)

ProMare Go

Reference number: M1-42-32-NB
Movement: automatic, Sellita Caliber SW200-1; ø 25.6 mm, height 4.6 mm; 26 jewels; 28,800 vph; woodpecker-neck adjustment, Mühle rotor, carefully reworked with special Mühle finish; 38-hour power reserve
Functions: hours, minutes, sweep seconds; date
Case: stainless steel, ø 42 mm, height 12.2 mm; bidirectional bezel, with 0-60 scale; sapphire crystal; transparent case back; screw-in crown; water-resistant to 30 atm
Band: rubber with leather layer, buckle
Price: $2,100

ProMare Lady

Reference number: M1-41-25-NB
Movement: automatic, Sellita Caliber SW200-1; ø 25.6 mm, height 4.6 mm; 26 jewels; 28,800 vph; woodpecker-neck adjustment, Mühle rotor, carefully reworked with special Mühle finish; 38-hour power reserve
Functions: hours, minutes, sweep seconds; date
Case: stainless steel, ø 39 mm, height 10.6 mm; sapphire crystal; transparent case back; screw-in crown; water-resistant to 30 atm
Band: rubber, with leather layer, buckle
Remarks: mother-of-pearl dial set with 6 diamonds
Price: $2,399
Variations: stainless steel band ($2,499)

Nivrel Uhren
Gerd Hofer GmbH
Kossmannstrasse 3
D-66119 Saarbrücken
Germany

Tel.:
+49-681-584-6576

E-mail:
info@nivrel.com

Website:
www.nivrel.com

Founded:
1978

Number of employees:
10, plus external staff members

Distribution:
Please contact headquarters for enquiries.

Most important collections/price range:
mechanical watches, most with complications / approx. $600 to $45,000

NIVREL

In 1891, master goldsmith Friedrich Jacob Kraemer founded a jewelry and watch shop in Saarbrücken that proved to be the place to go for fine craftsmanship. Gerd Hofer joined the family business in 1956, carrying it on into the fourth generation. However, his true passion was for watchmaking. In 1993, he and his wife, Gitta, bought the rights to use the Swiss name Nivrel, a brand that had been established in 1936, and integrated production of these watches into their German-based operations.

Today, Nivrel is led by the Hofers' daughter Anja, who is keeping both lineages alive. Mechanical complications with Swiss movements of the finest technical level and finishing as well as gold watches in the high-end design segment of the industry are manufactured with close attention to detail and an advanced level of craftsmanship. In addition to classic automatic watches, the brand has introduced everything from complicated chronographs and skeletonized watches to perpetual calendars and tourbillons. The movements and all the "habillage" of the watches—case, dial, crystal, crown, etc.—are made in Switzerland. Watch design, assembly, and finishing are done in Saarbrücken.

Nivrel watches are a perfect example of how quickly a watch brand incorporating a characteristic style and immaculate quality can make a respected place for itself in the industry. Affordable prices also play a significant role in this brand's success, but they do not keep the brand from innovating. Nivrel has teamed up with the Department of Metallic Materials of Saarland University to develop a special alloy for repeater springs that is softer and does not need as much energy to press.

Replique Classique Rote 12

Reference number: N 160.001 CAWEOS
Movement: automatic, ETA Caliber 2824-2; ø 25.6 mm, height 4.6 mm; 25 jewels; 28,800 vph; 38-hour power reserve
Functions: hours, minutes, sweep seconds
Case: stainless steel, ø 42 mm, height 11 mm; sapphire crystal; transparent case back; water-resistant to 5 atm
Band: calfskin, buckle
Price: $789

Replique Classique

Reference number: N 160.001 CAAES
Movement: automatic, ETA Caliber 2824-2; ø 25.6 mm, height 4.6 mm; 25 jewels; 28,800 vph; 38-hour power reserve
Functions: hours, minutes, sweep seconds
Case: stainless steel, ø 42 mm, height 11 mm; sapphire crystal; transparent case back; water-resistant to 5 atm
Band: calfskin, buckle
Price: $789

Replique Aviateur III

Reference number: N 123.001 CASDS
Movement: automatic, ETA Caliber 2824-2; ø 25.6 mm, height 4.6 mm; 25 jewels; 28,800 vph; 38-hour power reserve
Functions: hours, minutes, sweep seconds
Case: stainless steel, ø 42 mm, height 10.2 mm; sapphire crystal; transparent case back; water-resistant to 5 atm
Band: calfskin, buckle
Price: $730

NOMOS

Beethoven was born in 1770, and who should celebrate this event with a line of watches? Nomos, makers of sleek, often minimalist timepieces. The idea is not farfetched, since Beethoven was a fan of Johann Nepomuk Hummel's invention, the metronome. At any rate, calling a copper-dialed watch Götterfunken is the kind of deadpan humor Nomos has gone for since its founding in 1990 by Roland Schwertner and his associate Uwe Ahrendt.

Their emphasis on design meant that the brand needed its own calibers, and these supply engines to the thirteen model families that grace the company's portfolio. The first one was the manually wound Alpha (used in the Tetra Sinfonie line). But the one that made a splash was undoubtedly the DUW 4401 (Deutsche Uhrenwerke Nomos Glashütte), equipped with an in-house escapement with a spring "made in Germany." It will gradually be used in all the movements, including the new, automatic, ultrathin DUW 3001. The DUW 6101 features a safe and easy date correction, and it is a mere 3.6 millimeters high including the date, which fits well in the company's design efforts.

Speaking of design, the three hundred people working at Nomos include about forty design and communication staff at the Berlinblau in-house design studio and in the United States, where Nomos has offices (in New York) and about fifty points of sale. The key strategy: watches with a unique pared-down look at decent prices. Then comes the marketing, which is bold and humorous. Nomos, visibly, is a member of the *deutscher Werkbund*, precursor to the Bauhaus school, which essentially worked with basic forms and combined light with structure. This esthetic scrim, as it were, has produced the swimmer's watch Ahoi (as in "ship ahoy!"), with an optional synthetic strap like those that carry locker keys at Germany's public swimming pools. The Autobahn is a panegyric to Germany's favorite playground, the highway. And, as mentioned above, there are the Tetras named for Beethoven works.

Nomos Glashütte/SA
Roland Schwertner KG
Ferdinand-Adolph-Lange-Platz 2
01768 Glashütte
Germany

Tel.:
+49-35053-404-0

E-mail:
nomos@glashuette.com

Website:
nomos-glashuette.com

Founded:
1990

Number of employees:
approx. 300

U.S. distributor:
For the U.S. market, please contact:
NOMOS Glashuette USA Inc.
347 W. 36th St., Suite 600
New York, NY 10018
212-929-2575
contact@nomos-watches.com

Most important collections/price range:
Ahoi / $4,020 to $4,660; Autobahn / $4,800; Club / $1,500 to $4,060; Lambda / $17,000 to $20,000; Ludwig / $1,380 to $4,000; Lux / $19,500 to $21,500; Metro / $2,860 to $9,700; Orion / $1,600 to $4,350; Tangente / $1,440 to $4,980; Tangomat / $3,280 to $4,920; Tetra / $1,660 to $3,980; Zürich / $4,480 to $6,100

Tangente Neomatik 41 Update

Reference number: 180
Movement: automatic, Nomos Caliber DUW 6101; ø 35.2 mm, height 3.6 mm; 27 jewels; 21,600 vph; three-quarter plate, finely finished movement; 42-hour power reserve
Functions: hours, minutes, subsidiary seconds; date
Case: stainless steel, ø 40.5 mm, height 7.8 mm; sapphire crystal; transparent case back; water-resistant to 5 atm
Band: horse leather, buckle
Price: $4,100

Tangente Neomatik 41 Update Ruthenium

Reference number: 181
Movement: automatic, Nomos Caliber DUW 6101; ø 35.2 mm, height 3.6 mm; 27 jewels; 21,600 vph; three-quarter plate, finely finished movement; 42-hour power reserve
Functions: hours, minutes, subsidiary seconds; date
Case: stainless steel, ø 40.5 mm, height 7.8 mm; sapphire crystal; transparent case back; water-resistant to 5 atm
Band: horse leather, buckle
Price: $4,100

Tangente Sport Neomatik 42 Date

Reference number: 580
Movement: automatic, Nomos Caliber DUW 6101; ø 35.2 mm, height 3.6 mm; 27 jewels; 21,600 vph; three-quarter plate, finely finished movement; 42-hour power reserve
Functions: hours, minutes, subsidiary seconds; date
Case: stainless steel, ø 42 mm, height 10.9 mm; sapphire crystal; transparent case back; water-resistant to 30 atm
Band: stainless steel, folding clasp
Price: $4,980

Tangente

Reference number: 139
Movement: manually wound, Nomos Caliber Alpha; ø 23.3 mm, height 2.6 mm; 17 jewels; 21,600 vph; three-quarter plate, finely finished movement; 43-hour power reserve
Functions: hours, minutes, subsidiary seconds
Case: stainless steel, ø 35 mm, height 6.6 mm; sapphire crystal; transparent case back; water-resistant to 3 atm
Band: horse leather, buckle
Price: $2,330

Tangente 38 Nachtblau

Reference number: 167
Movement: manually wound, Nomos Caliber Alpha; ø 23.3 mm, height 2.6 mm; 17 jewels; 21,600 vph; three-quarter plate, finely finished movement; 43-hour power reserve
Functions: hours, minutes, subsidiary seconds
Case: stainless steel, ø 37.5 mm, height 6.8 mm; sapphire crystal; transparent case back; water-resistant to 3 atm
Band: suede, buckle
Price: $2,030

Tangente 33 Duo

Reference number: 120
Movement: manually wound, Nomos Caliber Alpha.2; ø 23.3 mm, height 2.6 mm; 17 jewels; 21,600 vph; three-quarter plate, finely finished movement; 43-hour power reserve
Functions: hours, minutes
Case: stainless steel, ø 32.8 mm, height 6.5 mm; sapphire crystal; water-resistant to 3 atm
Band: suede, buckle
Price: $1,440

Ludwig Neomatik 41 Date

Reference number: 261
Movement: automatic, Nomos Caliber DUW 6101; ø 35.2 mm, height 3.6 mm; 27 jewels; 21,600 vph; three-quarter plate, finely finished movement; 42-hour power reserve
Functions: hours, minutes, subsidiary seconds; date
Case: stainless steel, ø 40.5 mm, height 7.7 mm; sapphire crystal; transparent case back; water-resistant to 5 atm
Band: horse leather, buckle
Price: $4,000

Orion Neomatik 41 Date Night Blue

Reference number: 363
Movement: automatic, Nomos Caliber DUW 6101; ø 35.2 mm, height 3.6 mm; 27 jewels; 21,600 vph; three-quarter plate, finely finished movement; 42-hour power reserve
Functions: hours, minutes, subsidiary seconds; date
Case: stainless steel, ø 40.5 mm, height 9.4 mm; sapphire crystal; transparent case back; water-resistant to 5 atm
Band: horse leather, buckle
Price: $4,350

Metro Date Power Reserve

Reference number: 1101
Movement: manually wound, Nomos Caliber DUW 4401; ø 32.1 mm, height 2.8 mm; 23 jewels; 21,600 vph; three-quarter plate, finely finished movement; 42-hour power reserve
Functions: hours, minutes, subsidiary seconds; power reserve indicator; date
Case: stainless steel, ø 37 mm, height 7.7 mm; sapphire crystal; transparent case back; water-resistant to 3 atm
Band: horse leather, buckle
Price: $3,780

Autobahn Neomatik 41 Date Sportgray

Reference number: 1303
Movement: automatic, Nomos Caliber DUW 6101; ø 35.2 mm, height 3.6 mm; 27 jewels; 21,600 vph; three-quarter plate, finely finished movement; 42-hour power reserve
Functions: hours, minutes, subsidiary seconds; date
Case: stainless steel, ø 41 mm, height 10.5 mm; sapphire crystal; transparent case back; water-resistant to 10 atm
Band: textile, buckle
Price: $4,800

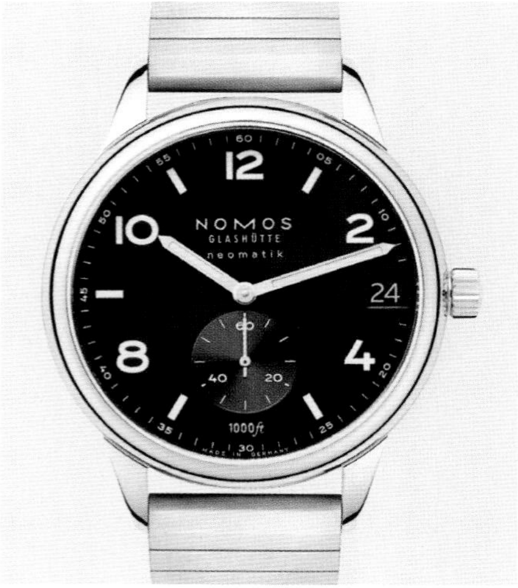

Club Sport Neomatik 42 Date Black

Reference number: 781
Movement: automatic, Nomos Caliber DUW 6101; ø 35.2 mm, height 3.6 mm; 27 jewels; 21,600 vph; three-quarter plate, finely finished movement; 42-hour power reserve
Functions: hours, minutes, subsidiary seconds; date
Case: stainless steel, ø 42 mm, height 10.2 mm; sapphire crystal; transparent case back; screw-in crown; water-resistant to 30 atm
Band: stainless steel, folding clasp
Price: $4,060

Ahoi

Reference number: 550
Movement: automatic, Nomos Caliber DUW 5001; ø 31 mm, height 4.3 mm; 26 jewels; 21,600 vph; three-quarter plate, finely finished movement; 43-hour power reserve
Functions: hours, minutes, subsidiary seconds
Case: stainless steel, ø 40.3 mm, height 10.6 mm; sapphire crystal; transparent case back; screw-in crown; water-resistant to 20 atm
Band: textile, buckle
Price: $4,060

Club Campus Neomatik

Reference number: 748
Movement: automatic, Nomos Caliber DUW 3001; ø 28.8 mm, height 3.2 mm; 27 jewels; 21,600 vph; three-quarter plate, finely finished movement; 43-hour power reserve
Functions: hours, minutes, subsidiary seconds
Case: stainless steel, ø 37 mm, height 8.3 mm; sapphire crystal; water-resistant to 20 atm
Band: stainless steel, sliding clasp
Price: $2,780

Club Campus 38 Nacht

Reference number: 736
Movement: manually wound, Nomos Caliber Alpha; ø 23.3 mm, height 2.6 mm; 17 jewels; 21,600 vph; three-quarter plate, finely finished movement; 43-hour power reserve
Functions: hours, minutes, subsidiary seconds
Case: stainless steel, ø 38.5 mm, height 8.5 mm; sapphire crystal; water-resistant to 10 atm
Band: suede, buckle
Price: $1,650

Zürich Weltzeit

Reference number: 805
Movement: automatic, DUW Caliber 5201; ø 31 mm, height 5.7 mm; 26 jewels; 21,600 vph; 42-hour power reserve
Functions: hours, minutes, subsidiary seconds; world time display (2nd time zone)
Case: stainless steel, ø 39.9 mm, height 10.8 mm; sapphire crystal; transparent case back; water-resistant to 3 atm
Band: horse leather, buckle
Price: $6,100

Tetra Fidelio

Reference number: 450
Movement: manually wound, Nomos Caliber Alpha; ø 23.3 mm, height 2.6 mm; 17 jewels; 21,600 vph; 43-hour power reserve
Functions: hours, minutes, subsidiary seconds
Case: stainless steel, 29.5 × 29.5 mm, height 6.5 mm; sapphire crystal; transparent case back; water-resistant to 3 atm
Band: suede, buckle
Price: $2,080

Tetra Götterfunken

Reference number: 444
Movement: manually wound, Nomos Caliber Alpha; ø 23.3 mm, height 2.6 mm; 17 jewels; 21,600 vph; 43-hour power reserve
Functions: hours, minutes, subsidiary seconds
Case: stainless steel, 29.5 × 29.5 mm, height 6.5 mm; sapphire crystal; transparent case back; water-resistant to 3 atm
Band: suede, buckle
Price: $2,080

Tetra Unsterbliche Geliebte

Reference number: 448
Movement: manually wound, Nomos Caliber Alpha; ø 23.3 mm, height 2.6 mm; 17 jewels; 21,600 vph; 43-hour power reserve
Functions: hours, minutes, subsidiary seconds
Case: stainless steel, 29.5 ×29.5 mm, height 6.5 mm; sapphire crystal; transparent case back; water-resistant to 3 atm
Band: suede, buckle
Price: $2,080

Caliber DUW 1001

Manually wound; swan-neck fine adjustment; double spring barrel, 84-hour power reserve
Functions: hours, minutes, subsidiary seconds; power reserve indicator
Diameter: 32 mm
Height: 3.6 mm
Jewels: 29, including 5 in screw-mounted gold chatons
Balance: screw balance
Frequency: 21,600 vph
Hairspring: Nivarox 1A
Shock protection: Incabloc
Remarks: hand-engraved balance cock, bevelled and polished edges, rhodium-plated movement with Glashütte sun-burst ribbing and perlage

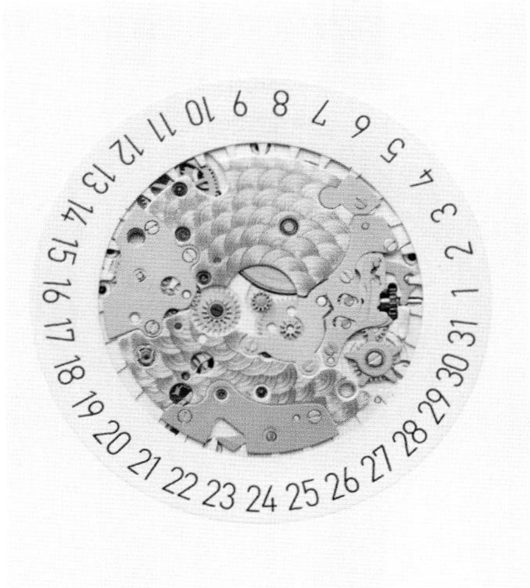

Caliber DUW 6101

Automatic; single spring barrel, 43-hour power reserve
Functions: hours, minutes, subsidiary seconds; date
Diameter: 35.2 mm
Height: 3.6 mm
Jewels: 27
Balance: in-house
Frequency: 21,600 vph
Hairspring: made in-house, heat-blued
Shock protection: Incabloc
Remarks: three-quarter plate, rhodium-plated movement with Glashütte ribbing and perlage, gold-plated engravings

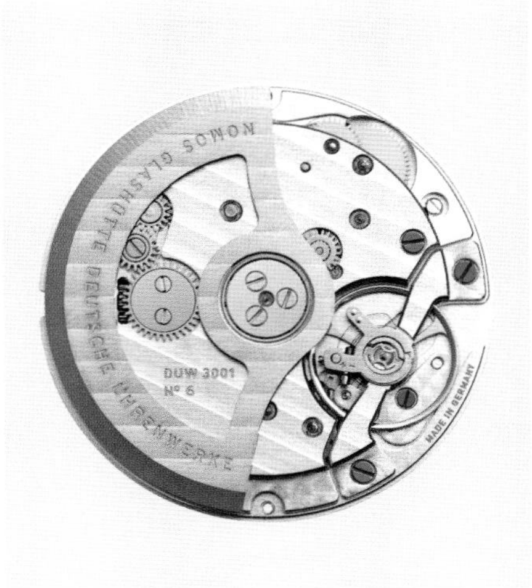

Caliber DUW 3001

Automatic; single spring barrel, 43-hour power reserve
Functions: hours, minutes, subsidiary seconds
Diameter: 28.8 mm
Height: 3.2 mm
Jewels: 27
Balance: made in-house
Frequency: 21,600 vph
Balance spring: made in-house, tempered-blue
Shock protection: Incabloc
Remarks: three-quarter plate, rhodium-plated movement with Glashütte ribbing and Nomos perlage

OMEGA

Omega SA
Jakob-Stämpfli-Strasse 96
CH-2502 Biel/Bienne
Switzerland

Tel.:
+41-32-343-9211

E-mail:
info@omegawatches.com

Website:
www.omegawatches.com

Founded:
1848

U.S. distributor:
Omega
703 Waterford Way, Suite 920
Miami, FL 33126
800-766-6342
www.omegawatches.com

As the largest brand in the SSIH Group, Omega had an important role to play during the quartz crisis that hit the Swiss watch industry in the 1970s. The Société Suisse de l'Industrie Horlogère and the Allgemeine Schweizerische Uhrenindustrie AG (ASUAG) merged to form the founding company of the Swatch Group. It became the flagship brand of the entire group and therefore had a leading position in terms of design, technology, and functionality.

With 20/20 hindsight, we can say that the industrializing of the special and complex escapement, which includes components requiring ultimate precision, is among the main achievements of the Group's various competence centers. Omega became quite naturally the first company to try out new materials like titanium and ceramic for the cases, or the central tourbillon, or the coaxial escapement designed originally by George Daniels. In the new Central Tourbillon, the two technologies are used side by side.

Technology and design are very much responsible for Omega's success. The 15,000-gauss amagnetic movement introduced a few years ago has also been used in many of the new products. And there is a plethora of new "Master Chronometer" movements, which not only meet the stringent requirements set out by the COSC but also have to pass the tests developed by Switzerland's Federal Institute of Metrology (METAS). The testing and certification process is performed in the new production building at the entirely renovated Swatch Group premises in Bienne/Biel. After promulgating the benefits of decentralization for years, Omega appears to be returning to the good old *manufacture* system of all crafts under a single roof. Swatch Group subsidiary Nivarox-FAR has finally mastered the production of the difficult, oil-free parts of the system designed by Englishman George Daniels, although the escapement continues to include lubrication, as the long-term results of "dry" coaxial movements are less than satisfactory. Thus, the most important plus for this escapement design remains high rate stability after careful regulation. Omega has even revived the Ladymatic, adding a silicon spring and the trademark coaxial escapement.

Speedmaster Moonwatch Caliber 321

Reference number: 311.30.40.30.01.001
Movement: manually wound, Omega Caliber 321B (base Lémania 2310); ø 27 mm, height 6.87 mm; 17 jewels; 18,000 vph; re-edition of a historic movement used in the first Speedmaster models; Breguet hairspring; column-wheel control of chronograph functions; finely finished movement; 55-hour power reserve
Functions: hours, minutes, subsidiary seconds; chronograph
Case: stainless steel, ø 39.7 mm, height 13.71 mm; sapphire crystal; transparent case back; water-resistant to 5 atm; **Band:** stainless steel, folding clasp
Price: $14,100

Seamaster Aqua Terra Master Chronometer

Reference number: 220.13.41.21.10.001
Movement: automatic, Omega Caliber 8900; ø 29 mm, height 5.5 mm; 39 jewels; 25,200 vph; 2 spring barrels, coaxial escapement, silicon balance and hairspring, amagnetic to 15,000 gauss; METAS-certified chronometer; 60-hour power reserve
Functions: hours, minutes, sweep seconds; date
Case: stainless steel, ø 41 mm, height 13.2 mm; sapphire crystal; transparent case back; screw-in crown; water-resistant to 15 atm
Band: reptile skin, folding clasp
Price: $5,400
Variations: various dial colors; stainless steel band; rubber strap

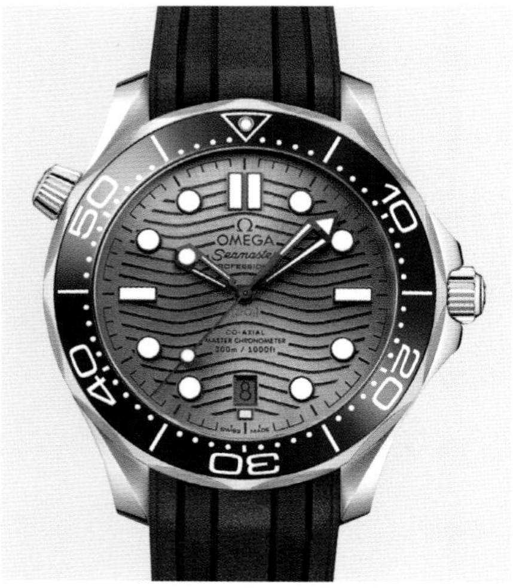

Seamaster Diver 300M

Reference number: 210.32.42.20.06.001
Movement: automatic, Omega Caliber 8800; ø 26 mm, height 4.6 mm; 35 jewels; 25,200 vph; 2 spring barrels, coaxial escapement, silicon balance and hairspring, amagnetic to 15,000 gauss; METAS-certified chronometer; 55-hour power reserve
Functions: hours, minutes, sweep seconds; date
Case: stainless steel, ø 42 mm, height 13.56 mm; unidirectional bezel with ceramic insert, with 0-60 scale; sapphire crystal; transparent case back; screw-in crown, helium valve; water-resistant to 30 atm
Band: rubber, folding clasp
Price: $4,900

Seamaster Diver Ceramic Titanium

Reference number: 210.92.44.20.01.001
Movement: automatic, Omega Caliber 8806; ø 26 mm, height 4.6 mm; 35 jewels; 25,200 vph; coaxial escapement, silicon balance and hairspring, amagnetic to 15,000 gauss; METAS-certified chronometer; 55-hour power reserve
Functions: hours, minutes, sweep seconds
Case: ceramic, ø 43.5 mm, height 14.17 mm; unidirectional titanium bezel with ceramic insert, with 0-60 scale; sapphire crystal; screw-in crown, helium valve; water-resistant to 30 atm
Band: rubber, buckle
Price: $8,100

Seamaster Diver 300M Chronograph

Reference number: 210.30.44.51.03.001
Movement: automatic, Omega Caliber 9900; ø 32.5 mm, height 7.6 mm; 54 jewels; 28,800 vph; 2 spring barrels, coaxial escapement, silicon balance and hairspring, amagnetic to 15,000 gauss; METAS-certified chronometer; 60-hour power reserve
Functions: hours, minutes, subsidiary seconds; chronograph; date
Case: stainless steel, ø 44 mm, height 17.2 mm; unidirectional bezel with ceramic insert, with 0-60 scale; sapphire crystal; screw-in crown and pushers, ceramic pushers, helium valve; water-resistant to 30 atm; **Band:** stainless steel, folding clasp
Price: $7,450

Seamaster Aqua Terra Worldtimer

Reference number: 220.12.43.22.03.001
Movement: automatic, Omega Caliber 8938; ø 29 mm, height 6.5 mm; 39 jewels; 25,200 vph; coaxial escapement, silicon balance and hairspring; amagnetic to 15,000 gauss; METAS-certified chronometer; 60-hour power reserve; COSC-certified chronometer
Functions: hours, minutes, sweep seconds; world time display (2nd time zone); date
Case: stainless steel, ø 43 mm, height 14.3 mm; sapphire crystal; transparent case back; screw-in crown; water-resistant to 15 atm
Band: rubber, buckle
Price: $8,900
Variations: stainless steel band

Seamaster Planet Ocean Deep Black Master Chronometer

Reference number: 215.92.46.22.01.001
Movement: automatic, Omega Caliber 8906; ø 29 mm, height 6 mm; 38 jewels; 25,200 vph; 2 spring barrels, coaxial escapement, silicon balance and hairspring, amagnetic to 15,000 gauss; METAS-certified chronometer; 60-hour power reserve
Functions: hours, minutes, sweep seconds; additional 24-hour display (2nd time zone); date
Case: ceramic, ø 43.5 mm, height 17.04 mm; unidirectional bezel with 0-60 scale; sapphire crystal; screw-in crown, helium valve; water-resistant to 60 atm
Band: rubber with textile layer, folding clasp
Price: $11,700

Seamaster Aqua Terra Railmaster

Reference number: 220.10.40.20.01.001
Movement: automatic, Omega Caliber 8806; ø 26 mm, height 4.6 mm; 35 jewels; 25,200 vph; coaxial escapement, silicon balance and hairspring, amagnetic to 15,000 gauss; METAS-certified chronometer; 55-hour power reserve
Functions: hours, minutes, sweep seconds
Case: stainless steel, ø 40 mm, height 12.65 mm; sapphire crystal; water-resistant to 15 atm
Band: stainless steel, folding clasp
Price: $5,200
Variations: various dials; calfskin strap; textile strap

Globemaster Master Chronometer

Reference number: 130.33.39.21.03.001
Movement: automatic, Omega Caliber 8900; ø 29 mm, height 5.5 mm; 39 jewels; 25,200 vph; coaxial escapement, silicon balance and hairspring, amagnetic to 15,000 gauss; METAS-certified chronometer; 60-hour power reserve
Functions: hours, minutes, sweep seconds; date
Case: stainless steel, ø 39 mm, height 12.53 mm; sapphire crystal; water-resistant to 10 atm
Band: reptile skin, folding clasp
Price: $6,900
Variations: various dials; stainless steel band; pink gold bezel; in pink gold

De Ville Prestige

Reference number: 424.10.40.20.01.002
Movement: automatic, Omega Caliber 2500; ø 25.6 mm, height 4.1 mm; 27 jewels; 25,200 vph; coaxial escapement; 48-hour power reserve; COSC-certified chronometer
Functions: hours, minutes, sweep seconds; date
Case: stainless steel, ø 39.5 mm, height 10.1 mm; sapphire crystal; water-resistant to 3 atm
Band: stainless steel, folding clasp
Price: $3,850
Variations: reptile skin strap; pink gold or yellow gold bezel

Speedmaster Dark Side of the Moon "Apollo 8"

Reference number: 311.92.44.30.01.001
Movement: manually wound, Omega Caliber 1869; ø 27 mm, height 6.87 mm; 19 jewels; 21,600 vph; 48-hour power reserve
Functions: hours, minutes, subsidiary seconds; chronograph
Case: ceramic, ø 44.25 mm, height 13.8 mm; sapphire crystal; transparent case back; water-resistant to 5 atm
Band: calfskin, buckle
Remarks: mainplate and bridges with carefully replicated moon surface
Price: $9,750

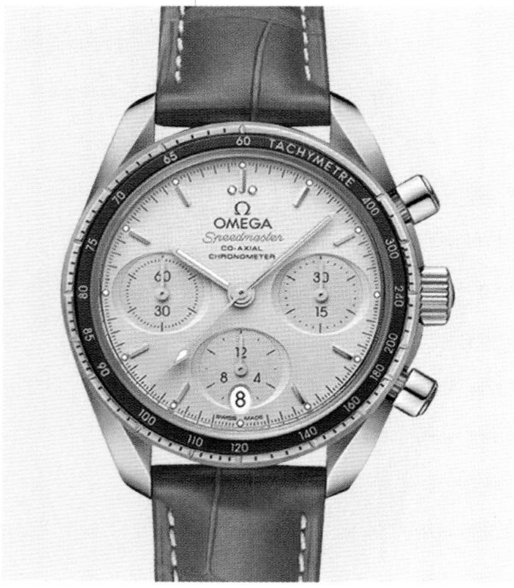

Speedmaster Co-Axial Chronometer 38 mm

Reference number: 324.63.38.50.02.003
Movement: automatic, Omega Caliber 3330; ø 30 mm, height 7.9 mm; 31 jewels; 28,800 vph; coaxial escapement, silicon balance and hairspring; 52-hour power reserve; COSC-certified chronometer
Functions: hours, minutes, subsidiary seconds; chronograph; date
Case: rose gold ("Sednagold"), ø 38 mm, height 14.7 mm; bezel with ceramic insert; sapphire crystal; water-resistant to 10 atm
Band: reptile skin, folding clasp
Price: $16,500
Variations: stainless steel

Speedmaster Moonphase

Reference number: 304.33.44.52.03.001
Movement: automatic, Omega Caliber 9904; ø 32.5 mm, height 8.35 mm; 54 jewels; 28,800 vph; 2 spring barrels, coaxial escapement, silicon balance and hairspring, amagnetic to 15,000 gauss; METAS-certified chronometer; 60-hour power reserve
Functions: hours, minutes, subsidiary seconds; chronograph; date, moon phase
Case: stainless steel, ø 44.25 mm, height 16.85 mm; bezel with ceramic insert; sapphire crystal; water-resistant to 10 atm
Band: reptile skin, folding clasp
Price: $10,600

Seamaster Diver James Bond Edition

Reference number: 210.90.42.20.01.001
Movement: automatic, Omega Caliber 8806; ø 26 mm, height 4.6 mm; 35 jewels; 25,200 vph; coaxial escapement, silicon balance and hairspring, amagnetic to 15,000 gauss; METAS-certified chronometer; 55-hour power reserve
Functions: hours, minutes, sweep seconds
Case: titanium, ø 42 mm, height 13.3 mm; unidirectional bezel with ceramic insert, with 0-60 scale; sapphire crystal; screw-in crown, helium valve; water-resistant to 30 atm
Band: titanium Milanese mesh, folding clasp
Price: $9,200

Speedmaster '57

Reference number: 331.10.42.51.01.002
Movement: automatic, Omega Caliber 9300; ø 32.5 mm, height 7.6 mm; 54 jewels; 28,800 vph; coaxial escapement, silicon balance and hairspring; 60-hour power reserve; COSC-certified chronometer
Functions: hours, minutes, subsidiary seconds; chronograph; date
Case: stainless steel, ø 41.5 mm, height 16.17 mm; sapphire crystal; water-resistant to 10 atm
Band: stainless steel, folding clasp
Price: $9,000
Variations: various dials; calfskin strap; pink gold; yellow gold

Caliber 8800

Automatic; coaxial escapement; amagnetic up to 15,000 gauss; METAS-certified chronometer; single spring barrel, 55-hour power reserve
Functions: hours, minutes, sweep seconds; date
Diameter: 26 mm
Height: 4.6 mm
Jewels: 35
Balance: silicon, without regulator
Frequency: 25,200 vph
Balance spring: silicon
Shock protection: Nivachoc
Remarks: blackened screws

Caliber 321B

Manually wound; Breguet hairspring; column-wheel control of chronograph functions; single spring barrel, 55-hour power reserve
Base caliber: Lémania 2310
Functions: hours, minutes, subsidiary seconds; chronograph
Diameter: 27 mm
Height: 6.87 mm
Jewels: 17
Frequency: 18,000 vph
Remarks: re-edition of historic movement used in first Speedmaster models; red gold–plated, finely finished

Caliber 8900

Automatic; coaxial escapement; amagnetic up to 15,000 gauss; METAS-certified chronometer; double spring barrel, 60-hour power reserve
Functions: hours, minutes, sweep seconds; date
Diameter: 29 mm
Height: 5.5 mm
Jewels: 39
Balance: silicon, without regulator
Frequency: 25,200 vph
Balance spring: silicon
Shock protection: Nivachoc
Remarks: mainplate, bridges, and rotor with "arabesque" côtes de Genève, rhodium-plated, spring barrels, blackened balance wheel and screws

Caliber 9900

Automatic; coaxial escapement; column-wheel control of chronograph functions; amagnetic up to 15,000 gauss; METAS-certified chronometer; double spring barrel, 60-hour power reserve
Functions: hours, minutes, subsidiary seconds; chronograph; date
Diameter: 32.5 mm
Height: 7.6 mm
Jewels: 5.4
Balance: silicon, without regulator
Frequency: 28,800 vph
Balance spring: silicon
Shock protection: Nivachoc
Remarks: mainplate, bridges, and rotor with "arabesque" côtes de Genève

Caliber 1861

Manually wound; single spring barrel, 48-hour power reserve
Base caliber: Lémania 1873
Functions: hours, minutes, subsidiary seconds; chronograph
Diameter: 27 mm
Height: 6.87 mm
Jewels: 18
Frequency: 21,600 vph
Balance spring: flat hairspring
Remarks: rhodium-plated, gold-plated engravings; 234 parts

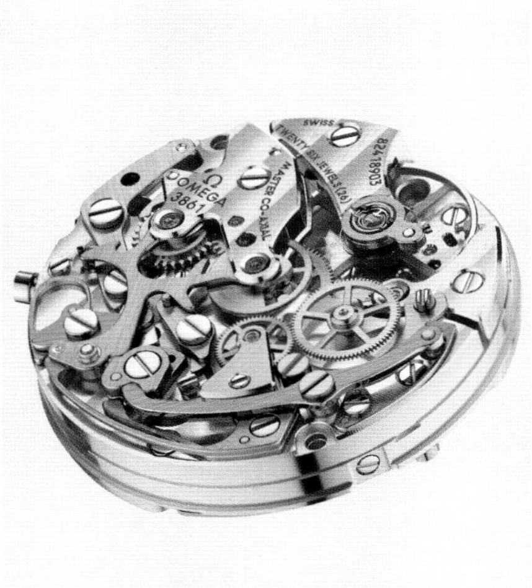

Caliber 3861

Manually wound; coaxial escapement, amagnetic protection to 15,000 gauss; METAS-certified chronometer; single spring barrel, 50-hour power reserve
Functions: hours, minutes, subsidiary seconds; chronograph
Diameter: 27 mm
Height: 6.87 mm
Jewels: 26
Frequency: 21,600 vph
Balance spring: silicon
Remarks: gold-plated movement ("Moonshine Gold"); 240 parts

ORIS

Oris, located near Basel, Switzerland, since its founding in 1904, has stuck to its strategic guns for as long as it has existed: affordable quality. The result has been growing international success, now with a portfolio divided up into four "product worlds," each with its own distinct identity: aviation, motor sports, diving, and culture. In utilizing specific materials—a tungsten bezel for the divers, for example—and functions based on these types, Oris makes certain that each will fit perfectly into the world for which it was designed. Yet the heart of every watch houses a small, high-quality "high-mech" movement identifiable by the brand's standard red rotor.

A bold step came in 2014 with the in-house Caliber 110, a plain, but technically efficient, manually wound movement. It was made together with the engineers from the Technical College of Le Locle, and features a massive 6-foot (1.8-meter) mainspring. Almost as regular as clockwork, the brand has produced further calibers.

The 111 provides ten days of power with even torque. The 112 has GMT function and day/night indication. The fourth in-house caliber, 113, was equipped with a clever sweep hand indication of calendar weeks that also shows the month. Add to that the apertures for date and day of the week, and you have a complete calendar for businesspeople and others who need to stay dialed into the date. And in 2018 came the 114, which is used in the ProPilot X, the first skeleton version of the watch, which suggests where the brand is going esthetically as well. Indeed, the structures remaining after skeletonization recall the grand old days of cast iron, at one time a very modern material in construction. To maintain the authentic look, the material was left unbeveled or -polished, and the dial section that is stretched across the movement like a net reveals soberly printed scales. The titanium case is completed by an integrated titanium bracelet.

Oris SA
Ribigasse 1
CH-4434 Hölstein
Switzerland

Tel.:
+41-61-956-1111

E-mail:
MyOris@oris.ch

Website:
www.oris.ch

Founded:
1904

Number of employees:
90

U.S. distributor:
Oris Watches USA
50 Washington Street, Suite 302
Norwalk, CT 06854
203-857-4769

Most important collections/price range:
Divers Sixty-Five, Big Crown, Artelier, Aquis, ProPilot / approx. $1,250 to $5,500

Big Crown ProPilot X Caliber 115

Reference number: 01 115 7759 7153
Movement: manually wound, Oris Caliber 115; ø 34 mm, height 6 mm; 38 jewels; 21,600 vph; skeletonized movement; centrally placed open mainspring; 240-hour power reserve
Functions: hours, minutes, subsidiary seconds; power reserve indicator
Case: titanium, ø 44 mm, height 12.5 mm; sapphire crystal; transparent case back; screw-in crown; water-resistant to 10 atm
Band: calfskin, folding clasp
Remarks: skeletonized dial
Price: $7,200

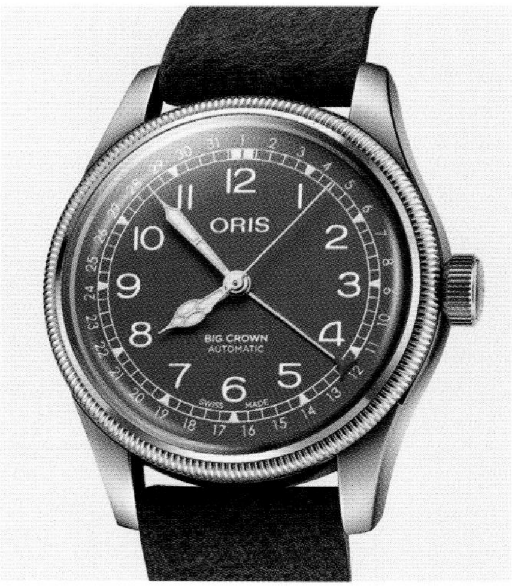

Big Crown Bronze Pointer Date

Reference number: 01 754 7741 3166
Movement: automatic, Oris Caliber 754 (base Sellita SW200-1); ø 25.6 mm, height 4.6 mm; 26 jewels; 28,800 vph; 38-hour power reserve
Functions: hours, minutes, sweep seconds; date
Case: bronze, ø 40 mm, height 11.8 mm; sapphire crystal; transparent case back; water-resistant to 5 atm
Band: calfskin, buckle
Price: $2,100

Big Crown ProPilot Big Date

Reference number: 01 751 7761 4063
Movement: automatic, Oris Caliber 751 (base Sellita SW220-1); ø 32.2 mm, height 5.05 mm; 26 jewels; 28,800 vph; 38-hour power reserve
Functions: hours, minutes, sweep seconds; date
Case: stainless steel, ø 41 mm, height 12.4 mm; sapphire crystal; transparent case back; screw-in crown; water-resistant to 10 atm
Band: stainless steel, folding clasp
Price: $1,900
Variations: black and anthracite dial; calfskin strap

Big Crown ProPilot Timer GMT

Reference number: 01 748 7756 4064
Movement: automatic, Oris Caliber 748 (base Sellita SW220-1); ø 32.2 mm, height 5.5 mm; 28 jewels; 28,800 vph; 38-hour power reserve
Functions: hours, minutes, subsidiary seconds; additional 24-hour display (2nd time zone); date
Case: stainless steel, ø 44 mm, height 12.8 mm; bidirectional bezel, with 0-60 scale; sapphire crystal; transparent case back; screw-in crown; water-resistant to 10 atm
Band: textile, folding clasp
Price: $2,600
Variations: stainless steel bracelet ($2,800); calfskin strap ($2,600)

Aquis Lake Baikal Limited Edition

Reference number: 01 733 7730 4175
Movement: automatic, Oris Caliber 733 (base Sellita SW200-1); ø 25.6 mm, height 4.6 mm; 26 jewels; 28,800 vph; 38-hour power reserve
Functions: hours, minutes, sweep seconds; date
Case: stainless steel, ø 43.5 mm, height 13.5 mm; unidirectional bezel with ceramic insert and 0-60 scale; sapphire crystal; screw-in crown; water-resistant to 30 atm
Band: stainless steel, folding clasp
Price: $2,400; limited to 1,999 pieces

Aquis Date 39.5

Reference number: 01 733 7732 4155
Movement: automatic, Oris Caliber 733 (base Sellita SW200-1); ø 25.6 mm, height 4.6 mm; 26 jewels; 28,800 vph; 38-hour power reserve
Functions: hours, minutes, sweep seconds; date
Case: stainless steel, ø 39.5 mm, height 12.6 mm; unidirectional bezel with ceramic insert, with 0-60 scale; sapphire crystal; screw-in crown; water-resistant to 30 atm
Band: stainless steel, folding clasp
Price: $2,200

Aquis Date 41.5

Reference number: 01 733 7766 4135
Movement: automatic, Oris Caliber 733 (base Sellita SW200-1); ø 25.6 mm, height 4.6 mm; 26 jewels; 28,800 vph; 38-hour power reserve
Functions: hours, minutes, sweep seconds; date
Case: stainless steel, ø 41.5 mm, height 12.7 mm; unidirectional bezel with ceramic insert, with 0-60 scale; sapphire crystal; screw-in crown; water-resistant to 30 atm
Band: stainless steel, folding clasp
Price: $2,200
Variations: rubber strap ($2,000)

Aquis Date Relief

Reference number: 01 733 7730 4153
Movement: automatic, Oris Caliber 733 (base Sellita SW200-1); ø 25.6 mm, height 4.6 mm; 26 jewels; 28,800 vph; 38-hour power reserve
Functions: hours, minutes, sweep seconds; date
Case: stainless steel, ø 43.5 mm, height 12.7 mm; unidirectional bezel with 0-60 scale; sapphire crystal; transparent case back; screw-in crown; water-resistant to 30 atm
Band: rubber, folding clasp, with extension link
Price: $1,900
Variations: stainless steel band ($2,100)

Aquis Chronograph

Reference number: 01 774 7743 4155
Movement: automatic, Oris Caliber 774 (base Sellita SW500); ø 30 mm, height 7.9 mm; 25 jewels; 28,800 vph; 48-hour power reserve
Functions: hours, minutes, subsidiary seconds; chronograph; date
Case: stainless steel, ø 45.5 mm, height 18.1 mm; unidirectional bezel with 0-60 scale; sapphire crystal; screw-in crown; water-resistant to 50 atm
Band: rubber, folding clasp
Price: $3,700
Variations: stainless steel band ($3,900)

Aquis GMT Date

Reference number: 01 798 7754 4135
Movement: automatic, Oris Caliber 798 (base Sellita SW330-1); ø 25.6 mm, height 4.1 mm; 25 jewels; 28,800 vph; 42-hour power reserve
Functions: hours, minutes, sweep seconds; additional 24-hour display (2nd time zone); date
Case: stainless steel, ø 43.5 mm, height 12.8 mm; bidirectional bezel with ceramic insert, with 0-24 scale; sapphire crystal; screw-in crown; water-resistant to 30 atm
Band: stainless steel, folding clasp
Price: $2,800
Variations: calfskin strap ($2,650); rubber strap ($2,600)

Aquis Date

Reference number: 01 733 7732 4157
Movement: automatic, Oris Caliber 733 (base Sellita SW200-1); ø 25.6 mm, height 4.6 mm; 26 jewels; 28,800 vph; 38-hour power reserve
Functions: hours, minutes, sweep seconds; date
Case: stainless steel, ø 39.5 mm, height 12.6 mm; unidirectional bezel with ceramic insert, with 0-60 scale; sapphire crystal; screw-in crown; water-resistant to 30 atm
Band: stainless steel, folding clasp
Price: $2,200
Variations: calfskin strap ($2,050); rubber strap ($2,000)

Divers Sixty-Five

Reference number: 01 733 7707 4357
Movement: automatic, Oris Caliber 733 (base Sellita SW200-1); ø 25.6 mm, height 4.6 mm; 26 jewels; 28,800 vph; 38-hour power reserve
Functions: hours, minutes, sweep seconds; date
Case: stainless steel, ø 40 mm, height 12.8 mm; unidirectional bronze bezel, with 0-60 scale; sapphire crystal; screw-in crown; water-resistant to 10 atm
Band: calfskin, buckle
Price: $2,100
Variations: stainless steel band ($2,300)

Divers Sixty-Five Bicolor

Reference number: 01 733 7707 4355
Movement: automatic, Oris Caliber 733 (base Sellita SW200-1); ø 25.6 mm, height 4.6 mm; 26 jewels; 28,800 vph; 38-hour power reserve
Functions: hours, minutes, sweep seconds; date
Case: stainless steel, ø 40 mm, height 12.8 mm; unidirectional bezel in bronze with 0-60 scale; sapphire crystal; screw-in crown; water-resistant to 10 atm
Band: stainless steel with bronze elements, folding clasp
Price: $2,450
Variations: calfskin strap ($2,200)

Divers Sixty-Five Chronograph

Reference number: 01 771 7744 4354
Movement: automatic, Oris Caliber 771 (base Sellita SW510-1); ø 30 mm, height 7.9 mm; 27 jewels; 28,800 vph; 48-hour power reserve
Functions: hours, minutes, subsidiary seconds; chronograph
Case: stainless steel, ø 43 mm, height 16.2 mm; unidirectional bezel in bronze; sapphire crystal; water-resistant to 10 atm
Band: calfskin, folding clasp
Price: $4,000
Variations: stainless steel band ($4,250)

Oris X Momotaro

Reference number: 01 733 7707 4337
Movement: automatic, Oris Caliber 733 (base Sellita SW200-1); ø 25.6 mm, height 4.6 mm; 26 jewels; 28,800 vph; 38-hour power reserve
Functions: hours, minutes, sweep seconds
Case: stainless steel, ø 40 mm, height 12.9 mm; unidirectional bezel in bronze with 0-60 scale; sapphire crystal; screw-in crown; water-resistant to 10 atm
Band: textile, buckle
Remarks: the model is a collaboration with Momotaro, a Japanese jeans label
Price: $2,200

Officine Panerai
Viale Monza, 259
I-20126 Milan
Italy

Tel.:
+39-02-363-138

Website:
www.panerai.com

Founded:
1860 in Florence, Italy

Number of employees:
approx. 250

U.S. distributor:
Panerai
645 Fifth Avenue
New York, NY 10022
877-PANERAI
concierge.usa@panerai.com; www.panerai.com

Most important collections/price range:
Luminor / $5,000 to $25,000; Luminor 1950 / $8,000 to $30,000; Radiomir / $7,000 to $25,000; Radiomir 1940 / $8,000 to $133,000; special editions / $10,000 to $125,000; clocks and instruments / $20,000 to $250,000

PANERAI

Officine Panerai (in English: Panerai Workshops) joined the Richemont Group in 1997. Since then, it has made an unprecedented rise from an insider niche brand to a lifestyle phenomenon. The company, founded in 1860 by Giovanni Panerai, supplied the Italian navy with precision instruments. In the 1930s, the Florentine engineers developed a series of waterproof wristwatches that could be used by commandos under especially extreme and risky conditions. After 1997, under the leadership of Angelo Bonati, the company came out with a collection of oversize wristwatches, both stylistically and technically based on these historical models.

In 2002, Panerai opened a *manufacture* in Neuchâtel, and by 2005 it was already producing its own movements (caliber family P.2000). In 2009, the new "little" Panerai *manufacture* movements (caliber family P.9000) were released. From the start, the idea behind them was to provide a competitive alternative to the base movements available until a couple of years ago. In 2014, a new *manufacture* was inaugurated in Neuchâtel to handle development, manufacturing, assembly, and quality control under one roof.

Parallel to consolidating, the brand has been steadily expanding its portfolio of new calibers. Fairly early on, it came out with an automatic chronograph with a flyback function, the P.9100. This was followed by a string of new calibers, almost one per year, to gradually replace "foreign" movements. Notorious is the P.4000, with an off-center winding rotor. At 3.95 millimeters, it is very thin for Panerai, but then again, it was developed for a new set of models.

Mechanics are not the only aspect of watchmaking that Panerai has sought to focus on. In the year of Covid, the company presented a number of models that make use of new materials, like the particularly radiant gold alloy the company named Goldtech and a carbon composite. Not only are these attractive to neophiles, but they also refresh the look of this brand without breaking any DNA rules.

Submersible EcoPangaea Tourbillon GMT 50mm "Mike Horn Edition"

Reference number: PAM01108
Movement: manually wound, Panerai Caliber P.2005/T; ø 36.6 mm, height 10.05 mm; 31 jewels; 28,800 vph; 3 spring barrels, 1-minute tourbillon; 144-hour power reserve
Functions: hours, minutes, subsidiary seconds; additional 24-hour display (2nd time zone), day/night indicator, power reserve indicator
Case: stainless steel, ø 50 mm, height 20.77 mm; unidirectional bezel with 0-60 scale; sapphire crystal; transparent case back; crown protector with hinged lever; water-resistant to 30 atm; **Band:** rubber, buckle
Price: $189,000; limited to 5 pieces

Luminor Submersible Carbotech 47mm

Reference number: PAM01616
Movement: automatic, Panerai Caliber P.9010; ø 31 mm, height 6 mm; 31 jewels; 28,800 vph; 2 spring barrels, 72-hour power reserve
Functions: hours, minutes, subsidiary seconds; date
Case: carbon fiber (Carbotech), ø 47 mm; unidirectional bezel, 0-60 scale; sapphire crystal; crown protector with hinged lever; water-resistant to 30 atm
Band: rubber, buckle
Price: $17,900

Luminor Marina 44mm

Reference number: PAM01117
Movement: automatic, Panerai Caliber P.9010; ø 31 mm, height 6 mm; 31 jewels; 28,800 vph; 2 spring barrels, 72-hour power reserve
Functions: hours, minutes, subsidiary seconds; date
Case: titanium, ø 44 mm, height 15.65 mm; sapphire crystal; crown protector with hinged lever; water-resistant to 30 atm
Band: textile, Velcro
Remarks: comes with additional rubber strap
Price: $21,500; limited to 270 pieces (only in Panerai boutiques)

Luminor Marina Goldtech 44mm

Reference number: PAM1112
Movement: automatic, Panerai Caliber P.9010; ø 31 mm, height 6 mm; 31 jewels; 28,800 vph; 2 spring barrels, 72-hour power reserve
Functions: hours, minutes, subsidiary seconds; date
Case: rose gold (Goldtech), ø 44 mm, height 14.5 mm; sapphire crystal; transparent case back; crown protector with hinged lever; water-resistant to 5 atm
Band: reptile skin, buckle
Remarks: comes with additional rubber strap
Price: $22,900; limited to 270 pieces

Luminor Luna Rossa GMT 44mm

Reference number: PAM01036
Movement: automatic, Panerai Caliber P.9010/GMT; ø 31 mm, height 6 mm; 31 jewels; 28,800 vph; 2 spring barrels, 72-hour power reserve
Functions: hours, minutes, subsidiary seconds; additional 12-hour display (2nd time zone); date
Case: titanium with black DLC, ø 44 mm, height 15.65 mm; sapphire crystal; crown protector with hinged lever; water-resistant to 30 atm
Band: calfskin, buckle
Remarks: dial made of sailcloth from the Luna Rossa; comes with additional rubber strap
Price: $11,200

Luminor Due 38mm

Reference number: PAM00926
Movement: automatic, Panerai Caliber P.900; ø 28.19 mm, height 4.2 mm; 23 jewels; 28,800 vph; 72-hour power reserve
Functions: hours, minutes, subsidiary seconds; date
Case: titanium, ø 38 mm, height 11.3 mm; sapphire crystal; crown protector with hinged lever; water-resistant to 3 atm
Band: reptile skin, buckle
Remarks: sandwich dial with luminous mass on lower dial
Price: $6,900

Luminor Marina Carbotech 44mm

Reference number: PAM01118
Movement: automatic, Panerai Caliber P.9010; ø 31 mm, height 6 mm; 31 jewels; 28,800 vph; 2 spring barrels, 72-hour power reserve
Functions: hours, minutes, subsidiary seconds; date
Case: carbon fiber (Carbotech), ø 44 mm, height 14.5 mm; sapphire crystal; crown protector with hinged lever; water-resistant to 30 atm
Band: textile, Velcro fastening
Remarks: comes with additional rubber strap
Price: $16,000; limited to 270 pieces (exclusive in Panerai boutiques)

Luminor Due 38mm

Reference number: PAM01045
Movement: automatic, Panerai Caliber P.900; ø 28.19 mm, height 4.2 mm; 23 jewels; 28,800 vph; 72-hour power reserve
Functions: hours, minutes, subsidiary seconds; date
Case: rose gold (Goldtech), ø 38 mm, height 11.2 mm; sapphire crystal; transparent case back; crown protector with hinged lever; water-resistant to 3 atm
Band: reptile skin, buckle
Price: $15,300

Luminor Due 42mm

Reference number: PAM00904
Movement: automatic, Panerai Caliber P.900; ø 28.19 mm, height 4.2 mm; 23 jewels; 28,800 vph; 72-hour power reserve
Functions: hours, minutes, subsidiary seconds; date
Case: stainless steel, ø 42 mm, height 10.7 mm; sapphire crystal; crown protector with hinged lever; water-resistant to 3 atm
Band: calfskin, buckle
Remarks: sandwich dial with luminous mass on lower dial
Price: $6,400

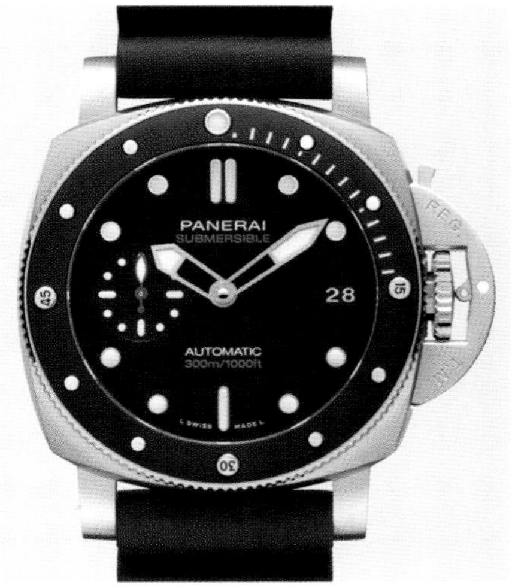

Luminor Submersible 42mm

Reference number: PAM00683
Movement: automatic, Panerai Caliber OPXXXIV; ø 28.19 mm, height 4.2 mm; 23 jewels; 28,800 vph; 72-hour power reserve
Functions: hours, minutes, subsidiary seconds; date
Case: stainless steel, ø 42 mm; unidirectional bezel with ceramic insert, with 0-60 scale; sapphire crystal; crown protector with hinged lever; water-resistant to 30 atm
Band: rubber, buckle
Price: $9,800

Luminor Submersible BMG-Tech 47mm

Reference number: PAM00799
Movement: automatic, Panerai Caliber P.9010; ø 31 mm, height 6 mm; 31 jewels; 28,800 vph; 2 spring barrels, 72-hour power reserve
Functions: hours, minutes, subsidiary seconds; date
Case: composite material BMG-Tech (alloy of zirconium, copper, aluminum, titanium, nickel), ø 47 mm; unidirectional carbon fiber bezel with 0-60 scale; sapphire crystal; crown protector with hinged lever; water-resistant to 30 atm
Band: rubber, buckle
Price: $15,300

Luminor Marina Fibratech 44mm

Reference number: PAM01663
Movement: automatic, Panerai Caliber P.9010; ø 31 mm, height 6 mm; 31 jewels; 28,800 vph; 2 spring barrels, 72-hour power reserve
Functions: hours, minutes, subsidiary seconds; date
Case: composite material (Fibratech), ø 44 mm, height 14.5 mm; carbon fiber (Carbotech) bezel and crown; sapphire crystal; crown protector with hinged lever; water-resistant to 30 atm
Band: textile, buckle
Remarks: comes with additional rubber strap
Price: $16,000

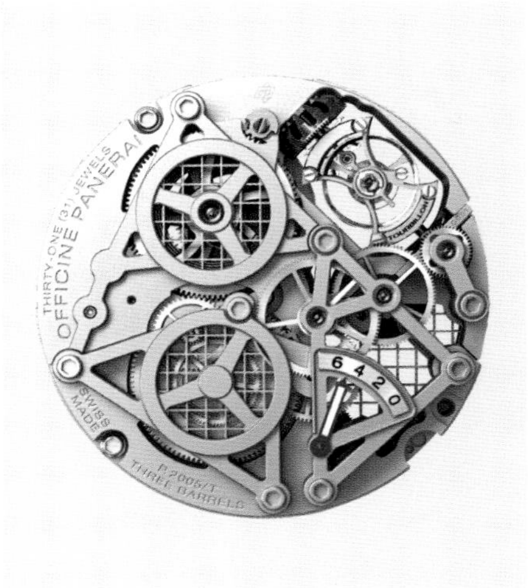

Caliber P.2005/T

Manually wound; skeletonized movement; 1-minute tourbillon perpendicular to balance pivot; triple, serially mounted spring barrels, 144-hour power reserve
Functions: hours, minutes, subsidiary seconds; additional 24-hour display (2nd time zone) with day/night indicator (on movement side)
Diameter: 36.6 mm
Height: 10.05 mm
Jewels: 31
Balance: glucydur
Frequency: 28,800 vph
Remarks: 277 parts

Caliber P.4002

Automatic; microrotor; double serial spring barrel, 72-hour power reserve
Functions: hours, minutes, subsidiary seconds; additional 12-hour display (2nd time zone); date
Diameter: 30 mm
Height: 4.8 mm
Jewels: 31
Balance: glucydur
Frequency: 28,800 vph
Hairspring: flat hairspring
Shock protection: Kif
Remarks: 288 parts

Caliber P.4001

Automatic; microrotor; crown-activated stop-seconds mechanism and zero-reset; double spring barrel, 72-hour power reserve
Functions: hours, minutes, subsidiary seconds; additional 24-hour display (2nd time zone), power reserve indicator (on back); date
Diameter: 30 mm
Height: 5.04 mm
Jewels: 31
Balance: glucydur
Frequency: 28,800 vph
Hairspring: flat hairspring
Shock protection: Kif
Remarks: 278 parts

PARMIGIANI

What began as the undertaking of a single man—a gifted watchmaker and reputable restorer of complicated vintage timepieces—in the small town of Fleurier in Switzerland's Val de Travers has now grown into an empire of sorts comprising several factories and more than 400 employees.

Michel Parmigiani is in fact just doing what he has done since 1976, when he began restoring vintage works. An exceptional talent, his output soon attracted the attention of the Sandoz Family Foundation, an organization established by a member of one of Switzerland's most famous families in 1964. The foundation bought 51 percent of Parmigiani Mesure et Art du Temps SA in 1996, turning what was practically a one-man show into a full-fledged and fully financed watch *manufacture*.

After the merger, Swiss suppliers were acquired by the partners, furthering the quest for horological autonomy. Atokalpa SA in Alle (Canton of Jura) manufactures parts such as pinions, wheels, and micro components. Bruno Affolter SA in La Chaux-de-Fonds produces precious metal cases, dials, and other specialty parts. Les Artisans Boitiers (LAB) and Quadrance et Habillage (Q&H) in La Chaux-de-Fonds manufacture cases out of precious metals and dials as well. Elwin SA in Moutier specializes in turned parts. In 2003, the movement development and production department officially separated from the rest as Vaucher Manufacture, now an autonomous entity with a sterling reputation. Parmigiani has enjoyed great independence and was growing strongly for a while, notably in the United States. The recent instabilities in the industry as a whole have led to some shifts in strategies, as CEO Davide Traxler has stated in interviews. The old relationship with Bugatti was terminated, and more emphasis has been placed on watches that can be used on a daily basis and are not quite what the rest of the industry considers "sportive." Parmigiani has always cut out his own turf.

Parmigiani Fleurier SA
Rue du Temple 11
CH-2114 Fleurier
Switzerland

Tel.:
+41-32-862-6630

E-mail:
info@parmigiani.ch

Website:
www.parmigiani.com

Founded:
1996

Number of employees:
425

Annual production:
approx. 6,000 watches

U.S. distributor:
Parmigiani Fleurier Distribution Americas LLC
2655 S. Le Jeune Road
Penthouse 1G
Coral Gables, FL 33134
305-260-7770; 305-269-7770
americas@parmigiani.com

Most important collections/price range:
Chronor, Kalpa, Tonda, Toric / approx. $7,800 to $700,000 for *haute horlogerie* watches; no limit for unique models

Tonda 1950

Reference number: PFC288-0000201-XA1442
Movement: automatic, Parmigiani Caliber PF701; ø 30 mm, height 2.6 mm; 21,600 vph; 42-hour power reserve
Functions: hours, minutes, subsidiary seconds
Case: stainless steel, ø 40 mm, height 8.2 mm; sapphire crystal; water-resistant to 3 atm
Band: reptile skin, folding clasp
Price: $11,900

Tonda 1950 Lune

Reference number: PFC284-1000200-HA1441
Movement: automatic, Parmigiani Caliber PF708; ø 30 mm, height 2.6 mm; 21,600 vph; 48-hour power reserve
Functions: hours, minutes, subsidiary seconds; date, moon phase (for northern and southern hemispheres)
Case: rose gold, ø 39.1 mm, height 9.6 mm; sapphire crystal; water-resistant to 3 atm
Band: reptile skin, folding clasp
Price: $26,900

Tonda Métrographe

Reference number: PFC274-0002500-XC1442
Movement: automatic, Parmigiani Caliber PF315; ø 28 mm, height 6 mm; 46 jewels; 28,800 vph; double spring barrel; finely finished with côtes de Genève; 42-hour power reserve
Functions: hours, minutes, subsidiary seconds; chronograph; date
Case: stainless steel, ø 40 mm, height 11.7 mm; sapphire crystal; transparent case back; water-resistant to 3 atm
Band: calfskin, folding clasp
Price: $11,900

Tonda Chronor

Reference number: PFH282-1000200-HA1241
Movement: manually wound, Parmigiani Caliber PF361; ø 30.6 mm, height 8.5 mm; 25 jewels; 36,000 vph; 2 column wheels to control chronograph functions; skeletonized movement; rose gold mainplate and bridges; 65-hour power reserve
Functions: hours, minutes, subsidiary seconds; flyback chronograph; large date
Case: rose gold, ø 42.1 mm, height 14.6 mm; sapphire crystal; water-resistant to 3 atm
Band: reptile skin, folding clasp
Price: $138,000

Toric Perpetual Calendar Rétrograde

Reference number: PFH427-1602400-HA1241
Movement: automatic, Parmigiani Caliber PF333; ø 27 mm, height 5.5 mm; 32 jewels; 28,800 vph; 50-hour power reserve
Functions: hours, minutes, sweep seconds; perpetual calendar with date (retrograde), weekday, month, moon phase (double), leap year
Case: pink gold, ø 42.5 mm, height 12.1 mm; sapphire crystal; water-resistant to 3 atm
Band: reptile skin, folding clasp
Price: $63,100

Toric Chronometer

Reference number: PFC423-1600201-HA1241
Movement: automatic, Parmigiani Caliber PF441; ø 25.6 mm, height 3.7 mm; 29 jewels; 28,800 vph; double spring barrel, 55-hour power reserve; COSC-certified chronometer
Functions: hours, minutes, sweep seconds; date
Case: pink gold, ø 40.8 mm, height 9.5 mm; sapphire crystal; water-resistant to 3 atm
Band: reptile skin, buckle
Price: $22,300

Tondagraphe

Reference number: PFH236-1000200-HA1241
Movement: manually wound, Parmigiani Caliber PF354; ø 29.9 mm, height 7.65 mm; 21,600 vph; 1-minute tourbillon; 72-hour power reserve
Functions: hours, minutes, subsidiary seconds; power reserve indicator; chronograph
Case: rose gold, ø 43 mm, height 13.4 mm; sapphire crystal; water-resistant to 3 atm
Band: reptile skin, buckle
Price: $199,000

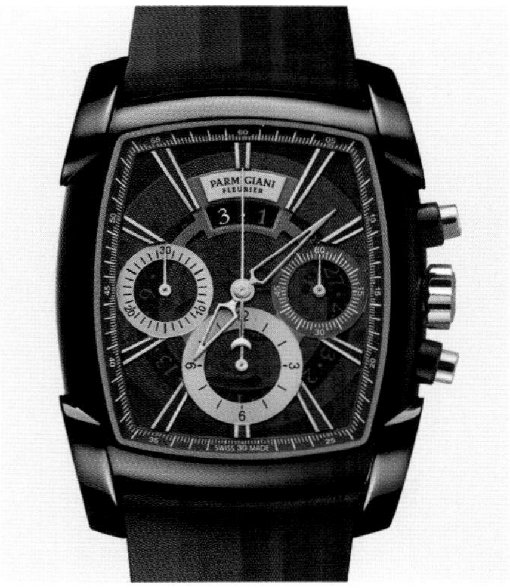

Kalpagraphe

Reference number: PFC128-0243200-XO1401
Movement: automatic, Parmigiani Caliber PF334; ø 30.3 mm, height 6.8 mm; 68 jewels; 28,800 vph; 50-hour power reserve
Functions: hours, minutes, subsidiary seconds; chronograph; date
Case: stainless steel with black DLC, 39.2 × 44.45 mm, height 12.8 mm; sapphire crystal; water-resistant to 3 atm
Band: rubber, buckle
Price: $17,600

Kalpagraphe Chronomètre

Reference number: PFC193-3044100-X01442
Movement: automatic, Parmigiani Caliber PF362; 31.9 × 39.7 mm, height 7 mm; 42 jewels; 36,000 vph; 65-hour power reserve; COSC-certified chronometer
Functions: hours, minutes, subsidiary seconds; chronograph; date
Case: titanium, 40.9 × 48.2 mm, height 14 mm; sapphire crystal; water-resistant to 3 atm
Band: rubber, folding clasp
Price: $36,700

Tonda 1950 Lune

Reference number: PFC284-1063300-HA2121
Movement: automatic, Parmigiani Caliber PF708; ø 30 mm, height 2.6 mm; 29 jewels; 21,600 vph; 48-hour power reserve
Functions: hours, minutes, subsidiary seconds; date, moon phase
Case: rose gold, ø 39.1 mm, height 9.6 mm; bezel set with 51 diamonds; sapphire crystal; water-resistant to 3 atm
Band: reptile skin, folding clasp
Remarks: mother-of-pearl dial
Price: $34,400

Tonda Métropolitaine Galaxy

Reference number: PFC800-1510320-HA3181
Movement: automatic, Parmigiani Caliber PF310; ø 23.9 mm, height 3.9 mm; 28 jewels; 28,800 vph; double spring barrel, 50-hour power reserve
Functions: hours, minutes, subsidiary seconds
Case: rose gold, ø 33.7 mm, height 8.95 mm; bezel set with 64 diamonds; sapphire crystal; transparent case back; water-resistant to 3 atm
Band: reptile skin, buckle
Remarks: aventurine dial
Price: $10,500

Tonda Métropolitaine

Reference number: PFC273-0063300-B00002
Movement: automatic, Parmigiani Caliber PF310; ø 23.9 mm, height 3.9 mm; 28 jewels; 28,800 vph; double spring barrel; finely finished with côtes de Genève; 50-hour power reserve
Functions: hours, minutes, subsidiary seconds; date
Case: stainless steel, ø 33.1 mm, height 8.65 mm; bezel set with 72 diamonds; sapphire crystal; transparent case back; water-resistant to 3 atm
Band: stainless steel, folding clasp
Remarks: mother-of-pearl dial
Price: $10,500
Variations: without diamonds

Tonda Métropolitaine

Reference number: PFC801-1510020-HC6181
Movement: automatic, Parmigiani Caliber PF310; ø 23.9 mm, height 3.9 mm; 28 jewels; 28,800 vph; double spring barrel; finely finished with côtes de Genève; 50-hour power reserve
Functions: hours, minutes, subsidiary seconds
Case: rose gold, ø 36 mm, height 8.95 mm; bezel set with 46 diamonds; sapphire crystal; transparent case back; water-resistant to 3 atm
Band: calfskin, buckle
Remarks: mother-of-pearl dial
Price: $29,500

Kalpagraphe Saphir

Reference number: PFC128-1002400-X02401
Movement: automatic, Parmigiani Caliber PF334; ø 30.3 mm, height 6.8 mm; 68 jewels; 28,800 vph; 50-hour power reserve
Functions: hours, minutes, subsidiary seconds; chronograph; date
Case: rose gold, 39.2 × 44.45 mm, height 12.8 mm; sapphire crystal; water-resistant to 3 atm
Band: rubber, buckle
Remarks: translucent sapphire crystal dial
Price: $35,200

Kalpa Donna

Reference number: PFC160-0020501-B00002
Movement: quartz
Functions: hours, minutes
Case: stainless steel, 24.8 × 34.8 mm, height 6.8 mm; sapphire crystal; water-resistant to 3 atm
Band: stainless steel, folding clasp
Remarks: case set with 43 diamonds
Price: $9,400
Variations: various dials

Caliber PF361

Manually wound; 2 column wheels to control chronograph functions; skeletonized construction; rose gold mainplate and bridges; single spring barrel, 65-hour power reserve
Functions: hours, minutes, subsidiary seconds; flyback chronograph; large date
Diameter: 30.6 mm
Height: 8.5 mm
Jewels: 25
Frequency: 36,000 vph
Remarks: 317 parts

Caliber PF702

Automatic; platinum microrotor; single spring barrel, 48-hour power reserve
Functions: hours, minutes, subsidiary seconds
Diameter: 30 mm
Height: 2.6 mm
Jewels: 29
Frequency: 21,600 vph

Caliber PF362

Automatic; column-wheel control of chronograph functions; single spring barrel, 65-hour power reserve; COSC-certified chronometer
Functions: hours, minutes, subsidiary seconds; chronograph; date
Measurements: 31.9 × 39.7 mm
Height: 7 mm
Jewels: 42
Frequency: 36,000 vph
Remarks: 332 parts

Caliber PF110

Manually wound; double mainspring barrel, 192-hour power reserve
Functions: hours, minutes, subsidiary seconds; power reserve indicator; date
Measurements: 29.3 × 23.6 mm
Height: 4.9 mm
Jewels: 28
Frequency: 21,600 vph

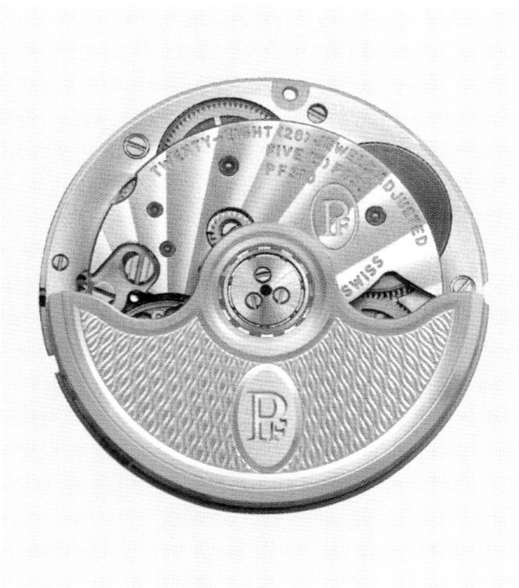

Caliber PF310

Automatic; gold rotor; double mainspring barrel, 50-hour power reserve
Functions: hours, minutes, subsidiary seconds; date
Diameter: 23.9 mm
Height: 3.9 mm
Jewels: 28
Frequency: 28,800 vph
Remarks: 189 parts

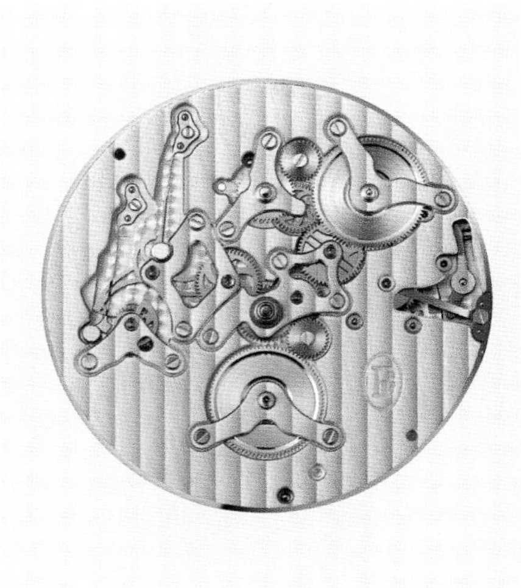

Caliber PF317

Automatic; rose gold microrotor; single spring barrel, 50-hour power reserve
Functions: hours, minutes, subsidiary seconds; additional 12-hour display (2nd time zone) with day/night indicator; date (retrograde)
Diameter: 35.6 mm
Height: 5.4 mm
Jewels: 28
Frequency: 28,800 vph
Remarks: 316 parts

PATEK PHILIPPE

In the Swiss watchmaking landscape, Patek Philippe has a special status as the last independent family-owned business. The company originated in 1839 with two Polish emigrés to Switzerland, Count Norbert Antoine de Patek and Frantiszek Czapek. In 1845, following the natural end of their contract, Patek sought another partner in the master watchmaker Jean Adrien Philippe, who had developed a keyless winding and time-setting mechanism. Ever since, Patek Philippe has been known for creating high-quality mechanical watches, some with extremely sophisticated complications. Even among its competition, the *manufacture* enjoys the greatest respect.

In 1932, Charles-Henri Stern took over the *manufacture*. His son Henri and grandson Philippe continued the tradition of solid leadership, steering the company through the notorious quartz crisis without ever compromising quality. The next in line, also Henri, heads the enterprise these days.

Producing an impressive 60,000-plus watches yearly demands ultramodern facilities. The year 2019 closed with the opening of large, new, ultramodern premises in Geneva, where various manufacturing activities can be performed under a single roof with an optimized workflow. The site is a complement to another industrial hub between La Chaux-de-Fonds and Le Locle, where case components are manufactured, cases are polished, and gem setting is done.

While Patek Philippe's main headquarters remains in Geneva, the *manufacture* no longer really has a need for that city's famed quality seal: All of its mechanical watches now feature the "Patek Philippe Seal," the criteria for which far exceed the requirements of the *Poinçon de Genève* and include specifications for the entire watch, not just the movement. Among the most recent creations to make that grade is the World Time Chronograph, a masterful extension of the company's large range of chronographs. To make space, there is no second hand and only a thirty-minute counter. A moving city ring and twenty-four-hour ring have a place on the dial as well, and the whole piece is just over 12 millimeters high.

Patek Philippe SA
Chemin du pont-du-centenaire 141
CH-1228 Plan-les-Ouates
Switzerland

Tel.:
+41-22-884-20-20

Website:
www.patek.com

Founded:
1839

Number of employees:
approx. 2,000 (estimated)

Annual production:
approx. 60,000 watches worldwide per year

U.S. distributor:
Patek Philippe USA
45 Rockefeller Center, Suite 401
New York, NY 10111
212-218-1240

Most important collections
Aquanaut, Calatrava, Ellipse, Gondolo, Nautilus / ladies' timepieces

Alarm Travel Time

Reference number: 5520P-001
Movement: automatic, Patek Philippe Caliber AL 30-660 S C FUS; ø 31 mm, height 6.6 mm; 52 jewels; 28,800 vph; silicon Spiromax hairspring, gold rotor; 42-hour power reserve
Functions: hours, minutes, sweep seconds; additional 12-hour display (2nd time zone), day/night indicator, alarm; date
Case: platinum, ø 42.2 mm, height 11.6 mm; sapphire crystal; transparent case back; water-resistant to 3 atm
Band: calfskin, buckle
Remarks: wake-up time (in separate window) based on local time, setting in 15-minute increments
Price: $260,216

Chronograph

Reference number: 5172G-001
Movement: manually wound, Patek Philippe Caliber CH 29-535 PS; ø 29.6 mm, height 5.35 mm; 33 jewels; 28,800 vph; Breguet hairspring, column-wheel control of chronograph functions; 65-hour power reserve
Functions: hours, minutes, subsidiary seconds; chronograph
Case: white gold, ø 41 mm, height 11.45 mm; sapphire crystal; transparent case back; water-resistant to 3 atm
Band: calfskin, folding clasp
Price: $78,420

Annual Calendar Chronograph

Reference number: 5905R-001
Movement: automatic, Patek Philippe Caliber CH 28-520 QA 24H; ø 33 mm, height 7.68 mm; 37 jewels; 28,800 vph; silicon Spiromax hairspring, gold rotor; 45-hour power reserve
Functions: hours, minutes; flyback chronograph; annual calendar with date, weekday, month
Case: platinum, ø 42 mm, height 14.3 mm; sapphire crystal; transparent case back; water-resistant to 3 atm
Band: reptile skin, buckle
Price: $70,377
Variations: rose gold ($70,377)

Regulator Annual Calendar

Reference number: 5235/50R-001
Movement: automatic, Patek Philippe Caliber 31-260 REG QA; ø 33 mm, height 5.08 mm; 31 jewels; 23,040 vph; Pulsomax escapement and silicon Spiromax hairspring, microrotor; 38-hour power reserve
Functions: hours (off-center), minutes, subsidiary seconds; annual calendar with date, weekday, month
Case: rose gold, ø 40.5 mm, height 10 mm; sapphire crystal; transparent case back; water-resistant to 3 atm
Band: reptile skin, buckle
Price: $55,592

Calatrava Weekly Calendar

Reference number: 5212A-001
Movement: automatic, Patek Philippe Caliber 26-330 S C J SE; ø 27 mm, height 4.82 mm; 50 jewels; 28,800 vph; silicon Spiromax hairspring, gold rotor; 35-hour power reserve
Functions: hours, minutes, sweep seconds; date, weekday, calendar week
Case: stainless steel, ø 40 mm, height 10.79 mm; sapphire crystal; transparent case back; water-resistant to 3 atm
Band: calfskin, buckle
Price: $35,484

Nautilus Annual Calendar

Reference number: 5726/1A-014
Movement: automatic, Patek Philippe Caliber 324 S QA LU 24H; ø 33.3 mm, height 5.78 mm; 34 jewels; 28,800 vph; silicon Spiromax hairspring, gold rotor; 35-hour power reserve
Functions: hours, minutes, sweep seconds; additional 24-hour display; annual calendar with date, weekday, month, moon phase
Case: stainless steel, ø 40.5 mm, height 11.3 mm; sapphire crystal; transparent case back; screw-in crown; water-resistant to 12 atm
Band: stainless steel, folding clasp
Price: $50,269

Aquanaut

Reference number: 5168G-010
Movement: automatic, Patek Philippe Caliber 324 S C; ø 27 mm, height 3.3 mm; 29 jewels; 28,800 vph; silicon Spiromax hairspring, gold rotor; 35-hour power reserve
Functions: hours, minutes, sweep seconds; date
Case: white gold, ø 42.2 mm, height 8.25 mm; sapphire crystal; transparent case back; screw-in crown; water-resistant to 12 atm
Band: rubber, folding clasp
Price: $43,764
Variations: blue dial and strap

Nautilus Ladies'

Reference number: 7118/1A-001
Movement: automatic, Patek Philippe Caliber 324 S C; ø 27 mm, height 3.3 mm; 29 jewels; 28,800 vph; silicon Spiromax hairspring, gold rotor; 35-hour power reserve
Functions: hours, minutes, sweep seconds; date
Case: stainless steel, ø 35.2 mm, height 8.62 mm; sapphire crystal; transparent case back; screw-in crown; water-resistant to 6 atm
Band: stainless steel, folding clasp
Price: $28,624

Nautilus

Reference number: 7118/1200R-001
Movement: automatic, Patek Philippe Caliber 324 S C; ø 27 mm, height 3.3 mm; 29 jewels; 28,800 vph; silicon Spiromax hairspring, gold rotor; 35-hour power reserve
Functions: hours, minutes, sweep seconds; date
Case: rose gold, ø 35.2 mm, height 8.62 mm; bezel set with 56 diamonds; sapphire crystal; transparent case back; water-resistant to 6 atm
Band: rose gold, folding clasp
Price: $59,140

Twenty4 Automatic

Reference number: 7300/1200R-001
Movement: automatic, Patek Philippe Caliber 324 S C; ø 27 mm, height 3.3 mm; 29 jewels; 28,800 vph; silicon Spiromax hairspring, gold rotor; 35-hour power reserve
Functions: hours, minutes, sweep seconds; date
Case: rose gold, ø 36 mm, height 10.05 mm; bezel set with 160 diamonds; sapphire crystal; transparent case back; water-resistant to 3 atm
Band: rose gold, folding clasp
Price: $48,495
Variations: various straps and cases, starting at $48,495

Twenty4 Automatic

Reference number: 7300/1200A-010
Movement: automatic, Patek Philippe Caliber 324 S C; ø 27 mm, height 3.3 mm; 29 jewels; 28,800 vph; silicon Spiromax hairspring, gold rotor; 35-hour power reserve
Functions: hours, minutes, sweep seconds; date
Case: stainless steel, ø 36 mm, height 10.05 mm; bezel set with 160 diamonds; sapphire crystal; transparent case back; water-resistant to 3 atm
Band: stainless steel, folding clasp
Price: $27,796
Variations: various straps and cases, starting at $27,796

Perpetual Calendar with Tourbillon and Minute Repeater

Reference number: 5207G-001
Movement: manually wound, Patek Philippe Caliber R TO 27 PS QI; ø 32 mm, height 9.33 mm; 37 jewels; 21,600 vph; 1-minute tourbillon; instantly changing perpetual calendar; chiming mechanism with traditional gongs; 38-hour power reserve
Functions: hours, minutes, subsidiary seconds; minute repeater; perpetual calendar with date, weekday, month, moon phase
Case: white gold, ø 41 mm, height 13.81 mm; sapphire crystal; transparent case back
Band: reptile skin, folding clasp
Price: on request

Chronograph Perpetual Calendar

Reference number: 5270P-001
Movement: manually wound, Patek Philippe Caliber CH 29 535 PS Q; ø 32 mm, height 7 mm; 33 jewels; 28,800 vph; 55-hour power reserve
Functions: hours, minutes, subsidiary seconds; day/night indicator; chronograph; perpetual calendar with date, weekday, month, moon phase, leap year
Case: platinum, ø 41 mm, height 12.4 mm; sapphire crystal; transparent case back; water-resistant to 3 atm
Band: reptile skin, folding clasp
Price: $205,807
Variations: rose gold ($212,904)

Perpetual Calendar

Reference number: 5320G-001
Movement: automatic, Patek Philippe Caliber 324 S Q; ø 32 mm, height 4.97 mm; 29 jewels; 28,800 vph; gold rotor; 35-hour power reserve
Functions: hours, minutes, sweep seconds; day/night indicator; perpetual calendar with date, weekday, month, moon phase, leap year
Case: white gold, ø 40 mm, height 11.1 mm; sapphire crystal; transparent case back; water-resistant to 3 atm
Band: reptile skin, folding clasp
Remarks: comes with additional white gold case back
Price: $92,259

Annual Calendar

Reference number: 5205G-013
Movement: automatic, Patek Philippe Caliber 324 S QA LU 24H; ø 32.6 mm, height 5.78 mm; 34 jewels; 28,800 vph; 35-hour power reserve
Functions: hours, minutes, sweep seconds; additional 24-hour display; annual calendar with date, weekday, month, moon phase
Case: rose gold, ø 40 mm, height 11.36 mm; sapphire crystal; transparent case back; water-resistant to 3 atm
Band: reptile skin, buckle
Price: $53,463

Calatrava Pilot Travel Time

Reference number: 5524R-001
Movement: automatic, Patek Philippe Caliber 324 S C FUS; ø 31 mm, height 4.82 mm; 29 jewels; 28,800 vph; silicon Spiromax hairspring; 35-hour power reserve
Functions: hours, minutes, sweep seconds; additional 12-hour display (2nd time zone), day/night indicator; date
Case: white gold, ø 42 mm, height 10.78 mm; sapphire crystal; transparent case back; water-resistant to 6 atm
Band: calfskin, buckle
Price: $53,818

Perpetual Calendar

Reference number: 5327G-001
Movement: automatic, Patek Philippe Caliber 240 Q; ø 27.5 mm, height 3.88 mm; 27 jewels; 21,600 vph; silicon Spiromax hairspring, microrotor; 38-hour power reserve
Functions: hours, minutes; additional 24-hour display; perpetual calendar with date, weekday, month, moon phase, leap year
Case: white gold, ø 39 mm, height 9.71 mm; sapphire crystal; transparent case back; water-resistant to 3 atm
Band: reptile skin, folding clasp
Remarks: comes with additional white gold case back
Price: $96,990
Variations: yellow and rose gold

World Time

Reference number: 5230R-012
Movement: automatic, Patek Philippe Caliber 240 HU; ø 27.5 mm, height 3.88 mm; 33 jewels; 21,600 vph; silicon Spiromax hairspring; 48-hour power reserve
Functions: hours, minutes; world time display (2nd time zone)
Case: rose gold, ø 38.5 mm, height 10.23 mm; pusher-activated inner bezel with city references; sapphire crystal; transparent case back; water-resistant to 3 atm
Band: reptile skin, folding clasp
Price: $52,044

Ellipse d'Or

Reference number: 5738R-001
Movement: automatic, Patek Philippe Caliber 240; ø 27.5 mm, height 2.53 mm; 27 jewels; 21,600 vph; gold microrotor; 48-hour power reserve
Functions: hours, minutes
Case: rose gold, 34.5 × 39.5 mm, height 5.9 mm; sapphire crystal
Band: reptile skin, buckle
Price: $34,065

Nautilus Perpetual Calendar

Reference number: 5740/1G-001
Movement: automatic, Patek Philippe Caliber 240 Q; ø 27.5 mm, height 3.88 mm; 27 jewels; 21,600 vph; 38-hour power reserve
Functions: hours, minutes; additional 24-hour display; perpetual calendar with date, weekday, month, moon phase, leap year
Case: white gold, ø 40 mm, height 8.42 mm; sapphire crystal; transparent case back; screw-in crown; water-resistant to 6 atm
Band: white gold, folding clasp
Price: $134,839

Aquanaut Chronograph

Reference number: 5968A-001
Movement: automatic, Patek Philippe Caliber CH 28-520 C; ø 30 mm, height 6.63 mm; 32 jewels; 28,800 vph; 45-hour power reserve
Functions: hours, minutes; chronograph; date
Case: stainless steel, ø 42.2 mm, height 11.9 mm; sapphire crystal; transparent case back; screw-in crown; water-resistant to 12 atm
Band: rubber, folding clasp
Price: $49,678

Caliber R TO 27 PS QI

Manually wound; 1-minute tourbillon; chiming mechanism with traditional gong; single spring barrel, 38-hour power reserve
Functions: hours, minutes, subsidiary seconds; minute repeater; perpetual calendar with date, weekday, month, moon phase
Diameter: 32 mm
Height: 9.33 mm
Jewels: 37
Balance: Gyromax
Frequency: 21,600 vph
Hairspring: Breguet
Remarks: 549 parts

Caliber CHR 29-535 PS Q

Manually wound; two wheels to control chronograph functions, flyback mechanism with isolator; single spring barrel, 65-hour power reserve
Functions: hours, minutes, subsidiary seconds; day/night indicator; flyback chronograph; perpetual calendar with date, weekday, month, moon phase, leap year
Diameter: 32 mm; **Height:** 8.7 mm
Jewels: 34
Balance: Gyromax, 4-armed, with 4 regulating weights
Frequency: 28,800 vph
Hairspring: Breguet
Remarks: 496 parts, including 182 for perpetual calendar and 42 for flyback mechanism with isolator

Caliber CH 29-535 PS

Manually wound; column-wheel control of chronograph functions, precisely jumping 30-minute totalizer; single spring barrel, 65-hour power
Functions: hours, minutes, subsidiary seconds; flyback chronograph
Diameter: 29.6 mm
Height: 7.1 mm
Jewels: 34
Balance: Gyromax, 4-armed, with 4 regulating weights
Frequency: 28,800 vph
Balance spring: Breguet
Shock protection: Incabloc
Remarks: 312 parts

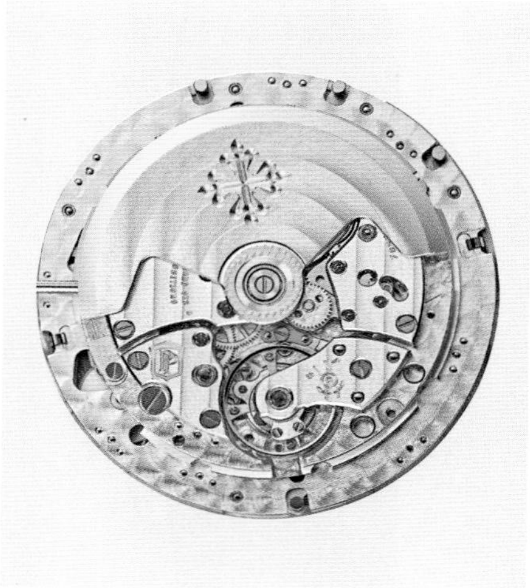

Caliber 324 S Q

Automatic; gold rotor; single spring barrel, 35-hour power reserve
Functions: hours, minutes, sweep seconds; day/night indicator; perpetual calendar with date, weekday, month, moon phase, leap year
Diameter: 32 mm
Height: 4.97 mm
Jewels: 29
Frequency: 28,800 vph

Caliber 324 S C

Automatic; gold rotor; single spring barrel, 35-hour power reserve
Functions: hours, minutes, sweep seconds; date
Diameter: 27 mm
Height: 3.3 mm
Jewels: 29
Balance: Gyromax
Frequency: 28,800 vph
Balance spring: Breguet
Variations: Caliber 324 S C FUS with additional 12-hour display (2nd time zone) and day/night indicator

Caliber 324 S QA LU 24H-303

Automatic; 21-kt-gold central rotor; single spring barrel, 45-hour power reserve
Functions: hours, minutes, sweep seconds; additional 24-hour display (2nd time zone); annual calendar with date, weekday, month, moon phase
Diameter: 32.6 mm
Height: 5.78 mm
Jewels: 34
Balance: Gyromax
Frequency: 28,800 vph
Hairspring: silicon Spiromax
Remarks: 347 parts

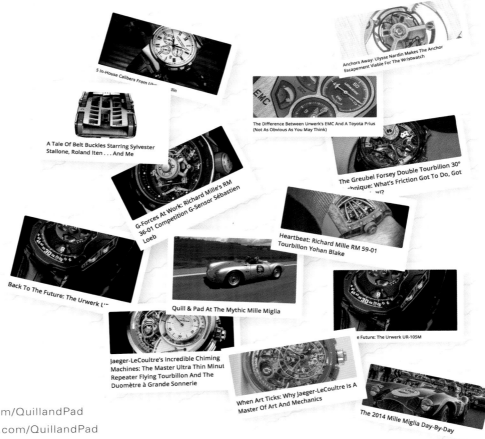

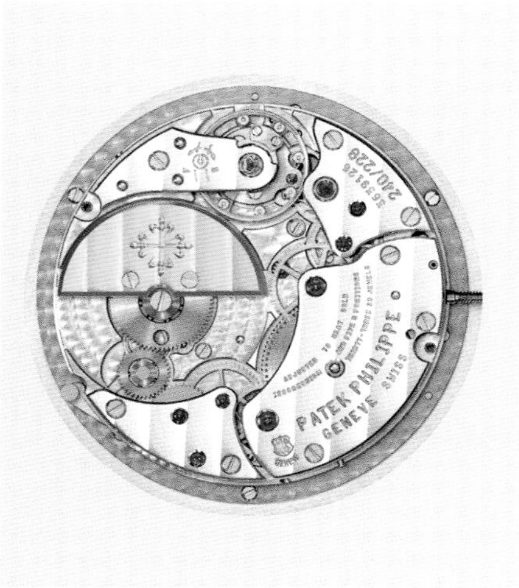

Caliber 240 HU

Automatic; off-center, ball bearing–mounted, unidirectional gold microrotor in 22-kt gold; single spring barrel, 48-hour power reserve
Functions: hours, minutes; world time display (2nd time zone)
Diameter: 27.5 mm
Height: 3.88 mm
Jewels: 33
Balance: Gyromax
Frequency: 21,600 vph
Remarks: 239 part

Caliber 240 Q

Automatic; gold microrotor; single spring barrel, 48-hour power reserve
Functions: hours, minutes; additional 24-hour display (2nd time zone); perpetual calendar with date, weekday, month, moon phase, leap year
Diameter: 30 mm
Height: 3.75 mm
Jewels: 27
Balance: Gyromax, with 8 masselotte regulating weights
Frequency: 21,600 vph
Balance spring: flat hairspring
Shock protection: Kif

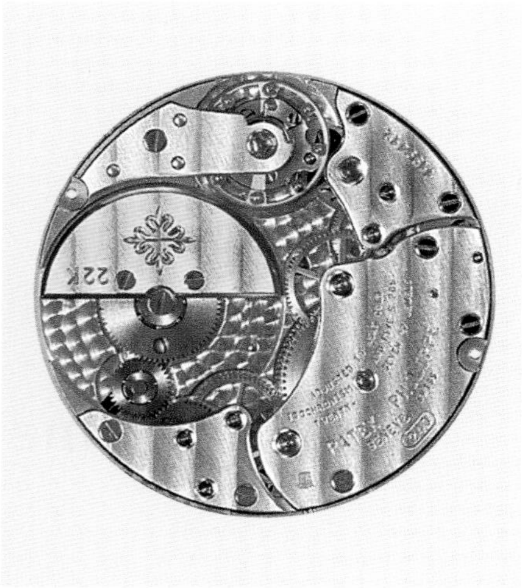

Caliber 240

Automatic; gold microrotor; single spring barrel, 48-hour power reserve
Functions: hours, minutes
Diameter: 27.5 mm
Height: 2.53 mm
Jewels: 27
Balance: Gyromax
Frequency: 21,600 vph
Balance spring: silicon Spiromax
Remarks: 161 parts

Caliber 26-330 S C J SE

Automatic; gold rotor; single spring barrel, 35-hour power reserve
Functions: hours, minutes, sweep seconds; date, weekday, calendar
Diameter: 27 mm
Height: 4.82 mm
Jewels: 50
Frequency: 28,800 vph
Hairspring: silicon Spiromax

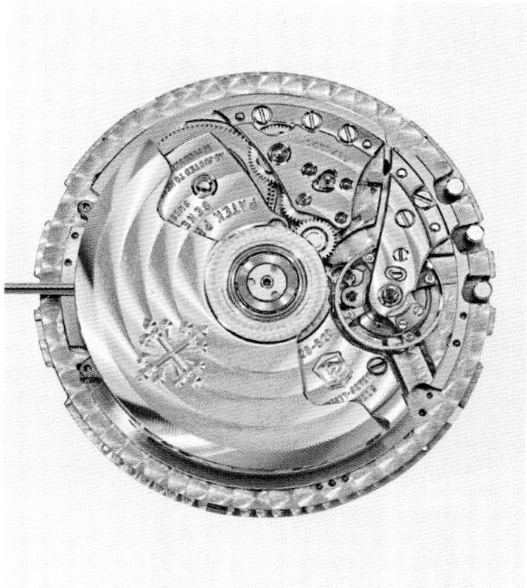

Caliber CH 28-520 QA 24H

Automatic; gold rotor; single spring barrel, 45-hour power reserve
Functions: hours, minutes; flyback chronograph; annual calendar with date, weekday, month
Diameter: 33 mm
Height: 7.68 mm
Jewels: 37
Frequency: 28,800 vph
Hairspring: silicon Spiromax

Caliber CH 28-520 C

Automatic; single spring barrel, 45-hour power reserve
Functions: hours, minutes; chronograph; date
Diameter: 30 mm
Height: 6.63 mm
Jewels: 32
Balance: Gyromax
Frequency: 28,800 vph
Balance spring: silicon Spiromax
Remarks: 308 parts

Paul Gerber
Uhren-Konstruktionen
Bockhornstrasse 69
CH-8047 Zürich
Switzerland

Tel.:
+41-44-401-4569

E-mail:
info@gerber-uhren.ch

Website:
www.gerber-uhren.ch

Founded:
1976

Annual production:
up to 50 watches

U.S. distributor:
Intro Swiss—Michel Schmutz
Michel Schmutz
6271 Corinth Rd.
Longmont, CO 80503
303-652-1520
introswiss@gmail.com

Most important collections/price range:
mechanical watches / from approx. $5,175 to $22,000; tourbillon desk clocks / from approx. $48,000 to $70,000

PAUL GERBER

In a world that often values hype more than the real thing, people like watchmaker Paul Gerber tend to get overlooked. And it's a shame, because this man, who works out of his basement, where he seems to be puttering around, has encyclopedic knowledge and experience of the industry. He has already developed a vast array of mechanisms and complications, including calendar movements, alarms, and tourbillons, for many brands. Gerber is the one who designed the complicated calendar mechanism for the otherwise minimalist MIH watch conceived by Ludwig Oechslin, curator of the International Museum of Horology (MIH) in La Chaux-de-Fonds and himself a watchmaker. To avoid cluttering a dial for a special customer, he recently devised a battery-run moon phase that fits in the watch strap. His work has twice appeared in *Guinness World Records*.

When his daily work for others lets up, Gerber gets around to building watches bearing his own name with such marvelous features as a retrograde second hand in an elegant thin case and a synchronously, unidirectional rotor system with miniature oscillating weights for his self-winding Retro Twin model. Gerber's works are all limited editions.

After designing a tonneau-shaped manually wound wristwatch with a three-dimensional moon phase display, Gerber created a simple three-hand watch with an automatic movement conceived and produced completely in-house. It features a 100-hour power reserve and is wound by three synchronically turning gold rotors. Gerber also offers the triple rotor and large date features in a watch with an ETA movement and lightweight titanium case as a classic pilot watch design or in a version with a more modern dial (the Synchron model). The Model 41 has an optional complication that switches the second hand from sweep to dead-beat motion by way of a pusher at 2 o'clock.

Gerber is allegedly retired. But a watchmaker never really does. Besides continuing to produce outstanding pieces, he occasionally gives three-day workshops for people wanting to get a real feel for the work.

Retro Twin

Reference number: 155
Movement: automatic, Gerber Caliber 15 (base ETA 7001); ø 28 mm, height 5.2 mm; 27 jewels; 21,600 vph; automatic winding with 2 synchronously rotating platinum rotors
Functions: hours, minutes, subsidiary seconds (retrograde)
Case: yellow gold, ø 36 mm, height 10.8 mm; sapphire crystal; transparent case back; water-resistant to 3 atm
Band: reptile skin, buckle
Price: $17,350
Variations: rose gold ($17,350) or white gold ($17,825); with platinum rotors set with brilliants (plus $3,175)

Modell 42

Reference number: 420 pilot (blue dial)
Movement: automatic, Gerber Caliber 42 (base ETA 2824); ø 36 mm, height 6.1 mm; 25 jewels; 28,800 vph; automatic winding with 3 synchronously rotating gold rotors
Functions: hours, minutes, sweep seconds; large quick-set date
Case: titanium, ø 42 mm, height 12 mm; sapphire crystal; transparent case back; screw-in crown; water-resistant to 10 atm
Band: calfskin, buckle
Price: $4,900
Variations: anthracite or synchron ($5,175); pilot's/synchron DaN (day and night) ($6,150); pilot's/synchron DT (Dual Time, $6,100)

Modell 42

Reference number: 420 DaN synchron
Movement: automatic, Gerber Caliber 42 (base ETA 2824); ø 36 mm, height 6.1 mm; 25 jewels; 28,800 vph; automatic winding with 3 synchronously rotating gold rotors
Functions: hours, minutes, sweep seconds; day/night indicator; date
Case: titanium, ø 42 mm, height 12 mm; sapphire crystal; transparent case back; screw-in crown; water-resistant to 10 atm
Band: calfskin, buckle
Price: $6,150
Variations: pilot's/synchron dial ($5,175); as Caliber42 pilot's/synchron 24-hour ($6,100)

PIAGET

Piaget SA
CH-1228 Plan-les-Ouates
Switzerland

Tel.:
+41-32-867-21-21

E-mail:
info@piaget.com

Website:
www.piaget.com

Founded:
1874

Number of employees:
900

Annual production:
about 25,000 watches

U.S. distributor:
Piaget North America
645 5th Avenue, 6th Floor
New York, NY 10022
212-909-4362
www.piaget.com

Most important collections:
Altiplano, Polo S, Limelight

One of the oldest watch manufacturers in Switzerland, Piaget began making watch movements in the secluded Jura village of La Côte-aux-Fées in 1874. For decades, those movements were delivered to other watch brands. The *manufacture* itself, strangely enough, remained in the background. It wasn't until the 1940s that the Piaget family began to offer complete watches under their own name.

Even today, Piaget, which long ago moved the business side of things to Geneva, still makes its watch movements at its main facility high in the Jura mountains.

In the late fifties, Piaget began investing in the design and manufacturing of ultrathin movements. This lends these watches the kind of understated elegance that became the company's hallmark. In 1957, Valentin Piaget presented the first ultrathin men's watch, the Altiplano, with the manual caliber 9P, which was 2 millimeters high. Shortly after, it came out with the 12P, an automatic caliber that clocked in at 2.3 millimeters.

The Altiplano has faithfully accompanied the brand for sixty years now. The movement has evolved over time. The recent 900P measures just 3.65 millimeters and is inverted to enable repairs, making the case back the mainplate with the dial set on the upper side. Striving for the thinnest watch produced, the Altiplano Ultimate Concept was released in 2018 for a very restricted community of extremely high-level collectors.

Worthy of note, too, is Piaget's concept watch that combines mechanical and quartz technology. The spring barrel, wound by hand or microrotor, drives a miniature generator that turns at a constant 5.33 rpm and replaces the escapement and balance wheel. It supplies the regulating quartz with power, which in turn regulates the movement. This inverted caliber is just 5.5 millimeters high. All the basic parts are on the dial side and partly visible thanks to skeletonized plates.

Altiplano Ultimate Concept

Reference number: G0A45502
Movement: manually wound, Piaget Caliber 900P-UC; ø 41 mm, height 2 mm (case and movement); 13 jewels; 28,800 vph; inverted construction in a single assembly with the case, flying mounting of wheels (on 1 side); 44-hour power reserve
Functions: hours, minutes (off-center)
Case: composite material with cobalt with black PVD, ø 41 mm, height 2 mm; sapphire crystal
Band: reptile skin, buckle
Remarks: currently the thinnest wristwatch; manufactured in a tiny series for collectors
Price: on request

Altiplano Ultimate Concept

Reference number: G0A45501
Movement: manually wound, Piaget Caliber 900P-UC; ø 41 mm, height 2 mm (case and movement); 13 jewels; 28,800 vph; inverted construction in single assembly with case, flying mounting of wheels (on 1 side); 44-hour power reserve
Functions: hours, minutes (off-center)
Case: composite material with cobalt with black PVD, ø 41 mm, height 2 mm; sapphire crystal
Band: textile strap, buckle
Remarks: currently the thinnest wristwatch; manufactured in a tiny series for collectors
Price: on request

Altiplano Ultimate Concept

Reference number: G0A45500
Movement: manually wound, Piaget Caliber 900P-UC; ø 41 mm, height 2 mm (case and movement); 13 jewels; 28,800 vph; inverted construction in a single assembly with the case, flying mounting of wheels (on 1 side); 44-hour power reserve
Functions: hours, minutes (off-center)
Case: composite material with cobalt with black PVD, ø 41 mm, height 2 mm; sapphire crystal
Band: reptile skin strap, buckle
Remarks: currently the thinnest wristwatch; manufactured in a tiny series for collectors
Price: on request

Altiplano Ultimate Automatic

Reference number: G0A45123
Movement: automatic, Piaget Caliber 910P; ø 41 mm, height 4.3 mm (case with movement); 30 jewels; 21,600 vph; inverted movement with case and hubless peripheral rotor; 50-hour power reserve
Functions: hours, minutes (off-center)
Case: white gold, ø 41 mm, height 4.3 mm; sapphire crystal
Band: reptile skin, buckle
Price: $27,300

Altiplano

Reference number: G0A44051
Movement: automatic, Piaget Caliber 1203P; ø 29.9 mm, height 3 mm; 25 jewels; 21,600 vph; rose gold microrotor; côtes de Genève; 44-hour power reserve
Functions: hours, minutes; date
Case: rose gold, ø 40 mm, height 6.36 mm; sapphire crystal; water-resistant to 3 atm
Band: reptile skin, folding clasp
Remarks: dial made of meteorite
Price: $24,600

Polo S Green

Reference number: G0A45005
Movement: automatic, Piaget Caliber 1110P; ø 25.58 mm, height 4 mm; 25 jewels; 28,800 vph; mainplate with perlage, blued screws, finely finished with côtes de Genève; 50-hour power reserve
Functions: hours, minutes, sweep seconds; date
Case: stainless steel, ø 42.4 mm, height 9.4 mm; sapphire crystal; transparent case back; water-resistant to 10 atm
Band: stainless steel, folding clasp
Price: $15,500; limited to 888 pieces

Polo S

Reference number: G0A44001
Movement: automatic, Piaget Caliber 1110P; ø 25.58 mm, height 4 mm; 25 jewels; 28,800 vph; mainplate with perlage, blued screws, finely finished with côtes de Genève; 50-hour power reserve
Functions: hours, minutes, sweep seconds; date
Case: stainless steel, ø 42.4 mm, height 9.4 mm; sapphire crystal; transparent case back; water-resistant to 10 atm
Band: reptile skin, folding clasp
Price: $8,400

Polo S

Reference number: G0A41002
Movement: automatic, Piaget Caliber 1110P; ø 25.58 mm, height 4 mm; 25 jewels; 28,800 vph; mainplate with perlage, blued screws, finely finished with côtes de Genève; 50-hour power reserve
Functions: hours, minutes, sweep seconds; date
Case: stainless steel, ø 42 mm, height 9.4 mm; sapphire crystal; transparent case back; water-resistant to 10 atm
Band: stainless steel, folding clasp
Price: $9,900

Polo S Chronograph

Reference number: G0A41006
Movement: automatic, Piaget Caliber 1160P; ø 25.58 mm, height 5.72 mm; 35 jewels; 28,800 vph; mainplate with perlage, blued screws, finely finished with côtes de Genève; 50-hour power reserve
Functions: hours, minutes; chronograph; date
Case: stainless steel, ø 42 mm, height 11.2 mm; sapphire crystal; transparent case back; water-resistant to 10 atm
Band: stainless steel, folding clasp
Price: $14,400
Variations: black dial; reptile skin band

Possession 29mm

Reference number: G0A45064
Movement: quartz
Functions: hours, minutes
Case: white gold, ø 29 mm, height 7.47 mm; bezel set with 42 diamonds; sapphire crystal; water-resistant to 3 atm
Band: reptile skin, buckle
Remarks: mother-of-pearl dial set with 11 diamonds
Price: $15,800

Possession 34mm

Reference number: G0A45074
Movement: quartz
Functions: hours, minutes
Case: white gold, ø 34 mm, height 7.47 mm; bezel set with 46 diamonds; sapphire crystal; water-resistant to 3 atm
Band: reptile skin, buckle
Remarks: mother-of-pearl dial set with 11 diamonds
Price: $19,300

Limelight Stella

Reference number: G0A44123
Movement: automatic, Piaget Caliber 584P; ø 26 mm; 21,600 vph; 42-hour power reserve
Functions: hours, minutes, sweep seconds; moon phase
Case: rose gold, ø 36 mm, height 9.9 mm; bezel set with 126 diamonds; sapphire crystal; transparent case back; water-resistant to 3 atm
Band: reptile skin, buckle
Remarks: dial set with 14 diamonds
Price: $37,200
Variations: white gold ($38,700)

Limelight Gala

Reference number: G0A45363
Movement: quartz
Functions: hours, minutes
Case: white gold, ø 32 mm, height 8.3 mm; bezel set with 20 diamonds and 22 sapphires; sapphire crystal; water-resistant to 3 atm
Band: reptile skin, buckle set with 15 diamonds
Remarks: mother-of-pearl dial
Price: $59,000

Limelight Gala Aventurine

Reference number: G0A45162
Movement: quartz
Functions: hours, minutes
Case: white gold, ø 32 mm, height 7.4 mm; bezel set with 62 diamonds; sapphire crystal; water-resistant to 3 atm
Band: reptile skin, buckle
Remarks: aventurine dial
Price: $32,800; limited to 300 pieces

Limelight Gala Automatic

Reference number: G0A45213
Movement: automatic, Piaget Caliber 501P; ø 20.5 mm, height 3.6 mm; 25 jewels; 21,600 vph; finely finished movement; 43-hour power reserve
Functions: hours, minutes
Case: rose gold, ø 26 mm, height 7 mm; bezel set with 62 diamonds; sapphire crystal; water-resistant to 3 atm
Band: rose gold Milanese mesh, sliding clasp
Price: $37,800

Caliber 900P-UC

Manually wound; inverted construction in a single assembly with the case, flying mounting of wheels (on 1 side); single spring barrel, 44-hour power reserve
Functions: hours, minutes (off-center)
Diameter: 41 mm
Height: 2 mm
Jewels: 13
Frequency: 28,800 vph
Remarks: 167 parts

Caliber 910P

Automatic; inverted construction in a single assembly with the case; hubless peripheral rotor; single spring barrel, 50-hour power reserve
Functions: hours, minutes, (off-center)
Diameter: 41 mm
Height: 4.3 mm
Jewels: 30
Balance: glucydur
Frequency: 21,600 vph
Hairspring: flat hairspring
Remarks: finely finished movement; 238 parts

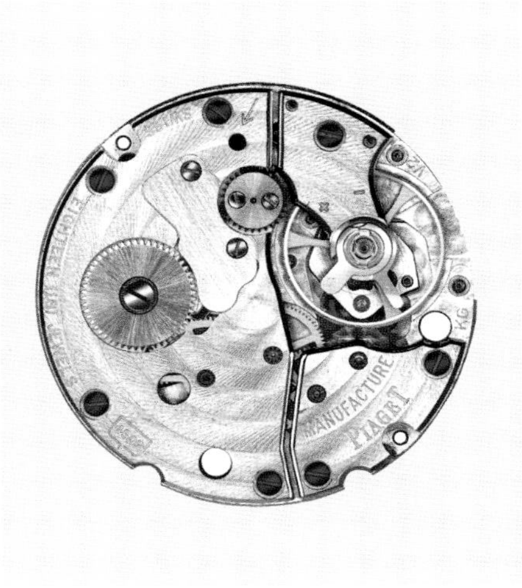

Caliber 450P

Manually wound; single spring barrel, 43-hour power reserve
Functions: hours, minutes, subsidiary seconds
Diameter: 20.5 mm
Height: 2.1 mm
Jewels: 18
Balance: glucydur
Frequency: 21,600 vph
Hairspring: flat hairspring
Remarks: finely finished movement; 131 parts

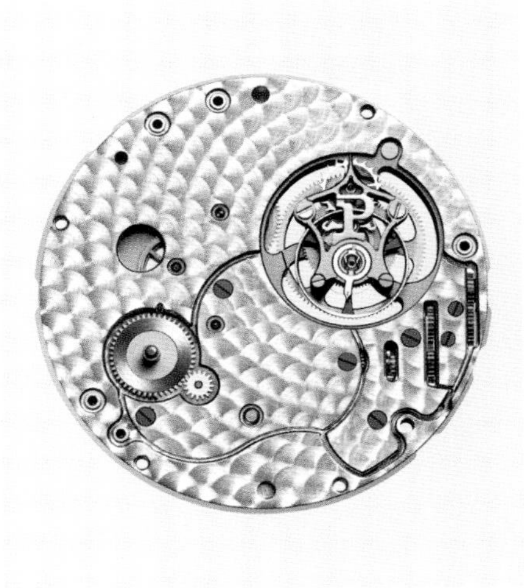

Caliber 670P

Manually wound; flying 1-minute tourbillon, titanium; single spring barrel, 48-hour power reserve
Functions: hours, minutes (off-center), subsidiary seconds (on tourbillon cage)
Diameter: 30.6 mm
Height: 4.6 mm
Jewels: 23
Balance: glucydur
Frequency: 21,600 vph
Remarks: finely finished movement; 157 parts

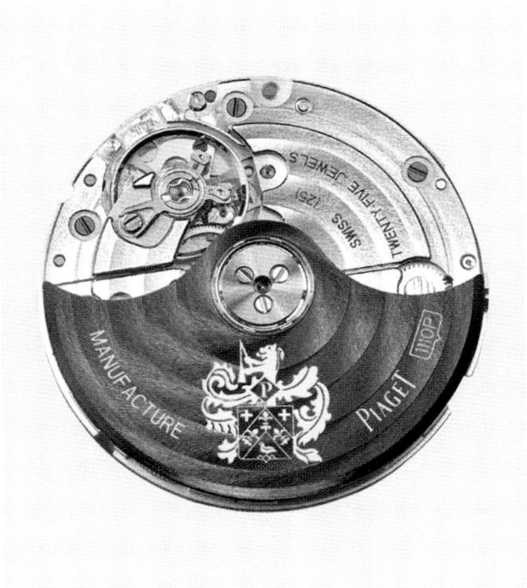

Caliber 1110P

Automatic; single spring barrel, 50-hour power reserve
Functions: hours, minutes, sweep seconds; date
Diameter: 25.58 mm
Height: 4 mm
Jewels: 25
Frequency: 28,800 vph
Remarks: perlage on mainplate, blued screws, finely finished with côtes de Genève; 180 parts

Caliber 1270S

Automatic; flying 1-minute tourbillon with titanium cage; microrotor of blackened platinum visible on dial; single spring barrel, 42-hour power reserve; Geneva Seal
Base caliber: 1270P
Functions: hours, minutes, subsidiary seconds (on tourbillon cage by the "1")
Diameter: 34.98 mm
Height: 5.05 mm
Jewels: 35
Balance: glucydur
Frequency: 21,600 vph
Remarks: fully skeletonized movement; 225 parts

PORSCHE DESIGN

In the past, Porsche Design has always made sure it was partnering with the best to manufacture its products. In 1978, it was the Schaffhausen-based brand IWC that produced watches under the name Porsche Design through a license agreement with the F. A. Porsche design firm. When the IWC license expired in 1998, Eterna, purchased by Porsche in 1995, took over manufacturing. In March 2014, Eterna and Porsche Design separated. Since then, all Porsche Design watches have been developed by the company subsidiary Porsche Design Timepieces in Solothurn, Switzerland, in collaboration with the well-established design studio in Zell-am-See, Austria.

Porsche Design was founded in 1972 by Professor Ferdinand Alexander Porsche, who died in April 2012. He created a string of classic objects at his "Studio," but sports car fans will always remember him for the Porsche 911.

In 2003, the Professor—a title bestowed by the Austrian government—founded a separate company to explore designs and different materials, notably for watches. In the 1970s, Porsche Design was already using black PVD-coated aluminum and titanium for its watches and cases. The Chronotimer collection harked back to this very avant-garde esthetic statement.

Porsche Design engineers obviously inspire themselves from the automobile industry when it comes to materials and functionality. The innovative rocker arm that activates the chronograph of the new Monobloc Actuator was inspired from the valve control of high-powered race cars using tappets. It improves ease of use and increases the mechanism's durability. A milestone was the release of the Caliber 01.200, in 2017, which featured a complex flyback mechanism. In 2019 came the innovative Caliber 04.110, with a very clever GMT switching mechanism that is setting new standards in the industry. The two new in-house calibers, 01.100 and 03.100, have expanded the company's portfolio of COSC-certified movements.

Porsche Design Group
Groenerstrasse 5
D-71636 Ludwigsburg
Germany

Tel.:
+49-711-911-0

E-mail:
contact@porsche-design.us

Website:
www.porsche-design.com

Founded:
1972

U.S. distributor:
Porsche Design of America, Inc.
Plaza Tower
600 Anton Blvd., Suite 1280
Costa Mesa, CA 92626
770-290-7500
contact@porsche-design.us

Most important collections
1919, Chronotimer Series 1, Monobloc Actuator, custom-made timepieces

1919 Chronotimer Flyback Blue & Leather

Reference number: 6023.6.04.006.07.2
Movement: automatic, Porsche Design Caliber Werk 01.200; ø 30 mm, height 7.9 mm; 25 jewels; 28,800 vph; 48-hour power reserve; COSC-certified chronometer
Functions: hours, minutes; rate control; flyback chronograph; date
Case: titanium, ø 42 mm, height 14.9 mm; sapphire crystal; transparent case back; screw-in crown; water-resistant to 10 atm
Band: calfskin, folding clasp with pusher
Price: $6,350

Sport Chrono Subsecond Titanium & Blue

Reference number: 6023.3.11.002.07.2
Movement: automatic, Porsche Design Caliber Werk 03.200; ø 25.6 mm, height 5.6 mm; 31 jewels; 28,800 vph; 38-hour power reserve; COSC-certified chronometer
Functions: hours, minutes, subsidiary seconds; date
Case: titanium, ø 42 mm, height 12.25 mm; sapphire crystal; screw-in crown; water-resistant to 10 atm
Band: calfskin, folding clasp with pusher
Price: $4,750

1919 Chrono Subsecond Titanium & Brown

Reference number: 6023.3.11.003.07.2
Movement: automatic, Porsche Design Caliber Werk 03.200 (base Sellita SW260-1); ø 25.6 mm, height 5.6 mm; 31 jewels; 28,800 vph; 38-hour power reserve; COSC-certified chronometer
Functions: hours, minutes, subsidiary seconds; date
Case: titanium, ø 42 mm, height 12.25 mm; sapphire crystal; screw-in crown; water-resistant to 10 atm
Band: calfskin, folding clasp
Price: $4,750

Sport Chrono Subsecond Titanium & Black

Reference number: 6023.3.11.001.07.2
Movement: automatic, Porsche Design Caliber Werk 03.200; ø 25.6 mm, height 5.6 mm; 31 jewels; 28,800 vph; 38-hour power reserve; COSC-certified chronometer
Functions: hours, minutes, subsidiary seconds; date
Case: titanium, ø 42 mm, height 12.25 mm; sapphire crystal; screw-in crown; water-resistant to 10 atm
Band: calfskin, folding clasp with pusher
Price: $4,750

Sport Chrono Black & Leather

Reference number: 6023.1.02.001.07.2
Movement: automatic, Porsche Design Caliber Werk 01.100; ø 30 mm, height 7.9 mm; 25 jewels; 28,800 vph; 48-hour power reserve; COSC-certified chronometer
Functions: hours, minutes; chronograph; date
Case: titanium with black carbide coating, ø 42 mm, height 14.9 mm; sapphire crystal; transparent case back; screw-in crown; water-resistant to 10 atm
Band: calfskin, folding clasp with pusher
Price: $6,150

Chronotimer Series 1 Flyback Acid Green

Reference number: 6013.6.05.005.08.2
Movement: automatic, Porsche Design Caliber Werk 01.200; ø 30 mm, height 7.9 mm; 25 jewels; 28,800 vph; 48-hour power reserve; COSC-certified chronometer
Functions: hours, minutes; rate control; flyback chronograph; date
Case: titanium with black titanium carbide coating, ø 42 mm, height 14.62 mm; sapphire crystal; transparent case back; screw-in crown; water-resistant to 5 atm
Band: calfskin, titanium folding clasp
Price: $6,700

Chronotimer Series 1 Flyback Racing Yellow

Reference number: 6013.6.12.004.08.2
Movement: automatic, Porsche Design Caliber Werk 01.200; ø 30 mm, height 7.9 mm; 25 jewels; 28,800 vph; 48-hour power reserve; COSC-certified chronometer
Functions: hours, minutes; rate control; flyback chronograph; date
Case: titanium with black titanium carbide coating, ø 42 mm, height 14.62 mm; sapphire crystal; screwed-in case back; black-tinted sapphire crystal opening; screw-in crown; water-resistant to 5 atm
Band: calfskin, titanium folding clasp
Price: $6,700

Monobloc Actuator Chronotimer Flyback Limited Edition Acid Green

Reference number: 6033.6.01.010.06.2
Movement: automatic, Porsche Design Caliber Werk 01.200; ø 30 mm, height 7.9 mm; 25 jewels; 28,800 vph; 48-hour power reserve; COSC-certified chronometer
Functions: hours, minutes; rate control; flyback chronograph; date
Case: titanium with black titanium carbide coating, ø 45.5 mm, height 15.6 mm; sapphire crystal; transparent case back; screw-in crown; water-resistant to 10 atm; **Band:** rubber, titanium folding clasp
Price: $8,500

1919 Globetimer UTC Titanium & Black

Reference number: 6023.4.05.001.07.2
Movement: automatic, Porsche Design Caliber Werk 04.110; ø 28.5 mm, height 6.94 mm; 26 jewels; 28,800 vph; 38-hour power reserve; COSC-certified chronometer
Functions: hours, minutes, sweep seconds; additional 24-hour display (2nd time zone), day/night indicator; date
Case: titanium, ø 42 mm, height 14.9 mm; sapphire crystal; screw-in crown; water-resistant to 10 atm
Band: calfskin, folding clasp with pusher
Price: $6,350

PRAMZIUS

Whatever their political affiliations or leanings, no one can deny that Eastern Europe, the Baltic states, and Russia, in particular, exert a considerable fascination on people. It may be the extreme quality of everything that comes from that part of the world that appeals to our need for drama—the long and troubled history; the brutal leaders; the staggeringly talented people, from musicians to chess players; the brooding novels about adultery, complex love, suicide, war, dark morality; the antics of modern-day Russians caught on smartphones and dashcams. That may explain the success of Détente Group and its boisterous watches celebrating Big Mechanics—not for the limp-wristed, by any stretch.

In 2017, Craig Hester, distributor of Vostok-Europe, Sturmanskie, and other brands, parlayed over 20 years' experience in the watch business into the launch of a series of watches that would pay tribute to this wild, dangerous, creative, and at times sincerely eccentric part of the world. The name Pramzius is a reference to the Baltic ruler of time, an ancient and, appropriately, pagan god. Funding for the project came from a Kickstarter campaign.

The first series of Pramzius was inspired by the renowned Trans-Siberian Railway and correspondingly themed pocket watch from back in the day. The Berlin Wall (2019) celebrated the fall of the infamous border: Its dial features graffiti from the last stretch of the Wall and a crown housing a bit of real Wall cement. The Iron Wolf was named after the legend behind the founding of the Lithuanian capital, Vilnius. It has become the official watch of a Lithuanian NATO brigade and its vehicle. Their insignia, a wolf's head, appears on the dial with the word *vilkas*, wolf. The Gauge Master (2020) is a replica of a gauge originally made in Switzerland, but installed on a vintage steam locomotive from Germany, whose trains also plied the Baltic coast. Train fans will enjoy the industrial look and the plate on the dial made from iron from a real hog.

Pramzius Watches
31 Halls Hill Road
Colchester, CT 06415

Website:
www.pramzius.com

E-mail:
info@pramzius.com

Founded:
2017

Number of employees:
4

Annual production:
2,500

Distribution:
direct sales

Most important collections/price range:
Trans-Siberian Railroad / $479; Berlin Wall Watch / $649 to $949; Military Iron Wolf Watch / $699; Master Gauge / $1,299

Gauge Master

Movement: automatic, Etoile Mechanica Caliber MS05G; ø 27.4 mm, height 5.67 mm; 21 jewels; 21,600 vph; bidirectional rotor; 42-hour power reserve
Functions: hours, minutes, subsidiary disk seconds; 24-hour indicator
Case: stainless steel, ø 53 × 45 mm, height 15 mm; water-resistant to 10 atm
Band: calfskin, buckle
Remarks: made partly of original steel from a vintage German locomotive
Price: $1,299

Military Iron Wolf Chronograph

Reference number: P715303
Movement: quartz, 6S21 Miyota Caliber; ø 34.6 mm, height 4.9 mm
Functions: hours, minutes, subsidiary seconds; 24-hour indicator
Case: stainless steel, ø 44 mm, height 14 mm; bezel with 0-120 scale; sapphire crystal; screw-down crown; water-resistant to 10 atm
Band: stainless steel, clasp
Remarks: full lume sandwich dial; bezel with "wolf teeth" indicators; comes with NATO nylon strap and bund strap
Price: $699

Berlin Wall Watch

Movement: automatic, Seiko Caliber NH35; ø 27.4 mm, height 5.32 mm; 24 jewels; 21,600 vph; bidirectional rotor; 41-hour power reserve
Functions: hours, minutes, sweep seconds; date
Case: stainless steel, ø 42 mm, height 14 mm; K1 mineral glass; screw-down crown; 3D rendering of Brandenburg Gate on case back; water-resistant to 10 atm
Band: calfskin strap, buckle
Remarks: genuine marble dial featuring original graffiti from Berlin Wall; bits of Berlin Wall in crown; comes with extra leather-nylon strap
Price: $649 leather; $699 bracelet
Variations: ETA 2824 movement ($899–$949); 48-millimeter case ($649–$699)

RADO

Rado Uhren AG
Bielstrasse 45
CH-2543 Lengnau
Switzerland

Tel.:
+41-32-655-6111

E-mail:
info@rado.com

Website:
www.rado.com
store.us.rado.com

Founded:
1957

Number of employees:
approx. 470

U.S. distributor:
Rado
The Swatch Group (U.S.), Inc.
703 Waterford Way, Suite 450
Miami, FL 33126
786-725-5393

Most important collections/price range:
HyperChrome / from approx $1,100; Diamaster / from approx. $1,500; Integral / from approx. $2,000; True / from approx. $1,400; Centrix / from approx. $800; Coupole Classic / from approx. $1,000; Tradition / from approx. $2,000

Rado is a relatively young brand, especially for a Swiss one. The company, which grew out of the Schlup clockwork factory, launched its first watches in 1957, but it achieved international fame only five years later, in 1962, when it surprised the world with a revolutionary invention. Rado's oval DiaStar was the first truly scratch-resistant watch ever, sporting a case made of the impervious alloy hardmetal. In 1985, its parent company, the Swatch Group, decided to put Rado's know-how and extensive experience in developing materials to good use, and from then on the brand intensified its research activities at its home in Lengnau, Switzerland, and continued to produce only watches with extremely hard cases. A record of sorts was even set in 2004, when they managed to create a 10,000-Vickers material, which is as hard as natural diamond.

Rado also made jewel watches, but over time it was the high-tech watches and pioneering spirit of the brand's ceramic researchers and engineers that won out. The company already holds more than thirty patents arising from research and production of new case materials. In 2011, for example, they produced the ultra-light Ceramos, which went into the D-Star collection. That spirit has returned in a series of slim automatics branded DiaMaster, which are scratch-resistant and come in a rosy gold or steely hue. Rado also uses a plasma-ceramic process to produce a material in warm metallic tones that keeps its sheen. Finally, there's the HyperChrome, which offers more resilience than regular ceramic, while weighing far less. This line goes back to the Golden Horse line from the 1950s and has been revived to meet the needs of a nostalgic market segment. The same applies to the Captain Cook line. As for the ceramic Trues, they not only reinforce the technicity of the brand but also offer consumers a modern-looking product, now in a square format.

Captain Cook Automatic Bronze

Reference number: R32504315
Movement: automatic, ETA Caliber C07.611; ø 25.6 mm, height 5.2 mm; 25 jewels; 21,600 vph; 80-hour power reserve
Functions: hours, minutes, sweep seconds; date
Case: bronze, ø 42 mm, height 12.5 mm; unidirectional bezel with ceramic insert, with 0-60 scale; sapphire crystal; screw-in crown; water-resistant to 30 atm
Band: calfskin, buckle
Price: $2,600
Variations: in brown and blue

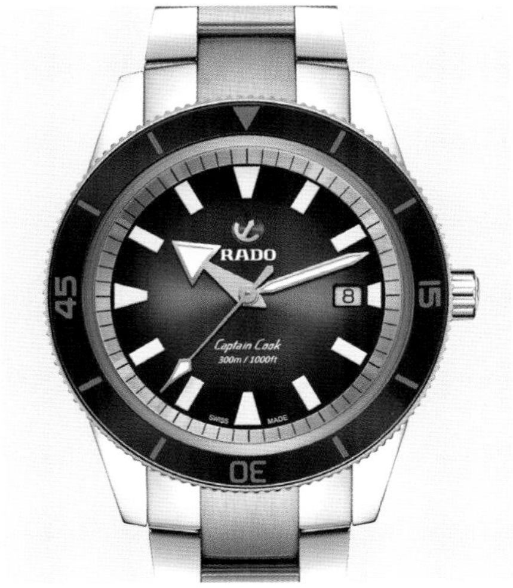

Captain Cook Automatic

Reference number: R32105203
Movement: automatic, ETA Caliber C07.611; ø 25.6 mm, height 5.2 mm; 25 jewels; 21,600 vph; 80-hour power reserve
Functions: hours, minutes, sweep seconds; date
Case: stainless steel, ø 42 mm, height 12.3 mm; unidirectional bezel with ceramic insert, with 0-60 scale; sapphire crystal; screw-in crown; water-resistant to 30 atm
Band: stainless steel, double folding clasp
Remarks: comes with additional textile and calfskin strap
Price: $2,400
Variations: blue or green dial

Captain Cook Automatic

Reference number: R32105103
Movement: automatic, ETA Caliber C07.611; ø 25.6 mm, height 5.2 mm; 25 jewels; 21,600 vph; 80-hour power reserve
Functions: hours, minutes, sweep seconds; date
Case: stainless steel, ø 42 mm, height 12.3 mm; unidirectional bezel with ceramic insert, with 0-60 scale; sapphire crystal; screw-in crown; water-resistant to 30 atm
Band: stainless steel, double folding clasp
Remarks: comes with additional textile and calfskin strap
Price: $2,000; limited to 999 pieces

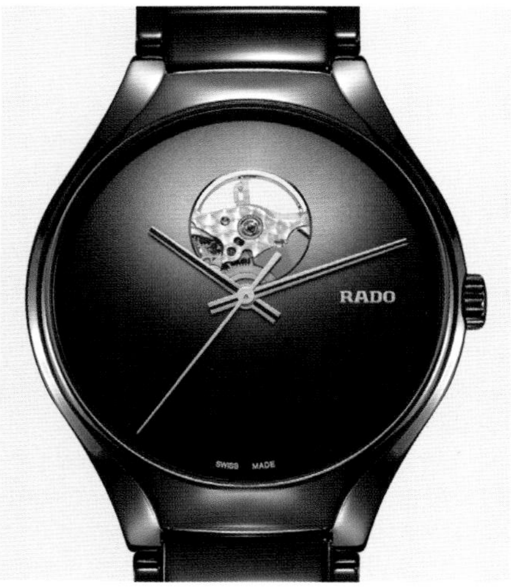

True Secret Automatic

Reference number: R27107152
Movement: automatic, ETA Caliber C07.611; ø 25.6 mm, height 5.2 mm; 25 jewels; 21,600 vph; 80-hour power reserve
Functions: hours, minutes, sweep seconds
Case: ceramic, ø 40 mm, height 9.2 mm; sapphire crystal; transparent case back; water-resistant to 5 atm
Band: ceramic, double folding clasp
Price: $1,900

True Square Automatic Open Heart

Reference number: R27086162
Movement: automatic, ETA Caliber C07.631; ø 25.6 mm, height 4.74 mm; 25 jewels; 21,600 vph; partially skeletonized mainplate and dial; 80-hour power reserve
Functions: hours, minutes, sweep seconds
Case: ceramic, 38 × 38 mm, height 9.7 mm; sapphire crystal; transparent case back; water-resistant to 5 atm
Band: ceramic, double folding clasp
Price: $2,350
Variations: white or plasma-colored ceramic with blue dial

True Square Automatic

Reference number: R27078162
Movement: automatic, ETA Caliber C07.611; ø 25.6 mm, height 5.2 mm; 25 jewels; 21,600 vph; 80-hour power reserve
Functions: hours, minutes, sweep seconds; date
Case: ceramic, 38 × 38 mm, height 9.6 mm; sapphire crystal; water-resistant to 5 atm
Band: ceramic, double folding clasp
Price: $1,950
Variations: various dials; set with stones

True Thinline Automatic

Reference number: R27113172
Movement: automatic, ETA Caliber A31.L02; ø 25.6 mm, height 4.6 mm; 25 jewels; 21,600 vph; 64-hour power reserve
Functions: hours, minutes, sweep seconds; date
Case: ceramic, ø 40 mm, height 9 mm; sapphire crystal; transparent case back; water-resistant to 3 atm
Band: ceramic, double folding clasp
Price: $2,300; limited to 2020 pieces

HyperChrome Classic "Golden Horse"

Reference number: R33930313
Movement: automatic, ETA Caliber C07.611; ø 25.6 mm, height 5.2 mm; 25 jewels; 21,600 vph; 80-hour power reserve
Functions: hours, minutes, sweep seconds; date
Case: stainless steel, ø 37 mm, height 10.8 mm; sapphire crystal; water-resistant to 5 atm
Band: stainless steel, double folding clasp
Price: $1,800; limited to 1,957 pieces
Variations: blue dial

Coupole Classic Open Heart

Reference number: R22894155
Movement: automatic, ETA Caliber C07.631; ø 25.6 mm, height 4.74 mm; 25 jewels; 21,600 vph; partially skeletonized mainplate and dial; 80-hour power reserve
Functions: hours, minutes, sweep seconds
Case: stainless steel, ø 41 mm, height 11.7 mm; sapphire crystal; transparent case back; water-resistant to 5 atm
Band: calfskin, folding clasp with adjustment link
Price: $1,550

Ressence Watches
Meirbrug 1
2000 Antwerp
Belgium

Tel.:
+32-3-446-0060

E-mail:
hello@ressence.be

Website:
www.ressencewatches.com

Founded:
2011

U.S. distributor:
Totally Worth It, LLC
76 Division Avenue
Summit, NJ 07901-2309
201-894-4710
724-263-2286
info@totallyworthit.com

Most important collections/price range:
Type 1 / from $20,600; Type 3 / from $42,200; Type 5 / from $35,800

RESSENCE

Belgian Benoit Mintiens had the luck of the newcomer at Baselworld 2010. He showed up at the last minute and found some space to show a strange watch with an almost two-dimensional dial. . . . He returned in 2011 with the Type 1001. It consisted of a large rotating dial carrying a hand that pointed to a minute track on the bezel. Hours, small seconds, and a day/night indication rotated on dedicated subsidiary dials. The ballet on the dial mesmerized those who saw it, so he sold all his fifty models off the bat.

The mechanics behind the Ressence watches—the name is a compounding of Renaissance of the Essential—are basically simple: A stripped-down and rebuilt ETA 2824 leaves the minute wheel as the main driver of the other wheels. Mintiens, however, was about to go further.

In 2012 came the Type 0 series, which included a few design changes. Then, in a successful bid to improve readability, he immersed the dial section in oil, giving the displays a very contemporary two-dimensional look, much like an electronic watch. The movement had to be kept separate from the oil and was connected to the dial using magnets and a set of superconductors and a Faraday cage to protect the movement from magnetism. Baffles compensate for the expanding and contracting of the oil due to temperature shifts. The Type 3 also lost the crown, the only obstacle to making a perfectly smooth watch, in favor of a clever setting and winding mechanism controlled by the case back. The watch was an automatic, of course. Not surprisingly, it won the Revelation Prize at the Grand Prix d'Horlogerie in Geneva in 2013.

The variations on the theme have been emerging from the Ressence studio at a regular pace. Several watches came with slightly different design. One was a diver's watch chic enough to wear for any occasion. The latest innovation is the e-Crown, which allows the wearer to reset the time electronically by discreetly tapping twice on the watch's crystal.

Type 5X

Movement: automatic, ROCS 5-1 (module base ETA 2824-2); ø 32 mm; 41 jewels; 28,800 vph; case back for winding and time setting; 25 gearwheels; 36-hour power reserve
Functions: minutes; hours and 90-second "runner" (Ressence Orbital Convex System: rotating minute dial with rotating satellites); oil temperature gauge
Case: titanium, ø 46 mm, height 15.5 mm; bidirectional bezel; sapphire crystal; water-resistant to 10 atm
Band: Alcantara, buckle
Remarks: 2 separately sealed case chambers; dial-side chamber filled with oil; display disks propelled by magnetic drive
Price: $36,500; limited 2020 model

Type 2G

Movement: automatic, Ressence Orbital Convex System (ROCS) 2 (module base ETA 2892A); ø 32 mm; 45 jewels; 28,800 vph; case back for winding and time setting; gear train with 37 gearwheels; e-Crown module activated by tapping sapphire crystal; 36-hour power reserve; **Functions:** hours, minutes, subsidiary seconds (ROCS: orbital minute dial with rotating satellites for additional indications); e-Crown functions (2nd time zone, energy saving, automatic time setting)
Case: polished titanium, ø 45 mm, height 12 mm; sapphire crystal; **Band:** calfskin, buckle
Remarks: e-Crown function monitors and controls mechanical movement; up to 3 months dark power reserve
Price: $48,000

Type 1B Slim

Movement: automatic, Ressence Orbital Convex System (ROCS) 1.3 (module base ETA 2892-A); ø 32 mm; 40 jewels; 28,800 vph; case back for winding and time setting; 27 gearwheels; 36-hour power reserve
Functions: hours, minutes, subsidiary seconds; orbiting minute dial with rotating satellites for additional displays; weekday (off-center, orbiting)
Case: titanium, ø 42 mm, height 11 mm; sapphire crystal
Band: reptile skin, buckle
Price: $20,600
Variations: white, blue, or silver dial

RGM

The traditional values of hard work and persistence are alive and well in Roland Murphy, founder of RGM, one of the U.S.'s most famous and exclusive watch companies. Murphy, born in Maryland, went through the watchmaker's drill, studying at the Bowman Technical School, then in Switzerland, and finally working with Swatch before launching his own business in 1992 in Pennsylvania, which could be considered a kind of "watch valley."

The secret to his success, however, has been always to stay in touch with fundamental American values and icons. His first watch, the Signature, resurrected vintage pocket watch movements developed by Hamilton. The Railroad series today is run on restored Hamilton movements. His second big project was the Caliber 801, the first "high-grade mechanical movement made in series in America since Hamilton stopped production of the 992 B in 1969," Murphy grins. This was followed by an all-American-made watch, the Pennsylvania Tourbillon.

And so, model by model, Murphy continues to expand his "Made in U.S.A." portfolio. "You cannot compare us to the big brands," says Murphy. "We are small and specialized, the needs are different. We work directly with the customer." This may account for the brand's diversity. There are retro-themed watches, sports-themed watches (honoring baseball or chess), a diver water-resistant to 70 atm, and the series 400 chronograph with a pulsometer and extra-large subdials for visibility.

Of late, Murphy has turned to the many crafts associated with watchmaking, notably engine-turned guilloché. He has also produced a series of dials with cloisonné enamel motifs or hand-painted images on mother of pearl. In 2020, he came out with a spectacular homage to Robert Falcon Scott's dramatic expedition to Antarctica from 1910–1913 on the ship *Terra Nova*.

RGM Watch Company
801 W. Main Street
Mount Joy, PA 17552

Tel.:
717-653-9799

E-mail:
sales@rgmwatches.com

Web:
www.rgmwatches.com

Founded:
1992

Number of employees:
12

Annual production:
200–300 watches

Distribution:
RGM deals directly with customers.
sales@rgmwatches.com

Most important collection/price range:
Pennsylvania Series (completely made in the U.S.) / $2,500 to $125,000

Cloisonné Model 25

Reference number: Model 25
Movement: automatic, RGM/Swiss movement with solid gold rotor; ø 25.6 mm; 21 jewels; 28,800 vph; rhodium finish with perlage and côtes de Genève; 42-hour power reserve
Functions: hours, minutes, sweep seconds
Case: stainless steel, ø 40 mm, height 11.2 mm; sapphire crystal; transparent case back; water-resistant to 5 atm
Band: calfskin, buckle
Remarks: custom cloisonné dial
Price: $13,900
Variations: custom dial design encouraged

Wood Marquetry Model 25

Reference number: Model 25
Movement: automatic, RGM/Swiss movement with solid gold rotor; ø 25.6 mm; 21 jewels; 28,800 vph; rhodium finish with perlage and côtes de Genève; 42-hour power reserve
Functions: hours, minutes, sweep seconds
Case: stainless steel, ø 40 mm, height 11.2 mm; sapphire crystal; transparent case back; water-resistant to 5 atm
Band: calfskin, buckle
Remarks: custom wood marquetry dial
Price: $13,900

Hand-painted Mother of Pearl Model 25

Reference number: Model 25
Movement: automatic, RGM/Swiss movement with solid gold rotor; ø 25.6 mm; 21 jewels; 28,800 vph; rhodium finish with perlage and côtes de Genève; 42-hour power reserve
Functions: hours, minutes, sweep seconds
Case: stainless steel, ø 40 mm, height 11.2 mm; sapphire crystal; transparent case back; water-resistant to 5 atm
Band: calfskin, buckle
Remarks: hand-painted on mother-of-pearl; case back with engraved map of Robert F. Scott's Terra Nova expedition 1910–1913
Price: on request

Type II Montgomery Marginal Minutes

Reference number: 222 RR
Movement: manually wound, restored Hamilton 921 or 923; ø 38.1 mm; 21 or 23 jewels; 18,000 vph; lever escapement; screw balance; U.S.-made movement; circular côtes de Genève; 42-hour power reserve
Functions: hours, minutes, subsidiary seconds
Case: stainless steel, ø 41 mm, height 12 mm; sapphire crystal; transparent case back; water-resistant to 5 atm; **Band:** leather, buckle
Remarks: grand-feu white glass enamel "boxcar" dial; blued hands
Price: $7,950 for the 923 movement; $5,950 for the 921

Model 207

Movement: automatic, RGM/ETA Caliber 2892-A2; ø 25.6 mm; 21 jewels; 28,800 vph; rhodium finish with perlage and côtes de Genève
Functions: hours, minutes, sweep seconds; date
Case: brushed or polished stainless steel, ø 38.5 mm, height 9.9 mm; sapphire crystal; transparent case back
Band: rubber or reptile skin, buckle
Remarks: date at 3 o'clock, 6 o'clock, or no date
Price: $2,750
Variations: without date; with black dial

Model 500-GMT

Movement: automatic, modified ETA Caliber 2893-2; ø 25.6 mm, height 4.1 mm; 21 jewels; 28,800 vph; bridges and plates with perlage and côtes de Genève; 48-hour power reserve
Functions: hours, minutes, sweep seconds; 2nd time zone on bezel; date
Case: brushed stainless steel, ø 41 mm, height 11.3 mm; sapphire crystal; bidirectional bezel with 0-24 scale and ceramic-filled numerals; screw-down back with Richard Sachs engraved design; screw-in crown; water-resistant to 10 atm
Band: rubber strap, buckle
Price: $4,750

Pennsylvania Tourbillon

Reference number: MM2
Movement: manually wound, in-house movement; ø 37.22 mm; 19 jewels; 18,000 vph; German silver and rose gold finish with perlage and côtes de Genève; 42-hour power reserve
Functions: hours, minutes; 1-minute tourbillon
Case: stainless steel, ø 43.5 mm, height 13.5 mm; guilloché dial; sapphire crystal; transparent case back
Band: reptile skin, buckle
Remarks: blued-steel minute and hour hands
Price: $95,000
Variations: rose gold ($125,000); platinum (price on request)

Classic Enamel

Reference number: PS 801 CE
Movement: manually wound, RGM Caliber 801; ø 37 mm; 19 jewels; lever escapement; screw balance; hand-engraved balance bridge with swan-neck regulator; U.S.-made bridges, mainplate, settings, 7-tooth winding click; circular côtes de Genève; 42-hour power reserve
Functions: hours, minutes, 3-armed second hand
Case: stainless steel, ø 43.3 mm, height 12.3 mm; sapphire crystal
Band: reptile skin, buckle
Remarks: grand-feu white glass double sunk enamel dial
Price: $11,900; limited edition
Variations: rose gold ($24,700)

Enamel Corps of Engineers

Reference number: 801 COE
Movement: manually wound, RGM Caliber 801; ø 37 mm; 19 jewels; lever escapement; screw balance; U.S.-made bridges, mainplate, settings, 7-tooth winding click; circular côtes de Genève; 42-hour power reserve
Functions: hours, minutes, subsidiary seconds
Case: stainless steel, ø 42 mm, height 10.5 mm; sapphire crystal; transparent case back; water-resistant to 5 atm
Band: leather, buckle
Remarks: grand-feu white glass enamel dial with aged luminous numbers
Price: $9,700
Variations: stainless steel bracelet ($10,450)

RICHARD MILLE

Richard Mille
c/o Horométrie SA
11, rue du Jura
CH-2345 Les Breuleux
Switzerland

Tel.:
+41-32-959-4353

E-mail:
info@richardmille.ch

Website:
www.richardmille.com

Founded:
2000

Annual production:
approx. 4,600 watches

U.S. distributor:
Richard Mille Americas
8701 Wilshire Blvd.
Beverly Hills, CA 90211
310-205-5555

Mille never stops delivering the wow to the watch world with what he calls his "race cars for the wrist." He is not an engineer, however, but rather a marketing expert who earned his first paychecks in the watch division of the French defense, automobile, and aerospace concern Matra in the early 1980s. "I have no historical relationship with watchmaking whatsoever," says Mille, "and so I have no obligations either. The mechanics of my watches are geared towards technical feasibility."

His early work was with the wizards at Audemars Piguet Renaud & Papi (APRP) in Le Locle, who would take on the Mille challenge. Audemars Piguet even tested some of those scandalous innovations—materials, technologies, functions—in a Richard Mille watch before daring to use them in its own collections (Tradition d'Excellence).

In 2007, Audemars Piguet finally became a shareholder in Richard Mille, and so the three firms are now closely bound. The assembly of the watches is done in the Franches-Montagnes region in the Jura, where Richard Mille opened the firm Horométrie.

To keep its fans happy, the brand never ceases to explore the lunatic fringe of the technically possible, like the collaboration with Airbus Corporate Jets, which gave rise to a case made of a lightweight titanium-aluminum alloy used in turbines. Then there is the superlight and tough material called graphene developed at the University of Manchester and used by McLaren. Richard Mille timepieces have also found their way onto the wrists of elite athletes, like tennis star Rafael Nadal and sprinter Yohan Blake. The 2018 watch for polo star Pablo Mac Donough features a unique, reinforced sapphire crystal. Formula One champion Alain Prost, who is a cycling fan, got a watch with a pusher-activated kilometer totalizer, and for action star Sylvester Stallone, Mille conceived an adventure watch with a tourbillon, a chronograph, and a detachable compass including a water level.

RM 07-01 Automatic Baguette Set

Reference number: RM 07-01
Movement: automatic, Richard Mille Caliber CRMA2; 22 × 29.9 mm, height 4.92 mm; 25 jewels; 28,800 vph; titanium mainplate and bridges, balance with 4 regulating screws, skeletonized rotor in pink gold with adjustable inertia and winding performance; 50-hour power reserve
Functions: hours, minutes
Case: white gold, 31.4 × 45.66 mm, height 11.85 mm; bezel and case sides set with diamonds; sapphire crystal; transparent case back; water-resistant to 5 atm; **Band:** rubber, folding clasp
Remarks: skeletonized dial set with diamonds
Price: CHF 601,000

RM 07-01 Automatic

Reference number: RM 07-01
Movement: automatic, Richard Mille Caliber CRMA2; 22 × 29.9 mm, height 4.92 mm; 25 jewels; 28,800 vph; titanium mainplate and bridges, balance with 4 regulating screws, skeletonized rotor in pink gold with adjustable inertia and winding performance; 50-hour power reserve
Functions: hours, minutes
Case: ceramic (pink gold case sides), 31.4 × 45.66 mm, height 11.85 mm; bezel set with diamonds; sapphire crystal; transparent case back; water-resistant to 5 atm
Band: rubber, folding clasp
Remarks: skeletonized dial set with diamonds
Price: CHF 195,000

RM 17-01 Tourbillon

Reference number: RM 017-01
Movement: manually wound, Richard Mille Caliber RM17-01; 29.45 × 31.2 mm, height 4.65 mm; 23 jewels; 21,600 vph; 1-minute tourbillon with ceramic end stone; partially skeletonized titanium plate; 70-hour power reserve
Functions: hours, minutes; power reserve indicator, crown position display
Case: pink gold, 39 × 48 mm, height 12.6 mm; sapphire crystal; transparent case back; water-resistant to 5 atm
Band: rubber, folding clasp
Remarks: case completely set with diamonds
Price: CHF 744,000

RM 030 Automatic

Reference number: RM 030
Movement: automatic, Caliber RMAR1; 28.45 × 30.25 mm, height 5.67 mm; 40 jewels; 28,800 vph; titanium mainplate and bridges, 2 spring barrels, automatically declutching winding rotor with adjustable inertia; 55-hour power reserve
Functions: hours, minutes, sweep seconds; power reserve indicator, rotor clutch function display; date
Case: pink gold, 42.7 × 50 mm, height 13.95 mm; sapphire crystal; transparent case back; water-resistant to 5 atm
Band: rubber, buckle
Price: CHF 133,000

RM 33-02 Automatic

Reference number: RM 33-02
Movement: automatic, Richard Mille Caliber RMXP1; ø 33 mm, height 2.6 mm; 29 jewels; 21,600 vph; partially skeletonized titanium mainplate, platinum microrotor; 45-hour power reserve
Functions: hours, minutes
Case: pink gold, ø 45.7 mm, height 6.3 mm; carbon fiber bezel and case back screwed onto case with 6 titanium screws; sapphire crystal; transparent case back; ceramic crown; water-resistant to 3 atm
Band: rubber, folding clasp
Remarks: skeletonized dial
Price: CHF 143,000

RM 037 Ceramic

Reference number: RM 037 TPT
Movement: automatic, Richard Mille Caliber CRMA1; 22.9 × 28 mm, height 4.82 mm; 25 jewels; 28,800 vph; skeletonized movement; winding rotor with variable geometry; 50-hour power reserve
Functions: hours, minutes; crown-activated functions; large date
Case: pink gold, 34.4 × 52.2 mm, height 12.5 mm; carbon fiber bezel and case back; sapphire crystal; transparent case back; pusher with crown function selector
Band: rubber, folding clasp
Remarks: bezel and skeletonized dial set with diamonds
Price: CHF 213,000

RM 39-01 Flyback Chronograph "Aviation E6-B"

Reference number: RM 39-01
Movement: manually wound, Richard Mille Caliber RMAC2; ø 39.15 mm, height 9 mm; 62 jewels; 21,600 vph; double spring barrel, skeletonized rotor in pink gold with adjustable inertia and winding performance; 70-hour power reserve; **Functions:** hours, minutes; additional 24-hour display (2nd time zone), power reserve display, function display; flyback-chronograph; full calendar with large date, month
Case: titanium, ø 50 mm, height 16.8 mm; bidirectional bezel with tachymeter and conversion table; sapphire crystal; transparent case back
Band: rubber, folding clasp
Price: CHF 152,000

RM 67-01 Automatic Extra-Thin

Reference number: RM 67-01
Movement: automatic, Richard Mille Caliber CRMA6; 29.1 × 31.25 mm, height 3.6 mm; 25 jewels; 28,800 vph; titanium mainplate and bridges, platinum winding rotor; 50-hour power reserve
Functions: hours, minutes; crown function display; date
Case: pink gold, 38.7 × 47.5 mm, height 7.75 mm; bezel set with diamonds and screwed to case back with 8 titanium screws; sapphire crystal; transparent case back; water-resistant to 3 atm
Band: rubber, folding clasp
Price: CHF 159,000

RM 70-01 Tourbillon Alain Prost

Reference number: RM 70-01
Movement: manually wound, Richard Mille Caliber RM70; 29.7 × 37.1 mm, height 10.7 mm; 32 jewels; 21,600 vph; 1-minute tourbillon; 5 switch-operated number rolls to add up the full distance traveled; 69-hour power reserve
Functions: hours, minutes; kilometer counter
Case: carbon fiber (TPT carbon); sapphire crystal; transparent case back; crown with torque limit; water-resistant to 5 atm
Band: rubber, folding clasp
Remarks: homage to Formula 1 world champion and passionate cyclist Alain Prost; comes with customized Colnago racing bike
Price: CHF 864.500; limited to 30 pieces

ROGER DUBUIS

Roger Dubuis has always been a *manufacture* committed to luxury and *"très haute horlogerie."* The brand makes some outstanding movement components—parts that, because of their quality and geographical origins, bear the coveted Seal of Geneva. Founder Roger Dubuis, who passed away in 2017, was steeped in watchmaking and the business. In 2008, he sold 60 percent of the company shares to Richemont Group, which benefited from the resulting synergies, especially Cartier, which gets its skeletonized movements from the Roger Dubuis *manufacture*. In early 2016, Richemont went all the way and acquired the remaining 40 percent of the Genevan brand.

Roger Dubuis was founded in 1995 as SOGEM SA (Société Genevoise des Montres) by name-giver Roger Dubuis and financier Carlos Dias, who came up with timepieces with unheard-of dimensions and incomparable complications. The meteoric development of this *manufacture* and the incredible frequency of its new introductions—even technical ones—continue to amaze colleagues and consumers alike. Today, Roger Dubuis develops all of its own movements, currently numbering more than thirty different mechanical calibers. In addition, it produces almost all components in-house, from base plates to escapements and balance springs. With this heavy-duty technological know-how in its quiver, the brand has been able to build some remarkable movements, like the massive RD101, with four balance springs and all manner of differentials and gear works to drive the Excalibur Quatuor, the equivalent in horology to a monster truck. Even in their more delicate versions, like the Brocéliande, featuring colored ivy leaves embracing the movement, Roger Dubuis watches always seem ready to jump off your wrist.

Recently, the brand has rubbed elbows with car racing. Its partnership with Pirelli has produced models using genuine Formula One rubber as straps on the crowns. The rubber has the original tire color coding for different driving options: wet, medium, soft, supersoft, ultrasoft, and hypersoft. Another partnership, with Lamborghini's motor sports division, Lamborghini Squadra Corse, has produced models inspired by the design of such cars as the Aventador and the Huracán.

Manufacture Roger Dubuis
2, rue André-De-Garrini - CP 149
CH-1217 Meyrin 2 (Geneva)
Switzerland

Tel.:
+41-22-783-2828

E-mail:
info@rogerdubuis.com

Website:
www.rogerdubuis.com

Founded:
1995

Annual production:
over 5,000 watches (estimated)

U.S. distributor:
Roger Dubuis New York
545 Madison Ave.
New York, NY 10022
212-651-3773
Roger Dubuis Beverly Hills
9490C Brighton Way
Beverly Hills, CA 90210
310-734-1855

Most important collections/price range:
Excalibur, Velvet / $12,000 to $1,100,000

Excalibur Huracán

Reference number: RDDBEX0749
Movement: automatic, Roger Dubuis Caliber RD630; ø 36.1 mm, height 7.78 mm; 29 jewels; 28,800 vph; 2 spring barrels; 60-hour power reserve
Functions: hours, minutes, sweep seconds; date
Case: titanium, ø 45 mm, height 13.3 mm; sapphire crystal; water-resistant to 5 atm
Band: rubber, folding clasp
Price: $47,000
Variations: gray dial; rose gold ($68,000)

Excalibur Huracán

Reference number: RDDBEX0829
Movement: automatic, Roger Dubuis Caliber RD630; ø 36.1 mm, height 7.78 mm; 29 jewels; 28,800 vph; 2 spring barrels; 60-hour power reserve
Functions: hours, minutes, sweep seconds; date
Case: titanium with black DLC, ø 45 mm, height 13.3 mm; sapphire crystal; water-resistant to 5 atm
Band: rubber, with leather layer, folding clasp
Price: $49,000
Variations: titanium without DLC ($47,000); rose gold ($68,000)

Excalibur Huracán

Reference number: RDDBEX0748
Movement: automatic, Roger Dubuis Caliber RD630; ø 36.1 mm, height 7.78 mm; 29 jewels; 28,800 vph; 2 spring barrels; 60-hour power reserve
Functions: hours, minutes, sweep seconds; date
Case: titanium, ø 45 mm, height 13.3 mm; sapphire crystal; water-resistant to 5 atm
Band: rubber, folding clasp
Price: $47,000
Variations: blue dial; rose gold ($68,000)

Excalibur Spider Pirelli Skeleton

Reference number: RDDBEX0747
Movement: automatic, Roger Dubuis Caliber RD820SQ; ø 36.1 mm, height 6.38 mm; 35 jewels; 28,800 vph; skeletonized movement, microrotor; 60-hour power reserve; Geneva Seal
Functions: hours, minutes
Case: titanium with black DLC coating, partially coated in rubber, ø 45 mm, height 14.02 mm; sapphire crystal; transparent case back; water-resistant to 5 atm
Band: rubber with leather inlay, folding clasp
Price: $72,000; limited to 88 pieces
Variations: various colors

Excalibur Aventador S

Reference number: RDDBEX0686
Movement: manually wound, Roger Dubuis Caliber RD103SQ; ø 36.1 mm, height 7.8 mm; 48 jewels; 57,600 vph; 2 coupled escapement systems with balances at a 90° angle, each beating at 28,8000 vph; power transmission and synchronization using planetary gears; skeletonized movement; 40-hour power reserve; Geneva Seal; **Functions:** hours, minutes, sweep seconds (jumping); power reserve indicator
Case: carbon fiber with titanium inner case partially covered in rubber, ø 45 mm, height 14.05 mm; sapphire crystal; transparent case back; rubber-covered crown; water-resistant to 5 atm
Band: rubber, with calfskin layer, folding clasp
Price: $209,000; limited to 88 pieces

Excalibur Skeleton Automatic

Reference number: RDDBEX0777
Movement: automatic, Roger Dubuis Caliber RD820SQ; ø 36.1 mm, height 6.38 mm; 35 jewels; 28,800 vph; skeletonized movement, microrotor; 60-hour power reserve; Geneva Seal
Functions: hours, minutes
Case: carbon fiber, ø 42 mm, height 11.9 mm; sapphire crystal; transparent case back; water-resistant to 3 atm
Band: rubber, folding clasp
Price: $65,500
Variations: white gold ($82,500); rose gold ($76,000)

Excalibur 45 Automatic

Reference number: RDDBEX0602
Movement: automatic, Roger Dubuis Caliber RD830; ø 29.21 mm, height 4 mm; 27 jewels; 28,800 vph; 48-hour power reserve
Functions: hours, minutes, subsidiary seconds; date
Case: titanium, ø 45 mm, height 14.7 mm; sapphire crystal; transparent case back; water-resistant to 5 atm
Band: rubber, folding clasp
Price: $16,700
Variations: various straps, cases, and dials

Excalibur 36 Automatic

Reference number: RDDBEX0789
Movement: automatic, Roger Dubuis Caliber RD830; ø 29.21 mm, height 4 mm; 27 jewels; 28,800 vph; 48-hour power reserve
Functions: hours, minutes, subsidiary seconds; date
Case: rose gold, ø 36 mm, height 13.3 mm; bezel set with 48 brilliant-cut diamonds; sapphire crystal; transparent case back; water-resistant to 5 atm
Band: reptile skin, folding clasp
Remarks: mother-of-pearl dial
Price: $75,500
Variations: various straps, cases, and dials

Excalibur 45 Automatic

Reference number: RDDBEX0567
Movement: automatic, Roger Dubuis Caliber RD830; ø 29.21 mm, height 4 mm; 27 jewels; 28,800 vph; 48-hour power reserve
Functions: hours, minutes, subsidiary seconds; date
Case: titanium with black DLC coating, ø 45 mm, height 14.7 mm; sapphire crystal; transparent case back; water-resistant to 5 atm
Band: rubber, folding clasp
Price: $16,700
Variations: various straps, cases, and dials

Caliber RD630

Automatic; skeletonized movement; winding rotor shaped like a tire rim; double spring barrel, 60-hour power reserve
Functions: hours, minutes, sweep seconds; date
Diameter: 36.1 mm
Height: 7.78 mm
Jewels: angled at 12°
Frequency: 28,800 vph
Remarks: bead-blasted plates and bridges, NAC-coated; 233 parts

Caliber RD 103SQ

Manually wound; double sprung balance with angled balance wheels, 28,800 vph each; power transmission and synchronization via planetary gears; skeletonized movement; single spring barrel, 40-hour power reserve; Geneva Seal
Functions: hours, minutes, sweep seconds (jumping); power reserve indicator
Diameter: 36.1 mm
Height: 7.8 mm
Jewels: 48
Frequency: 57,600 vph

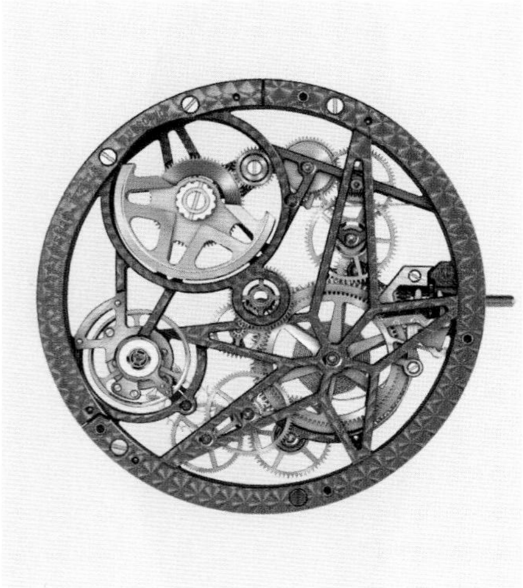

Caliber RD820SQ

Automatic; skeletonized movement; microrotor; single spring barrel, 60-hour power reserve; Geneva Seal
Functions: hours, minutes
Diameter: 36.1 mm
Height: 6.38 mm
Jewels: 35
Frequency: 28,800 vph
Remarks: rhodium-plated movement, finely finished with perlage; 167 parts

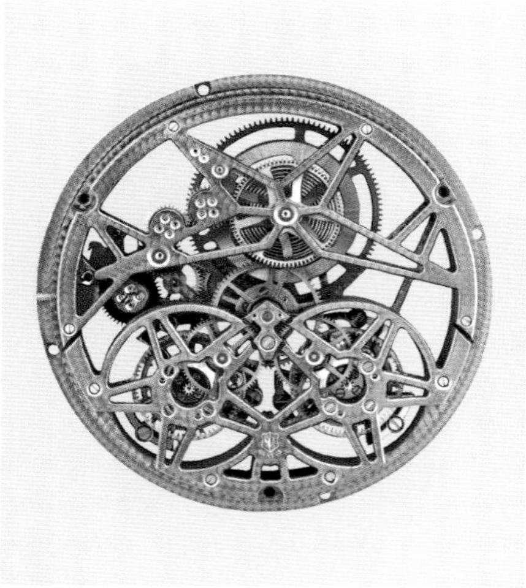

Caliber RD01SQ

Manually wound; 2 flying 1-minute tourbillons with equalizing differential skeletonized movement; single spring barrel, 48-hour power reserve; Geneva Seal, COSC-certified chronometer
Functions: hours, minutes
Diameter: 37.8 mm
Height: 7.67 mm
Jewels: 28
Balance: glucydur variable inertia balance
Frequency: 21,600 vph
Remarks: 319 components

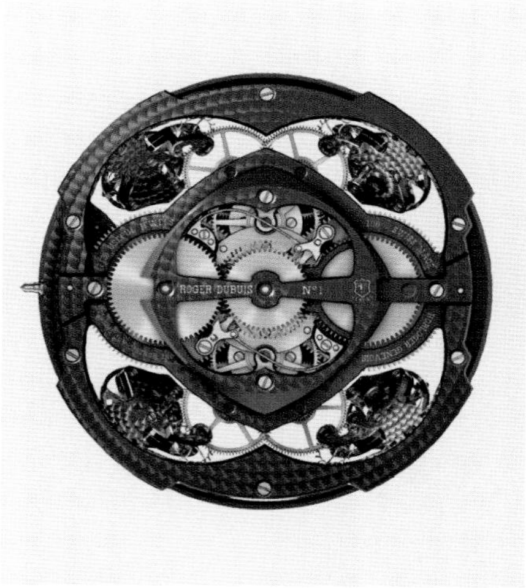

Caliber RD101

Manually wound; 4 radially assembled lever escapements, synchronized with 3 balancing differentials; additional planetary gears for winding and power reserve indicator; skeletonized movement; double spring barrel, 40-hour power reserve; Geneva Seal
Functions: hours, minutes; power reserve indicator
Diameter: 37.9 mm
Height: 10.6 mm
Jewels: 113
Balance: glucydur (4×)
Frequency: 28,800 vph
Balance spring: flat hairspring
Remarks: galvanic black movement, beveled and with perlage; 590 parts

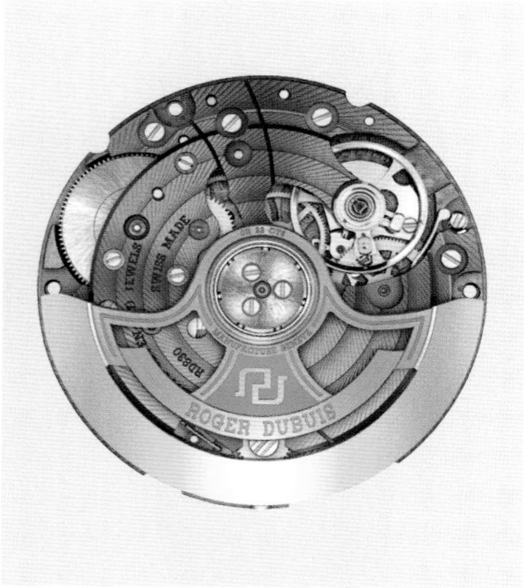

Caliber RD830

Automatic; rotor in rose gold; single spring barrel, 48-hour power reserve
Functions: hours, minutes, subsidiary seconds; date
Diameter: 29.21 mm
Height: 4 mm
Jewels: 27
Frequency: 28,800 vph
Remarks: finely finished with côtes de Genève; 183 parts

Rolex SA
Rue François-Dussaud 3
CH-1211 Geneva 26
Switzerland

Website:
www.rolex.com

Founded:
1908

Number of employees:
over 2,000 (estimated)

Annual production:
approx. 1,000,000 watches (estimated)

U.S. distributor:
Rolex Watch U.S.A., Inc.
Rolex Building
665 Fifth Avenue
New York, NY 10022-5358
212-758-7700
www.rolex.com

ROLEX

Essentially, the Rolex formula for success has always been "what you see is what you get"—and plenty of it. For over a century now, the company has made wristwatch history without a need for *grandes complications*, perpetual calendars, tourbillons, or exotic materials. And its output in sheer quantity is phenomenal, at not quite a million watches per year. But make no mistake about it: The quality of these timepieces is legendary.

For as long as anyone can remember, this brand has held the top spot in the COSC's statistics, and year after year Rolex delivers just about half of all of the official institute's successfully tested mechanical chronometer movements. The brand has also pioneered several fundamental innovations: Rolex founder Hans Wilsdorf invented the hermetically sealed Oyster case in the 1920s, which he later outfitted with a screwed-in crown and an automatic movement wound by rotor. Shock protection, water resistance, the amagnetic Parachrom hairspring, and automatic winding are some of the virtues that make wearing a Rolex timepiece much more comfortable and reliable. As for movements, the automatic caliber 3255 features new materials (nickel-phosphorus), special micromanufacturing technology (LIGA) to make the pallet fork and balance wheel of the Chronergy escapement, and a barrel spring that can store up more energy than ever.

Rolex watches are produced in four different locations in Switzerland. Headquarters in Geneva handles final assembly and quality control and sales. All development, manufacturing, and quality control is done a few miles away in new premises in Plan-les-Ouates. Jewel-setting and dials are made in the Chêne-Bourg district of Geneva, and movements come from a factory in Bienne/Biel.

Meanwhile the company has built up representation in nearly one hundred countries in the world, with over thirty subsidiaries with customer service centers. The network also includes around four thousand watchmakers trained according to Rolex standards.

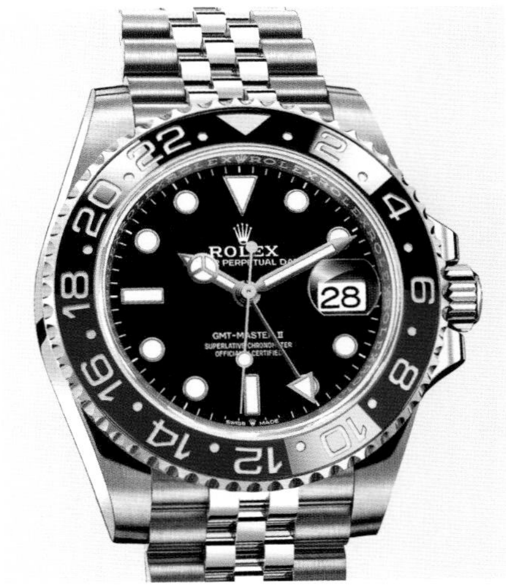

Oyster Perpetual GMT-Master II

Reference number: 126710BLNR
Movement: automatic, Rolex Caliber 3285; ø 28.5 mm, height 6.4 mm; 31 jewels; 28,800 vph; Parachrom hairspring, Paraflex shock absorber, Chronergy escapement; 70-hour power reserve; COSC-certified chronometer
Functions: hours (switched via crown), minutes, sweep seconds; additional 24-hour display (2nd time zone); date
Case: stainless steel, ø 40 mm, height 13 mm; bidirectional bezel with ceramic insert, with 0-24 scale; sapphire crystal; screw-in crown; water-resistant to 10 atm; **Band:** Jubilee stainless steel, folding clasp with safety lock and extension link
Price: $9,700

Oyster Perpetual GMT-Master II

Reference number: 126719BLRO
Movement: automatic, Rolex Caliber 3285; ø 28.5 mm, height 6.4 mm; 31 jewels; 28,800 vph; Parachrom hairspring, Paraflex shock absorber, Chronergy escapement; 70-hour power reserve; COSC-certified chronometer
Functions: hours (switched via crown), minutes, sweep seconds; additional 24-hour display (2nd time zone); date
Case: white gold, ø 40 mm, height 13 mm; bidirectional bezel with ceramic insert, with 0-24 scale; sapphire crystal; screw-in crown; water-resistant to 10 atm; **Band:** Jubilee stainless steel, folding clasp with safety lock and extension link
Price: $55,000

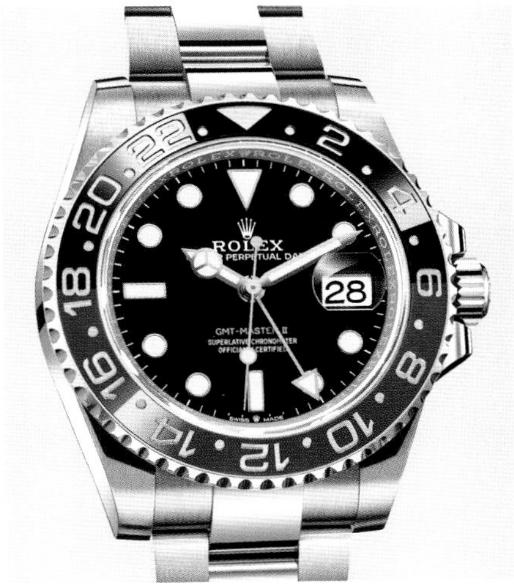

Oyster Perpetual GMT-Master II

Reference number: 126715CHNR
Movement: automatic, Rolex Caliber 3285; ø 28.5 mm, height 6.4 mm; 31 jewels; 28,800 vph; Parachrom hairspring, Paraflex shock absorber, Chronergy escapement; 70-hour power reserve; COSC-certified chronometer
Functions: hours (switched via crown), minutes, sweep seconds; additional 24-hour display (2nd time zone); date
Case: rose gold, ø 40 mm, height 13 mm; bidirectional bezel with ceramic insert, with 0-24 scale; sapphire crystal; screw-in crown; water-resistant to 10 atm; **Band:** Jubilee stainless steel, folding clasp with safety lock and extension link
Price: $38,250

Oyster Perpetual Deepsea

Reference number: 126660
Movement: automatic, Rolex Caliber 3235; ø 29.1 mm; 31 jewels; 28,800 vph; Parachrom hairspring, Paraflex shock absorber, Chronergy escapement, glucydur balance with Microstella regulating bolts; 70-hour power reserve; COSC-certified chronometer
Functions: hours, minutes, sweep seconds; date
Case: stainless steel, ø 44 mm; unidirectional bezel with ceramic insert, with 0-60 scale; sapphire crystal; screw-in crown; helium valve; water-resistant to 390 atm; **Band:** Oystersteel, folding clasp, with safety lock and extension link
Price: $12,250
Variations: blue-black dial ($12,550)

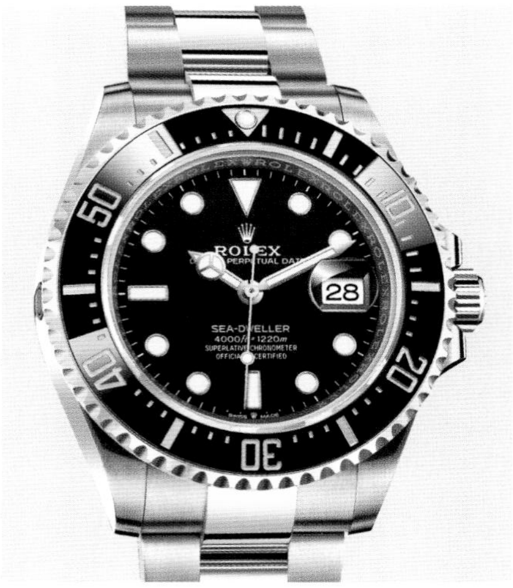

Oyster Perpetual Sea-Dweller

Reference number: 126603
Movement: automatic, Rolex Caliber 3235; ø 29.1 mm, 31 jewels; 28,800 vph; Parachrom hairspring, Paraflex shock absorber, Chronergy escapement, glucydur balance with Microstella regulating bolts; 70-hour power reserve; COSC-certified chronometer
Functions: hours, minutes, sweep seconds; date
Case: stainless steel, ø 44 mm; unidirectional bezel in yellow gold with ceramic insert, with 0-60 scale; sapphire crystal; screw-in crown; helium valve; water-resistant to 390 atm
Band: Oystersteel with yellow gold elements, folding clasp, with safety lock and extension link
Price: $12,250; **Variations:** blue-black dial ($12,550)

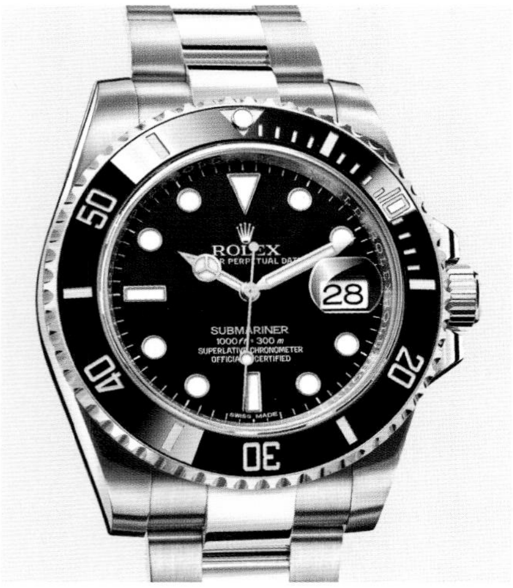

Oyster Perpetual Submariner Date

Reference number: 116613LN
Movement: automatic, Rolex Caliber 3135; ø 28.5 mm, height 6 mm; 31 jewels; 28,800 vph; Parachrom hairspring, glucydur balance with Microstella regulating bolts; 48-hour power reserve; COSC-certified chronometer
Functions: hours, minutes, sweep seconds; date
Case: stainless steel, ø 40 mm, height 12.5 mm; unidirectional bezel in yellow gold with ceramic insert, with 0-60 scale; sapphire crystal; screw-in crown; water-resistant to 30 atm
Band: Oystersteel with yellow gold elements, folding clasp, with extension link
Price: $14,000
Variations: stainless steel ($9,150)

Oyster Perpetual Air-King

Reference number: 116900
Movement: automatic, Rolex Caliber 3131; ø 28.5 mm; 31 jewels; 28,800 vph; Parachrom hairspring, glucydur balance with Microstella regulating bolts; soft iron cap for amagnetic protection; 48-hour power reserve; COSC-certified chronometer
Functions: hours, minutes, sweep seconds
Case: stainless steel, ø 40 mm; sapphire crystal; screw-in crown; water-resistant to 10 atm
Band: Oystersteel, folding clasp, with safety lock and extension link
Price: $6,200

Oyster Perpetual Explorer

Reference number: 214270
Movement: automatic, Rolex Caliber 3132; ø 28.5 mm; 31 jewels; 28,800 vph; Parachrom hairspring, glucydur balance with Microstella regulating bolts; 48-hour power reserve; COSC-certified chronometer
Functions: hours, minutes, sweep seconds
Case: stainless steel, ø 39 mm; sapphire crystal; screw-in crown; water-resistant to 10 atm
Band: Oystersteel, folding clasp, with extension link
Price: $6,550

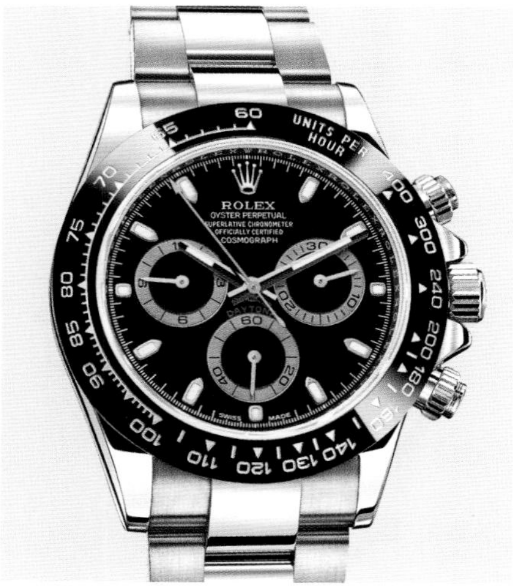

Oyster Perpetual Cosmograph Daytona

Reference number: 116500LN
Movement: automatic, Rolex Caliber 4130; ø 30.5 mm, height 6.5 mm; 44 jewels; 28,800 vph; Parachrom hairspring, glucydur balance with Microstella regulating bolts; 72-hour power reserve; COSC-certified chronometer
Functions: hours, minutes, subsidiary seconds; chronograph
Case: stainless steel, ø 40 mm, height 12.8 mm; Cerachrom bezel; sapphire crystal; screw-in crown and pushers; water-resistant to 10 atm
Band: Oystersteel, folding clasp, with safety lock and extension link
Price: $12,400; **Variations:** white dial

Oyster Perpetual Yacht-Master II

Reference number: 116681
Movement: automatic, Rolex Caliber 4161 (base Caliber 4130); ø 31.2 mm, height 8.05 mm; 42 jewels; 28,800 vph; Parachrom hairspring, glucydur balance with Microstella regulating bolts; 72-hour power reserve; COSC-certified chronometer
Functions: hours, minutes, subsidiary seconds; programmable regatta countdown with memory
Case: stainless steel, ø 44 mm, height 13.8 mm; bidirectional rose gold bezel with ceramic insert; sapphire crystal; screw-in crown; water-resistant to 10 atm; **Band:** Oystersteel with rose gold elements, folding clasp, with safety lock and extension link
Price: $24,995; **Variations:** yellow gold ($47,950); stainless steel ($16,995)

Oyster Perpetual Yacht-Master 42

Reference number: 116659
Movement: automatic, Rolex Caliber 3135; ø 28.5 mm, height 6 mm; 31 jewels; 28,800 vph; Parachrom hairspring, glucydur balance with Microstella regulating bolts; 48-hour power reserve; COSC-certified chronometer
Functions: hours, minutes, sweep seconds; date
Case: white gold, ø 42 mm, height 11.9 mm; bidirectional bezel with ceramic insert and 0-60 scale; sapphire crystal; screw-in crown; water-resistant to 10 atm
Band: elastomer with metal mesh inside, folding clasp
Price: $27,800

Oyster Perpetual Yacht-Master 37

Reference number: 268655
Movement: automatic, Rolex Caliber 2236; ø 20 mm, height 5.5 mm; 31 jewels; 28,800 vph; Parachrom hairspring, glucydur balance with Microstella regulating bolts; 48-hour power reserve; COSC-certified chronometer
Functions: hours, minutes, sweep seconds; date
Case: rose gold, ø 37 mm, height 11 mm; bidirectional bezel with ceramic insert and 0-60 scale; sapphire crystal; screw-in crown; water-resistant to 10 atm
Band: elastomer with metal mesh inside, folding clasp, with extension link
Price: $11,250

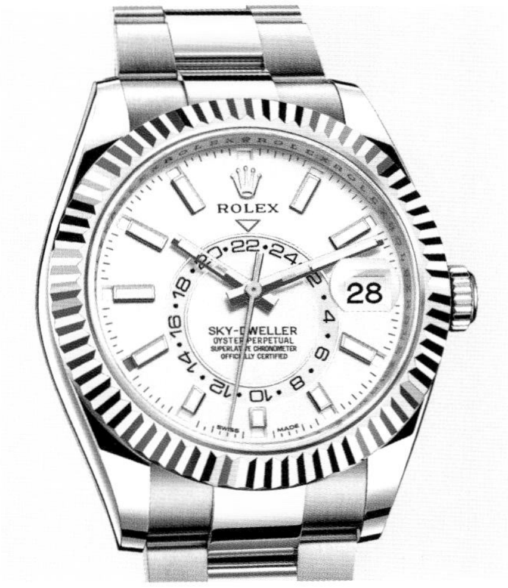

Oyster Perpetual Sky-Dweller

Reference number: 326933
Movement: automatic, Rolex Caliber 9001; ø 33 mm, height 8 mm; 40 jewels; 28,800 vph; Parachrom hairspring, Paraflex shock absorption, glucydur balance with Microstella regulating bolts; 72-hour power reserve; COSC-certified chronometer; **Functions:** hours, minutes, sweep seconds; additional 24-hour display (2nd time zone); annual calendar with date, month
Case: stainless steel, ø 42 mm, height 14.1 mm; bidirectional yellow gold bezel to control functions; sapphire crystal; screw-in crown; water-resistant to 10 atm; **Band:** Oystersteel with yellow gold elements, folding clasp, with extension link
Price: $17,150
Variations: stainless steel /white gold ($37,000)

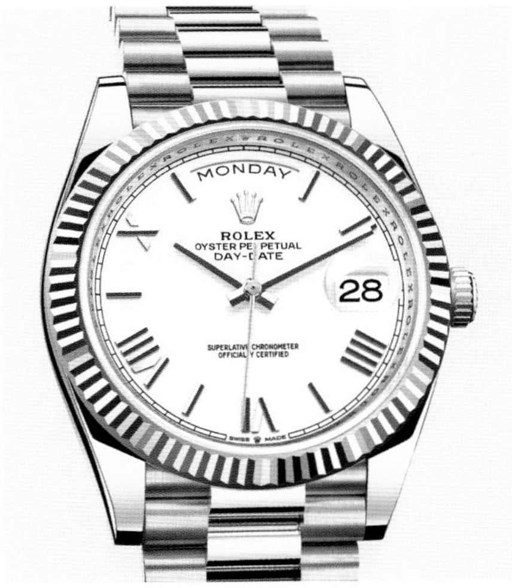

Oyster Perpetual Day-Date 40

Reference number: 228238
Movement: automatic, Rolex Caliber 3255; ø 29.1 mm, height 5.4 mm; 31 jewels; 28,800 vph; Parachrom hairspring, Paraflex shock absorption, Chronergy escapement, glucydur balance with Microstella regulating bolts; 70-hour power reserve; COSC-certified chronometer
Functions: hours, minutes, sweep seconds; date, weekday
Case: yellow gold, ø 40 mm, height 11.6 mm; sapphire crystal; screw-in crown; water-resistant to 10 atm
Band: President yellow gold, folding clasp
Price: $34,850
Variations: white gold ($37,550); Everose gold ($37,550)

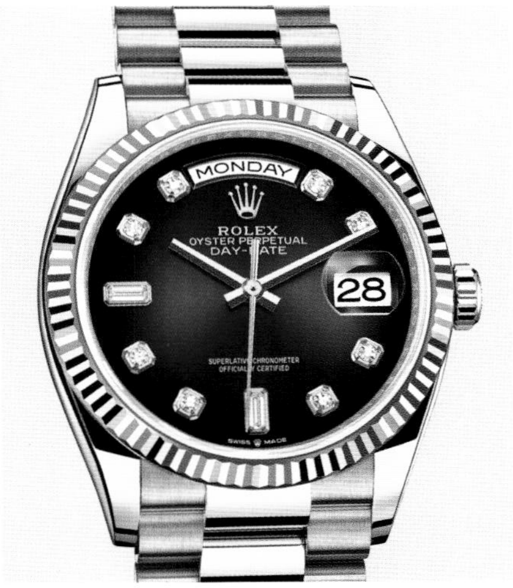

Oyster Perpetual Day-Date 36

Reference number: 128238
Movement: automatic, Rolex Caliber 3255; ø 29.1 mm, height 5.4 mm; 31 jewels; 28,800 vph; Parachrom hairspring, Paraflex shock absorption, Chronergy escapement, glucydur balance with Microstella regulating bolts; 70-hour power reserve; COSC-certified chronometer
Functions: hours, minutes, sweep seconds; date, weekday
Case: yellow gold, ø 36 mm, height 11.1 mm; sapphire crystal; screw-in crown; water-resistant to 10 atm
Band: President yellow gold, folding clasp
Remarks: dial with brilliant-cut diamond indices
Price: $34,550
Variations: white gold ($37,250); rose gold ($37,250)

Oyster Perpetual Datejust 41

Reference number: 126300
Movement: automatic, Rolex Caliber 3235; ø 29.1 mm; 31 jewels; 28,800 vph; Parachrom hairspring, Paraflex shock protection, Chronergy escapement, glucydur balance with Microstella regulating bolts; 70-hour power reserve; COSC-certified chronometer
Functions: hours, minutes, sweep seconds; date
Case: Oystersteel, ø 41 mm, height 11.6 mm; white gold bezel; sapphire crystal; screw-in crown; water-resistant to 10 atm
Band: Jubilee stainless steel, folding clasp, with extension link
Price: $7,900

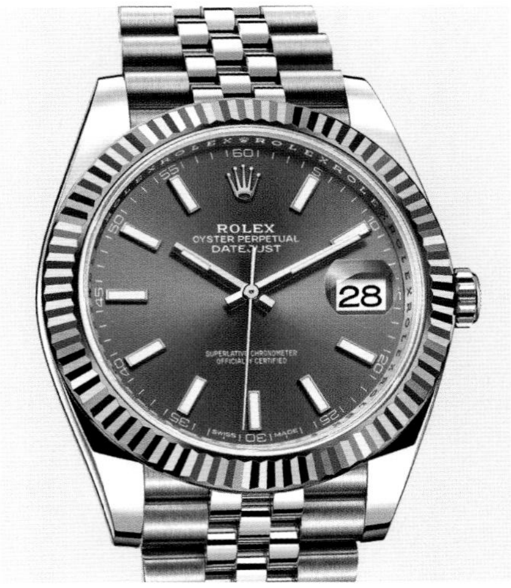

Oyster Perpetual Datejust 41

Reference number: 126334
Movement: automatic, Rolex Caliber 3235; ø 29.1 mm; 31 jewels; 28,800 vph; Parachrom hairspring, Paraflex shock protection, Chronergy escapement, glucydur balance with Microstella regulating bolts; 70-hour power reserve; COSC-certified chronometer
Functions: hours, minutes, sweep seconds; date
Case: Oystersteel, ø 41 mm, height 11.6 mm; white gold bezel; sapphire crystal; screw-in crown; water-resistant to 10 atm
Band: Jubilee stainless steel, folding clasp, with extension link
Price: $7,900

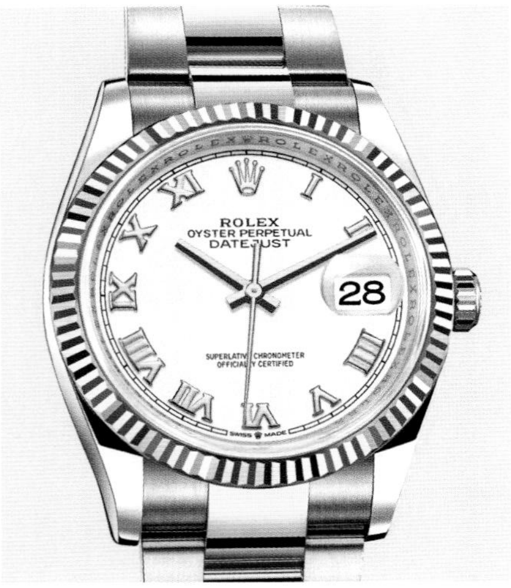

Oyster Perpetual Datejust 36

Reference number: 126233
Movement: automatic, Rolex Caliber 3235; ø 29.1 mm; 31 jewels; 28,800 vph; Parachrom hairspring, Paraflex shock protection, Chronergy escapement, glucydur balance with Microstella regulating bolts; 70-hour power reserve; COSC-certified chronometer
Functions: hours, minutes, sweep seconds; date
Case: stainless steel, ø 36 mm, height 11.3 mm; yellow gold bezel; sapphire crystal; screw-in crown, in yellow gold; water-resistant to 10 atm
Band: Oystersteel with yellow gold elements, folding clasp, with extension link
Price: $16,000

Cellini Moonphase

Reference number: 50535
Movement: automatic, Rolex Caliber 3195; ø 28.5 mm; 31 jewels; 28,800 vph; Parachrom hairspring, Paraflex shock protection, Chronergy escapement; 48-hour power reserve; COSC-certified chronometer
Functions: hours, minutes, sweep seconds; date, moon phase
Case: rose gold, ø 39 mm; sapphire crystal; screw-in crown; water-resistant to 5 atm
Band: reptile skin, folding clasp
Remarks: blue enameled celestial disk with rhodium-plated meteorite as a moon
Price: $26,750

Cellini Time

Reference number: 50509
Movement: automatic, Rolex Caliber 3132 (base 3130); ø 28.5 mm; 31 jewels; 28,800 vph; Parachrom Breguet hairspring; 48-hour power reserve; COSC-certified chronometer
Functions: hours, minutes, sweep seconds
Case: white gold, ø 39 mm; sapphire crystal; screw-in crown; water-resistant to 5 atm
Band: reptile skin, buckle
Price: $15,200
Variations: rose gold ($12,700); with date ($17,000)

Cellini Dual Time

Reference number: 50529
Movement: automatic, Rolex Caliber 3180 (base Rolex Caliber 3187 with module); 28,800 vph; Parachrom-Hairspring; 48-hour power reserve; COSC-certified chronometer
Functions: hours, minutes, sweep seconds; additional 12-hour display (2nd time zone), day/night indicator
Case: white gold, ø 39 mm; sapphire crystal; screw-in crown; water-resistant to 5 atm
Band: reptile skin, buckle
Price: $17,460
Variations: various dials; rose gold ($19,400)

Caliber 3255

Automatic; optimized Chronergy escapement, nickel phosphorus pallet lever and escape wheel made using LIGA process; single spring barrel, 70-hour power reserve; COSC-certified chronometer
Functions: hours, minutes, sweep seconds; date, weekday
Diameter: 29.1 mm
Height: 5.4 mm
Jewels: 31
Balance: glucydur with Microstella regulating bolts
Frequency: 28,800 vph
Balance spring: Parachrom Breguet hairspring
Shock protection: Paraflex
Remarks: used in Day-Date 40

Caliber 3235

Automatic; optimized Chronergy escapement, nickel phosphorus pallet lever and escape wheel made using LIGA process; single spring barrel, 70-hour power reserve; COSC-certified chronometer
Functions: hours, minutes, sweep seconds; date
Diameter: 28.5 mm
Height: 6 mm
Jewels: 31
Balance: glucydur with Microstella regulating bolts
Frequency: 28,800 vph
Balance spring: Parachrom Breguet hairspring
Shock protection: Paraflex
Remarks: used in Datejust

Caliber 2236

Automatic; single spring barrel, 55-hour power reserve; COSC-certified chronometer
Functions: hours, minutes, sweep seconds; date
Diameter: 20 mm
Height: 5.95 mm
Jewels: 31
Balance: glucydur with Microstella regulating bolts
Frequency: 28,800 vph
Balance spring: Parachrom flat hairspring
Shock protection: Kif
Remarks: used in Lady Datejust

Caliber 4130

Automatic; single spring barrel, 72-hour power reserve; COSC-certified chronometer
Functions: hours, minutes, subsidiary seconds; chronograph
Diameter: 30.5 mm
Height: 6.5 mm
Jewels: 44
Balance: glucydur with Microstella regulating bolts
Frequency: 28,800 vph
Balance spring: Parachrom Breguet hairspring
Shock protection: Kif
Remarks: used in Daytona

Caliber 4161

Automatic; single spring barrel, 72-hour power reserve; COSC-certified chronometer
Base caliber: Caliber 4130
Functions: hours, minutes, subsidiary seconds; programmable regatta countdown with memory
Diameter: 31.2 mm
Height: 8.05 mm
Jewels: 42
Balance: glucydur with Microstella regulating bolts
Frequency: 28,800 vph
Balance spring: Parachrom Breguet hairspring
Shock protection: Kif
Remarks: used in Yacht-Master II

Caliber 9001

Automatic; single spring barrel, 72-hour power reserve; COSC-certified chronometer
Functions: hours, minutes, sweep seconds; additional 24-hour display (2nd time zone); annual calendar with date, month
Diameter: 33 mm
Height: 8 mm
Jewels: 40
Balance: glucydur with Microstella regulating bolts
Frequency: 28,800 vph
Balance spring: Parachrom Breguet hairspring
Shock protection: Kif
Remarks: used in Sky-Dweller

SCHAUMBURG WATCH

If you are searching for a brand whose brand strategy is anti-brand, then Schaumburg is your brand. Frank Dilbakowski is the owner of this small watchmaking business in Rinteln, Westphalia, which has been producing very unusual yet affordable timepieces since 1998. The name Schaumburg comes from the surrounding region. The firm has gained a reputation for high-performance timepieces for rugged sports and professional use. But expect to be surprised. The portfolio includes such pieces as the chronometer line Aquamatic, with water resistance to 1,000 meters, and the Aquatitan models, secure to 2,000 meters. If you are into the worn-down-industrial look, there is the Steam Punk collection, which looks as if it had been buried in someone's garden and has now been unearthed, cleaned up, but not restored. It is a particular way to surf the vintage wave.

The watches work well, of course, because Dilbakowski has prioritized traditional watchmaking. The Rinteln workbenches produce the plates and bridges and provide all the finishing as well (perlage, engraving, skeletonizing). Some of the bracelets, cases, and dials are even manufactured here, but the base movements come from Switzerland. Besides unadorned one-hand watches like the recent Squarematic Loyalty, which hints at 1970s-style modernity, the current portfolio of timepieces includes such outstanding creations as a special moon phase, which, rather than simply showing a moon, has a "shadow" crossing over an immobile photo-like reproduction of the moon. The watches can be complicated with regard to design, like the skeletonized watch called the Steel Flower, or they can be simple. The Unikatorium, in contrast, leaves space on the dial for a special guilloché pattern designed in-house and for lots of hand-engraving on bridges and the mainplate visible through the case back. And, of course, the Schaumburg workshop also produces unique pieces.

Schaumburg Watch
Lindburgh & Benson
Kirchplatz 5 and 6
D-31737 Rinteln
Germany

Tel.:
+49-5751-923-351

E-mail:
info@lindburgh-benson.com

Website:
www.schaumburgwatch.com

Founded:
1998

Number of employees:
7

Distribution:
retail

U.S. distributor:
Schaumburg Watch
About Time Luxury Group
210 Bellevue Avenue
Newport, RI 02840
401-846-0598
nicewatch@aol.com

Most important collections/price range:
mechanical wristwatches / approx. $1,500 to $13,000

MooN Aventurine

Reference number: SWMA20
Movement: automatic, Caliber SW 11 (base MAB 88); ø 25.6 mm, height 3.6 mm; 25 jewels; 28,800 vph; astronomically precise moon phase
Functions: hours, minutes; date, moon phase
Case: stainless steel, ø 43 mm, height 12.4 mm; sapphire crystal; water-resistant to 5 atm
Band: reptile skin, folding clasp
Remarks: aventurine dial with photorealistic lunar cycle
Price: $6,000

Unikatorium Classic III

Reference number: SWC320
Movement: manually wound, Caliber SW 07.1 (base ETA 6497); ø 36.6 mm, height 4.5 mm; 17 jewels; 18,000 vph; three-quarter plate; skeletonized spring barrel; finely finished and guillochéed movement; 38-hour power reserve
Functions: hours, minutes, subsidiary seconds
Case: stainless steel, ø 42 mm, height 11 mm; sapphire crystal; transparent case back
Band: calfskin, buckle
Price: $2,400

Squarematic Loyalty

Reference number: SWSM20
Movement: automatic, Caliber SW-SJ20; ø 25.6 mm, height 4.6 mm; 26 jewels; 28,800 vph; 38-hour power reserve
Functions: hours (5-minute indices)
Case: stainless steel, 39 × 39 mm, height 10.9 mm; sapphire crystal; transparent case back
Band: sheep leather, buckle
Price: $1,795

Schwarz Etienne SA
Route de L'Orée-du-Bois 5
CH-2300 La Chaux-de-Fonds
Switzerland

Tel.:
+41-32-967-9420

E-mail:
info@schwarz-etienne.ch

Website:
www.schwarz-etienne.ch

Founded:
1902

Number of employees:
16

Annual production:
300 to 500

Distribution:
Contact main office in Switzerland.

Most important collections:
La Chaux-de-Fonds, Roma, Roswell, Fiji

SCHWARZ ETIENNE

When Raffaello Radicchi, who hails from Perugia, Italy, talks about his business, you might think he was talking about a little shop he set up in Neuchâtel. Ask him why he went into watchmaking, he answers, "I was allergic to the metal and could only wear a gold watch." Subtext: He could not afford a gold watch, so he founded a watch company.

Radicchi is a genuine maverick and a lone figure in this somewhat hermetic industry. He arrived in Switzerland at 18, a mason. He retrained as a carpenter and started buying and renovating homes, and soon he was earning some serious money. In the early aughts, an acquaintance bought up a watch brand in La Chaux-de-Fonds and suggested that Radicchi buy the building that came with it. The brand, once a big name in the industry and a supplier of movements (to Chanel, among others), had originally been founded by Paul Schwarz and Olga Etienne.

By 2008, Radicchi owned the whole package. He understood that the company needed independence to survive. Having a number of outstanding suppliers locally to partner with was a good start. But Schwarz Etienne needed movements. By 2013, he had two, and a third came in 2015. These calibers drive a series of watches, including a tourbillon, that are classical in look, yet very modern-technical, thanks to the inverted movement construction that puts the off-center microrotor on the dial. They've recently started appearing in the watches of other brands and the great Kari Voutilainen was invited to do the decoration on a limited edition of three-hand Romas.

For all its traditionalism, the brand still maintains a feeling of youthful creativity. The Roswell's case, for example, is shaped like a comic-book UFO. And if you have seven figures to spend, you can purchase a special box of seven watches honoring the days of the week, their planets, and their astrological sign. Not surprisingly, Schwarz Etienne came up with a particularly distinctive ladies' watch called Fiji. The dials are in various colors, or enriched with a spread of diamonds, and with droplet indices. The subsidiary seconds dial is cut out in such a way as to create a floral animation with the underlying dial.

Fiji Floral Seconds Joaillerie

Reference number: WFI04MA01RBW01-A
Movement: automatic, Schwarz Etienne Caliber ASE 200.00 with microrotor; ø 30.40 mm, height 5.35 mm; 33 jewels; 21,600 vph; 86-hour power reserve
Functions: hours, minutes, subsidiary seconds as animated floral display
Case: red gold, ø 38 mm, height 10.76 mm; red gold crown; sapphire crystal; water-resistant to 5 atm
Remarks: case set with 512 diamonds, dial with 236
Band: calfskin, folding clasp
Price: $56,200
Variations: black dial

Roma Manufacture Small Second

Reference number: WROVMA03SSCUBCLTD-A
Movement: automatic, Schwarz Etienne Caliber ASE 100.00; ø 30.4 mm, height 5.35 mm; 34 jewels; 21,600 vph; 96-hour power reserve
Functions: hours, minutes, subsidiary seconds
Case: stainless steel, ø 39 mm, height 11 mm; sapphire crystal; transparent case back; water-resistant to 5 atm
Band: leather, buckle
Remarks: hand-guilloché and movement decoration by the Ateliers Kari Voutilainen
Price: $30,140; limited to 50 pieces
Variations: white dial

La Chaux-de-Fonds Tourbillon Petite Seconde Rétrograde

Reference number: WCF09TSE06RB21AA
Movement: automatic, Schwarz Etienne Caliber TSE PSR 122.00; ø 30.40 mm, height 7.05 mm; 40 jewels; 21,600 vph; 1-minute flying tourbillon; plate/bridges sandblasted and chamfered; 72-hour power reserve
Functions: off-center hours, minutes, subsidiary seconds (retrograde)
Case: stainless steel, ø 44 mm, height 13.70 mm; sapphire crystal; transparent case back; water-resistant to 5 atm
Remarks: lapis lazuli numeral track
Band: reptile skin, folding clasp
Price: $69,995

SEIKO

The Japanese watch giant is a part of the Seiko Holding Company, but the development and production of its watches are fully self-sufficient. Seiko makes every variety of portable timepiece and offers mechanical watches with both manual and automatic winding, quartz watches with battery and solar power or with the brand's own mechanical "Kinetic" power generation, as well as the groundbreaking "Spring Drive" hybrid technology. This intelligent mix of mechanical energy generation and electronic regulation is reserved for Seiko's top models.

Also in the top segment of the brand is the Grand Seiko line, a group of watches that enjoys cult status among international collectors. Only recently did the Tokyo-based company offer a large collection to the global market. Today, there are several watches with the Spring Drive technology, but most new Grand Seikos (see page 166) are conventional mechanical hand-wound and automatic watches.

Classic Seikos are designed for tradition-conscious buyers. The Astron, however, with its automatic GPS-controlled time setting, suggests the watch of the future. In its second incarnation, the Astron is 30 percent more compact, and the energy required by the GPS system inside is supplied by a high-tech solar cell on the dial. As for the new Prospex collection, released for the fiftieth anniversary of the first Seiko diver's watches, it has an unmistakably modern look. The old protective case of the Marinemaster is now made of ceramic instead of plastic.

Seiko Holdings
Ginza, Chuo, Tokyo
Japan

Website:
www.seikowatches.com

Founded:
1881

U.S. distributor:
Seiko Corporation of America
1111 MacArthur Boulevard
Mahwah, NJ 07430
201-529-5730
custserv@seikousa.com
www.seikousa.com

Most important collections/price range:
Astron / approx. $1,850 to $3,400; Presage / approx. $425 to $4,500; Prospex / approx. $395 to $6,000

Prospex Automatic Hi-Beat 200m Diver's Limited Edition

Reference number: SLA037J1
Movement: automatic, Seiko Caliber 8L55; ø 28.4 mm, height 6 mm; 37 jewels; 36,000 vph; 55-hour power reserve
Functions: hours, minutes, sweep seconds; date
Case: stainless steel (with hard coating), ø 39.9 mm, height 14.7 mm; unidirectional bezel with 0-60 scale; sapphire crystal; screw-in crown; water-resistant to 20 atm
Band: silicone, buckle
Remarks: replica of the Prospex automatic diver's watch of 1965
Price: $6,300; limited to 1,100 pieces

Prospex Automatic Hi-Beat 300m Diver's Limited Edition

Reference number: SLA039J1
Movement: automatic, Seiko Caliber 8L55; ø 28.4 mm, height 6 mm; 37 jewels; 36,000 vph; 55-hour power reserve
Functions: hours, minutes, sweep seconds; date
Case: stainless steel, ø 44.8 mm, height 15.7 mm; unidirectional bezel with 0-60 scale; sapphire crystal; screw-in crown; water-resistant to 30 atm
Band: silicone, buckle
Remarks: replica of the Prospex automatic diver's watch of 1968
Price: $6,800; limited to 1,100 pieces

Prospex Automatic 200m Diver's

Reference number: SPB143J1
Movement: automatic, Seiko Caliber 6R35; ø 27.4 mm, height 4.95 mm; 24 jewels; 21,600 vph; 70-hour power reserve
Functions: hours, minutes, sweep seconds; date
Case: stainless steel (with hard coating), ø 40 mm, height 13 mm; unidirectional bezel with 0-60 scale; sapphire crystal; screw-in crown; water-resistant to 20 atm
Band: stainless steel, folding clasp, with safety catch and extension link (with hard coating)
Price: $1,200

Prospex Automatic "Save the Ocean" Special Edition

Reference number: SRPE07K1
Movement: automatic, Seiko Caliber 4R36; ø 27 mm, height 4.95 mm; 24 jewels; 21,600 vph; 41-hour power reserve
Functions: hours, minutes, sweep seconds; date, weekday
Case: stainless steel, ø 45 mm, height 13.2 mm; unidirectional bezel with 0-60 scale; sapphire crystal; screw-in crown; water-resistant to 20 atm
Band: silicone, buckle
Price: $595

Prospex Automatic "Alpinist"

Reference number: SPB121J1
Movement: automatic, Seiko Caliber 6R35; ø 27.4 mm, height 4.95 mm; 24 jewels; 21,600 vph; 70-hour power reserve
Functions: hours, minutes, sweep seconds; date
Case: stainless steel, ø 40 mm, height 12 mm; crown-activated inner bezel with 360° scale; sapphire crystal; transparent case back; screw-in crown; water-resistant to 20 atm
Band: calfskin, folding clasp
Price $725

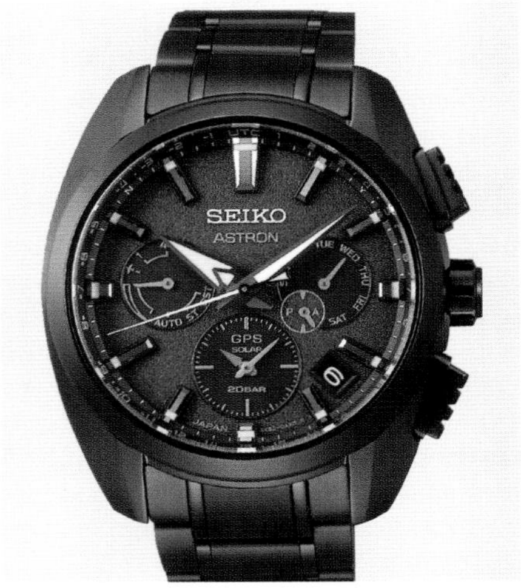

Astron GPS Solar Dual Time

Reference number: SSH069J1
Movement: quartz, Seiko Caliber 5X53; autonomous energy from solar cells on dial
Functions: hours, minutes, sweep seconds; additional 12-hour display (2nd time zone), world time function (39 time zones), flight mode, signal reception indication, daylight saving time indication; perpetual calendar, date, weekday
Case: titanium (with black hard coating), ø 41.4 mm, height 13.3 mm; sapphire crystal with superclear coating; water-resistant to 10 atm
Band: titanium with black hard coating, folding clasp
Price: $2,700

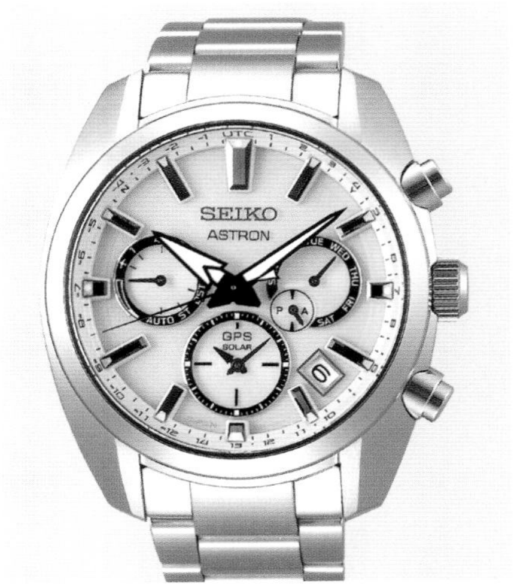

Astron GPS Solar Dual Time

Reference number: SSH047J1
Movement: quartz, Seiko Caliber 5X53; autonomous energy from solar cells on dial
Functions: hours, minutes, sweep seconds; additional 12-hour display (2nd time zone), world time function (39 time zones), flight mode, signal reception indication, daylight saving time indication; perpetual calendar, date, weekday
Case: stainless steel (with hard coating), ø 41.4 mm, height 13.3 mm; sapphire crystal with superclear coating; water-resistant to 10 atm
Band: stainless steel with hard coating, folding clasp
Price: $2,000

Presage Automatic Multifunction

Reference number: SPB161J1
Movement: automatic, Seiko Caliber 6R27; ø 27.4 mm, height 6 mm; 29 jewels; 28,800 vph; 45-hour power reserve
Functions: hours, minutes, sweep seconds; power reserve indicator; date
Case: stainless steel, ø 40 mm, height 13 mm; sapphire crystal; transparent case back; water-resistant to 10 atm
Band: horse leather, folding clasp
Remarks: enamel dial
Price: $1,300

Presage Automatic "Cocktail"

Reference number: SSA405J1
Movement: automatic, Seiko Caliber 4R38; ø 27 mm, height 4.95 mm; 24 jewels; 21,600 vph; 41-hour power reserve
Functions: hours, minutes, sweep seconds
Case: stainless steel, ø 41 mm, height 13 mm; acryl glass; transparent case back; water-resistant to 5 atm
Band: calfskin, folding clasp
Remarks: opening in dial and mainplate over the balance
Price: $475

SINN

Pilot and flight instructor Helmut Sinn began manufacturing watches in Frankfurt am Main because he thought the pilot's watches on the market were too expensive. The resulting combination of top quality, functionality, and a good price-performance ratio turned out to be an excellent sales argument. Sinn Spezialuhren zu Frankfurt am Main is a brand with origins in technology. There is hardly another source that offers watch lovers such a sophisticated and reasonable collection of sporty watches, many conceived to survive in extreme conditions by conforming to German DIN industrial norms.

In 1994, Lothar Schmidt took over the brand, and his product developers began looking for inspiration in other industries and the sciences. They did so out of a practical technical impulse without any plan for launching a trend. Research and development are consistently aimed at improving the functionality of the watches. This includes application of special Sinn technology such as moisture-proofing cases by pumping in an inert gas like argon. Other Sinn innovations include the Diapal (a lubricant-free lever escapement), the Hydro (an oil-filled diver's watch), and tegiment processing (for hardened steel and titanium surfaces). Having noticed a lack of norms for aviator watches, Schmidt negotiated a partnership with the Aachen Technical University to create the *Technischer Standard Fliegeruhren* (TESTAF, or Technical Standard for Pilot's Watches), which is housed at the Eurocopter headquarters.

Sinn recently joined forces with two German watch companies, the Sächsische Uhrentechnologie Glashütte (SUG) and the Uhren-Werke-Dresden (UWD). The latter produced the outstanding UWD 33.1 caliber with Sinn as chaperone. That movement was then used to drive the Meisterbund I, which translates as "master alliance."

All these moves have brought the company enough wherewithal to open new headquarters in the Sossenheim district of Frankfurt. The building offers nearly 25,000 square feet of space, most of which is devoted to assembly and manufacturing. At the heart of the two-story construction is a grandiose atrium with a skylight offering lots of natural light. The roof was also turned into an open-air terrace.

Sinn Spezialuhren GmbH
Wilhelm-Fay-Strasse 21
D-65936 Frankfurt/Main
Germany

Tel.:
+49-69-9784-14-200

E-mail:
info@sinn.de

Website:
www.sinn.de

Founded:
1961

Number of employees:
approx. 120

Annual production:
approx. 14,000 watches

U.S. distributor:
WatchBuys
888-333-4895
www.watchbuys.com

Most important collections/price range:
Financial District, U-Models, Diapal / from approx. $1,000 to $17,000

1739 St I S

Reference number: 1739.012
Movement: automatic, Sellita Caliber SW300-1; ø 25.6 mm, height 3.6 mm; 25 jewels; 28,800 vph; amagnetic according to German Industrial Norm (DIN); 42-hour power reserve
Functions: hours, minutes
Case: stainless steel, ø 39 mm, height 9.1 mm; sapphire crystal; transparent case back; water-resistant to 10 atm
Band: calfskin, buckle
Price: $2,170
Variations: silver-colored dial

206 St Ar

Reference number: 206.010
Movement: automatic, ETA Caliber 7750; ø 30 mm, height 7.9 mm; 25 jewels; 28,800 vph; amagnetic according to German Industrial Norm (DIN); 42-hour power reserve
Functions: hours, minutes, subsidiary seconds; chronograph; date, weekday
Case: stainless steel, ø 43 mm, height 17 mm; unidirectional bezel with 0-60 scale; sapphire crystal; transparent case back; water-resistant to 30 atm
Band: calfskin, buckle
Remarks: certified according to European diving norm, dehumidifying technology (protective gas)
Price: $3,930
Variations: stainless steel bracelet or silicone strap

EZM 12

Reference number: 112.010
Movement: automatic, ETA Caliber 2836-2; ø 25.6 mm, height 5.05 mm; 25 jewels; 28,800 vph; protected from magnetic fields up to 80,000 A/m; 38-hour power reserve; **Functions:** hours, minutes, sweep seconds; date, weekday
Case: tegimented stainless steel, black hard coating, ø 44 mm, height 14 mm; bidirectional bezel with 0-60 scale (counting downward); crown-activated inner ring with 0-60 scale (counting upward); sapphire crystal; water-resistant to 20 atm
Band: silicone, folding clasp with extension link
Remarks: developed for emergency medical professionals; comes with pocketknife; dehumidifying technology (protective gas)
Price: $3,780

EZM 10 TESTAF

Reference number: 950.011
Movement: automatic, Sinn Caliber SZ 01 (base ETA 7750); ø 30 mm, height 7.9 mm; 29 jewels; 28,800 vph; sweep minute counter, lubrication-free escapement (Diapal), shockproof and amagnetic
Functions: hours, minutes, subsidiary seconds; 2nd 24-hour display; chronograph; date
Case: tegimented titanium, ø 46.5 mm, height 15.6 mm; bidirectional bezel with 0-60 scale; sapphire crystal; screw-in crown; water-resistant to 20 atm; **Band:** calfskin, buckle
Remarks: certified according to Technical Standard for Pilot's Watches (TESTAF); dehumidifying technology (protective gas)
Price: $5,680; **Variations:** titanium bracelet ($5,910)

3006 Hunting Watch

Reference number: 3006.010
Movement: automatic, ETA Caliber 7751; ø 30 mm, height 7.9 mm; 25 jewels; 28,800 vph; shock-resistant and amagnetic according to German Industrial Norm (DIN); 42-hour power reserve
Functions: hours, minutes, subsidiary seconds; additional 24-hour display (2nd time zone); chronograph; date, weekday, month, moon phase
Case: tegimented stainless steel, ø 44 mm, height 15.5 mm; sapphire crystal; transparent case back; screw-in crown; water-resistant to 20 atm
Band: calfskin, buckle
Remarks: dehumidifying technology (special gas)
Price: $3,980; **Variations:** stainless steel bracelet ($4,340); silicone strap ($4,100)

936

Reference number: 936.010
Movement: automatic, Sinn Caliber SZ 05 (base ETA 7750); ø 30 mm, height 7.9 mm; 26 jewels; 28,800 vph; shock-resistant and amagnetic according to German Industrial Norm (DIN); magnetic protection to 80,000 A/m; 42-hour power reserve
Functions: hours, minutes, subsidiary seconds; chronograph; date
Case: tegimented stainless steel, ø 43 mm, height 15 mm; sapphire crystal; screw-in crown; water-resistant to 10 atm
Band: calfskin, buckle
Price: $3,390
Variations: stainless steel band ($3,690)

EZM 9 TESTAF

Reference number: 949.010
Movement: automatic, Sellita Caliber SW200-1; ø 25.6 mm, height 4.6 mm; 26 jewels; 28,800 vph; shock-resistant and amagnetic according to German Industrial Norm (DIN); 38-hour power reserve
Functions: hours, minutes, sweep seconds; date
Case: tegimented titanium, ø 44 mm, height 12 mm; bidirectional bezel, with 0-60 scale; sapphire crystal; screw-in crown; water-resistant to 20 atm; **Band:** tegimented titanium, folding clasp, with safety catch
Remarks: certified according to Technical Standard for Pilot's Watches (TESTAF); dehumidifying technology (protective gas)
Price: $3,940; **Variations:** leather strap ($3,620); silicone strap ($3,940)

T1

Reference number: 1014.010
Movement: automatic, ETA Caliber 2892-A2; ø 25.6 mm, height 3.6 mm; 21 jewels; 28,800 vph; shock-resistant and amagnetic according to German Industrial Norm (DIN); 42-hour power reserve
Functions: hours, minutes, sweep seconds; date
Case: titanium with perlage, ø 45 mm, height 12.5 mm; unidirectional bezel with 0-60 scale; sapphire crystal; screw-in crown; water-resistant to 100 atm
Band: titanium, folding clasp, with safety catch
Remarks: certified according to European diving norm, dehumidifying technology (protective gas)
Price: $3,440
Variations: silicone strap ($3,490)

U50

Reference number: 1050.010
Movement: automatic, Sellita Caliber SW300-1; ø 25.6 mm, height 3.6 mm; 25 jewels; 28,800 vph; shock-resistant and amagnetic according to German Industrial Norm (DIN); 42-hour power reserve
Functions: hours, minutes, sweep seconds; date
Case: stainless steel (submarine steel), ø 41 mm, height 11.15 mm; unidirectional bezel with 0-60 scale; sapphire crystal; screw-in crown; water-resistant to 50 atm; **Band:** silicone, folding clasp, with safety catch
Remarks: certified according to European diving norm
Price: $2,380; **Variations:** U50 SDR with blackened bezel on bracelet ($3,120); U50 S with blackened case ($2,980)

U212 EZM 16

Reference number: 212.040
Movement: automatic, Sellita Caliber SW300-1; ø 25.6 mm, height 3.6 mm; 25 jewels; 28,800 vph; shock-resistant and amagnetic according to German Industrial Norm (DIN); 42-hour power reserve
Functions: hours, minutes, sweep seconds; date
Case: stainless steel (submarine steel), ø 47 mm, height 14.5 mm; unidirectional bezel with 0-60 scale; sapphire crystal; screw-in crown; water-resistant to 100 atm; **Band:** silicone, folding clasp, with safety catch and extension link
Remarks: certified according to European diving norm, dehumidifying technology (protective gas)
Price: $2,920; **Variations:** stainless steel band ($2,970); textile strap

556 A RS

Reference number: 556.0141
Movement: automatic, Sellita Caliber SW200-1; ø 25.6 mm, height 4.6 mm; 26 jewels; 28,800 vph; amagnetic according to German Industrial Norm (DIN); 38-hour power reserve
Functions: hours, minutes, sweep seconds; date
Case: stainless steel, ø 41 mm, height 11 mm; sapphire crystal; transparent case back; screw-in crown; water-resistant to 20 atm
Band: stainless steel, folding clasp, with safety catch
Price: $1,510
Variations: Index-dial ($1,690)

836

Reference number: 836.010
Movement: automatic, ETA Caliber 2892-A2; ø 25.6 mm, height 3.6 mm; 21 jewels; 28,800 vph; amagnetic according to German Industrial Norm (DIN), magnetic protection up to 80,000 A/m; 42-hour power reserve
Functions: hours, minutes, sweep seconds; date
Case: tegimented stainless steel, ø 43 mm, height 10.6 mm; sapphire crystal; screw-in crown; water-resistant to 10 atm
Band: calfskin, buckle
Price: $1,980
Variations: stainless steel band ($2,280)

104 St Sa I W

Reference number: 104.012
Movement: automatic, Sellita Caliber SW220-1; ø 25.6 mm, height 5.05 mm; 26 jewels; 28,800 vph; amagnetic according to German Industrial Norm (DIN); 38-hour power reserve
Functions: hours, minutes, sweep seconds; date, weekday
Case: stainless steel, ø 41 mm, height 11.5 mm; bidirectional bezel, with 0-60 scale; sapphire crystal; transparent case back; screw-in crown; water-resistant to 20 atm
Band: calfskin, buckle
Price: $1,440
Variations: blue or black dial ($1,440)

144 St Diapal

Reference number: 144.068
Movement: automatic, modified ETA Caliber 7750; ø 30 mm, height 8.4 mm; 25 jewels; 28,800 vph; lubricant-free mechanism (Diapal), amagnetic according to German Industrial Norm (DIN); 46-hour power reserve; **Functions:** hours, minutes, subsidiary seconds; with additional 12-hour display (2nd time zone); chronograph; date
Case: stainless steel, ø 41 mm, height 14.5 mm; sapphire crystal; transparent case back; water-resistant to 20 atm
Band: stainless steel, folding clasp, with safety catch
Remarks: dehumidifying technology (protective gas)
Price: $2,490
Variations: without Diapal technology ($2,490)

356 Sa Flieger III

Reference number: 356.072
Movement: automatic, modified Sellita Caliber SW500; ø 30.4 mm, height 7.9 mm; 26 jewels; 28,800 vph; shock-resistant and amagnetic according to German Industrial Norm (DIN); 42-hour power reserve
Functions: hours, minutes, subsidiary seconds; chronograph; date, weekday
Case: stainless steel, ø 38.5 mm, height 15 mm; sapphire crystal; transparent case back; screw-in crown; water-resistant to 10 atm
Band: calfskin, buckle
Price: $2,320
Variations: with acryl glass ($1,990); black dial ($2,320); copper-colored dial ($2,680)

Speake-Marin
Avenue de Miremont 33C
1206 Geneva
Switzerland

Tel.:
+41-21-695-26-55

E-mail:
info@speake-marin.com

Website:
www.speake-marin.com

Founded:
2002

Number of employees:
9

Annual production:
400 watches

U.S. Sales
Watches of Switzerland
844-4-USAWOS (844-487-2967)
jkloiber@battalionpr.com

Most important collections:
One & Two, Art Series, Vintage, Haute Horlogerie

SPEAKE-MARIN

So many brands these days bear the name of great watchmakers from the distant past. Speake-Marin is an exception. Peter Speake-Marin is very much alive, but is no longer connected with his company, other than through his name and style.

He hails from Essex, England, and learned the trade at Hackney College and the famous WOSTEP. He restored antique watches at Somlo's in Piccadilly and then, in 1996, moved to Le Locle, Switzerland, to work with Renaud et Papi, when he also set about making his own pieces. A dual-train tourbillon (the Foundation Watch) opened the door to the prestigious AHCI.

His watches always feel connected to the industry's traditions. The topping tool logo suggests the expert handicraft that goes into making a watch, rather than hyper-modern CNC machines. He has also had his skilled fingers in a number of iconic timepieces, like the HM1 of MB&F, the Chapter One for Maîtres du Temps, and the Harry Winston Excenter Tourbillon.

And then, in 2017, he decided to leave the brand he had given birth to and shaped for sixteen years. In a brief letter, then new CEO, Christelle Rosnoblet, promised to maintain the brand's characteristic "British elegance and impertinence." What the "new" Speake-Marin has produced is very high-end, notably the double tourbillon with a special mechanism to regulate and harmonize the rate of the two tourbillons. Longtime Speake-Marin fans might recognize the boldness in the technical concepts, but they will also recognize the conical crown and the famous Piccadilly case, now remodeled. It reappears in the Academic line and in the new London Chronograph Triple Date. The latter runs on an iconic Valjoux 88 caliber from the 1950s, a fine movement that can be seen through the transparent case back.

London Chronograph Triple Date

Reference number: 514208050
Movement: manually wound, Valjoux 88 Caliber; ø 29.5 mm, height 7.2 mm; 33 jewels; 18,000 vph; 44-hour power reserve
Functions: hours, minutes, subsidiary seconds; chronograph; sweep date, weekday, month; moon phase
Case: titanium, ø 42 mm, height 15 mm; sapphire crystal; water-resistant to 3 atm
Remarks: in the traditional Piccadilly case from the early Speake-Marin years
Band: calfskin, folding clasp
Price: $24,000; limited to 15 pieces
Variations: blue dial

One & Two Academic Metallic Blue

Reference number: 414212010
Movement: automatic, SMA03 Caliber; ø 32 mm, height 4.2 mm; 31 jewels; 28,800 vph; microrotor bridges with côtes de Genève; 50-hour power reserve
Functions: hours, minutes, subsidiary seconds
Case: titanium, ø 42 mm, height 10.5 mm; sapphire crystal; water-resistant to 3 atm
Band: reptile skin, folding clasp
Price: $13,500; limited to 16 pieces
Variations: silvery-white dial ($13,500, limited to 26 pieces); with 38-mm case ($12,900, limited to 38 pieces)

Double-Tourbillon Openworked

Reference number: 934681150
Movement: automatic, SMA-HH06 Caliber; ø 38.4 mm, height 8.75 mm; 56 jewels; 21,600 vph; two 1-minute tourbillons, patented rate equalizer for the two regulators; double barrel springs; open-worked dial, 72-hour power reserve
Functions: hours, minutes, subsidiary seconds
Case: white gold, ø 46 mm, height 10.5 mm; sapphire crystal; water-resistant to 3 atm
Band: reptile skin, buckle
Price: $305,000; unique piece

STOWA

Stowa GmbH & Co. KG
Gewerbepark 16
D-75331 Engelsbrand
Germany

Tel.:
+49-7082-942630

E-mail:
info@stowa.com

Website:
www.stowa.de

Founded:
1927

Number of employees:
20

Annual production:
around 4,500 watches

Distribution:
Direct sales; please contact company in Germany; orders taken by phone Monday through Friday 9 a.m. to 5 p.m. European time. Note: Prices are determined according to daily exchange rate.

When a watch brand organizes a museum for itself, it is usually with good reason. The firm Stowa may not be the biggest fish in the horological pond, but it has been around for more than eighty years, and its products are well worth taking a look at as expressions of German watchmaking culture. Stowa began in Pforzheim, then moved to the little industrial town of Rheinfelden, and now operates in Engelsbrand, a "suburb" of Pforzheim. After a history as a family-owned company, today the brand is headed by Jörg Schauer, who has maintained the goal and vision of original founder Walter Storz: delivering quality watches at a reasonable price.

Stowa is one of the few German brands to have operated without interruption since the start of the twentieth century, albeit with a new owner as of 1990. Besides all the political upheavals, it survived the quartz crisis of the 1970s, during which Europe was flooded with cheap watches from Asia and many traditional German watchmakers were put out of business. Storz managed to keep Stowa going, but even a quality fanatic has to pay a price during times of trouble: With huge input from his son, Werner, Storz restructured the company so that it was able to begin encasing reasonably priced quartz movements rather than being strictly an assembler of mechanical ones.

Schauer bought the brand in 1996. Spurred on by the success of his own eponymous line, he also steered Stowa back toward mechanical watches, taking inspiration from older Stowa timepieces but using Swiss ETA movements. Retro can be a trap out of which some brands fail to escape, but thanks to a clever collaboration with designer Hartmut Esslinger, the watches produced by this unusual brand always manage to have a modern, contemporary touch, albeit not "in your face." This applies equally to the line of Flieger (pilot) watches.

Flieger Bronze Vintage

Reference number: FliegerBronzeVintage
Movement: manually wound, ETA Caliber 2804-2; ø 25.6 mm, height 3.35 mm; 17 jewels; 28,800 vph; 42-hour power reserve
Functions: hours, minutes, sweep seconds
Case: bronze, ø 40 mm, height 9.2 mm; sapphire crystal; water-resistant to 5 atm
Band: calfskin, buckle
Price: $1,450

Marine Original

Reference number: MarineOriginalpolweissarabisch
Movement: manually wound, ETA Caliber 6498-1; ø 36.6 mm, height 4.5 mm; 17 jewels; 18,000 vph; screw balance, swan-neck fine adjustment, côtes de Genève, blued screws; 46-hour power reserve
Functions: hours, minutes, subsidiary seconds
Case: stainless steel, ø 41 mm, height 12 mm; sapphire crystal; transparent case back; water-resistant to 5 atm
Band: calfskin, buckle
Price: $1,505
Variations: silver dial ($1,669)

Chronograph 1938 Black

Reference number: chronograph1938schwarz
Movement: automatic, ETA Caliber 7753; ø 30 mm, height 7.9 mm; 27 jewels; 28,800 vph; 48-hour power reserve
Functions: hours, minutes, subsidiary seconds; chronograph
Case: stainless steel, ø 41 mm, height 13.7 mm; sapphire crystal; transparent case back; water-resistant to 5 atm
Band: calfskin, buckle
Price: $2,171
Variations: manually wound movement ($2,498)

TAG Heuer
Branch of LVMH SA
6a, rue L.-J.-Chevrolet
CH-2300 La Chaux-de-Fonds
Switzerland

Tel.:
+41-32-919-8164

E-mail:
info@tagheuer.com

Website:
www.tagheuer.com

Founded:
1860

Number of employees:
1,600 employees internationally

U.S. distributor:
TAG Heuer/LVMH Watch & Jewelry USA
966 South Springfield Avenue
Springfield, NJ 07081
973-467-1890

Most important collections/price range:
TAG Heuer Formula 1, Aquaracer, Link, Carrera, Connected, Monaco, Heritage / from approx. $1,300 to $20,000

TAG HEUER

Measuring speed accurately in ever greater detail was always the goal of TAG Heuer, a company founded in 1860 in St. Imier, Switzerland, by Edouard Heuer. With this in mind, the brand strove for a number of technical milestones, including the first automatic chronograph caliber with a microrotor, created in 1969 with Hamilton-Büren, Breitling, and Dubois Dépraz. That was before Techniques d'Avant Garde (TAG), a high-tech firm, bought the company.

In 1999, TAG Heuer became part of LVMH Group and in addition to producing its own watches also, later, served as an extended workbench for companion brands Zenith and Hublot.

TAG Heuer has continued to break world speed records for mechanical escapements. The Caliber 360 combined a standard movement with a 360,000-vph (50-Hz) chronograph mechanism able to measure hundredths of a second. In 2011, the Mikrograph 1/100th brought time display and measurement on a single plate. Shortly after, the Mikrotimer Flying 1000 broke the thousandth-of-a-second barrier. A year later, the Mikrogirder 2000 doubled the frequency using a vibrating metal strip instead of a balance wheel. The MikrotourbillonS features a separate chronograph escapement driven at a record-breaking 360,000 vph.

Under the new LVMH coordinator, Jean-Claude Biver of Hublot fame, the company decided to cut back on the top end of the pricing scale. CEO Guy Sémon, a scientist with a PhD in physics, heads the company's Research Institute. He has experimented with electromagnetic, hairspring-less pendulum watches and new materials, like graphene, a synthetic material that does not need to be processed as a blank but can be easily shaped right from the drawing board. And true to its tradition of innovation, TAG Heuer has also become one of the leaders in connected watches that embody the company's competence in mechanical watchmaking with the latest communication technologies.

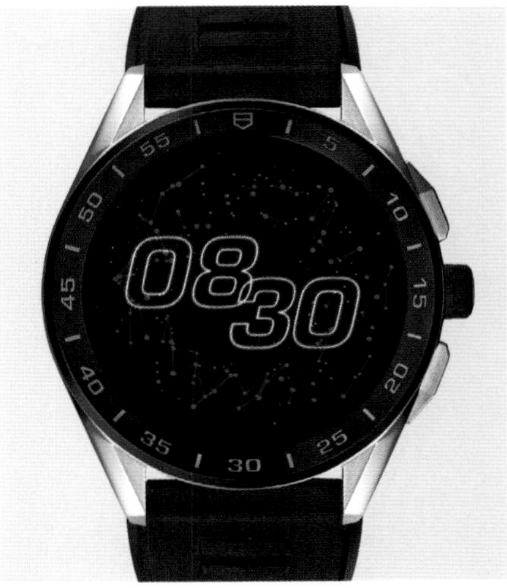

Connected

Reference number: SBG8A10.BT6219
Movement: quartz; Qualcomm Snapdragon Wear 3100 processor; smartwatch with wear operating system from Google; 430-mAh lithium-ion battery
Functions: hours, minutes, seconds (digital); sensors for pulse, compass, speed; near-field communication (NFC), microphone; various installable micro-apps
Case: stainless steel, ø 45 mm; bezel with ceramic insert; sapphire crystal; water-resistant to 5 atm
Band: rubber, folding clasp
Price: $2,600

Formula 1 Calibre 6

Reference number: WAZ2012.BA0842
Movement: automatic, TAG Heuer Caliber 6 (base SW260-1); ø 25.6 mm, height 4.35 mm; 27 jewels; 28,800 vph; 42-hour power reserve
Functions: hours, minutes, subsidiary seconds; date
Case: stainless steel, ø 43 mm, height 12 mm; unidirectional bezel with 0-60 scale; sapphire crystal; water-resistant to 20 atm
Band: stainless steel, folding clasp
Price: $1,800
Variations: white or blue dial

Formula 1 Calibre 16

Reference number: CAZ2010.BA0876
Movement: automatic, TAG Heuer Caliber 16 (base ETA 7750); ø 30.4 mm, height 7.9 mm; 25 jewels; 28,800 vph
Functions: hours, minutes, subsidiary seconds; chronograph; date
Case: stainless steel, ø 44 mm, height 15 mm; sapphire crystal; screw-in crown; water-resistant to 20 atm
Band: stainless steel, folding clasp
Price: $2,850

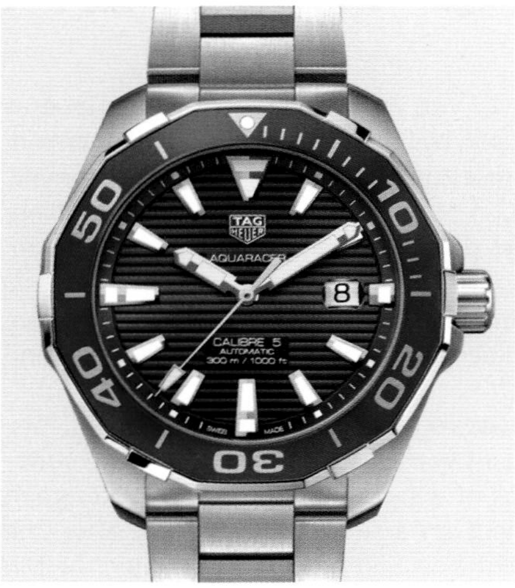

Aquaracer 300M Calibre 5

Reference number: WAY201S.BA0927
Movement: automatic, TAG Heuer Caliber 5 (base ETA 2824-2); ø 26 mm, height 4.6 mm; 25 jewels; 28,800 vph
Functions: hours, minutes, sweep seconds; date
Case: stainless steel, ø 43 mm; unidirectional bezel with 0-60 scale; sapphire crystal; screw-in crown; water-resistant to 30 atm
Band: stainless steel, folding clasp
Price: $2,750

Aquaracer 300M Calibre 5

Reference number: WAY201A.BA0927
Movement: automatic, TAG Heuer Caliber 5 (base ETA 2824-2); ø 26 mm, height 4.6 mm; 25 jewels; 28,800 vph
Functions: hours, minutes, sweep seconds; date
Case: stainless steel, ø 43 mm; unidirectional bezel with 0-60 scale; sapphire crystal; screw-in crown; water-resistant to 30 atm
Band: stainless steel, folding clasp, with safety lock and extension link
Price: $2,750

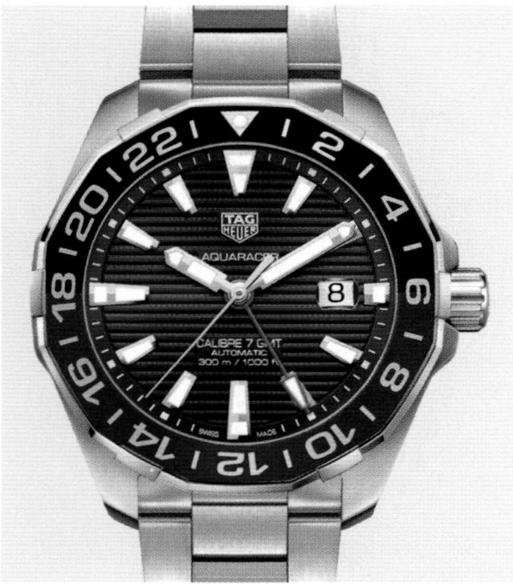

Aquaracer 300M Calibre 7 GMT

Reference number: WAY201T.BA0927
Movement: automatic, TAG Heuer Caliber 7 (base ETA 2893-2); ø 26 mm, height 4.1 mm; 21 jewels; 28,800 vph; 42-hour power reserve
Functions: hours, minutes, sweep seconds; additional 24-hour display (2nd time zone); date
Case: stainless steel, ø 43 mm; bidirectional bezel with aluminum insert, with 0-24 scale; sapphire crystal; screw-in crown; water-resistant to 30 atm
Band: stainless steel, folding clasp, with safety lock and extension link
Price: $3,050

Link Calibre 5

Reference number: WBC2110.BA0603
Movement: automatic, TAG Heuer Caliber 5 (base ETA 2824-2); ø 26 mm, height 4.6 mm; 25 jewels; 28,800 vph
Functions: hours, minutes, sweep seconds; date
Case: stainless steel, ø 41 mm; sapphire crystal; water-resistant to 10 atm
Band: stainless steel, folding clasp
Price: $2,900
Variations: white dial

Link Calibre 17

Reference number: CBC2110.BA0603
Movement: automatic, TAG Heuer Caliber 17 (base ETA 2894-2); ø 28.6 mm, height 6.1 mm; 37 jewels; 28,800 vph; 42-hour power reserve
Functions: hours, minutes, subsidiary seconds; chronograph; date
Case: stainless steel, ø 41 mm; sapphire crystal; transparent case back; water-resistant to 10 atm
Band: stainless steel, folding clasp
Price: $4,500
Variations: blue dial

TAG Heuer Carrera Calibre 5

Reference number: WAR211A.BA0782
Movement: automatic, TAG Heuer Caliber 5 (base ETA 2824-2); ø 26 mm, height 4.6 mm; 25 jewels; 28,800 vph
Functions: hours, minutes, sweep seconds; date
Case: stainless steel, ø 39 mm, height 12 mm; sapphire crystal; transparent case back; water-resistant to 10 atm
Band: stainless steel, folding clasp
Price: $2,550
Variations: various dial colors; reptile skin strap ($2,550)

TAG Heuer Carrera Calibre 5 Day-Date

Reference number: WAR201E.FC6292
Movement: automatic, TAG Heuer Caliber 5 (base ETA 2836-2); ø 26 mm, height 5.05 mm; 25 jewels; 28,800 vph
Functions: hours, minutes, sweep seconds; date, weekday
Case: stainless steel, ø 41 mm, height 13 mm; sapphire crystal; transparent case back; water-resistant to 10 atm
Band: reptile skin, folding clasp
Price: $2,800
Variations: various dials; stainless steel band ($2,800)

TAG Heuer Carrera Calibre 16

Reference number: CBM2110.BA0651
Movement: automatic, TAG Heuer Caliber 16 (base ETA 7750); ø 30.4 mm, height 7.9 mm; 25 jewels; 28,800 vph
Functions: hours, minutes, subsidiary seconds; chronograph; date
Case: stainless steel, ø 41 mm; ceramic bezel; sapphire crystal; screw-in crown; water-resistant to 10 atm
Band: stainless steel, folding clasp
Price: $4,600

TAG Heuer Carrera Calibre Heuer 02

Reference number: CBG2A10.FT6168
Movement: automatic, TAG Heuer Caliber Heuer 02; ø 31 mm, height 6.9 mm; 33 jewels; 28,800 vph; 80-hour power reserve
Functions: hours, minutes, subsidiary seconds; chronograph; date
Case: stainless steel, ø 45 mm; ceramic bezel; sapphire crystal; transparent case back; water-resistant to 10 atm
Band: rubber, folding clasp
Price: $5,900

TAG Heuer Carrera Calibre Heuer 02

Reference number: CBG2A90.BH0653
Movement: automatic, TAG Heuer Caliber Heuer 02; ø 31 mm, height 6.9 mm; 33 jewels; 28,800 vph; 80-hour power reserve
Functions: hours, minutes, subsidiary seconds; chronograph; date
Case: ceramic, ø 45 mm; sapphire crystal; transparent case back; water-resistant to 10 atm
Band: ceramic, double folding clasp
Price: $6,950

Carrera Calibre Heuer 02 GMT

Reference number: CBG2A1Z.BA0658
Movement: automatic, TAG Heuer Caliber Heuer 02; ø 31 mm, height 6.9 mm; 33 jewels; 28,800 vph; 80-hour power reserve
Functions: hours, minutes, subsidiary seconds; additional 24-hour display (2nd time zone); chronograph; date
Case: stainless steel, ø 45 mm; bezel with ceramic insert; sapphire crystal; transparent case back; water-resistant to 10 atm
Band: stainless steel, folding clasp
Price: $6,550
Variations: rubber strap ($5,900)

Carrera Calibre Heuer 02 Tourbillon C.O.S.C. Black Titanium

Reference number: CAR5A8Y.FC6377
Movement: automatic, TAG Heuer Caliber Heuer 02 T; ø 31 mm, height 6.9 mm; 33 jewels; 28,800 vph; 1-minute tourbillon; COSC-certified chronometer
Functions: hours, minutes; chronograph
Case: titanium with black titanium carbide coating, ø 45 mm; sapphire crystal; water-resistant to 10 atm
Band: reptile skin, folding clasp
Price: $17,300

Monaco Calibre 11

Reference number: CAW211P.FC6356
Movement: automatic, TAG Heuer Caliber 11 (base Sellita SW300 with Module 2006 from Dubois Dépraz); ø 30 mm, height 7.3 mm; 59 jewels; 28,800 vph
Functions: hours, minutes, subsidiary seconds; chronograph; date
Case: stainless steel, 39 × 39 mm, height 14.5 mm; sapphire crystal; transparent case back; water-resistant to 10 atm
Band: calfskin, folding clasp
Price: $6,350

Monaco Calibre 11 Special Edition Gulf

Reference number: CAW211R.FC6401
Movement: automatic, TAG Heuer Caliber 11 (base Sellita SW300 with Module 2006 from Dubois Dépraz); ø 30 mm, height 7.3 mm; 59 jewels; 28,800 vph
Functions: hours, minutes, subsidiary seconds; chronograph; date
Case: stainless steel, 39 × 39 mm, height 14.5 mm; sapphire crystal; transparent case back; water-resistant to 10 atm
Band: calfskin, folding clasp
Price: $6,550

Monaco Calibre Heuer 02

Reference number: CBL2111.FC6453
Movement: automatic, TAG Heuer Caliber Heuer 02; ø 31 mm, height 6.9 mm; 33 jewels; 28,800 vph; 80-hour power reserve
Functions: hours, minutes, subsidiary seconds; chronograph; date
Case: stainless steel, 39 × 39 mm, height 14.5 mm; sapphire crystal; water-resistant to 10 atm
Band: reptile skin, folding clasp
Price: $6,350

Monaco Calibre Heuer 02 Limited Edition Grand Prix de Monaco Historique

Reference number: CBL2114.FC6486
Movement: automatic, TAG Heuer Caliber Heuer 02; ø 31 mm, height 6.9 mm; 33 jewels; 28,800 vph; 80-hour power reserve
Functions: hours, minutes, subsidiary seconds; chronograph; date
Case: stainless steel, 39 × 39 mm, height 14.5 mm; sapphire crystal; water-resistant to 10 atm
Band: calfskin, folding clasp
Price: $7,050; limited to 1,000 pieces

Heuer Autavia Calibre 5 C.O.S.C.

Reference number: WBE5116.EB0173
Movement: automatic, TAG Heuer Caliber 5 (base ETA 2824-2); ø 26 mm, height 4.6 mm; 25 jewels; 28,800 vph; COSC-certified chronometer
Functions: hours, minutes, sweep seconds; date
Case: stainless steel, ø 42 mm; bidirectional ceramic bezel with 0-60 scale; sapphire crystal; water-resistant to 10 atm
Band: stainless steel, folding clasp
Price: $3,350

Autavia Calibre 5 C.O.S.C.

Reference number: WBE5190.FC8268
Movement: automatic, TAG Heuer Caliber 5 (base ETA 2824-2); ø 26 mm, height 4.6 mm; 25 jewels; 28,800 vph; COSC-certified chronometer
Functions: hours, minutes, sweep seconds; date
Case: bronze, ø 42 mm; bidirectional ceramic bezel with 0-60 scale; sapphire crystal; water-resistant to 10 atm
Band: calfskin, buckle
Price: $3,850

Temption GmbH
Raistinger Str. 46
D-71083 Herrenberg
Germany

Tel.:
+49-7032-977-954

E-mail:
ftemption@aol.com

Website:
www.temption.info

Founded:
1997

Number of employees:
4

Annual production:
700 watches

U.S. distributor:
Debby Gordon
3306 Arrow Creek Dr.
Granbury, TX 76049
debby@temptionusa.com
Toll-free number: 1-888-400-4293

Most important collections/price range:
automatics (three-hand), GMT, chronographs, and chronographs with complications / approx. $1,900 to $4,200

TEMPTION

Temption has been operating under the leadership of Klaus Ulbrich since 1997. Ulbrich is an engineer with special training in the construction of watches and movements, and right from the start, he intended to develop timekeepers that were modern in their esthetics but not subject to the whims of zeitgeist. Retro watches would have no place in his collections. The design behind all Temption models is inspired more by the Bauhaus or the Japanese concept of wabi sabi. Reduction to what is absolutely necessary is the golden rule here. Beauty emerges from clarity, or in other words, less is more.

Ulbrich sketches all the watches himself. Some of the components are even made in-house, but all the pieces are assembled in the company facility in Herrenberg, a town just to the east of the Black Forest. The primary functions are always easy to read, even in low light. The company logo is discreetly included on the dial.

Ulbrich works according to a model he calls the "information pyramid." Hours and minutes are at the tip, with all other functions subordinated. To maintain this hierarchy, the dials are dark, the date windows are in the same hue, and all subdials are not framed in any way. The most unimportant information for reading time comes at the end of the "pyramid"; it is shiny black on black: the logo, which can only be identified in lateral light.

The Cameo rectangular model is a perfect example of Ulbrich's esthetic concept and his consistent technological approach: Because rectangular sapphire crystals can hardly be made water-resistant, the Cameo's crystal is chemically bonded to the case and water-resistant to 10 atm. The frame for the sapphire was metalized inside to hide the bonded edge. The overall look is one of stunning simplicity and elegance. With the CGK205 chronograph, Ulbrich took the concept out of the case. Whether it be the leather strap or the stainless steel bracelet, the watch's attachment is seamlessly integrated into the case, without any visible split.

Chronograph Classic "Curare"

Reference number: CLV2316WCSST
Movement: automatic, Caliber T17.1 (base ETA 7750); ø 30 mm, height 7.8 mm; 25 jewels; 28,800 vph; finely finished movement; 42-hour power reserve
Functions: hours, minutes, subsidiary seconds; chronograph; date, weekday
Case: stainless steel with black PVD, ø 43 mm, height 14.8 mm; sapphire crystal; transparent case back; screw-in crown and pushers, with amber cabochons; water-resistant to 10 atm
Band: calfskin, folding clasp
Price: $2,900
Variations: rubber strap

Chronograph CGK205-V2

Reference number: 205V2316BSST
Movement: automatic, Caliber T18.1 (base ETA 7751); ø 30 mm, height 7.8 mm; 25 jewels; 28,800 vph; finely finished movement; 42-hour power reserve
Functions: hours, minutes, subsidiary seconds; additional 24-hour display; chronograph; full calendar with date, weekday, month, moon phase
Case: stainless steel, ø 43 mm, height 14 mm; sapphire crystal; transparent case back; screw-in crown and pushers, with onyx cabochons; water-resistant to 10 atm
Band: stainless steel, folding clasp
Remarks: comes with additional calfskin strap
Price: $3,475

Cameo-S

Reference number: CAMSIBFS151
Movement: automatic, Caliber T15.1 (base Soprod A10); ø 25.6 mm, height 3.6 mm; 21 jewels; 28,800 vph; finely finished movement; 42-hour power reserve
Functions: hours, minutes, sweep seconds; date
Case: stainless steel, 37 × 41 mm, height 9.9 mm; sapphire crystal; transparent case back; screw-in crown; water-resistant to 10 atm
Band: calfskin, double folding clasp
Price: $1,775

TISSOT

Tissot SA
Chemin des Tourelles, 17
CH-2400 Le Locle
Switzerland

Tel.:
+41-32-933-3111

E-mail:
info@tissot.ch

Website:
www.tissotwatches.com

Founded:
1853

U.S. distributor:
Tissot
The Swatch Group (U.S.), Inc.
703 Waterford Way
Suite 450
Miami, FL 33126
www.tissotwatches.com/en-us

Most important collections/price range:
Ballade / from $925; T-Touch / from $850; NBA Collection / from $375; Chemin des Tourelles / from $795; Seastar from $495; Swissmatic from $395

The Swiss watchmaker Tissot was founded in 1853 in the town of Le Locle in the Jura mountains. In the century that followed, it gained international recognition for its Savonnette pocket watch. And even when the wristwatch became popular in the early twentieth century, time and again Tissot managed to attract attention to its products. To this day, the Banana Watch of 1916 and its first watches in the art deco style (1919) remain design icons of that epoch. The watchmaker has always been at the top of its technical game as well: The first amagnetic watch (1930), the first mechanical plastic watch (Astrolon, 1971), and its touch-screen T-Touch (1999) all bear witness to Tissot's remarkable capacity for finding unusual and modern solutions.

Today, Tissot belongs to the Swatch Group and, with its wide selection of quartz and inexpensive mechanical watches, serves as the group's entry-level brand. Within this price segment, Tissot offers something special for the buyer who values traditional watchmaking but is not of limitless financial means. The brand has been cultivating a sportive image of late, expanding into everything from basketball to superbike racing, from ice hockey to fencing—and water sports, of course. Partnerships with several NBA teams have been signed, notably with the Houston Rockets, Chicago Bulls, and Washington Wizards in October 2018. The chronograph Couturier line is outfitted with the new ETA chronograph caliber C01.211. This caliber features a number of plastic parts: another step in simplifying, and lowering the cost of, mechanical movements.

Increasingly, in addition, a number of Tissot models are being equipped with the automatic caliber Powermatic 80, which boasts a silicon hairspring, which has outstanding isochronous oscillation and is impervious to magnetic fields and changes in temperature. And for the buyer, it means only a slight increase in price.

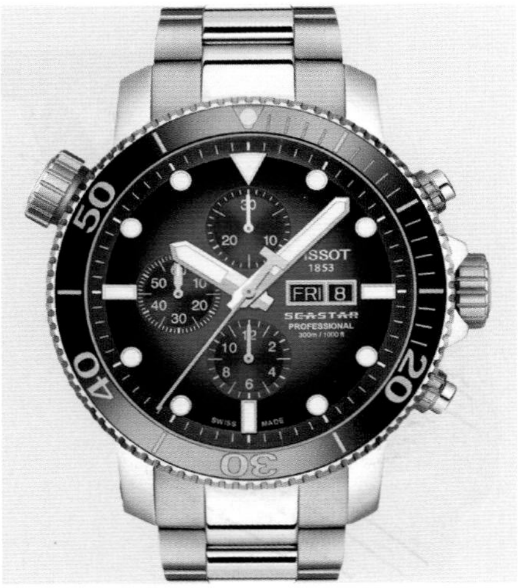

Seastar 1000 Professional

Reference number: T120.614.11.041.00
Movement: automatic, ETA Caliber A05.H21; ø 30 mm, height 7.9 mm; 25 jewels; 28,800 vph; 60-hour power reserve
Functions: hours, minutes, subsidiary seconds; chronograph; date, weekday
Case: stainless steel, ø 48 mm, height 17.9 mm; unidirectional bezel with ceramic insert, with 0-60 scale; sapphire crystal; transparent case back, helium valve; water-resistant to 30 atm
Band: stainless steel, folding clasp, with safety lock
Price: $2,200; limited to 1,000 pieces

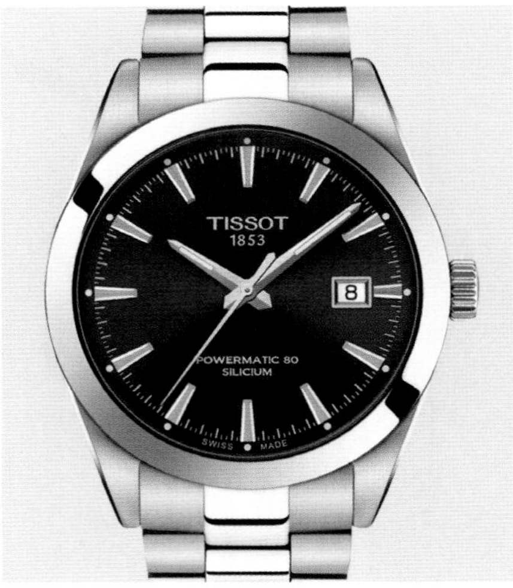

Gentleman Powermatic 80 Silicium

Reference number: T127.407.11.041.00
Movement: automatic, ETA Caliber Powermatic 80 Silicium (base ETA 2824-2); ø 25.6 mm, height 4.74 mm; 25 jewels; 21,600 vph; silicon hairspring; 80-hour power reserve
Functions: hours, minutes, sweep seconds; date
Case: stainless steel, ø 40 mm, height 11.5 mm; sapphire crystal; transparent case back; water-resistant to 10 atm
Band: stainless steel, folding clasp
Price:$775

Supersport Chrono

Reference number: T125.617.16.041.00
Movement: quartz, ETA Caliber G10.212 Powerdrive
Functions: hours, minutes, subsidiary seconds; chronograph; date
Case: stainless steel, ø 45.5 mm, height 11.92 mm; sapphire crystal; water-resistant to 10 atm
Band: calfskin, buckle
Price: $400

Seastar 1000 Powermatic 80

Reference number: T120.407.11.091.00
Movement: automatic, ETA Caliber Powermatic 80 (base ETA 2824-2); ø 25.6 mm, height 4.6 mm; 23 jewels; 21,600 vph; 80-hour power reserve
Functions: hours, minutes, sweep seconds; date
Case: stainless steel, ø 43 mm, height 12.7 mm; unidirectional bezel with ceramic insert, with 0-60 scale; sapphire crystal; transparent case back; water-resistant to 30 atm
Band: stainless steel Milanese mesh, folding clasp
Price: $725

PRC 200 Chronograph

Reference number: T114.417.17.037.02
Movement: quartz, ETA Caliber G10.212 Powerdrive
Functions: hours, minutes, subsidiary seconds; chronograph; date
Case: stainless steel, ø 43 mm, height 12.02 mm; sapphire crystal; water-resistant to 20 atm
Band: rubber, buckle
Price: $425

Race MotoGP 2020 Automatic Chronograph

Reference number: T115.427.27.057.00
Movement: automatic, ETA Caliber C01.211 (base ETA 7750); ø 31 mm, height 8.44 mm; 15 jewels; 21,600 vph; 46-hour power reserve
Functions: hours, minutes, subsidiary seconds; chronograph; date
Case: stainless steel, ø 45 mm, height 16.58 mm; sapphire crystal; transparent case back; water-resistant to 10 atm
Band: calfskin with rubber filling, buckle
Price: $1,295; limited to 3,333 pieces

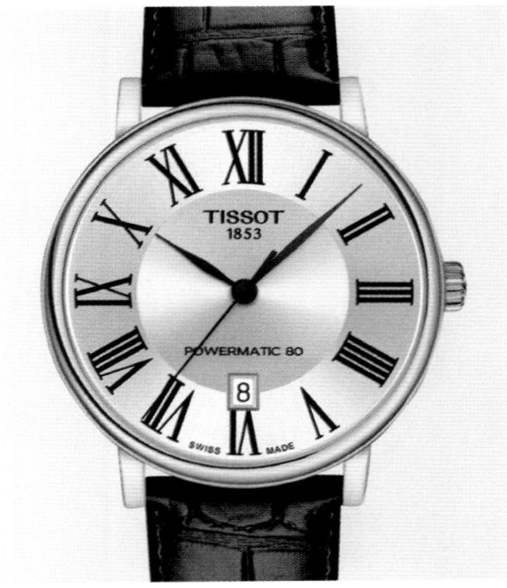

Carson Premium Powermatic 80

Reference number: T122.407.36.033.00
Movement: automatic, ETA Caliber Powermatic 80 (base ETA 2824-2); ø 25.6 mm, height 4.6 mm; 23 jewels; 21,600 vph; 80-hour power reserve
Functions: hours, minutes, sweep seconds; date
Case: stainless steel with rose gold PVD, ø 40 mm, height 10.25 mm; sapphire crystal; transparent case back; water-resistant to 5 atm
Band: calfskin, buckle
Price: $695

Le Locle Automatique Small Second

Reference number: T006.428.22.032.00
Movement: automatic, ETA Caliber 2825-2; ø 25.6 mm, height 6.6 mm; 25 jewels; 28,800 vph; 42-hour power reserve
Functions: hours, minutes, subsidiary seconds; date
Case: stainless steel, ø 39.3 mm, height 11.55 mm; bezel and crown with yellow gold PVD; sapphire crystal; transparent case back; water-resistant to 3 atm
Band: stainless steel, folding clasp
Price: $725

Heritage Porto Mechanical

Reference number: T128.505.16.012.00
Movement: manually wound, ETA Caliber 7001; ø 23.3 mm, height 2.5 mm; 17 jewels; 21,600 vph; 45-hour power reserve
Functions: hours, minutes, subsidiary seconds
Case: stainless steel, 31.1 × 42.45 mm, height 10.47 mm; sapphire crystal; water-resistant to 3 atm
Band: calfskin, folding clasp
Price: $1,025

TOURBY WATCHES

Tourby Watches
Königstrasse 78
D-58300 Wetter an der Ruhr
Hagen in Westfalen
Germany

Tel:
+49 176 83118382

E-mail:
info@tourbywatches.com

Website:
www.tourbywatches.com

Founded:
2007

Number of employees:
5

Annual production:
500

Distribution:
Tourby deals directly with customers.

Most important collections/price range:
Lawless Diver / from $1,400; Art Deco Classic / from $1,800; Ottoman / from $1,575; Planetarium / $9,000; special sets

Tourby Watches from the town of Wetter in Westphalia, Germany, manufactures mechanical wristwatches whose design is inspired by classic models. The story began when Erdal Yildiz inherited a pocket watch from his grandfather. The Unitas movement inside was in need of serious revision. So he looked around for a proper watchmaker, and was soon enamored with the craft itself. The world of mechanical watches became a genuine passion during his studies. He then contacted a number of suppliers in Germany and Switzerland, and in 2007 founded his own brand. The name Tourby has nothing to do with tourbillons, which his company does not manufacture. Rather, it is his nickname, it is short and memorable, and the domain name was still available!

All raw materials are purchased from top-notch suppliers in Germany and Switzerland. Some of the parts are ready to use on delivery; others need to be reworked in the company's own workshops in the cities of Bochum and Hagen. The cases are finished by hand, for example, as are the movements—all Swiss ETA calibers—which are extensively decorated, and the dials, in part at least. The leather straps are stitched by hand, as well. Final assembly, quality control, and after-sales service are all done by the company.

Tourby Watches produces series, but also does made-to-order pieces. The customer can choose his or her case, dial, hands, strap, and even the movement with its decoration. Another option is skeletonization. It's a good way to get hold of a unique piece.

This little brand has already quite a following in the U.S., notably. A pilot's watch was made especially for the dangerous deployments of the Strike Fighters Weapons School Pacific, a U.S. Navy training school for fighter pilots. For collectors, Yildiz managed to convince a "well-known American artist" who wished to remain anonymous to paint each inhabited continent on five dials for a special set. The watches are run on a heavily modified ETA 6498, with more power reserve and a higher beat.

Art Deco 40

Reference number: 2042
Movement: manually wound, ETA Caliber 6498-1, 37 mm; 17 jewels; 18,000 vph, adjusted in 5 positions; côtes de Genève; sunburst wheels; blued screws; 48-hour power reserve
Functions: hours, minutes, subsidiary seconds
Case: stainless steel, 40.5 mm, height 10.6 mm; arched sapphire crystal; transparent case back; water-resistant to 5 atm
Band: reptile skin, buckle
Remarks: sterling silver dial
Price: $2,040
Variations: skeletonized and modified movement ETA 6498-2 ($3,540)

Art Deco 43

Reference number: 2040.2
Movement: manually wound, ETA Caliber 6498-1; 37 mm; 17 jewels; 18,000 vph, adjusted in 5 positions; côtes de Genève; sunburst wheels; blued screws; 48-hour power reserve
Functions: hours, minutes, subsidiary seconds
Case: stainless steel, rose gold–plated, 43 mm, height 10.4 mm; arched sapphire crystal; transparent case back; water-resistant to 5 atm
Band: reptile skin, buckle
Remarks: sterling silver dial
Price: $2,040; **Variations:** skeletonized and modified movement ETA 6498-2 ($3,540); different sizes (40, 43, and 45 mm) and different dial colors (silver, black, anthracite)

Art Deco Sector Dial 40

Reference number: 2030
Movement: manually wound, ETA Caliber 6498-1; 37 mm; 17 jewels; 18,000 vph, adjusted in 5 positions; côtes de Genève; sunburst wheels; blued screws; 48-hour power reserve
Functions: hours, minutes, subsidiary seconds
Case: stainless steel, 40.5 mm, height 10.6 mm; arched sapphire crystal; transparent case back; water-resistant to 5 atm
Band: reptile skin, buckle
Remarks: sterling silver dial
Price: $2,040
Variations: skeletonized and modified movement ETA 6498-2 ($3,540)

Art Deco Sector Dial Vintage Rose 43

Reference number: 2034
Movement: manually wound, ETA Caliber 6498-1; 37 mm; 17 jewels; 18,000 vph, adjusted in 5 positions; côtes de Genève; sunburst wheels; blued screws; 48-hour power reserve
Functions: hours, minutes, subsidiary seconds
Case: stainless steel, rose gold–plated, 43 mm, height 10.4 mm; arched sapphire crystal; transparent case back; water-resistant to 5 atm
Band: reptile skin, buckle
Remarks: sterling silver dial
Price: $2,290; **Variations:** skeletonized and modified movement ETA 6498-2 ($3,780); different sizes (40, 43, and 45 mm) and different dial colors (silver, black)

Enamel 40

Reference number: 2010.1
Movement: manually wound, ETA Caliber 6498-1; 37 mm; 17 jewels; 18,000 vph, adjusted in 5 positions; côtes de Genève; sunburst wheels; blued screws; 48-hour power reserve
Functions: hours, minutes, subsidiary seconds
Case: stainless steel, 40.5 mm, height 10.6 mm; arched sapphire crystal; transparent case back; water-resistant to 5 atm
Band: reptile skin, buckle
Remarks: enamel-coated dial
Price: $1,900
Variations: skeletonized and modified movement ETA 6498-2 ($3,400)

Old Military Enamel 40

Reference number: 1404
Movement: manually wound, ETA Caliber 6498-1; 37 mm; 17 jewels; 18,000 vph, adjusted in 5 positions; côtes de Genève; sunburst wheels; blued screws; 48-hour power reserve
Functions: hours, minutes, subsidiary seconds
Case: stainless steel, 40.5 mm, height 10.6 mm; arched sapphire crystal; transparent case back; water-resistant to 5 atm
Band: cordovan strap, buckle
Price: $1,680
Variations: black dial and different sizes (43 or 45 mm)

Pilot Automatic Ottoman 40

Reference number: 2095
Movement: automatic, ETA Caliber 2824-2; 25.6 mm; 25 jewels; 28,800 vph, adjusted in 5 positions; 36-hour power reserve
Functions: hours, minutes, sweep second
Case: stainless steel, 40.5 mm, height 10.6 mm; arched sapphire crystal; transparent case back; water-resistant to 5 atm
Band: cordovan strap, buckle
Price: $1,620
Remarks: old Ottoman numbers
Variations: different sizes (40, 43, and 45 mm)

Starry Heavens 40

Reference number: 7005
Movement: manually wound, ETA Caliber 6498-1; 37 mm; 17 jewels; 18,000 vph, adjusted in 5 positions; côtes de Genève; sunburst wheels; blued screws; 48-hour power reserve
Functions: hours, minutes, subsidiary seconds
Case: stainless steel, 40.5 mm, height 10.6 mm; arched sapphire crystal; transparent case back; water-resistant to 5 atm
Band: reptile skin, buckle
Remarks: hand-painted dial
Price: $2,400
Variations: skeletonized and modified movement ETA 6498-2 ($3,900)

Around the World America

Reference number: 0000
Movement: manually wound, ETA Caliber 6498-2; 37 mm; 17 jewels; 21,600 vph, adjusted in 5 positions; côtes de Geneve; sunburst wheels; blued screws; 60-hour power reserve
Functions: hours, minutes, subsidiary seconds
Case: stainless steel, 40.5 mm, height 10.6 mm; arched sapphire crystal; transparent case back; water-resistant to 5 atm
Band: reptile skin, buckle
Remarks: hand-painted dial
Price: $12,000
Variations: comes in set with 5 watches: America, Asia, Australia, Arabia, and Europe ($60,000)

TOWSON WATCH COMPANY

After over forty years repairing high-grade watches, repeaters, and chronographs, and making his own tourbillons, George Thomas, a master watchmaker, met Hartwig Balke, a graduate in mechanical engineering and also a talented watchmaker, by chance in a bar in Annapolis. The two men, each well on his way to retirement, decided to turn their passion into a business and, in 2000, founded the Towson Watch Company. Thomas's first tourbillon pocket watches are displayed at the National Watch and Clock Museum in Columbia, Pennsylvania. In 1999, Balke made his first wrist chronograph, the STS-99 Mission, for a NASA astronaut and mission specialist. It was worn during the first shuttle mission in the new millennium, in the year 2000. The two also restored one of the world's oldest watches, one belonging to Philip Melanchton. In 2009, Thomas was invited to open up a pocket watch belonging to President Lincoln and revealed a secret message engraved by a servicing watchmaker and Union supporter working in Maryland: "Jonathan Dillon April 13-1861 Fort Sumpter [sic] was attacked by the rebels on the above date J Dillon." Towson timepieces pay tribute to local sites, like the Choptank and Potomac rivers. The timepieces are imaginative, a touch retro, a bit nostalgic perhaps, and very personal—not to mention affordable. A number of chronographs give the brand a sportive look. For the Dress Chronograph, Towson recruited the German watchmaker and dial specialist Jochen Benzinger.

Their local commitment is also shared by entrepreneur and former University of Maryland football captain Kevin Plank, who launched the technological sports apparel company Under Armour. In early 2016, the company announced it had bought a 25 percent stake in Towson, to boost its market presence and ensure its future. The two founders had been thinking of succession. Those concerns have now been laid to rest: "The brand will continue to grow and thrive for a long time to come," they told the *Baltimore Sun*.

Towson Watch Co.
502 Dogwood Lane
Towson, MD 21286

Tel.:
410-823-1823

E-mail:
towsonwatchco@aol.com

Website:
towsonwatchcompany.com

Founded:
2000

Number of employees:
4

Annual production:
200 watches

Distribution:
retail

Most important collections/price range:
Skipjack GMT / approx. $2,950; Mission / approx. $2,500; Potomac / approx. $2,000; Choptank / approx. $4,500; Martin / approx. $3,950 / custom design / $10,000 to $35,000

Dress Chronograph

Reference number: BCH 25
Movement: automatic, Caliber 7750 Valjoux; diameter ø 30 mm, height 7.9 mm; 21 jewels; 28,800 vph; finely finished with côtes de Genève
Functions: hours, minutes, subsidiary seconds; chronograph; date
Case: stainless steel, ø 42 mm, height 15.8 mm; sapphire crystal; screw-down transparent case back; water-resistant to 5 atm
Band: reptile skin, folding clasp
Remarks: elaborate silver dial with guilloché by Jochen Benzinger
Price: $8,100

Mission Moon SC

Reference number: MM250-CS
Movement: automatic ETA Caliber 7751; ø 25.6 mm, height 3.6 mm; 21 jewels; 28,800 vph; fine finishing with côtes de Genève
Functions: hours, minutes, subsidiary seconds; weekday, month, date; moon phase; 24-hour display; chronograph
Case: stainless steel, 40 mm, height 13.5 mm; sapphire crystal; screw-down back with engraving; water-resistant to 5 atm
Band: calfskin, orange stitching, folding clasp
Price: $4,160
Variations: stainless steel bracelet ($4,460)

Choptank Moon Chrono Special

Reference number: CT025-G
Movement: automatic, ETA Caliber 7751 Valjoux; ø 30 mm, height 7.9 mm; 25 jewels; 28,800 vph; fine finishing with côtes de Genève
Functions: hours, minutes, subsidiary seconds; weekday, month, date; moon phase; 24-hour display; chronograph
Case: stainless steel, 40 mm × 44 mm, height 13.5 mm; sapphire crystal at front; transparent screw-down back; water-resistant to 5 atm
Band: reptile skin with folding clasp
Price: $8,500
Variations: mesh stainless steel bracelet ($8,850)

Sagamore (Three-Diamond Watch)

Reference number: SAG100
Movement: manually wound, Soprod Unitas Caliber 6498; ø 36.6 mm, height 4.5 mm; 17 jewels; 18,000 vph; 46-hour power reserve
Functions: hours, minutes, subsidiary seconds
Case: stainless steel, ø 42 mm, height 12.5 mm; sapphire crystal; transparent case back; water-resistant to 5 atm
Remarks: silver and rhodium-plated dial, 3 diamonds at 3 o'clock
Band: reptile skin, 14-kt rose gold buckle
Price: $1,550

North.er

Reference number: NP100
Movement: automatic, ETA Caliber 2893-2; ø 25.6 mm, height 4.1 mm; 21 jewels; 28,800 vph; 38-hour power reserve
Functions: hours, minutes, sweep seconds; date; 2nd time zone hand
Case: stainless steel, 42 mm, height 13.5 mm; sapphire crystal; transparent case back; water-resistant to 5 atm
Band: calfskin, folding clasp
Price: $2,500

14-kt Gold Potomac

Reference number: GP 001-14K
Movement: manually wound, Soprod Unitas Caliber 6497; ø 37.2 mm, height 4.5 mm; 17 jewels; 18,000 vph; swan-neck fine adjustment; barley and solar guilloché on dial, rhodium-plated dial; skeletonized movement
Functions: hours, minutes, subsidiary seconds
Case: 14-kt rose gold, ø 42 mm, height 12.5 mm; sapphire crystal; transparent case back; water-resistant to 3 atm
Band: reptile skin, 14-kt rose gold buckle
Price: $23,500

Martin M-130

Reference number: CC100
Movement: automatic, ETA Caliber 7750 Valjoux; ø 30 mm; height 7.9 mm; 25 jewels; 28,800 vph; fine finishing with côtes de Genève
Functions: hours, minutes, subsidiary seconds; chronograph, date
Case: stainless steel, ø 42 mm, height 13.5 mm; sapphire crystal; screw-down back with engraving; water-resistant to 5 atm
Band: leather, folding clasp
Price: $3,950
Variations: mesh stainless steel bracelet ($4,250)

Potomac

Reference number: PO250-S
Movement: manually wound, Soprod Unitas Caliber 6498; ø 37.2 mm, height 4.5 mm; 17 jewels; 18,000 vph
Functions: hours, minutes, subsidiary seconds
Case: stainless steel, ø 42 mm, height 12.5 mm; domed sapphire crystal; screw-down transparent back; water-resistant to 3 atm
Band: calfskin, buckle
Price: $1,995
Variations: black dial with gold numerals and black calfskin strap; stainless steel mesh bracelet ($2,345)

Skipjack GMT

Reference number: SKJ100-S
Movement: Automatic Caliber ETA 2893-2; ø 25.6 mm, height 4.1 mm; 21 jewels; 28,800 vph; fine finish with côtes de Genève
Functions: hours, minutes, sweep seconds; date; 24-hour adjustable hand
Case: stainless steel, cannelage; ø 41.5 mm; sapphire crystal; screw-down transparent back with sapphire crystal; water-resistant to 5 atm
Band: calfskin, folding clasp
Price: $2,950
Variations: black dial with rhodium-plated numerals and leather strap with deployment clasp; stainless steel bracelet ($3,250)

TUDOR

Montres Tudor SA
Rue François-Dussaud 3-5-7
1211 Geneva 26
Switzerland

Tel.:
+41-22-302-2200

Website:
www.tudorwatch.com

Founded:
1946

U.S. distributor:
Tudor Watch U.S.A., LLC
665 Fifth Avenue
New York, NY 10022
212-897-9900
www.tudorwatch.com

Most important collections/price range:
Black Bay / $2,475 to $6,800; Heritage / $2,675 to $6,175; Pelagos / $4,450; 1926 / $1,725 to $3,475

The Tudor brand came out of the shadow cast by its "big sister" Rolex in 2007 and worked hard to develop its own personality. The strategy focuses on distinctive models that draw inspiration from the brand's rich past but remain in the "affordable quality watch segment."

Rolex founder Hans Wilsdorf started Tudor in 1946 as a second brand in order to offer the legendary reliability of his watches to a broader public at a more affordable price. To this day, Tudor still benefits from the same industrial platform as Rolex, especially in the area of cases and bracelets, assembly, and quality assurance, not to mention distribution and after-sales. However, the movements themselves are usually delivered by ETA and "Tudorized" according to the company's own esthetic and technical criteria.

After the Heritage Black Bay diver's watch, based on a 1954 model, came the blue-highlighted 1973 Chronograph Montecarlo. In 2014, Tudor completed the Heritage collection with the Ranger, a sports watch with an urban-adventurer feel, inspired by the same "tool watch" from the 1960s. For 2019 it was the turn of the diver's project "Commando," a 1960s prototype that finally saw the light of day under the name Black Bay P-01, whose rotating bezel is held in place with a clip.

Tudor has also been in the movement business. The MT-5621 made its debut in the simple North Flag and was built as a three-hander (MT-5612) for the Pelagos models. Two other caliber iterations are used for the new Black Bay models.

The M5601/5602 calibers, with three hands and a date, were followed by an attractive automatic chronograph using Breitling's B01 Caliber in exchange for the three-hand MT5912. Meanwhile, the Tudor engineers came up with the automatic MT5652, which powers a brand-new GMT. These exchanges between the two brands give both of them independence from the large suppliers of movements.

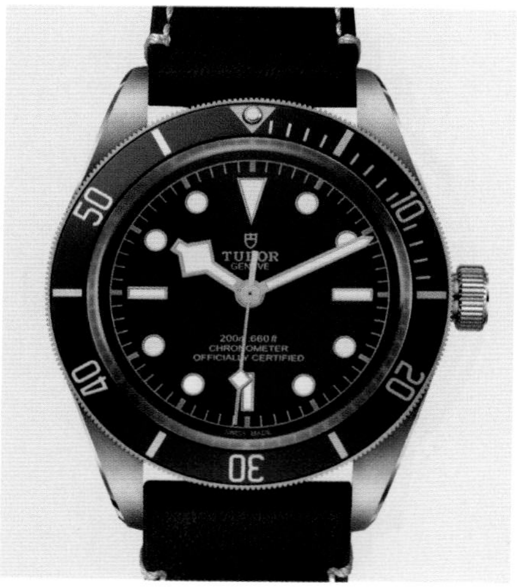

Black Bay Fifty-Eight Navy Blue

Reference number: 79030B
Movement: automatic, Tudor Caliber MT5402; ø 26 mm, height 4.99 mm; 27 jewels; 28,800 vph; silicon hairspring; 70-hour power reserve; COSC-certified chronometer
Functions: hours, minutes, sweep seconds
Case: stainless steel, ø 39 mm; unidirectional bezel with aluminum insert, with 0-60 scale; sapphire crystal; screw-in crown; water-resistant to 20 atm
Band: "soft touch" synthetic, buckle
Price: $3,700
Variations: textile strap ($3,375)

Black Bay Fifty-Eight Navy Blue

Reference number: 79030B
Movement: automatic, Tudor Caliber MT5402; ø 26 mm, height 4.99 mm; 27 jewels; 28,800 vph; silicon hairspring; 70-hour power reserve; COSC-certified chronometer
Functions: hours, minutes, sweep seconds
Case: stainless steel, ø 39 mm; unidirectional bezel with aluminum insert, with 0-60 scale; sapphire crystal; screw-in crown; water-resistant to 20 atm
Band: stainless steel, folding clasp
Price: $4,595
Variations: textile strap ($4,445)

Black Bay P01

Reference number: 70150
Movement: automatic, Tudor Caliber MT5612; ø 31.8 mm, height 6.5 mm; 26 jewels; 28,800 vph; silicon hairspring, balance with variable inertia; 70-hour power reserve; COSC-certified chronometer
Functions: hours, minutes, sweep seconds; date
Case: stainless steel, ø 42 mm; bidirectional bezel, 0-12 scale, with stop system (hinged element on upper lug); sapphire crystal; screw-in crown; water-resistant to 20 atm
Band: stainless steel, folding clasp with safety lock
Remarks: release of 1960s prototype for U.S. Navy that was never manufactured serially
Price: $3,950

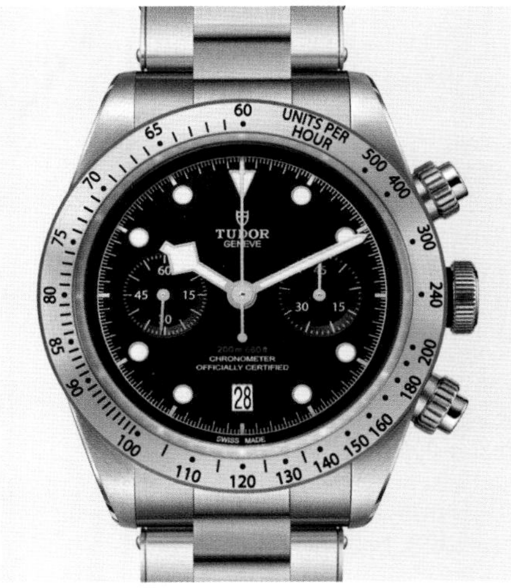

Black Bay Chrono

Reference number: 79350
Movement: automatic, Tudor Caliber MT5813; ø 30.4 mm, height 7.23 mm; 41 jewels; 28,800 vph; silicon hairspring, balance with variable inertia; 70-hour power reserve; COSC-certified chronometer
Functions: hours, minutes, subsidiary seconds; chronograph; date
Case: stainless steel, ø 41 mm; sapphire crystal; screw-in crown and pushers; water-resistant to 20 atm
Band: stainless steel, folding clasp
Remarks: comes with additional textile strap
Price: $5,225
Variations: leather strap ($5,125)

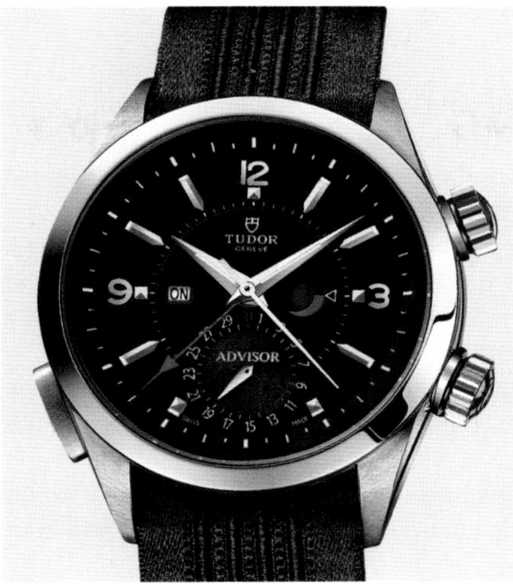

Heritage Advisor

Reference number: 79620TN
Movement: automatic, Tudor Caliber 2892 with special module (base ETA 2892-A2); ø 25.6 mm; 21 jewels; 28,800 vph; 42-hour power reserve
Functions: hours, minutes, sweep seconds; alarm; date
Case: stainless steel, titanium, ø 42 mm; sapphire crystal; water-resistant to 10 atm
Band: silk, buckle
Price: $5,850
Variations: stainless steel band ($6,175); reptile skin strap ($5,950)

Heritage Chrono

Reference number: 70330B
Movement: automatic, Tudor Caliber 2892 with special module (base ETA 2892-A2); ø 25.6 mm; 21 jewels; 28,800 vph; 42-hour power reserve
Functions: hours, minutes, subsidiary seconds; chronograph; date
Case: stainless steel, ø 42 mm; bidirectional bezel, with 0-12 scale; sapphire crystal; screw-in crown; water-resistant to 15 atm
Band: textile, buckle
Price: $4,150
Variations: stainless steel band ($4,475); black dial

North Flag

Reference number: 91210N
Movement: automatic, Tudor Caliber MT5621; ø 33.8 mm, height 6.5 mm; 28 jewels; 28,800 vph; silicon hairspring; 70-hour power reserve; COSC-certified chronometer
Functions: hours, minutes, sweep seconds; power reserve indicator; date
Case: stainless steel, ø 40 mm; bezel with ceramic ring; sapphire crystal; transparent case back; screw-in crown; water-resistant to 10 atm
Band: stainless steel, folding clasp
Price: $3,850
Variations: calfskin strap ($3,750)

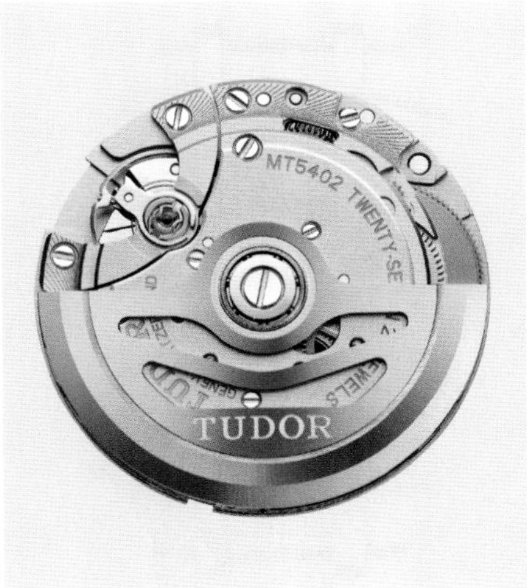

Caliber MT5402

Automatic; single spring barrel, 70-hour power reserve; COSC-certified chronometer
Functions: hours, minutes, sweep seconds
Diameter: 26 mm
Height: 4.99 mm
Jewels: 27
Balance: glucydur with weighted screws
Frequency: 28,800 vph
Hairspring: silicon

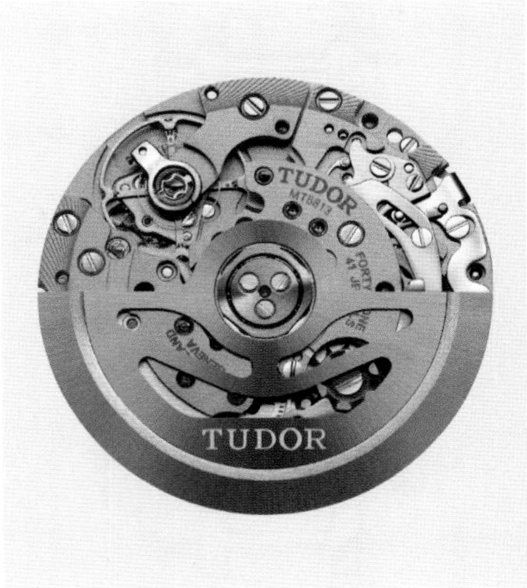

Caliber MT5813

Automatic; single spring barrel, 70-hour power reserve; COSC certified chronometer
Functions: hours, minutes, subsidiary seconds; chronograph; date
Diameter: 30.4 mm
Height: 7.23 mm
Jewels: 41
Balance: glucydur with weighted screws
Frequency: 28,800 vph
Hairspring: silicon

TUTIMA

Tutima Uhrenfabrik GmbH Ndl. Glashütte
Altenberger Strasse 6
D-01768 Glashütte
Germany

Tel.:
+49-35053-320-20

E-mail:
info@tutima.com

Website:
www.tutima.com

Founded:
1927

Number of employees:
approx. 60

U.S. distributor:
Tutima USA, Inc.
P.O. Box 983
Torrance, CA 90508
1-TUTIMA-1927
info@tutimausa.com
www.tutima.com

Most important collections/price range:
Patria, Saxon One, M2, Grand Flieger, Hommage / approx. $1,650 to $29,500

The name Glashütte is synonymous with watches in Germany. The area, also known for precision engineering, already had quite a watchmaking industry going when World War I closed off markets, followed by the hyperinflation of the early twenties. To rebuild the local economy, a conglomerate was created to produce finished watches, under the leadership of jurist Dr. Ernst Kurtz, consisting of the movement manufacturer UROFA Glashütte AG and UFAG. The top watches were given the name Tutima, derived from the Latin *tutus*, meaning whole, sound. Among the brand's most famous timepieces was a pilot's watch that set standards in terms of esthetics and functionality.

A few days before World War II ended, Kurtz left Glashütte and founded Uhrenfabrik Kurtz in southern Germany. A young businessman and former employee of Kurtz by the name of Dieter Delecate is credited with keeping the manufacturing facilities and the name Tutima going even as the company sailed through troubled waters. In founding Tutima Uhrenfabrik GmbH in Ganderkesee, this young, resolute entrepreneur prepared the company's strategy for the coming decades.

Delecate has had the joy of seeing Tutima return to its old home and vertically integrated operations, meaning it is once again a genuine *manufacture*. Under renowned designer Rolf Lang, it has developed an in-house minute repeater. In 2013, Tutima proudly announced a genuine made-in-Glashütte movement (at least 50 percent must be produced in the town), Caliber 617.

In addition to technically advanced and sportive watches, Tutima Glashütte has started reviving the great watchmaking crafts that have made the region world famous. There is the Hommage minute repeater and the three-hand Patria. In 2017, the brand introduced the Tempostopp, a flyback chronograph run on the Caliber 659, a replica of the legendary Urofa Caliber 59 from the 1940s with a few necessary improvements in the details. And then there are the models for everyday usage based on military watches, like the M2 Coastline, of lightweight titanium but with soft edges that will not ruin a silk shirt cuff.

Saxon One Chronograph Racing Red

Reference number: 6420-07
Movement: automatic, Tutima Caliber 521 (base ETA 7750); ø 30 mm, height 7.9 mm; 25 jewels; 28,800 vph; sweep minute counter, rotor with gold seal; 48-hour power reserve
Functions: hours, minutes, subsidiary seconds; additional 24-hour display (2nd time zone); chronograph; date
Case: stainless steel, ø 43 mm, height 15.7 mm; bidirectional bezel with reference markers; sapphire crystal; transparent case back; screw-in crown; water-resistant to 20 atm
Band: stainless steel, folding clasp
Price: $6,500

Saxon One M

Reference number: 6121-03
Movement: automatic, Tutima Caliber 330 (base ETA 2836-2); ø 25.6 mm, height 5.05 mm; 25 jewels; 28,800 vph; rotor with gold seal; 38-hour power reserve
Functions: hours, minutes, sweep seconds; date, weekday
Case: stainless steel, ø 40 mm, height 13 mm; sapphire crystal; transparent case back; screw-in crown; water-resistant to 10 atm
Band: stainless steel, folding clasp
Price: $2,350
Variations: calfskin band ($1,950)

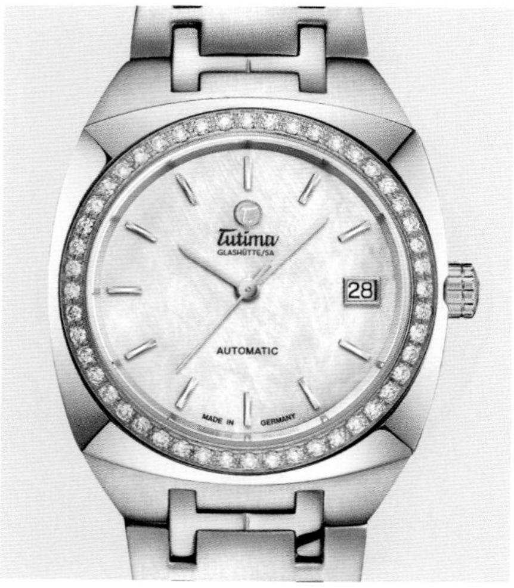

Saxon One Lady Diamonds

Reference number: 6701-01
Movement: automatic, Tutima Caliber 340 (base ETA 2892-A2); ø 25.6 mm, height 3.6 mm; 25 jewels; 28,800 vph; rotor with gold seal; 42-hour power reserve
Functions: hours, minutes, sweep seconds; date
Case: stainless steel, ø 36 mm, height 10.7 mm; bezel set with 48 diamonds; sapphire crystal; transparent case back; screw-in crown; water-resistant to 10 atm
Band: stainless steel, folding clasp
Remarks: mother-of-pearl dial
Price: $6,500

M2

Reference number: 6450-03
Movement: automatic, Tutima Caliber 521 (base ETA 7750); ø 30 mm, height 7.9 mm; 25 jewels; 28,800 vph; sweep minute counter, rotor with gold seal; 48-hour power reserve
Functions: hours, minutes, subsidiary seconds; additional 24-hour display; chronograph; date
Case: titanium, ø 46 mm, height 15.5 mm; sapphire crystal; screw-in crown; water-resistant to 30 atm
Band: titanium, folding clasp
Remarks: soft-iron inner case for amagnetic protection
Price: $6,500
Variations: Kevlar strap ($5,900)

M2 Coastline Chronograph

Reference number: 6430-05
Movement: automatic, Tutima Caliber 310 (base ETA 7750); ø 30 mm, height 7.9 mm; 25 jewels; 28,800 vph; 48-hour power reserve
Functions: hours, minutes, subsidiary seconds; chronograph; date
Case: titanium, ø 43 mm, height 13 mm; sapphire crystal; screw-in crown; water-resistant to 20 atm
Band: rubber, with textile layer, folding clasp
Price: $3,300

M2 Seven Seas

Reference number: 6151-04
Movement: automatic, Tutima Caliber 330 (base ETA 2836-2); ø 25.6 mm, height 5.05 mm; 25 jewels; 28,800 vph; rotor with gold seal; 38-hour power reserve
Functions: hours, minutes, sweep seconds; date, weekday
Case: titanium, ø 44 mm, height 13 mm; unidirectional bezel with 0-60 scale; sapphire crystal; screw-in crown; water-resistant to 50 atm
Band: titanium, folding clasp
Price: $2,300

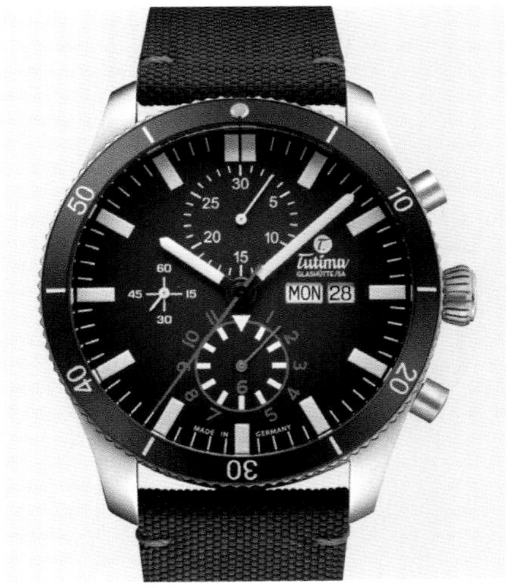

Grand Flieger Airport Chronograph

Reference number: 6406-03
Movement: automatic, Tutima Caliber 310 (base ETA 7750); ø 30 mm, height 7.9 mm; 25 jewels; 28,800 vph; rotor with gold seal; 48-hour power reserve
Functions: hours, minutes, subsidiary seconds; chronograph; date, weekday
Case: stainless steel, ø 43 mm, height 16 mm; bidirectional bezel with ceramic insert, with 0-60 scale; sapphire crystal; transparent case back; screw-in crown; water-resistant to 20 atm
Band: textile, folding clasp
Price: $3,900

Grand Flieger Airport

Reference number: 6106-01
Movement: automatic, Tutima Caliber 330 (base ETA 2836-2); ø 25.6 mm, height 5.05 mm; 25 jewels; 28,800 vph; rotor with gold seal; 38-hour power reserve
Functions: hours, minutes, sweep seconds; date, weekday
Case: stainless steel, ø 43 mm, height 13 mm; bidirectional bezel with ceramic insert, with 0-60 scale; sapphire crystal; transparent case back; screw-in crown; water-resistant to 20 atm
Band: textile, folding clasp
Price: $2,500

Flieger

Reference number: 6105-31
Movement: automatic, Tutima Caliber 330 (base ETA 2836-2); ø 25.6 mm, height 5.05 mm; 25 jewels; 28,800 vph; rotor with gold seal; 38-hour power reserve
Functions: hours, minutes, sweep seconds; date
Case: stainless steel, ø 41 mm, height 13 mm; sapphire crystal; transparent case back; screw-in crown; water-resistant to 10 atm
Band: calfskin, buckle
Price: $1,650
Variations: various colors

Patria Admiral Blue

Reference number: 6610-01
Movement: manually wound, Tutima Caliber 617; ø 31 mm, height 4.78 mm; 20 jewels; 21,600 vph; screw balance with weighted screws and Breguet hairspring; Glashütte three-quarter plate; winding wheels with click; gold-plated and finely finished movement; 65-hour power reserve
Functions: hours, minutes, subsidiary seconds
Case: stainless steel, ø 43 mm, height 11.2 mm; sapphire crystal; transparent case back; water-resistant to 5 atm
Band: reptile skin, buckle
Price: $6,900

Tempostopp

Reference number: 6650-01
Movement: manually wound, Tutima Caliber 659; ø 33.7 mm, height 6.6 mm; 28 jewels; 21,600 vph; screw balance with gold weight screws and Breguet hairspring; winding wheels with click; hand-engraved balance cock, gold-plated and finely finished movement; 65-hour power reserve
Functions: hours, minutes, subsidiary seconds; flyback chronograph
Case: rose gold, ø 43 mm, height 12.95 mm; sapphire crystal; transparent case back
Band: reptile skin, buckle
Remarks: optimized replica of legendary UROFA Caliber 59 from 1940s
Price: $33,100

Hommage

Reference number: 6800-02
Movement: manually wound, Tutima Caliber 800; ø 32 mm, height 7.2 mm; 42 jewels; 21,600 vph; screw balance with gold weight screws and Breguet hairspring; Glashütte three-quarter plate; winding wheels with click; gold-plated and finely finished movement; hand-engraved balance cock; 65-hour power reserve
Functions: hours, minutes, subsidiary seconds; minute repeater
Case: rose gold, ø 43 mm, height 13.4 mm; sapphire crystal; transparent case back
Band: reptile skin, buckle
Price: on request

Caliber Tutima 618

Manually wound; 3 screw-mounted gold chatons, Glashütte three-quarter plate; winding wheels with click; single spring barrel, 65-hour power reserve
Functions: hours, minutes, subsidiary seconds; power reserve indicator
Diameter: 31 mm
Height: 4.78 mm
Jewels: 27
Balance: screw balance with gold weight screws
Frequency: 21,600 vph
Balance spring: Breguet hairspring
Remarks: gold-plated and finely finished movement

Caliber Tutima 659

Manually wound; column-wheel control of chronograph functions; single spring barrel, 65-hour power reserve
Functions: hours, minutes, subsidiary seconds; flyback chronograph
Diameter: 33.7 mm
Height: 6.6 mm
Jewels: 28
Balance: screw balance with gold weight screws
Frequency: 21,600 vph
Balance spring: Breguet hairspring
Remarks: optimized replica of the legendary UROFA Caliber 59; gold-plated and finely finished movement

Caliber Tutima 800

Manually wound; 4 screw-mounted gold chatons, Glashütte three-quarter plate, 2 gongs, winding wheels with click; single spring barrel, 65-hour power reserve
Functions: hours, minutes, subsidiary seconds; minute repeater
Diameter: 32 mm
Height: 7.2 mm
Jewels: 42
Balance: screw balance with gold weight screws
Frequency: 21,600 vph
Balance spring: Breguet hairspring
Remarks: gold-plated and finely finished movement

Ulysse Nardin SA
3, rue du Jardin
CH-2400 Le Locle
Switzerland

Tel.:
+41-32-930-7400

Website:
www.ulysse-nardin.com

Founded:
1846

U.S. distributor:
Ulysse Nardin Inc.
7900 Glades Rd., Suite 200
Boca Raton, FL 33434
646 500 8664
usa@ulysse-nardin.com

Most important collections:
Blast Collection, Marine chronometers and diver's watches; Dual Time (also ladies' watches); complications (alarm clocks, perpetual calendar, tourbillons, minute repeaters, jacquemarts, astronomical watches)

ULYSSE NARDIN

At the beginning of the 1980s, following the infamous quartz crisis, Rolf Schnyder revived the venerable Ulysse Nardin brand, which once upon a time had a reputation for marine chronometers and precision watches. He had the luck to meet the multitalented Dr. Ludwig Oechslin, who developed a host of innovations for Ulysse Nardin, from intelligent calendar movements to escapement systems. He was the first to use silicon and synthetic diamonds. In fact, just about every Ulysse Nardin has become famous for some spectacular technical innovation, be it the Moonstruck with its stunning moon phase accuracy or the outlandish Freak series that more or less does away with the dial.

After Schnyder's death in 2011, the brand developed a strategy of partnerships and acquisitions, notably of the enameler Donzé Cadrans SA, which gave rise to the Marine Chronometer Manufacture, powered by the Caliber UN-118.

In 2014, the French luxury group Kering, owner of Girard-Perregaux, purchased Ulysse Nardin. The two companies are neighbors in La Chaux-de-Fonds, Switzerland, and this has created synergies. Ulysse Nardin's creative power remains strong, with such innovations as a new blade-driven anchor escapement and the regatta countdown watch with a second hand that runs counterclockwise first before running clockwise like a conventional chronograph once the race has started.

A joint venture with Sigatec in Sion and its sister company, Mimotec, which specialize in lithogalvanics (LIGA) and processing silicon, allowed Ulysse Nardin to continue developing its advanced technologies, producing, among others, the dual Ulysse escapement in the recent Freaks and the "Anchor Escapement" for the Caliber 178 with tourbillon.

Marine Torpilleur

Reference number: 1182-310/40
Movement: automatic, Caliber UN-118; ø 31.6 mm, height 6.45 mm; 50 jewels; 28,800 vph; DIAMonSIL escapement, silicon hairspring; 60-hour power reserve; COSC-certified chronometer
Functions: hours, minutes, subsidiary seconds; power reserve indicator; date
Case: rose gold, ø 42 mm, height 13 mm; sapphire crystal; transparent case back; screw-in crown; water-resistant to 10 atm
Band: reptile skin, folding clasp
Price: $17,900
Variations: black dial; rubber strap $19,900

Marine Torpilleur

Reference number: 1183-310/40
Movement: automatic, Caliber UN-118; ø 31.6 mm, height 6.45 mm; 50 jewels; 28,800 vph; DIAMonSIL escapement, silicon hairspring; 60-hour power reserve; COSC-certified chronometer
Functions: hours, minutes, subsidiary seconds; power reserve indicator; date
Case: stainless steel, ø 42 mm, height 13 mm; sapphire crystal; transparent case back; screw-in crown; water-resistant to 5 atm
Band: reptile skin, folding clasp
Price: $6,900
Variations: blue dial; rubber strap ($6,900); stainless steel band ($7,600)

Marine Chronometer Annual Calendar

Reference number: 1133-210/E3
Movement: automatic, Caliber UN-113; ø 31.6 mm, height 6.65 mm; 55 jewels; silicon balance and hairspring; 60-hour power reserve; COSC-certified chronometer
Functions: hours, minutes, subsidiary seconds; power reserve indicator; annual calendar with date, month
Case: stainless steel, ø 43 mm; sapphire crystal; transparent case back; screw-in crown; water-resistant to 10 atm
Band: reptile skin, double folding clasp
Remarks: enamel dial
Price: $12,900; **Variations:** rubber strap ($12,800)

Marine Chronometer

Reference number: 1186-126-3/43
Movement: automatic, Caliber UN-118; ø 31.6 mm, height 6.45 mm; 50 jewels; 28,800 vph; DIAMonSIL balance, silicon hairspring; 60-hour power reserve; COSC-certified chronometer
Functions: hours, minutes, subsidiary seconds; power reserve indicator; date
Case: rose gold, ø 43 mm, height 13 mm; sapphire crystal; transparent case back; screw-in crown; water-resistant to 10 atm
Band: rubber, with rose gold element, folding clasp
Price: $33,300
Variations: reptile skin strap ($31,900)

Marine Chronograph Annual Calendar Manufacture

Reference number: 1533-150-3/43
Movement: automatic, Caliber UN-153; ø 31 mm, height 7.37 mm; 53 jewels; 28,800 vph; silicon escapement; 52-hour power reserve
Functions: hours, minutes, subsidiary seconds; chronograph; annual calendar with date, month
Case: stainless steel, ø 43 mm, height 14.8 mm; sapphire crystal; transparent case back; screw-in crown; water-resistant to 10 atm
Band: reptile skin, folding clasp
Price: $11,900
Variations: white dial with blue rubber strap ($11,800)

Marine Chronograph Annual Calendar Manufacture

Reference number: 1532-150/43
Movement: automatic, Caliber UN-153; ø 31 mm, height 7.37 mm; 53 jewels; 28,800 vph; silicon escapement; 52-hour power reserve
Functions: hours, minutes, subsidiary seconds; chronograph; annual calendar with date, month
Case: rose gold, ø 43 mm, height 14.8 mm; sapphire crystal; transparent case back; screw-in crown; water-resistant to 10 atm
Band: reptile skin, folding clasp
Price: $33,000
Variations: white dial; rubber strap and rose gold element ($34,600)

Marine Tourbillon Manufacture

Reference number: 1283-181/E3
Movement: automatic, Caliber UN-128; ø 31 mm, height 6.45 mm; 50 jewels; 28,800 vph; flying 1-minute tourbillon; silicon balance and hairspring; 60-hour power reserve
Functions: hours, minutes; power reserve indicator
Case: stainless steel, ø 43 mm, height 12.2 mm; sapphire crystal; transparent case back; screw-in crown, with rubber coating; water-resistant to 10 atm
Band: reptile skin, double folding clasp
Remarks: enamel dial
Price: $28,000
Variations: rubber strap ($27,900)

Diver

Reference number: 8163-175/93
Movement: automatic, Caliber UN-816 (base Sellita SW300); ø 25.6 mm, height 3.6 mm; 25 jewels; 28,800 vph; 42-hour power reserve
Functions: hours, minutes, sweep seconds; date
Case: stainless steel, ø 42 mm, height 10.75 mm; unidirectional bezel with rubber insert, with 0-60 scale; sapphire crystal; screw-in crown; water-resistant to 30 atm
Band: textile, buckle
Price: $5,800
Variations: blue dial; stainless steel band ($6,500)

Diver Chronometer

Reference number: 1183-170-3/93
Movement: automatic, Caliber UN-118; ø 31.6 mm, height 6.45 mm; 50 jewels; 28,800 vph; DIAMonSIL balance, silicon hairspring; 60-hour power reserve; COSC-certified chronometer
Functions: hours, minutes, subsidiary seconds; power reserve indicator; date
Case: titanium, ø 44 mm, height 13.1 mm; unidirectional bezel with rubber insert, with 0-60 scale; sapphire crystal; transparent case back; screw-in crown; water-resistant to 30 atm
Band: rubber, buckle
Price: $7,900
Variations: blue dial; stainless steel band ($8,600)

Diver Chronometer

Reference number: 1185-170-3/BLACK
Movement: automatic, Caliber UN-118; ø 31.6 mm, height 6.45 mm; 50 jewels; 28,800 vph; DIAMonSIL balance, silicon hairspring; 60-hour power reserve; COSC-certified chronometer
Functions: hours, minutes, subsidiary seconds; power reserve indicator; date
Case: titanium with black PVD, ø 44 mm, height 13.1 mm; unidirectional rose gold bezel with rubber insert, with 0-60 scale; sapphire crystal; transparent case back; screw-in crown; water-resistant to 30 atm
Band: rubber, buckle
Price: $12,000

Diver X

Reference number: 1183-170LE-3/90-ANT
Movement: automatic, Caliber UN-118; ø 31.6 mm, height 6.45 mm; 50 jewels; 28,800 vph; DIAMonSIL balance, silicon hairspring; 60-hour power reserve
Functions: hours, minutes, subsidiary seconds, date
Case: titanium, ø 44 mm, height 13.1 mm; unidirectional bezel with 0-60 scale; sapphire crystal; water-resistant to 30 atm
Band: rubber
Price: $8,900

Blast

Reference number: 1723-400-3A/00
Movement: automatic, Caliber UN-172; ø 37 mm, height 6.1 mm; 25 jewels; 1-minute tourbillon; platinum microrotor; 72-hour power reserve
Functions: hours, minutes
Case: titanium/ceramic, ceramic case barrel, ø 45 mm, height 13 mm; ceramic bezel; sapphire crystal; transparent case back; water-resistant to 5 atm
Band: rubber, folding clasp
Price: $46,000
Variations: textured rubber strap ($46,000)

Blast

Reference number: 1723-400/BLACK
Movement: automatic, Caliber UN-172; ø 37 mm, height 6.1 mm; 25 jewels; 1-minute tourbillon; platinum microrotor; 72-hour power reserve
Functions: hours, minutes
Case: titanium with black DLC, ceramic case barrel, ø 45 mm, height 13 mm; ceramic bezel; sapphire crystal; transparent case back; water-resistant to 5 atm
Band: reptile skin, folding clasp
Price: $46,000
Variations: rubber strap ($46,000); red and black rubber strap ($46,000)

Skeleton X Titanium

Reference number: 3713-260-3/03
Movement: manually wound, Caliber UN-371; ø 37 mm, height 5.86 mm; 23 jewels; 18,000 vph; skeletonized movement; double spring barrel; silicon escape wheel and hairspring; 96-hour power reserve
Functions: hours, minutes
Case: titanium, ø 42 mm, height 10.85 mm; bezel with blue PVD coating; sapphire crystal; transparent case back; water-resistant to 5 atm
Band: rubber, buckle
Price: $17,500
Variations: black bezel; carbonium gold ($21,000); rose gold ($29,000)

Skeleton X Titanium

Reference number: 3713-260/03
Movement: manually wound, Caliber UN-371; ø 37 mm, height 5.86 mm; 23 jewels; 18,000 vph; skeletonized movement; double spring barrel; silicon escape wheel and hairspring; 96-hour power reserve
Functions: hours, minutes
Case: rose gold, ø 42 mm, height 10.05 mm; titanium bezel with blue PVD coating; sapphire crystal; transparent case back; water-resistant to 5 atm
Band: rubber, buckle
Price: $17,500
Variations: rubber strap

Freak X

Reference number: 2303-270/03
Movement: automatic, Caliber UN-230; ø 31 mm; 19 jewels; 28,800 vph; baguette movement on peripheral carousel; silicon escapement and hairspring, movement parts serve as hands; time-setting via bezel, conventional winding and time-setting by crown; 72-hour power reserve
Functions: hours, minutes
Case: titanium, ø 43 mm, height 13.5 mm; sapphire crystal; transparent case back
Band: calfskin, folding clasp
Price: $21,000

Freak X

Reference number: 2305-270/02
Movement: automatic, Caliber UN-230; ø 31 mm; 19 jewels; 28,800 vph; baguette movement on peripheral carousel; silicon escapement and hairspring, movement parts serve as hands; time-setting via bezel, conventional winding and time-setting by crown; 72-hour power reserve
Functions: hours, minutes
Case: pink gold and titanium with DLC, ø 43 mm, height 13.5 mm; sapphire crystal; transparent case back
Band: reptile skin, folding clasp
Price: $30,000

Freak Vision

Reference number: 2505-250
Movement: automatic, Caliber UN-250; ø 31 mm; 19 jewels; 18,000 vph; flying 1-minute tourbillon on rotating carousel, automatic "grinder" winding system with pawl and flexible control, constant force lever escapement; silicon escapement and hairspring, movement components used as hands, time-setting via bezel; 50-hour power reserve
Functions: hours, minutes
Case: platinum, ø 45 mm, height 14.1 mm; bidirectional bezel with rubber insert to set hands; sapphire crystal; transparent case back
Band: reptile skin, folding clasp
Price: $95,000
Variations: rose gold ($95,000)

Caliber UN-118

Automatic; DIAMonSIL escapement (patented); single spring barrel, approx. 60-hour power reserve
Functions: hours, minutes, subsidiary seconds; power reserve indicator; date
Diameter: 31.6 mm
Height: 6.45 mm
Jewels: 50
Balance: with variable inertia
Frequency: 28,800 vph
Balance spring: silicon
Shock protection: Incabloc
Remarks: perlage on mainplate, bridges with concentric côtes de Genève ("côtes circulaires")

Caliber UN-334

Automatic; silicon escapement; single spring barrel, 48-hour power reserve
Functions: hours, minutes, subsidiary seconds; additional 24-hour display (2nd time zone); large date
Jewels: 49
Balance: with variable inertia
Frequency: 28,800 vph
Balance spring: silicon
Shock protection: Incabloc
Remarks: patented rapid time adjustment for 2nd time zone; perlage on mainplate, bridges with concentric côtes de Genève ("côtes circulaires")

Caliber UN-155

Automatic; silicon escapement; column-wheel control of chronograph functions; single spring barrel, 52-hour power reserve
Functions: hours, minutes, subsidiary seconds; chronograph with integrated 10-minute backward countdown; date
Diameter: 34 mm
Height: 8.28 mm
Jewels: 67
Frequency: 28,800 vph
Balance spring: silicon
Remarks: for regatta countdown, second hand runs backward first, then reverses when it reaches its target time (can be set accurately to the minute); 650 parts

Urban Jürgensen
Route Boujean 77
CH-2502 Biel-Bienne
Switzerland

Tel.:
+41-32-365-1526

E-mail:
info@urbanjurgensen.com

Website:
www.urbanjurgensen.com

Founded:
1773

Annual production:
several hundred watches

U.S. distributor:
Martin Pulli
4337 Main Street
Philadelphia, PA 19127
215-508-4610
martin@martinpulli.com
www.martinpulli.com

Most important collections:
High-end references with in-house movements; some are sold exclusively from the workshop with a private pickup visit arrangement.

URBAN JÜRGENSEN & SØNNER

For all aficionados and collectors of fine timekeepers, the name Urban Jürgensen & Sønner is synonymous with outstanding watches. The company was founded in 1773 and has always strived for the highest rungs of the horological art. Technical perfection consistently combines with imaginative cases. A lot of attention is given to dials and hands.

Today, Urban Jürgensen & Sønner—originally a Danish firm—manufactures watches in Switzerland, where a team of eight superbly qualified watchmakers do the work in three ateliers. For over a quarter century now, they have been making highly complicated unique pieces and very upmarket wristwatches in small editions of 50 to 300 pieces. The series were based mostly on *ébauches* by Frédéric Piguet. Like all keen watchmakers, those at Urban Jürgensen have also sought to make their own movements, which would meet the highest standards of precision and reliability and not require too much servicing.

In 2003, a team began collaborating with a well-known external design engineer to construct a base movement, the UJS-P8, a traditional Swiss lever escapement with, in one iteration, a pivoting chronometer escapement.

The esthetic concept behind the brand's watches is clearly vintage. Urban Jürgensen & Sønner timepieces have the broad, open face of old pocket watches and classic hands, including a Breguet-type hour hand. The lugs on the 1741 recall the link to the watch chain. CEO Søren Jenry Petersen, an industrialist and watch lover, has kept up that watchmaking concept. The 1140 series is composed of classical watches with a modernized eighteenth-century feel. The Jürgensen One's case is one of the more modern timepieces made by this high-end brand. A detail worth noting is the complex "grenage" technique used to create that grainy look on the dial.

Jürgensen One

Reference number: 5541 GMT
Movement: automatic, Urban Jürgensen Caliber P5; ø 32 mm, height 6.6 mm; 34 jewels; 21,600 vph; 2 spring barrels, 72-hour power reserve
Functions: hours, minutes, sweep seconds; 2nd time zone at 6 o'clock
Case: stainless steel, 41 mm, height 12.1 mm at bezel; sapphire crystal; transparent case back; water-resistant to 12 atm
Band: stainless steel, integrated, double folding clasp with security lock
Remarks: 2nd time zone forward/backward adjustment with pushers at 8 and 10 o'clock
Price: $36,950

Reference 1741

Reference number: 1741 PT
Movement: manually wound, Urban Jürgensen Caliber P4 base with special module; ø 32 mm, height 5.2 mm; 35 jewels; 21,600 vph, double spring barrel, 72-hour power reserve
Functions: hours, minutes, sweep seconds; perpetual calendar with date, weekday, month, moon phase, leap year
Case: platinum, ø 41 mm, height 12.3 mm; sapphire crystal; transparent case back; water-resistant to 3 atm
Band: reptile skin, buckle
Price: $98,600
Variations: on request

Reference 2140 White Gold

Reference number: 2140 WG Black
Movement: manually wound, Urban Jürgensen Caliber P4; ø 32 mm, height 5.2 mm; 23 jewels; 21,600 vph; 2 spring barrels, 72-hour power reserve
Functions: hours, minutes, subsidiary seconds
Case: white gold, 40 mm, height 12.1 mm at bezel; sapphire crystal; transparent case back; water-resistant to 3 atm
Band: reptile skin, buckle
Remarks: hand-made guilloché on black dial
Price: $31,500
Variations: gray or blue dial; as GMT ($37,200)

URWERK

Felix Baumgartner and designer Martin Frei count among the living legends of innovative horology. They founded their company, Urwerk, in 1997 with a name that is a play on the words *Uhrwerk*, for movement, and *Urwerk*, meaning a sort of primal mechanism. Their specialty is inventing surprising time indicators featuring digital numerals that rotate like satellites and display the time in a relatively linear depiction on a small "dial" at the front of the flattened case, which could almost—but not quite—be described as oval. Their inspiration goes back to the so-called night clock of the eighteenth-century Campanus brothers, but the realization is purely *2001: A Space Odyssey*.

Urwerk's debut was with the Harry Winston Opus 5. Later, they created the Black Cobra, which displays time using cylinders and other clever ways to recoup energy for driving rather heavy components. The Torpedo is another example of high-tech watchmaking, again based on the satellite system of revolving and turning hands. These pieces remind one of the frenetic engineering that has transformed the planet since the eighteenth century. And with each return to the drawing board, Baumgartner and Frei find new ways to explore what has now become an unmistakable form, using high-tech materials, like aluminum titanium nitride (AlTiN), or finding new functions for the owner to play with.

Urwerk is continually pushing the envelope, even by its own standards. The "Transformator" added a rotatable, pivotable case to the watch. The latest model UR-105 CT Maverick is like the older Kryptonite, but now with a bronze case that will age along with the wearer. Far more portable is the 111C, where time is given more fluidly on wheels, including the digital seconds. And the latest implemented idea is the continuation of the minute hand trajectory along a 20-minute scale representing the 555 kilometers (345 miles) you would travel if standing that long on the equator. A scale opposite tracks your 20-minute journey around the sun as 35,740 kilometers (22,216 miles).

Urwerk SA
114, rue du Rhône
CH-1204 Geneva
Switzerland

Tel:
+41-22-900-2027

E-mail:
info@urwerk.com

Website:
www.urwerk.com

Founded:
1995

Annual production:
150 watches

U.S. distributor:
Ildico Inc.
8701 Wilshire Blvd.
Beverly Hills, CA 90211
310-205-5555

UR-100V Iron

Movement: automatic, Caliber UR 12.02; 52 jewels; winding system steered by 2 turbines; 28,800 vph; wandering hour satellites with beryllium-bronze Geneva Cross control and planetary transmission, finely finished, winding system regulated by fluid dynamics decoupling; 48-hour power reserve
Functions: hours (digital, rotating), minutes (segment display), rotational distance at the equator and orbital distance in 20-minute increments
Case: titanium and stainless steel, 41 × 49.7 mm, height 14 mm; sapphire crystal; water-resistant to 3 atm
Band: reptile skin, buckle
Price: $53,000; limited edition of 25 pieces

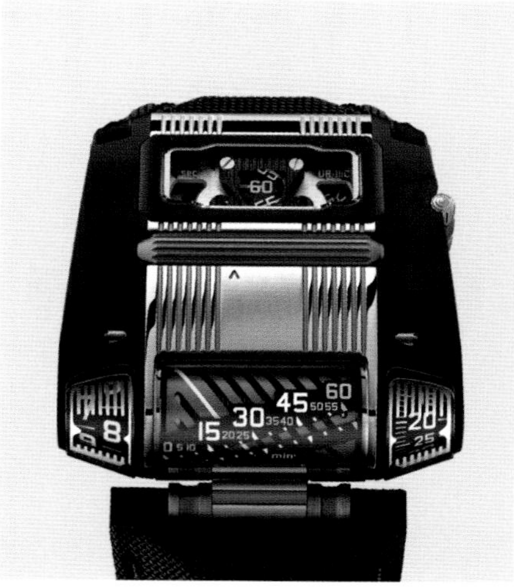

UR-111C TT

Movement: automatic, Caliber UR 7.10; 51 jewels; 28,800 vph; 37 jewels; 48-hour power reserve
Functions: jumping hours; retrograde linear minutes; digital seconds on 2 wheels
Case: stainless steel with gunmetal finish coated steel, 46 × 42 mm, height 15 mm; sapphire crystal; water-resistant to 3 atm
Remarks: digital seconds carried by network of optical fibers, 2 wheels cut by LIGA
Band: textile, buckle
Price: $133,000; limited to 25 pieces
Variations: polished steel

UR-220 "The Falcon Project"

Movement: manually wound, Caliber UR 7.20; 28,800 vph; 59 jewels; revolving satellite hours and 3D minute indicator; 48-hour power reserve
Functions: hours (digital, rotating), minutes; double power reserve indicator; oil change service indicator
Case: carbon and titanium, 43.8 mm × 53.6 mm, height 14.8 mm; sapphire crystal; transparent case back with black DLC on titanium; water-resistant to 3 atm
Band: rubber, buckle and Velcro fastening
Price: $162,000

UTS Watches, Inc.
P.O. Box 6293
Los Osos, CA 93412

Tel.:
877-887-0123 or 805-528-9800

E-mail:
info@utswatches.com

Website:
www.utswatches.com

Founded:
1999

Number of employees:
2

Annual production:
fewer than 500

Distribution:
direct sales only

Most important collections/price range:
sports and diver's watches, chronographs / from $2,500 to $7,000

UTS

UTS, or "Uhren Technik Spinner," was the natural outgrowth of a company based in Munich and manufacturing CNC tools and machines for the watch industry. Nicolaus Spinner, a mechanical engineer and aficionado in his own right, learned the nitty-gritty of watchmaking by the age-old system of taking watches apart. From there to making robust diver's watches was just a short step. The collection has grown considerably since he started production in 1999. The watches are built mainly around ETA calibers. Some, like the new 4000M, feature a unique locking bezel using a stem, a bolt, and a ceramic ball bearing system invented by Spinner. Another specialty is the 6-mm sapphire crystal, which guarantees significant water resistance. Spinner's longtime friend and business partner, Stephen Newman, is the owner of the UTS trademark in the United States. He not only has worked on product development, but has also contributed his own design ideas and handles sales and marketing for the small brand. A new watch released in 2014, the 4000M Diver, boasts an extreme depth rating even without the need for a helium escape valve and is available in a GMT version. The collection is small, but UTS has a faithful following in Germany and the United States. The key for the fan club is a unique appearance coupled with mastery of the technology. These are pure muscle watches with no steroids.

Diver 4000M GMT

Movement: automatic, ETA Caliber 2893-2; ø 25.6 mm, height 4.6 mm; 25 jewels; 28,800 vph; 42-hour power reserve
Functions: hours, minutes, sweep seconds; date; 2nd time zone
Case: stainless steel, ø 45 mm, height 17.5 mm; bidirectional bezel with 0-60 scale; 6-mm sapphire crystal, antireflective on back; screwed-down case back; screw-in crown and buttons; locking bezel; water-resistant to 400 atm
Band: stainless steel with diver's extension folding clasp or rubber or leather strap
Price: $6,800

2000M

Movement: automatic, ETA Caliber 2824-2; ø 25.6 mm, height 4.6 mm; 25 jewels; 28,800 vph; 42-hour power reserve
Functions: hours, minutes, sweep seconds; date
Case: stainless steel, ø 44 mm, height 16.5 mm; unidirectional bezel with 0-60 scale; automatic helium escape valve; sapphire crystal, antireflective on back; screwed-down case back; screw-in crown and buttons; water-resistant to 200 atm
Band: stainless steel with diver's extension folding clasp, comes with rubber leather strap
Price: $3,950

Adventure Manual Wind

Movement: manually wound, ETA Unitas Caliber 6497; ø 36.6 mm, height 5.4 mm; 18 jewels; 18,000 vph; 48-hour power reserve
Functions: hours, minutes, subsidiary seconds
Case: stainless steel, ø 46 mm, height 14 mm; screw-in crown; antireflective sapphire crystal; screwed-down sapphire crystal case back; water-resistant to 50 atm
Band: leather, buckle
Price: $3,400
Variations: rubber strap

VACHERON CONSTANTIN

The origins of this oldest continuously operating watch *manufacture* can be traced back to 1755 when Jean-Marc Vacheron opened his workshop in Geneva. His highly complex watches were particularly appreciated by clients in Paris. The development of such an important outlet for horological works there had a lot to do with the emergence of a wealthy class around the powerful French court. The Revolution put an end to all the financial excesses of that market, however, and the Vacheron company suffered as well, until the arrival of marketing wizard François Constantin in 1819.

Fast-forward to the late twentieth century: The brand with the Maltese cross logo had evolved into a tradition-conscious keeper of *haute horlogerie* under the aegis, starting in the mid-1990s, of the Vendôme Luxury Group (today's Richemont SA).

Vacheron Constantin is one of the last luxury brands to have abandoned the traditional way of dividing up labor. Today, most of its basic movements are made in-house at the production facilities and headquarters in Plan-les-Ouates and the workshops in Le Brassus in Switzerland's Jura region.

Products range from the world's most complicated watch, like the 57260, and the finely crafted Les Cabinotiers collection of unique pieces, with, in 2020, a watch combining a minute repeater, a chronograph, an equation display, and lots more. For daily use, there are the Overseas models, and the entry-level collection, the Fiftysix, with a basic movement and no Geneva Seal. In 2019, the brand's competence in movements produced a genuine novelty: a perpetual calendar driven by the "Twin Beat" escapement. It runs at 36,000 vph on the wearer's arm, and can be switched to 8,640 vph when stored, giving it a 65-day power reserve.

Vacheron Constantin
Chemin du Tourbillon
CH-1228 Plan-les-Ouates
Switzerland

Tel.:
+41-22-930-2005

E-mail:
info@vacheron-constantin.com

Website:
www.vacheron-constantin.com

Founded:
1755

Number of employees:
approx. 800

Annual production:
over 20,000 watches (estimated)

U.S. distributor:
Vacheron Constantin
Richemont North America
645 Fifth Avenue
New York, NY 10022
877-701-1755

Most important collections:
Harmony, Patrimony, Traditionnelle, Historiques, Métiers d'Art, Malte, Overseas, Egérie, Fiftysix, Quai de l'Île, unique pieces

Les Cabinotiers "La Musique du Temps"

Reference number: 9740C/000R-B692
Movement: manually wound, Vacheron Constantin Caliber 2756; ø 33.3 mm, height 16.35 mm; 40 jewels; 18,000 vph; 1-minute tourbillon; 65-hour power reserve; Geneva Seal; **Functions:** hours, minutes; additional 24-hour display (2nd time zone), minute repeater; flyback chronograph; perpetual calendar with date, weekday, month, leap year on rear; moon phase and moon age (retrograde); equation display; sunrise and sundown times, day/night duration
Case: rose gold, ø 50 mm, height 21 mm; sapphire crystal; transparent case back
Band: reptile skin, folding clasp
Price: on request; unique piece

Traditionnelle Tourbillon Chronograph

Reference number: 5100T/000R-B623
Movement: manually wound, Vacheron Constantin Caliber 3200; ø 32.8 mm, height 6.7 mm; 39 jewels; 18,000 vph; 1-minute tourbillon; crown pusher control of chronograph functions; 65-hour power reserve; Geneva Seal
Functions: hours, minutes, subsidiary seconds (on tourbillon cage); power reserve indicator; chronograph
Case: rose gold, ø 42.5 mm, height 11.7 mm; sapphire crystal; transparent case back; water-resistant to 3 atm
Band: reptile skin, folding clasp
Price: on request

Traditionnelle Twin Beat Perpetual Calendar

Reference number: 3200T/000P-B578
Movement: manually wound, Vacheron Constantin Caliber 3610; ø 32 mm, height 6 mm; 64 jewels; 36,000 or 8,640 vph; movement with Twin-Beat escapement system, switchable between active and passive mode (e.g., for storage in a safe), 96-hour or up to 65-day power reserve; Geneva Seal
Functions: hours, minutes; mode indicator, double power reserve indicator for active and passive mode; perpetual calendar with date, month, leap year
Case: platinum, ø 42 mm, height 12.3 mm; sapphire crystal; transparent case back; water-resistant to 3 atm; **Band:** reptile skin, buckle
Price: on request

Fiftysix Automatik

Reference number: 4600E/000A-B442
Movement: automatic, Vacheron Constantin Caliber 1326; ø 26.2 mm, height 4.3 mm; 25 jewels; 28,800 vph; 48-hour power reserve
Functions: hours, minutes, sweep seconds; date
Case: stainless steel, ø 40 mm, height 9.6 mm; sapphire crystal; transparent case back; water-resistant to 3 atm
Band: reptile skin, folding clasp
Price: $12,000
Variations: rose gold ($19,900)

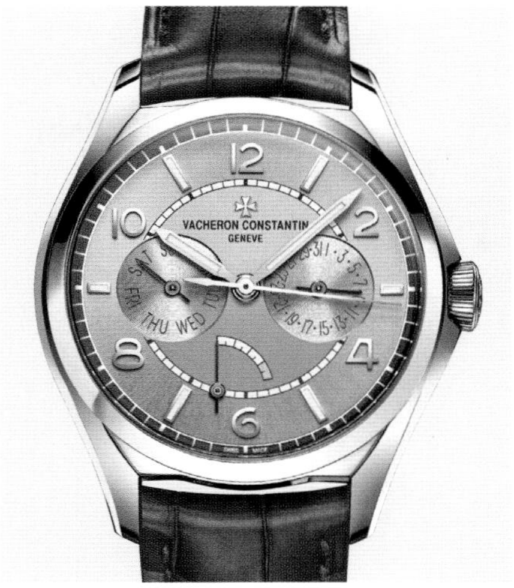

Fiftysix Day/Date

Reference number: 4400E/000A-B437
Movement: automatic, Vacheron Constantin Caliber 2475SC/2; ø 26.2 mm, height 5.7 mm; 27 jewels; 28,800 vph; 40-hour power reserve; Geneva Seal
Functions: hours, minutes, sweep seconds; power reserve indicator; date, weekday
Case: stainless steel, ø 40 mm, height 11.6 mm; sapphire crystal; transparent case back; water-resistant to 3 atm
Band: reptile skin, folding clasp
Price: $17,400
Variations: pink gold ($32,600)

Fiftysix Automatik

Reference number: 4600E/000R-B576
Movement: automatic, Vacheron Constantin Caliber 1326; ø 26.2 mm, height 4.3 mm; 25 jewels; 28,800 vph; 48-hour power reserve
Functions: hours, minutes, sweep seconds; date
Case: rose gold, ø 40 mm, height 9.6 mm; sapphire crystal; transparent case back; water-resistant to 3 atm
Band: calfskin, buckle
Price: $19,900

Fiftysix Complete Calendar

Reference number: 4000E/000R-B438
Movement: automatic, Vacheron Constantin Caliber 2460 QCL/1; ø 29 mm, height 5.4 mm; 27 jewels; 28,800 vph; 40-hour power reserve; Geneva Seal
Functions: hours, minutes, sweep seconds; full calendar with date, weekday, month
Case: pink gold, ø 40 mm, height 11.6 mm; sapphire crystal; transparent case back; water-resistant to 3 atm
Band: reptile skin, folding clasp
Price: $36,800
Variations: stainless steel ($23,500)

Fiftysix Full Calendar

Reference number: 4000E/000A-B548
Movement: automatic, Vacheron Constantin Caliber 2460QCL/1; ø 29 mm, height 5.4 mm; 27 jewels; 28,800 vph; 40-hour power reserve; Geneva Seal
Functions: hours, minutes, sweep seconds; full calendar with date, weekday, month, moon phase
Case: stainless steel, ø 40 mm, height 11.6 mm; sapphire crystal; transparent case back; water-resistant to 3 atm
Band: reptile skin, folding clasp
Price: $21,700
Variations: rose gold ($33,800)

Historique "Cornes de Vache" 1955

Reference number: 5000H/000A-B582
Movement: automatic, Vacheron Constantin Caliber 1142; ø 27.5 mm, height 5.57 mm; 21 jewels; 21,600 vph; 48-hour power reserve; Geneva Seal
Functions: hours, minutes, subsidiary seconds; chronograph
Case: stainless steel, ø 38.5 mm, height 10.9 mm; sapphire crystal; transparent case back; water-resistant to 3 atm
Band: calfskin, buckle
Price: $42,200
Variations: platinum; rose gold

Overseas Perpetual Calendar Extra-Thin

Reference number: 4300V/120R-B509
Movement: automatic, Vacheron Constantin Caliber 1120 QP/1; ø 29.6 mm, height 4.05 mm; 36 jewels; 19,800 vph; 40-hour power reserve; Geneva Seal
Functions: hours, minutes; perpetual calendar with date, weekday, month, moon phase, leap year
Case: rose gold, ø 41.5 mm, height 8.1 mm; sapphire crystal; transparent case back; water-resistant to 5 atm
Band: rose gold, triple folding clasp
Remarks: amagnetic soft-iron cage; comes with additional reptile skin strap
Price: $78,500

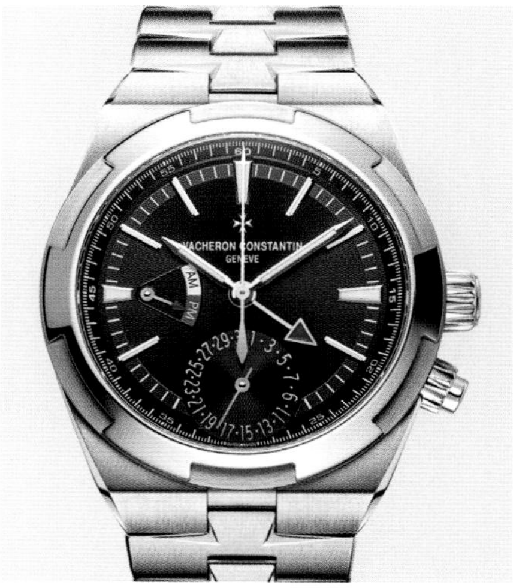

Overseas Dual-Time

Reference number: 7900V/110A-B546
Movement: automatic, Vacheron Constantin Caliber 5110 DT; ø 30.6 mm, height 6 mm; 37 jewels; 28,800 vph; 60-hour power reserve; Geneva Seal
Functions: hours, minutes, sweep seconds; additional 12-hour display (2nd time zone), day/night indicator; date
Case: stainless steel, ø 41 mm, height 12.8 mm; sapphire crystal; transparent case back; water-resistant to 15 atm
Band: stainless steel, triple folding clasp
Remarks: amagnetic soft-iron cage; comes with additional reptile skin or rubber strap
Price: $25,200

Overseas Perpetual Calendar Extra-Thin Skeleton

Reference number: 4300V/120R-B547
Movement: automatic, Vacheron Constantin Caliber 1120 QPSQ/1; ø 29.6 mm, height 4.05 mm; 36 jewels; 19,800 vph; completely skeletonized movement; 40-hour power reserve; Geneva Seal
Functions: hours, minutes; perpetual calendar with date, weekday, month, moon phase, leap year
Case: rose gold, ø 41.5 mm, height 8.1 mm; sapphire crystal; transparent case back; water-resistant to 5 atm
Band: rose gold, triple folding clasp
Remarks: amagnetic soft-iron cage; comes with additional reptile skin or rubber strap
Price: on request

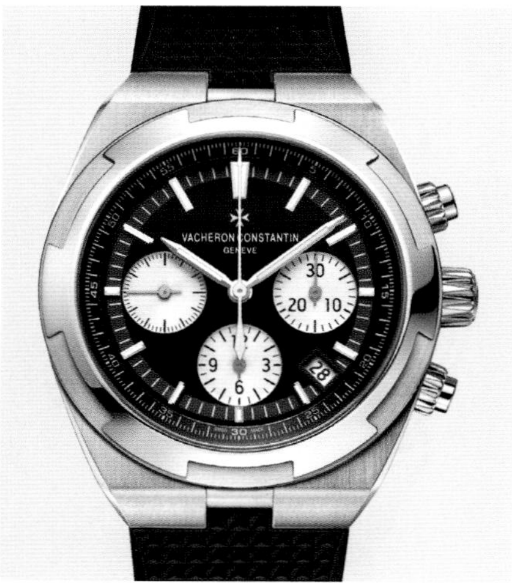

Overseas Chronograph

Reference number: 5500V/110A-B481
Movement: automatic, Vacheron Constantin Caliber 5200; ø 30.6 mm, height 6.6 mm; 54 jewels; 28,800 vph; column-wheel control of chronograph functions; gold rotor; 52-hour power reserve; Geneva Seal
Functions: hours, minutes, subsidiary seconds; chronograph; date
Case: stainless steel, ø 42.5 mm, height 13.7 mm; sapphire crystal; transparent case back; screw-in crown and pushers; water-resistant to 15 atm
Band: rubber, double folding clasp
Price: $27,800
Variations: reptile skin band

Overseas Automatic

Reference number: 4500V/110A-B128
Movement: automatic, Vacheron Constantin Caliber 5100; ø 30.6 mm, height 4.7 mm; 37 jewels; 28,800 vph; gold rotor; 60-hour power reserve; Geneva Seal
Functions: hours, minutes, sweep seconds; date
Case: stainless steel, ø 41 mm, height 11 mm; sapphire crystal; transparent case back; water-resistant to 15 atm
Band: stainless steel, double folding clasp
Price: $20,400
Variations: reptile skin strap; rubber strap

Overseas Small Model

Reference number: 2305V/100R-B077
Movement: automatic, Vacheron Constantin Caliber 5300; ø 22.6 mm, height 4 mm; 31 jewels; 28,800 vph; gold rotor; 44-hour power reserve; Geneva Seal
Functions: hours, minutes, subsidiary seconds
Case: rose gold, ø 37 mm, height 10.8 mm; with 84 diamonds; sapphire crystal; transparent case back; water-resistant to 15 atm
Band: rose gold, double folding clasp
Price: $25,400
Variations: reptile skin and rubber strap; stainless steel

Patrimony Automatic

Reference number: 85180/000R-B515
Movement: automatic, Vacheron Constantin Caliber 2450 Q6; ø 26.2 mm, height 3.6 mm; 27 jewels; 28,800 vph; 40-hour power reserve; Geneva Seal
Functions: hours, minutes, sweep seconds; date
Case: rose gold, ø 40 mm, height 8.55 mm; sapphire crystal; water-resistant to 3 atm
Band: reptile skin, buckle
Price: $25,600

Patrimony Retrograde Date and Weekday

Reference number: 4000U/000R-B516
Movement: automatic, Vacheron Constantin Caliber 2460 R31R7/2; ø 27.2 mm, height 5.4 mm; 27 jewels; 28,800 vph; 40-hour power reserve; Geneva Seal
Functions: hours, minutes; date, weekday (retrograde)
Case: rose gold, ø 42.5 mm, height 9.7 mm; sapphire crystal; water-resistant to 3 atm
Band: reptile skin, folding clasp
Price: $42,500

Égérie Automatic

Reference number: 4605F/110A-B495
Movement: automatic, Vacheron Constantin Caliber 1088; ø 20.8 mm, height 3.8 mm; 26 jewels; 28,800 vph; 40-hour power reserve
Functions: hours, minutes, sweep seconds; date
Case: stainless steel, ø 35 mm, height 9.32 mm; bezel set with 58 diamonds; sapphire crystal; transparent case back; crown with moonstone cabochon; water-resistant to 3 atm
Band: stainless steel, triple folding clasp
Remarks: dial set with 34 diamonds
Price: $21,200
Variations: rose gold

Égérie Moon Phase

Reference number: 8005F/000R-B498
Movement: automatic, Vacheron Constantin Caliber 1088 L; ø 30 mm, height 5 mm; 26 jewels; 28,800 vph; 40-hour power reserve
Functions: hours, minutes, sweep seconds; moon phase
Case: rose gold, ø 37 mm, height 10.08 mm; bezel set with 58 diamonds; sapphire crystal; transparent case back; crown with moonstone cabochon; water-resistant to 3 atm
Band: reptile skin, buckle
Remarks: dial set with 36 diamonds; comes with 2 additional reptile skin straps
Price: $34,300
Variations: stainless steel

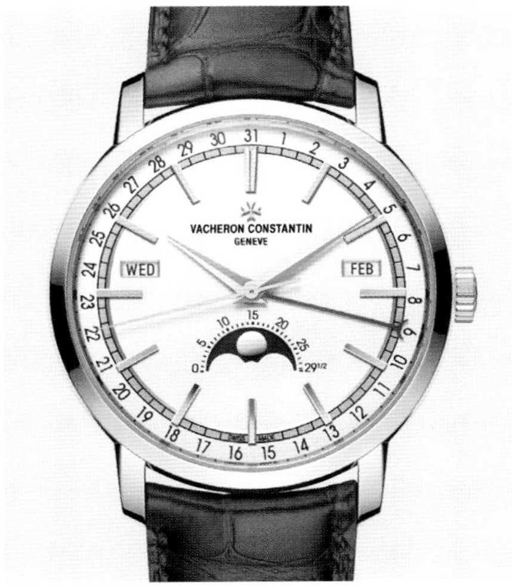

Traditionnelle Full Calendar

Reference number: 4010T/000R-B344
Movement: manually wound, Vacheron Constantin Caliber 2460 QCL; ø 29 mm, height 5.4 mm; 27 jewels; 28,800 vph; 40-hour power reserve; Geneva Seal
Functions: hours, minutes, sweep seconds; full calendar with date, weekday, month, moon phase
Case: rose gold, ø 41 mm, height 10.7 mm; sapphire crystal; transparent case back; water-resistant to 3 atm
Band: reptile skin, folding clasp
Price: on request

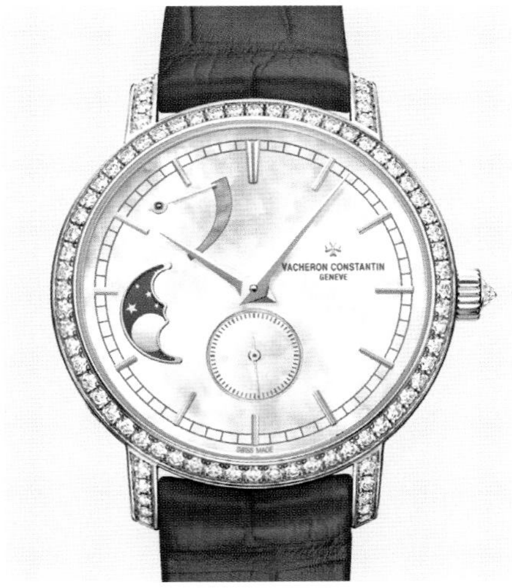

Traditionnelle Moon Phase

Reference number: 83570/000G-9916
Movement: manually wound, Vacheron Constantin Caliber 1410 AS; ø 26 mm, height 4.2 mm; 22 jewels; 28,800 vph; 40-hour power reserve; Geneva Seal
Functions: hours, minutes, subsidiary seconds; power reserve indicator; moon phase
Case: white gold, ø 36 mm, height 9.1 mm; bezel and lugs set with 81 diamonds; sapphire crystal; transparent case back; crown with diamond; water-resistant to 3 atm
Band: reptile skin, buckle
Remarks: mother-of-pearl dial
Price: $40,200

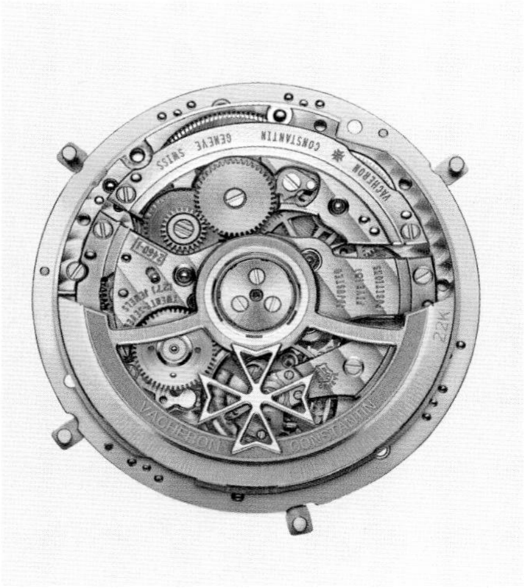

Caliber 2460 QCL/1

Automatic; stop-seconds mechanism; single spring barrel, 40-hour power reserve; Geneva Seal
Functions: hours, minutes, sweep seconds; full calendar with date, weekday, month
Diameter: 29 mm
Height: 5.4 mm
Jewels: 27
Balance: glucydur
Frequency: 28,800 vph
Remarks: gold rotor; 308 parts

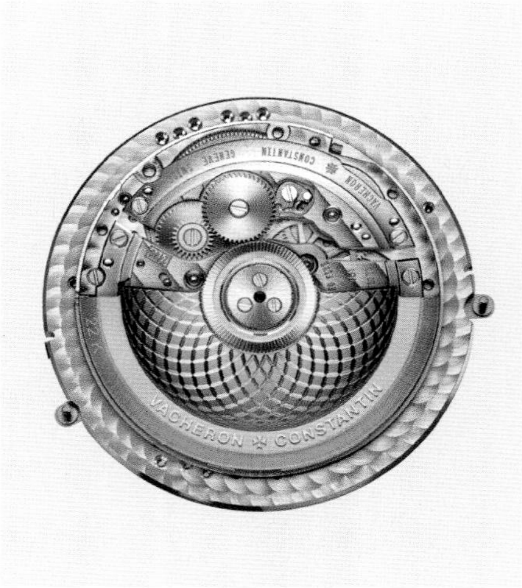

Caliber 2460 G4/1

Automatic; single spring barrel, 40-hour power reserve; Geneva Seal
Functions: disk display for hours, minutes; disk display for date, weekday
Diameter: 31 mm
Height: 6.05 mm
Jewels: 27
Balance: glucydur
Frequency: 28,800 vph
Remarks: gold rotor; 237 parts

Caliber 3300

Manually wound; column-wheel control of chronograph functions, horizontal clutch; single spring barrel, 65-hour power reserve; Geneva Seal
Functions: hours, minutes, subsidiary seconds; power reserve indicator; chronograph with crown pusher
Diameter: 32.8 mm
Height: 6.7 mm
Jewels: 35
Balance: glucydur
Frequency: 21,600 vph
Remarks: 252 parts

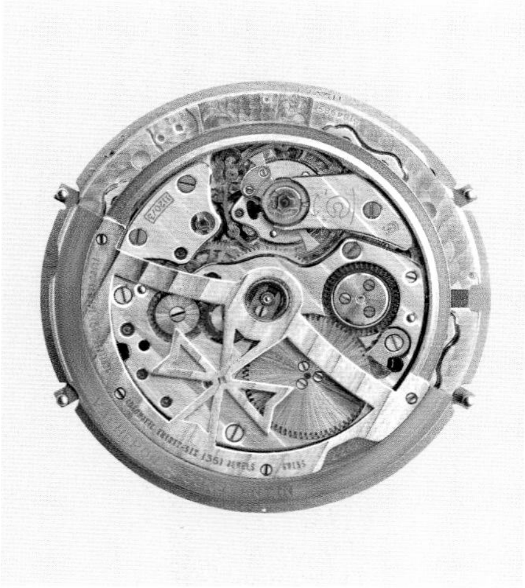

Caliber 1120 QP

Automatic; extra-thin construction; winding rotor with supporting ring; single spring barrel, 40-hour power reserve; Geneva Seal
Functions: hours, minutes; perpetual calendar with date, weekday, month, moon phase, leap year
Diameter: 29.6 mm
Height: 4.05 mm
Jewels: 36
Balance: glucydur
Frequency: 19,800 vph
Remarks: skeletonized rotor with gold oscillating mass; 276 parts

Caliber 1731

Manually wound; single spring barrel, 65-hour power reserve; Geneva Seal
Functions: hours, minutes, subsidiary seconds; hour, quarter-hour, and minute repeater
Diameter: 32.8 mm
Height: 3.9 mm
Jewels: 36
Balance: glucydur
Frequency: 21,600 vph
Remarks: perlage on mainplate, beveled edges, bridges with côtes de Genève

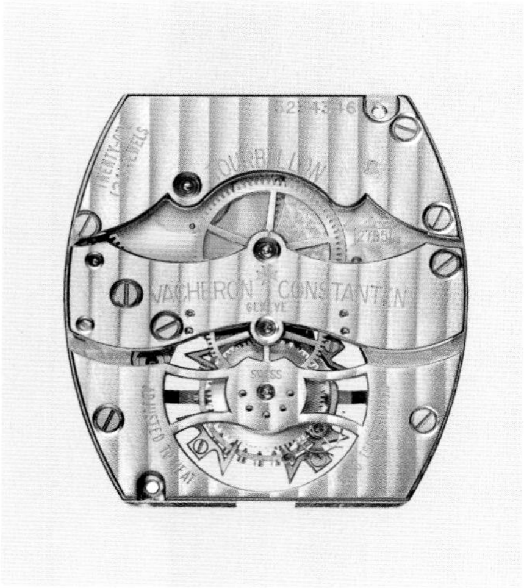

Caliber 2795

Automatic; 1-minute tourbillon; single spring barrel, 45-hour power reserve; Geneva Seal
Functions: hours, minutes, subsidiary seconds (on tourbillon cage)
Dimensions: 27.37 × 29.3 mm
Height: 6.1 mm
Jewels: 27
Balance: glucydur
Frequency: 18,000 vph
Remarks: tonneau-shaped

ITAY NOY
JERUSALEM
N°0101

VAN CLEEF & ARPELS

In 1999, while shopping around for more companies to add to its roster of high-end jewelers, Richemont Group decided to purchase Van Cleef & Arpels. The venerable jewelry brand had a lot of name recognition, thanks in part to a host of internationally known customers, like Jacqueline Kennedy Onassis, whose two marriages each involved a Van Cleef & Arpels ring. It also had a reputation for the high quality of its workmanship. It was Van Cleef & Arpels that came up with the mystery setting using a special rail and cut totally hidden from the casual eye.

Van Cleef & Arpels was a family business that came to be when a young stonecutter, Alfred van Cleef, married Estelle Arpels in 1896, and ten years later opened a business on Place Vendôme in Paris with Estelle's brother Charles. More of Estelle's brothers joined the firm, which was soon booming and serving, quite literally, royalty.

Watches were always a part of the portfolio. But after joining Richemont, Van Cleef now had the support of a very complete industrial portfolio that would allow it to make stunning movements that could bring dials to life. A collaboration with Jean-Marc Wiederrecht and Agenhor produced outstanding combinations of artistry in design and crafts, with horological excellence that made the watch-loving public take notice. The brand has come up with some genuine innovations: The Midnight Nuit Lumineuse lights up six diamonds with a pusher using a ceramic band and the phenomenon of piezoelectricity. The Lady Arpels Planétarium won the Ladies' Complication Prize at the prestigious GPHG in 2018. The watch features an extraordinary complication: Mercury, Venus, and Earth rotating in real time around the sun, with the Moon rotating around Earth, and a shooting star fulfilling wishes all day long on an aventurine sky.

Van Cleef & Arpels
2, rue du Quatre-Septembre
F-75002 Paris
France

Tel.:
+33-1-70-70-36-56

Website:
www.vancleefarpels.com

Founded:
1906

U.S. distributor:
1-877-VAN-CLEEF

Most important collections:
Charms; Pierre Arpels; Poetic Complications

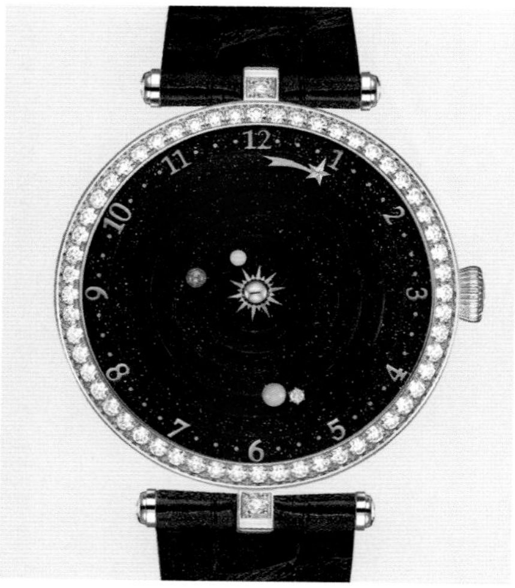

Lady Arpels Planétarium

Reference number: VCAROAR500
Movement: automatic, Valfleurier Q020 with exclusive module (van der Klaauw); 34 jewels; 40-hour power reserve
Functions: retrograde hours and minutes
Case: white gold, ø 38 mm, height 11.8 mm; white gold bezel with round diamonds; sculpted bridge; diamond on crown
Band: reptile skin, white gold buckle
Remarks: planetarium with aventurine dial, pink gold sun and white gold shooting star, pink mother-of-pearl Mercury, green enamel Venus, turquoise Earth, diamond Moon; planets rotate at actual speed
Price: $245,000
Variation: on diamond bracelet ($330,000)

Midnight Nuit Lumineuse

Reference number: VCARO5YB00
Movement: automatic, Valfleurier Q020, exclusive caliber developed for Van Cleef & Arpels; 50 jewels; 40-hour power reserve
Functions: retrograde hours; minutes
Case: white gold, ø 42 mm, height 12.1 mm; white gold bezel set with diamonds; round diamond on crown; water-resistant up to 3 atm
Remarks: six LEDs backlight diamonds on the dial to form the Unicorn constellation on the dial, lit by piezoelectricity
Band: reptile skin, buckle
Remarks: aventurine dial with miniature painting and diamonds
Price: on request

Pierre Arpels Heure d'ici & Heure d'ailleurs

Reference number: VCARO4II00
Movement: automatic, exclusive Agenhor caliber; 48-hour power reserve
Functions: double jumping hours and retrograde minutes; dual time zone
Case: rose gold, ø 42 mm, height 7.97 mm; white gold bezel; crown with round diamond; sapphire case back; water-resistant up to 3 atm
Remarks: black lacquer dial with sunburst motif on the edge
Band: reptile skin, white gold buckle
Price: $28,300
Variations: in white gold and white lacquer dial with "piqué" motif ($40,900)

Vortic Watch Co.
517 N. Link Lane, Unit A
Fort Collins, CO 80524

Tel.:
855-285-7884

E-mail:
info@vorticwatches.com

Website:
vorticwatches.com

Founded:
2013

Number of employees:
5

Most important collections/price range:
American Artisan Series, Railroad Edition, Military Edition, "Convert Your Watch" service / $1,495 to $7,495

VORTIC WATCH COMPANY

The U.S. watch industry produced some very fine timepieces back in the nineteenth century, like Ball, Elgin, Hamilton, and Waltham. So where did the millions of pocket watches go?

Enter R.T. Custer from Pennsylvania. He heard about companies gathering cases of old pocket watches for their gold and silver, and throwing out the movements, dials, hands, and anything deemed worthless. So he took some classes in industrial design, learned all about 3D printing, graduated, and moved out to Colorado. With crowdfunded seed money, and a few friends, he started printing simple cases.

This process, known as upcycling, did not please one brand, Hamilton, whose name appears on some of the dials. It decided to use the staggering power of its parent group, Swatch, to stomp out the upstart in Colorado. After five years of litigation, a judge at the Southern District of New York finally ended the absurd battle in RT's favor. Vortic promptly did a victory lap with the Lancaster 065.

Vortic continues to use printed titanium cases for the American Artisan series, which features a crystal of Corning's very robust Gorilla Glass. Watch fans can also send in an old pocket watches for reconditioning and wrist conversion with personal configuration. The Railroad Edition offers vintage railroad watches featuring a lever under the removable bezel, a system that prevents the watches from being accidentally reset.

The latest family of watches, the Military Edition, comes from a stock of pocket watches originally manufactured for the U.S. Army Air Corps. RT is now successful enough to "give back": Five hundred dollars from the sale of each watch will go to the Veterans Watchmaker Initiative, which provides training for U.S. military veterans who wish to become professional watchmakers.

American Artisan Series "The Lancaster 065"

Movement: manually wound, antique Hamilton Watch Company movement (built in 1930), 12 size (39 mm); 23 jewels; 36-hour power reserve
Functions: hours, minutes, sweep seconds
Case: titanium with "bronzed" finish, 46 mm, height 12 mm; Gorilla Glass crystal; transparent case back, water-resistant to 1 atm
Band: calfskin with special "oxblood" finish, buckle
Remarks: special "victory" watch to celebrate legal victory against a major group
Price: $1,995 to $3,995; all unique pieces
Variations: cases in 3D-printed titanium, machined titanium, black DLC titanium; machined bronze

The Railroad Edition "The Lancaster Railroad 016"

Movement: antique Hamilton movement (built 1945); 16 size (43 mm); 21 jewels, lever set, 36-hour power reserve; **Functions:** hours, minutes, subsidiary seconds
Case: titanium, 51 mm, height 15 mm; special bezel system allows access to railroad lever setting mechanism; Gorilla Glass crystal; transparent case back; water-resistant to 1 atm; **Band:** calfskin, buckle
Remarks: in no way associated with modern-day Hamilton Watch Company; the piece shown here was a family heirloom, antique pocket watch
Price: $3,995 to $9,995; all unique pieces
Variations: titanium; black DLC titanium; machined bronze

The Military Edition (Second Edition)

Movement: antique Hamilton Watch Company movement (1938–1950), 16 size (43 mm); 22 jewels; 36-hour power reserve
Functions: hours, minutes, deadbeat seconds
Case: titanium with black PVD, ø 49 mm, height 15 mm; German glass; transparent case back (Gorilla Glass); water-resistant to 5 atm
Band: calfskin, buckle
Remarks: movement originally manufactured for US Army Air Corps in World War II; comes with additional canvas strap and strap of authentic bomber jacket
Price: $5,995; limited to 50 pieces

VOSTOK-EUROPE

Koliz Vostok Co. Ltd.
Naugarduko 41
LT-03227 Vilnius
Lithuania

Tel.:
+370-5-2106342

E-mail:
info@vostok-europe.com

Website:
www.vostok-europe.com

Founded:
2003

Number of employees:
24

Annual production:
30,000 watches

U.S. distributor:
Vostok-Europe
Détente Watch Group
244 Upton Road, Suite 4
Colchester, CT 06415
877-486-7865
www.detentewatches.com

Most important collections/price range:
Anchar collection / from $759; Mriya / from $649

Vostok-Europe is a young brand with old roots. In 2014, it celebrated its tenth anniversary.

What started as a joint venture between the original Vostok company—a wholly separate entity—deep in the heart of Russia and a start-up in the newly minted European Union member nation of Lithuania has grown into something altogether different over the years. Originally, every Vostok model had a proprietary Russian engine, a 32-jewel automatic built by Vostok in Russia. Over the years, demand and the need for alternative complications expanded the portfolio of movements to include Swiss and Japanese ones. While the heritage of the eighty-year Russian watch industry is still evident in the inspirations and designs of Vostok-Europe, the watches built today have become favorites of extreme athletes the world over.

"Real people doing real things," is the mantra that Igor Zubovskij, managing director of the company, often repeats. "We don't use models to market our watches. Only real people test our watches in many different conditions."

That community of "real people" includes cross-country drivers in the Dakar Rally, one of the most famous aerobatic pilots in the world, a team of spelunkers who literally went to the bottom of the world in the Krubera Cave, and world free-diving champions. Much of the Vostok-Europe line is of professional dive quality. For illumination, some models incorporate tritium tube technology, which offers about twenty-five years of constant lighting. The Lunokhod 2, the current flagship of the brand, incorporates vertical tubes in a "candleholder" design for full 360-degree illumination.

The watches are assembled in Vilnius, Lithuania, and Zubvoskij still personally oversees quality control operations. The Mriya, named after the world's largest cargo airplane, was the first watch in the world to carry the new Seiko NE88 column-wheel chronograph movement.

Expedition Everest Underground Automatic

Reference number: YN84-597A543
Movement: automatic, Seiko Epson YN84; ø 29.36 mm; 22 jewels; 21,600 vph; 40-hour power reserve; **Functions:** hours, minutes, sweep seconds; power reserve indication, 24-hour display
Case: stainless steel, ø 48 mm, height 17.5 mm; unidirectional bezel with 0-60 scale, hardened antireflective K1 mineral glass; screw-in crown; water-resistant to 20 atm; **Band:** leather, buckle
Remarks: "Trigalight" constant tritium illumination; comes with additional silicone strap, changing tool, and dry box
Price: $769; limited and numbered edition of 3,000 pieces

Expedition Everest Underground

Reference number: YM8J-597E546
Movement: quartz, Seiko Epson YM8J
Functions: hours, minutes, sweep seconds; world time with city references; weekday, date, 24-hour chronograph, 24-hour countdown, 24-hour sound alarm
Case: stainless steel, ø 47 mm, height 17.5 mm; unidirectional bezel with 0-60 scale, hardened antireflective K1 mineral glass; screw-in crown; water-resistant to 20 atm; **Band:** leather, buckle
Remarks: "Trigalight" constant tritium illumination; comes with additional silicone strap, changing tool, and dry box
Price: $599; limited and numbered edition of 3,000 pieces

Lunokhod 2 Chrono & Alarm & Perpetual Calendar "Tritium Gaslight"

Reference number: YM86-620A506
Movement: S. Epson YM86; ø 27 mm, height 3.7 mm
Functions: hours, minutes, subsidiary seconds; 24-hour chronograph; 24-hour sound alarm; perpetual calendar; days of the week
Case: stainless steel, ø 49 mm, height 17.5 mm; unidirectional bezel with 0-60 scale, hardened antireflective K1 mineral glass; water-resistant to 30 atm, helium release valve
Band: calfskin, buckle
Remarks: with 2nd silicone strap, screwdriver, and dry box; "Trigalight" constant tritium illumination
Price: $899

Energia 2

Reference number: YN84-575A539
Movement: automatic, Seiko Epson YN84; ø 29.36 mm; 22 jewels; 21,600 vph; 40-hour power reserve; **Functions:** hours, minutes, sweep seconds; power reserve indication, 24-hour display
Case: stainless steel, ø 48 mm, height 17.5 mm; unidirectional bezel with 0-60 scale, hardened antireflective K1 mineral glass; screw-in crown; water-resistant to 30 atm; helium release valve; **Band:** stainless steel bracelet; buckle with diver's extension
Remarks: "Trigalight" constant tritium illumination; comes with additional silicone strap, changing tool, and dry box
Price: $1,210; limited and numbered edition of 3,000 pieces

N-1 Rocket

Reference number: NE57-225A562/B
Movement: automatic, Seiko Caliber NH57; ø 29.36 mm, height 5.32 mm; 29 jewels, 21,600 vph; 41-hour power reserve
Functions: hours, minutes, sweep seconds; sweep power reserve; date
Case: stainless steel, ø 46 mm, height 17 mm; unidirectional bezel with 0-120 scale, K1 hardened antireflective mineral glass; water-resistant to 20 atm, helium release valve
Band: leather, buckle
Price: $799

Energia 2

Reference number: YN84/575O540
Movement: automatic, Seiko Caliber YN84; ø 26.6 mm, height 5.32 mm; 22 jewels; 21,600 vph; 41-hour power reserve
Functions: hours, minutes, sweep seconds; power reserve indicator; 24-hour indication
Case: bronze, ø 48 mm, height 17 mm; unidirectional bezel with 0-60 scale, K1 hardened antireflective mineral glass; water-resistant to 30 atm; helium release valve
Band: leather, buckle
Remarks: with 2nd silicone strap, screwdriver, and dry box; "Trigalight" constant tritium illumination
Price: $1,079; limited and numbered edition of 3,000 pieces

Anchar Men's Diver Watch

Reference number: 6S21-510O586
Movement: Quartz, Miyota 6S21; ø 34.3 mm, height 4.13 mm
Functions: hours, minutes, date, central hand chronograph
Case: bronze, ø 48 mm, height 16 mm; unidirectional bezel with 0-60 scale, hardened antireflective K1 mineral glass; screw-in crown; water-resistant to 30 atm
Band: calfskin, buckle
Remarks: comes with 2nd silicone band, 2 screwdrivers, and dry box; "Trigalight" constant tritium illumination
Price: $899
Variations: various dial colors

Expedition North Pole

Movement: automatic, Seiko Caliber SII NH35; ø 29.36 mm, height 5.32 mm; 24 jewels; 21,600 vph; bidirectional winding; 41-hour power reserve
Functions: hours, minutes, sweep seconds; date
Case: stainless steel, ø 43 mm, height 15.5 mm; hardened antireflective K1 mineral crystal; screw-in crown; transparent case back; water-resistant to 20 atm
Band: calfskin, buckle
Price: $439

Limousine

Reference number: YN84-565E550
Movement: automatic, Seiko Epson YN84; ø 27.4 mm, height 5.77 mm; 22 jewels; 21,600 vph; 40-hour power reserve
Functions: hours, minutes, sweep seconds; 24-hour indicator; power reserve; date
Case: bicolor stainless steel and rose gold, ø 45 mm, height 14 mm; hardened antireflective K1 mineral crystal; water-resistant to 5 atm
Remarks: "Trigalight" constant tritium illumination; open balance
Band: calfskin, buckle
Price: $859
Variations: yellow gold, blue PVD bezel

WALDAN

Oscar Waldan, born in Poland, has a remarkable life story. He was already a watch fan by the time he ended up in Terezin concentration camp, where he befriended a fellow prisoner who was a watchmaker. After the war, he plunged headfirst into the industry, supplying various high-profile retailers in the United States with in-house-branded timepieces. He also worked with major brands like Omega. And then, Waldan decided he had the experience and the wherewithal and the ideas to produce his own timepieces. In 1979, he launched Waldan International. The quartz crisis was still weighing on the industry, but he designed a series of mechanical watches and built his cases and dials to reflect the quality Swiss engines within. These early Waldans included such counterintuitive pieces as a moon phase chronograph, and they remain collector's favorites, embodying what a fine luxury wristwatch should be: a mechanical complication with top-quality components inside and out and a design that will never go out of style.

The first generation of Waldan watches (now known as the Classic collection) are Swiss Made timepieces crafted in 18-kt gold or platinum. In 2018, Oscar's son Andrew took the reins and decided it was time to evolve by adding a new line that would take the classic look of the existing Waldans and build a high-quality watch priced to appeal to a much wider audience. The Heritage collection is crafted in steel, sapphire, and fine leather, and is now built in the USA. While the Classic collection remains available to high-end collectors, the new Heritage collection embraces a retail price segment under $500, with a goal of offering the timeless Waldan design(s) to a far wider audience.

Waldan Watches
600 5th Ave.
FLR 2
New York, NY 10020

Tel.:
212-308-5310

E-mail:
info@waldanwatches.com

Website:
www.waldanwatches.com

Founded:
1979

Number of employees:
6

Annual production:
approx. 6,000

Distribution:
See headquarters.

Most important collections/price range:
Waldan Heritage / $299 to-$1,000; Waldan Classic / $8,000 to $18,000

Heritage Professional

Reference number: 0196OA
Movement: quartz, Ameriquartz Caliber 70200 all-metal
Functions: hours, minutes, subseconds
Case: stainless steel stepped case; ø 40 mm, height 8.6 mm; sapphire crystal, water-resistant to 5 atm
Band: calfskin, buckle
Price: $299

Heritage Professional

Reference number: 0196D
Movement: quartz, Ameriquartz Caliber 70200 all-metal
Functions: hours, minutes, subseconds
Case: stainless steel stepped case; ø 40mm, height 8.6 mm; sapphire crystal, water-resistant to 5 atm
Band: calfskin, buckle
Price: $299

Heritage Sportline

Reference number: 0196SA
Movement: quartz, Ameriquartz Caliber 70200 all-metal
Functions: hours, minutes, subseconds
Case: stainless steel stepped case; ø 40 mm, height 8.6 mm; sapphire crystal, water-resistant to 5 atm
Band: calfskin, buckle
Price: $299

Heritage Sportline

Reference number: 0196SB
Movement: quartz, Ameriquartz Caliber 70200 all-metal
Functions: hours, minutes, subseconds
Case: stainless steel stepped case; ø 40 mm, height 8.6 mm; sapphire crystal; water-resistant to 5 atm
Band: calfskin, buckle
Price: $299

Retro Alarm

Movement: manually wound, caliber AS 1931; ø 25.6 mm, height 6.9 mm; 17 jewels; 21,600 vph; dual spring barrels; 13-second alarm; 48-hour power reserve
Functions: hours, minutes, sweep seconds; date; mechanical alarm
Case: rose gold, ø 38 mm, height 12 mm; sapphire crystal; full case back; water-resistant to 3 atm
Band: reptile skin, buckle
Remarks: 1970–1974 Vintage NOS retro alarm movement; white porcelain enamel dial
Price: $8,000

World Time Chronometer

Movement: automatic, ETA 2893-3 Caliber; ø 25.6 mm, height 4.1 mm; 21 jewels; 28,800 vph; decorated movement and rotor; COSC-certified movement; 38-hour power reserve
Functions: hours, minutes, sweep seconds; world time indicator
Case: rose gold, ø 40 mm; sapphire crystal; transparent case back; water-resistant to 3 atm
Price: $18,000

Astronic Chronometer

Movement: automatic, ETA 2824-2 Caliber; ø 25.6 mm, height 4.6 mm; 21 jewels; 28,800 vph; decorated bridges and rotor (with signature); COSC-certified movement; 38-hour power reserve
Functions: hours, minutes, sweep seconds; sweep date, weekday, month, moon phase
Case: rose gold, ø 39 mm; sapphire crystal; transparent case back; water-resistant to 3 atm
Band: reptile skin, buckle
Remarks: enamel dial with black or gold applied numerals
Price: $8,000

Astronic Chronograph

Movement: automatic, 1969 Zenith "El Primero" Caliber 3019 PHF; ø 30 mm, height 6.5 mm; 31 jewels; 36,000 vph; 50-hour power reserve
Functions: hours, minutes, seconds on subdial, 12-hour chronograph, day of week, date, month, moon phase
Case: pink gold, ø 39.5mm, height 20 mm; sapphire crystal; transparent case back; water-resistant to 3 atm
Band: reptile skin, buckle
Remarks: enamel dial with applied gold Breguet numerals
Price: $16,000

Chronograph Chronometer

Movement: automatic, Valjoux 7751; ø 30 mm, height 7.9 mm; 25 jewels; 28,800 vph; bidirectional rotor, côte de Genève; COSC-certified movement; 42-hour power reserve
Functions: hours, minutes, subsidiary seconds; chronograph; 2nd time zone, day, weekday, date, moon phase
Case: pink gold; ø 38 mm; sapphire crystal; transparent case back; jacketed chronograph pushers; water-resistant to 3 atm
Band: reptile skin
Remarks: enamel dial with applied Arabic-style numerals, black or gold Breguet-style hands
Price: $10,600
Variations: platinum case

WEMPE GLASHÜTTE I/SA

Ever since 2005, the global jewelry chain Gerhard D. Wempe KG has been putting out watches under its own name again. It was probably inevitable: Gerhard D. Wempe, who founded the company in the late nineteenth century in Oldenburg, was himself a watchmaker. And in the 1930s, the company also owned the Hamburg chronometer works that made watches for seafarers and pilots.

Today, while Wempe remains formally in Hamburg, its manufacturing is done in Glashütte. The move to the fully renovated and expanded Urania observatory in the hills above town was engineered by Eva-Kim Wempe, great-granddaughter of the founder. There, the company does all its after-sales service and tests watches using the strict German Industrial Norm (DIN 8319), with official blessings from the Saxon and Thuringian offices for measurement and calibration, and according to international norms paid out by the German Calibration Service.

The move to Glashütte coincided with a push to verticalize by creating a line of in-house movements for the exclusive Chronometerwerke models, like the very retro Chronometerwerke Power Reserve. The calibers, bearing the initials CW, are made in partnership with companies like Nomos in Glashütte or the Swiss workshop MHVJ.

The second Wempe line is called Zeitmeister, or Master of Time. This collection uses reworked, ETA or Sellita calibers. It meets all the requirements of the high art of watchmaking and, thanks to its accessible pricing, is attractive for budding collectors. In 2020, Wempe joined a large community of brands with sportive-elegant timepieces. The Iron Walker series is supposed to be inspired by the workers who built the great skyscrapers of New York in the 1920s. The line is characterized by the elegant bracelet that integrates almost seamlessly into the case. The skyscrapers are hinted at in the shape of the hands.

Gerhard D. Wempe KG
Steinstrasse 23
D-20095 Hamburg
Germany

Tel.:
+49-40-334-480

E-mail:
info@wempe.de

Website:
www.wempe.com

Founded:
1878

Number of employees:
845 worldwide; 65 at Wempe Glashütte I/SA

Annual production:
5,000 watches

U.S. distributor:
Wempe
700 Fifth Avenue
New York, NY 10019
212-397-9000
www.wempe.com

Most important collections/price range:
Wempe Zeitmeister / approx. $1,000 to $4,500; Wempe Chronometerwerke / approx. $6,000 to $56,500; Wempe Iron Walker / $1,950 to $4,250

Chronometerwerke Power Reserve

Reference number: WG 080003
Movement: manually wound, Wempe Caliber CW3; ø 32 mm, height 6.1 mm; 40 jewels; 28,800 vph; three-quarter plate, 3 screw-mounted gold chatons, hand-engraved balance cock; 42-hour power reserve; DIN-certified chronometer
Functions: hours, minutes, subsidiary seconds; power reserve indicator
Case: stainless steel, ø 43 mm, height 12.5 mm; sapphire crystal; transparent case back; water-resistant to 3 atm
Band: reptile skin, buckle
Price: $6,300

Chronometerwerke Automatic Pilot's Watch Limited

Reference number: WG 090005
Movement: automatic, Wempe Caliber CW4; ø 32.8 mm, height 6 mm; 35 jewels; 28,800 vph; 2 spring barrels, three-quarter plate, hand-engraved balance cock, 6 gold chatons, tungsten microrotor, finely finished with Glashütte ribbing; ISO 3159-certified chronometer; 90-hour power reserve
Functions: hours, minutes, sweep seconds
Case: stainless steel with black PVD, ø 41 mm, height 11.7 mm; sapphire crystal; transparent case back; water-resistant to 3 atm
Band: calfskin, buckle
Price: $6,300; limited to 100 pieces

Chronometerwerke Automatic

Reference number: WG 090003
Movement: automatic, Wempe Caliber CW4; ø 32.8 mm, height 6 mm; 35 jewels; 28,800 vph; 2 spring barrels, three-quarter plate, hand-engraved balance cock, 6 gold chatons, tungsten microrotor, finely finished with Glashütte ribbing; ISO 3159-certified chronometer; 92-hour power reserve
Functions: hours, minutes, sweep seconds; date
Case: stainless steel, ø 41 mm, height 11.7 mm; sapphire crystal; transparent case back; water-resistant to 3 atm
Band: reptile skin, buckle
Price: $6,900
Variations: yellow gold ($14,950)

Zeitmeister World Time

Reference number: WM 340001
Movement: automatic, ETA Caliber 2893-2; ø 25.6 mm, height 4.1 mm; 21 jewels; 28,800 vph; ISO 3159-certified chronometer; 42-hour power reserve
Functions: hours, minutes, sweep seconds; world time display (2nd time zone); date
Case: stainless steel, ø 42 mm, height 11 mm; sapphire crystal; water-resistant to 5 atm
Band: reptile skin, buckle
Price: $2,135

Zeitmeister Moon Phase Full Calendar

Reference number: WM 350001
Movement: automatic, ETA Caliber 2892-A2 with module; ø 25.6 mm, height 5.35 mm; 21 jewels; 28,800 vph; ISO 3159-certified chronometer; 42-hour power reserve
Functions: hours, minutes, sweep seconds; full calendar with date, weekday, month, moon phase
Case: stainless steel, ø 42 mm, height 14.1 mm; sapphire crystal; water-resistant to 5 atm
Band: reptile skin, folding clasp
Price: $2,890

Zeitmeister Classic Automatic

Reference number: WM 140001
Movement: automatic, ETA Caliber 2892-A2; ø 25.6 mm, height 3.6 mm; 21 jewels; 28,800 vph; ISO-3195-certified chronometer; 42-hour power reserve
Functions: hours, minutes, sweep seconds; date
Case: stainless steel, ø 38 mm, height 11 mm; sapphire crystal; water-resistant to 5 atm
Band: reptile skin, buckle
Price: $1,620

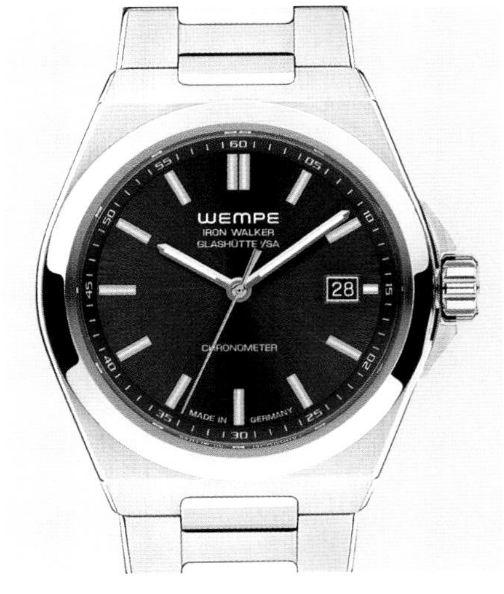

Iron Walker Automatic Men's Watch

Reference number: WI 100006
Movement: automatic, ETA Caliber 2892-A2; ø 25.6 mm, height 3.6 mm; 21 jewels; 28,800 vph; ISO-3195-certified chronometer; 42-hour power reserve
Functions: hours, minutes, sweep seconds; date
Case: stainless steel, ø 40 mm, height 9.75 mm; sapphire crystal; water-resistant to 10 atm
Band: stainless steel, folding clasp, with safety catch
Price: $2,750
Variations: white or black dial

Iron Walker Automatic Diver's Watch

Reference number: WI 200001
Movement: automatic, ETA Caliber 2892-A2; ø 25.6 mm, height 3.6 mm; 21 jewels; 28,800 vph; ISO-3195-certified chronometer; 42-hour power reserve
Functions: hours, minutes, sweep seconds; date
Case: stainless steel, ø 42 mm, height 11.7 mm; crown-activated inner bezel with 0-60 scale; sapphire crystal; screw-in crown; water-resistant to 30 atm
Band: stainless steel, folding clasp, with safety catch and extension link
Price: $3,450
Variations: blue dial

Iron Walker Automatic Chronograph

Reference number: WI 300002
Movement: automatic, ETA Caliber 7753; ø 30 mm, height 7.9 mm; 27 jewels; 28,800 vph; ISO-3195-certified chronometer; 48-hour power reserve
Functions: hours, minutes, subsidiary seconds; chronograph; date
Case: stainless steel, ø 42 mm, height 13.95 mm; sapphire crystal; screw-in crown; water-resistant to 10 atm
Band: stainless steel, folding clasp, with safety catch
Price: $4,250
Variations: black dial

ZEITWINKEL

Zeitwinkel is turning fifteen in 2021, but that is not really important for this small, independent company based in St.-Imier, one of the hubs of the watch industry in Switzerland. The key attributes of the brand, ones that many watch manufacturers aspire to endow their creations with, are "timeless, simple, and sustainable." What are fifteen years compared to timelessness?

The models produced by Zeitwinkel (the name means "time angle") are deceptively classical: The simplest exemplar is a two-hand watch; the most complicated, the 273°, a three-hand timepiece with power reserve display and large date. The most decoration one will find on the dials is a spangling of stylized *W*s, for *Winkel* (angle). The cases feature a delicate interplay of sandblasted and polished areas, but they are discreetly elegant, in a fairly "German" way, which comes as no surprise, because Zeitwinkel's founders, Ivica Maksimovic and Peter Nikolaus, hail from there. Some details will catch the eye, notably the extralarge subsidiary seconds dial or the aperture for the patented large date, found beside the 11 o'clock marker.

The most valuable part of the watches is their veritable *manufacture* movements, plates and bridges made of German silver, which is fairly rare in the business. The calibers were developed by Laurent Besse and his *artisans horlogers,* or watchmaking craftspeople. All components come courtesy of longtime independent suppliers not far from Zeitwinkel's workshop in Saint-Imier, where all movements as well as all watches are assembled and regulated by hand. The 273° Saphir Fumé comes with a smoked sapphire crystal dial. The enamel dial of the 082° Email Grand Feu is smaller, but the brilliance of the enamel is a perfect backdrop to the gentle blue numerals and indices that recall timepieces of a past era.

In keeping with the company's ideals, you won't find any alligator in Zeitwinkel watch straps. Choices here are exclusively rubber, calfskin, or calfskin with an alligator-like pattern.

Zeitwinkel Montres SA
Rue Pierre-Jolissaint 35
CH-2610 Saint-Imier
Switzerland

Tel.:
+41-32-940-17-71

E-mail:
info@zeitwinkel.ch

Website:
www.zeitwinkel.ch

Founded:
2006

Annual production:
approx. 800 watches

U.S. distributor:
Tourneau
510 Madison Avenue
New York, NY 10022
212-758-5830
RightTime
7110 E. County Line Road
Highlands Ranch, CO 80126
303-862-3900

Most important collections/price range:
mechanical wristwatches / starting at around $6,900

082° Email Grand Feu

Reference number: 082-3.S02-01-23
Movement: automatic, Caliber ZW0102; ø 30.4 mm, height 5.7 mm; 30 jewels; 28,800 vph; German silver three-quarter plate with côtes de Genève and perlage; polished screws and edges; 72-hour power reserve
Functions: hours, minutes, sweep seconds
Case: stainless steel, ø 39 mm, height 11.6 mm; sapphire crystal; transparent case back; water-resistant to 5 atm
Band: calfskin, folding clasp
Remarks: white enamel dial, grand feu
Price: $12,200
Variations: different bands

181°

Reference number: 181-21-01-21
Movement: automatic, Caliber ZW0102; ø 30.4 mm, height 5.7 mm; 28 jewels; 28,800 vph; German silver three-quarter plate and bridges, guilloché, polished screws and edges; 72-hour power reserve
Functions: hours, minutes, subsidiary seconds; date
Case: stainless steel, ø 42.5 mm, height 11.7 mm; sapphire crystal; transparent case back; water-resistant to 5 atm
Remarks: heat-blued second hand
Band: calfskin, folding clasp
Price: $7,900
Variations: various dial colors

273° Saphir Fumé

Reference number: 273-4.S01-01-21
Movement: automatic, Caliber ZW0103; ø 30.4 mm, height 8 mm; 49 jewels; 28,800 vph; German silver three-quarter plate and bridges, côtes de Genève, polished screws and edges; perlage on dial side; 72-hour power reserve
Functions: hours, minutes, subsidiary seconds; power reserve indicator; patented big date mechanism
Case: stainless steel, ø 42.5 mm, height 13.8 mm; sapphire crystal; transparent case back; water-resistant to 5 atm
Band: calfskin, folding clasp
Remarks: smoky black sapphire crystal dial
Price: $16,300
Variations: various dial colors; different bands

Zenith SA
34, rue des Billodes
CH-2400 Le Locle
Switzerland

Tel.:
+41-32-930-6262

Website:
www.zenith-watches.com

Founded:
1865

Number of employees:
over 330 employees worldwide

U.S. distributor:
Zenith Watches
966 South Springfield Avenue
Springfield, NJ 07081
866-675-2079
contact.zenith@lvmhwatchjewelry.com

Most important collections/price range:
Academy / from $80,900; Elite / from $4,700; Chronomaster / from $6,700; Pilot / from $5,700; Defy / from $5,900

ZENITH

The tall, narrow building in Le Locle, with its closely spaced, high windows to let in daylight, is a testimony to Zenith's history as a self-sufficient *manufacture* in the entrepreneurial spirit of the Industrial Revolution. The company, founded in 1865 by Georges Favre-Jacot as a small watch reassembly workshop, has produced and distributed every type of watch from the simple pocket watch to the most complicated calendar. But it remains primarily linked with the El Primero caliber, the first wristwatch chronograph movement boasting automatic winding and a frequency of 36,000 vph, allowing for measurements of a tenth of a second. That was the year 1969, and only a few watch manufacturers had risked such a high oscillation frequency—and none of them with such complexity as the integrated chronograph mechanism and bilaterally winding rotor of the El Primero.

Purchase of the brand by LVMH Group in 1999 gave the company new technical possibilities. Zenith was dusted off and modernized. The historic complex in Le Locle, which was put on UNESCO's World Heritage list in 2009, was thoroughly renovated. Over eighty different crafts are practiced here, from watchmaking to design, from art to prototyping. Synergies with the Group companion Hublot and TAG Heuer produced the Defy 21, a complex chronograph movement based on the 36,000-vph El Primero. It features two separate gear trains and escapements for time and chronograph functions, respectively. The chronograph movement beats at 360,000 vph, allowing the hundredths of a second to be displayed. The other technical feat is the Zero G that keeps the escapement system in the horizontal position.

The vintage movement has also produced nostalgic pilot's watches chez Zenith, and more recently a re-edition of a number of historic models housed in identifiably classic cases. The original El Primero is often used to drive the hands, but in 2020 the company released the El Primero 3600 caliber, a modernized version of the old one with a little more power reserve.

Chronomaster Revival Shadow

Reference number: 97.T384.4061.21.C822
Movement: automatic, Zenith Caliber 4061 "El Primero"; ø 30 mm, height 6.6 mm; 31 jewels; 36,000 vph; 50-hour power reserve
Functions: hours, minutes, subsidiary seconds; chronograph
Case: titanium, ø 37 mm; sapphire crystal; water-resistant to 5 atm
Band: rubber, double folding clasp
Remarks: titanium case based on a case prototype from 1970 (A384 blackened)
Price: $8,200

Chronomaster Revival Manufacture Edition

Reference number: 03.Z386.400.60.C843
Movement: automatic, Zenith Caliber 400 "El Primero"; ø 30 mm, height 6.6 mm; 31 jewels; 36,000 vph; 50-hour power reserve
Functions: hours, minutes, subsidiary seconds; chronograph; date
Case: stainless steel, ø 38 mm, height 12.45 mm; sapphire crystal; transparent case back; water-resistant to 5 atm
Band: reptile skin, buckle
Remarks: dial in 3 blue hues like an A386 prototype from 1969
Price: $8,700

El Primero Chronomaster 2

Reference number: 95.3001.3600.69.C817
Movement: automatic, Zenith Caliber 3600 "El Primero"; ø 30 mm, height 6.6 mm; 31 jewels; 36,000 vph; partially skeletonized movement; 60-hour power reserve
Functions: hours, minutes, subsidiary seconds; chronograph; date
Case: titanium, ø 42 mm, height 12.75 mm; ceramic bezel; sapphire crystal; transparent case back; water-resistant to 10 atm
Band: reptile skin, double folding clasp
Price: $9,600

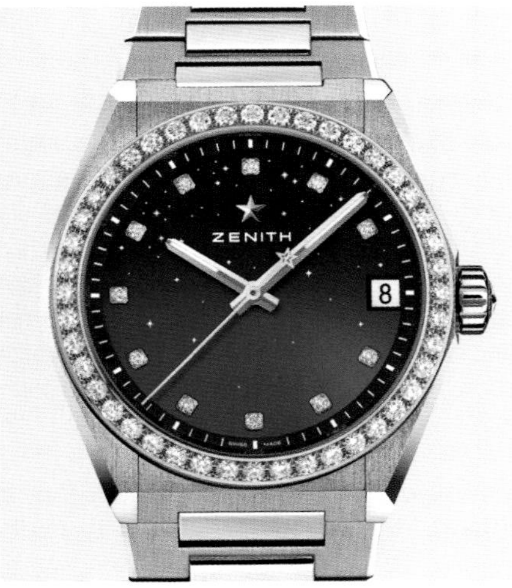

Defy Classic Midnight

Reference number: 16.9200.670.01.MI001
Movement: automatic, Zenith Caliber 670 SK "Elite"; ø 25.6 mm, height 3.88 mm; 27 jewels; 28,800 vph; skeletonized movement; 48-hour power reserve
Functions: hours, minutes, sweep seconds; date
Case: stainless steel, ø 36 mm; bezel set with 44 diamonds; sapphire crystal; transparent case back; water-resistant to 10 atm
Band: stainless steel, folding clasp
Remarks: dial set with 11 diamonds; comes with 2 additional reptile skin straps
Price: $10,700

Defy Classic Midnight

Reference number: 16.9200.670.03.MI001
Movement: automatic, Zenith Caliber 670 SK "Elite"; ø 25.6 mm, height 3.88 mm; 27 jewels; 28,800 vph; skeletonized movement; 48-hour power reserve
Functions: hours, minutes, sweep seconds; date
Case: stainless steel, ø 36 mm; bezel set with 44 diamonds; sapphire crystal; transparent case back; water-resistant to 10 atm
Band: stainless steel, folding clasp
Remarks: dial set with 11 diamonds; comes with 2 additional reptile skin straps
Price: $10,700

Defy El Primero 21 "Land Rover"

Reference number: 97.9000.9004.01.R787
Movement: automatic, Zenith Caliber 9004 "El Primero"; ø 32 mm, height 7.9 mm; 53 jewels; 36,000 vph; independent chronograph mechanism with its own escapement (360,000 vph) and power management system; Timelab-tested chronometer; 50-hour power reserve
Functions: hours, minutes, subsidiary seconds; power reserve indicator (for chronograph functions); chronograph (with 1/100th second display)
Case: titanium, ø 44 mm, height 14.5 mm; sapphire crystal; transparent case back; water-resistant to 10 atm
Band: rubber, with reptile skin layer, double folding clasp
Remarks: comes with additional textile strap
Price: $13,600; limited to 250 pieces

Defy El Primero 21 Carl Cox Edition

Reference number: 10.9001.9004.99.R941
Movement: automatic, Zenith Caliber 9004 "El Primero"; ø 32 mm, height 7.9 mm; 53 jewels; 36,000 vph; independent chronograph mechanism with its own escapement (360,000 vph) and power management system; Timelab-tested chronometer; 50-hour power reserve; **Functions:** hours, minutes, subsidiary seconds; power reserve indicator (for chronograph functions); chronograph (with 1/100th second display)
Case: carbon fiber mixed with Luminova (glows under UV light), ø 44 mm, height 14.5 mm; sapphire crystal; transparent case back; water-resistant to 10 atm
Band: rubber with textile layer, double folding clasp
Remarks: homage to DJ Carl Cox
Price: $19,100; limited to 200 pieces

Defy El Primero 21 Ultraviolet

Reference number: 97.9001.9004.80.R922
Movement: automatic, Zenith Caliber 9004 "El Primero"; ø 32 mm, height 7.9 mm; 53 jewels; 36,000 vph; independent chronograph mechanism with its own escapement (360,000 vph) and power management system; bridges with violet PVD; Timelab-tested chronometer; 50-hour power reserve
Functions: hours, minutes, subsidiary seconds; power reserve indicator (for chronograph functions); chronograph (with 1/100th second display)
Case: titanium, ø 44 mm, height 14.5 mm; sapphire crystal; transparent case back; water-resistant to 10 atm
Band: rubber with textile layer, double folding clasp
Price: $13,100; limited to 200 pieces

Defy El Primero Double Tourbillon

Reference number: 40.9000.9020.78.R582
Movement: automatic, Zenith Caliber 9020 "El Primero"; ø 35.8 mm, height 7.9 mm; 59 jewels; 36,000 vph; 2 independent tourbillon escapements; chronograph mechanism with its own escapement (360,000 vph) and power management system; Timelab-tested chronometer; 50-hour power reserve
Functions: hours, minutes, subsidiary seconds; power reserve indicator (for chronograph functions); chronograph (with 1/100th second display)
Case: platinum, ø 46 mm, height 14.5 mm; sapphire crystal; transparent case back; water-resistant to 10 atm
Band: rubber, with reptile skin layer, double folding clasp
Price: $141,000; limited to 10 pieces

Pilot Type 20 Rescue Chronograph

Reference number: 03.2434.4069.20.I010
Movement: automatic, Zenith Caliber 4069 "El Primero"; ø 30 mm, height 6.6 mm; 35 jewels; 36,000 vph; 50-hour power reserve
Functions: hours, minutes, subsidiary seconds; chronograph
Case: stainless steel, ø 45 mm, height 14.25 mm; sapphire crystal; water-resistant to 10 atm
Band: calfskin, buckle
Price: $7,700

Pilot Type 20 Rescue

Reference number: 03.2434.679.20.I010
Movement: automatic, Zenith Caliber 679 "Elite"; ø 25.6 mm, height 3.85 mm; 27 jewels; 28,800 vph; 50-hour power reserve
Functions: hours, minutes, sweep seconds
Case: stainless steel, ø 45 mm, height 14.25 mm; sapphire crystal; water-resistant to 10 atm
Band: calfskin, buckle
Price: $7,200

Elite Classic 36mm

Reference number: 22.3200.670.01.C831
Movement: automatic, Zenith Caliber 670 SK "Elite"; ø 25.6 mm, height 3.88 mm; 27 jewels; 28,800 vph; skeletonized movement; 50-hour power reserve
Functions: hours, minutes, sweep seconds; date
Case: rose gold, ø 36 mm; bezel set with 75 diamonds; sapphire crystal; transparent case back; water-resistant to 5 atm
Band: reptile skin, buckle
Price: $14,600

Elite Classic

Reference number: 18.3100.670.01.C920
Movement: automatic, Zenith Caliber 670 SK "Elite"; ø 25.6 mm, height 3.88 mm; 27 jewels; 28,800 vph; skeletonized movement; 50-hour power reserve
Functions: hours, minutes, sweep seconds; date
Case: rose gold, ø 40.5 mm; sapphire crystal; transparent case back; water-resistant to 5 atm
Band: reptile skin, buckle
Price: $12,600

Elite Classic

Reference number: 03.3100.670.02.C922
Movement: automatic, Zenith Caliber 670 SK "Elite"; ø 25.6 mm, height 3.88 mm; 27 jewels; 28,800 vph; skeletonized movement; 50-hour power reserve
Functions: hours, minutes, sweep seconds; date
Case: stainless steel, ø 40.5 mm; sapphire crystal; transparent case back; water-resistant to 5 atm
Band: reptile skin, double folding clasp
Price: $5,800

Elite Moonphase

Reference number: 18.3100.692.01.C922
Movement: automatic, Zenith Caliber 692 SK "Elite"; ø 25.6 mm, height 3.97 mm; 27 jewels; 28,800 vph; 48-hour power reserve
Functions: hours, minutes, subsidiary seconds; moon phase
Case: rose gold, ø 40.5 mm; sapphire crystal; transparent case back; water-resistant to 5 atm
Band: reptile skin, buckle
Price: $13,600

Caliber 9004 El Primero

Automatic; independent chronograph mechanism with separate escapement (360,000 vph) and power management; COSC-certified chronometer; 2 hairsprings of nanotube carbon matrix, impervious to magnetic fields and temperature fluctuations; single spring barrel, 50-hour power reserve; Timelab-certified chronometer
Functions: hours, minutes, subsidiary seconds; power reserve indicator (for chronograph functions); chronograph displays 1/100th of a second
Diameter: 32.8 mm; **Height:** 7.9 mm
Jewels: 53
Balance: glucydur
Frequency: 36,000 vph
Remarks: côtes de Genève; 293 parts

Caliber 670 Elite

Automatic; skeletonized movement; single spring barrel, 50-hour power reserve
Functions: hours, minutes, sweep seconds; date
Diameter: 25.6 mm
Height: 3.88 mm
Jewels: 27
Balance: glucydur
Frequency: 28,800 vph
Balance spring: flat hairspring
Shock protection: Kif
Remarks: 187 parts

Caliber 679 Elite

Automatic; single spring barrel, 50-hour power reserve
Functions: hours, minutes, sweep seconds
Diameter: 25.6 mm
Height: 3.85 mm
Jewels: 27
Balance: glucydur
Frequency: 28,800 vph
Balance spring: flat hairspring
Shock protection: Kif
Remarks: perlage on plate, rotor (removed for image) and bridges finely finished with côtes de Genève; 126 parts

Caliber 400 El Primero

Automatic; column-wheel control of chronograph functions; single spring barrel, 50-hour power reserve
Functions: hours, minutes, subsidiary seconds; chronograph; date
Diameter: 30 mm
Height: 6.5 mm
Jewels: 31
Balance: glucydur
Frequency: 36,000 vph
Balance spring: flat hairspring
Shock protection: Kif
Remarks: 278 parts

Caliber 692 Elite

Automatic; single spring barrel, 48-hour power reserve
Functions: hours, minutes, subsidiary seconds; moon phase
Diameter: 25.6 mm
Height: 3.97 mm
Jewels: 27
Balance: glucydur
Frequency: 28,800 vph
Hairspring: flat hairspring
Shock protection: Kif
Remarks: mainplate with perlage, finely finished rotor (not featured in image) and bridges with côtes de Genève

Caliber 4047 El Primero

Automatic; single spring barrel, 50-hour power reserve
Functions: hours, minutes; chronograph; large date; sun and moon phase (integrated day/night indicator)
Diameter: 30.5 mm
Height: 9.05 mm
Jewels: 41
Balance: glucydur
Frequency: 36,000 vph
Balance spring: flat hairspring
Shock protection: Kif

Zero West LTD
41 Bridgefoot Path
Emsworth
Hampshire
United Kingdom
PO10 7EB

Tel.:
+44 (0)1243 376 676

E-mail:
time@zerowest.co.uk

Website:
www.zerowest.watch

Founded:
2015

Number of employees:
5

Distribution:
Contact the manufacturer directly.

Most important collections:
Aviation (Spitfire S1/S2/S3/S4 P9427) / Marine (Longitude L1, Longitude L2) / Motorsport (TT-58, Café Racer CR-1 Chronograph, Land Speed LS-1 Chronograph)

ZERO WEST

Time, place, and, indeed, history are the reference points for Zero West, a company founded in 2015 by Andrew Brabyn and Graham Collins, an expert marketing designer and an aerospace engineer, respectively. The company name itself refers to the coordinates of the Greenwich Royal Observatory. Their first watch was a statement: The Longitude L1 paid homage to an icon of British—even world—horology, John Harrison's remarkable H4 maritime clock that managed to keep accurate time on a ship in 1761 and contributed to the establishment of the Greenwich prime meridian by George Airy in 1851.

It was a solid launch into the evolving world of modern British watchmaking. The company has since defined three core collections for their brand: automotive, aviation, and marine. Their latest aviation model, for example, celebrates an icon, the Spitfire S4. This classic pilot watch is inspired from the avionic instruments found in an MKI Spitfire. The case back is an engraved disk from the casing of the Merlin engine from a Spitfire plane. In fact, the original plane was built just thirty miles from where Zero West assembled the watch, some eighty years later.

The automotive portfolio includes the Café Racer chronograph, a reference to the biker gangs who would race between all-night cafés along Great Britain's postwar motorways. The LS-1 Land Speed remembers Daytona Beach, March 29, 1927, when Harry Seagraves broke the 200-mph barrier in his Sunbeam. The chronograph comes in a bullhead case, with the pushers at 11 and 1 o'clock.

The watches are designed and assembled at the company's workshop and headquarters on the South Coast of England. It is where the two founders do their historical research and brainstorm each new watch dial. It is also where Graham Collins makes the straps for the collections. Low volume ensures high quality. The geographical location on the dials and case backs relates to the watch's theme. Each watch is powered by tried-and-true Swiss calibers, like the ETA 2824, and Valjoux 7750 for the chronographs.

Spitfire

Reference Number: S4 P9427
Movement: automatic, ETA Caliber 2824; ø 25.6 mm, height 4.6 mm; 25 jewels; 28,800 vph; 38-hour power reserve
Functions: hours, minutes
Case: vapor-blasted stainless steel, ø 44 mm, height 14.1 mm; black PVD on lugs; brass-finished "joystick" winding crown; transparent case back; water-resistant to 10 atm; **Band:** calfskin, buckle
Remarks: case back features engraved disk made from Merlin engine casing from Spitfire plane, serial number P9427
Price: $3,300; limited to 80 pieces
Variations: without Merlin engraved case back ($2,900; limited to 300 pieces)

Café Racer

Reference Number: CR-1
Movement: automatic Valjoux Caliber 7750; ø 30 mm; height 7.9 mm; 25 jewels; 28,800 vph; custom-decorated rotor; 48-hour power reserve
Function: hours, minutes, subsidiary seconds; date, day; chronograph
Case: stainless steel, ø 44 mm, height 16.3 mm; sapphire crystal; transparent case back; water-resistant 10 atm
Band: calfskin, buckle
Remarks: coordinates reference Ace Café; Arabic dial from period-correct race plates
Price: $4,350; limited to 100 pieces

Land Speed

Reference Number: LS-1
Movement: automatic Valjoux Caliber 7750; ø 30 mm, height 7.9 mm; 25 jewels; 28,800 vph; 48-hour power reserve
Functions: hours, minutes, subsidiary seconds; chronograph
Case: stainless steel with black PVD, ø 44 mm, height 15.7 mm; sapphire crystal; screw-in crown; water-resistant to 10 atm
Remarks: "bullhead" case references in-car rally timers; date and coordinates reference Sir Henry Seagrave's land speed record of 203.79 mph in 1927 on Daytona Beach
Price: $4,350; limited to 100 pieces

CONCEPTO

The Concepto Watch Factory, founded in 2006 in La Chaux-de-Fonds, is the successor to the family-run company Jaquet SA, which changed its name to La Joux-Perret a little while ago and then moved to a different location on the other side of the hub of watchmaking. In 2008, Valérien Jaquet, son of the company founder Pierre Jaquet, began systematically building up a modern movement and watch component factory on an empty floor of the building.

Today, the Concepto Watch Factory employs eighty people in various departments, such as Development/Prototyping, Decoparts (partial manufacturing using lathes, machining, or wire erosion), Artisia (production of movements and complications in large series), as well as Optimo (escapements). In addition to the standard family of calibers, the C2000 (based on the Valjoux) and the vintage chronograph movement C7000 (the evolution of the Venus Caliber), the company's product portfolio includes various tourbillon movements (Caliber C8000) and several modules for adding onto ETA movements (Caliber C1000). A brand-new caliber series, the C3000, features a retrograde calendar and seconds, a power reserve indicator, and a chronograph. The C4000 chronograph caliber with automatic winding is currently in pre-series testing.

One of Concepto's greatest assets is its flexibility. Most of the company's movements are not sold off the shelf, as it were, but rather designed according to the specific requirements of the customer with regard to form or technical DNA. Complicated movements are assembled entirely and tested by the company's watchmakers, while others are sold as kits for assembly by the watchmakers. Annual production is somewhere between 30,000 and 40,000 units, with additional hundreds of thousands of components made for contract manufacturing.

Caliber 1053

Automatic; inverted construction with dial-side escapement; bidirectional off-center winding rotor; single spring barrel; 42-hour power reserve
Functions: hours, minutes, subsidiary seconds (all off-center)
Diameter: 33 mm
Height: 3.75 mm
Jewels: 31
Balance: glucydur
Frequency: 28,800 vph
Balance spring: flat hairspring
Remarks: black finishing on movement

Caliber 2904 (dial side)

Inverted construction with dial-side escapement; single spring barrel; 48-hour power reserve
Functions: hours, minutes, subsidiary seconds
Diameter: 30.4 mm
Height: 4.6 mm
Jewels: 31
Balance: screw balance
Frequency: 28,800 vph
Balance spring: flat hairspring

Caliber 3041 Skeleton (dial side)

Manually wound; skeletonized symmetrical construction; single spring barrel; 48-hour power reserve
Functions: hours, minutes
Diameter: 32.6 mm
Height: 5.5 mm
Jewels: 21
Balance: screw balance
Frequency: 28,800 vph
Balance spring: flat hairspring
Remarks: extensive personalization options for finishing and accessories

Caliber 2000-RAC

Automatic; column wheel control of chronograph functions; stop-second system; single spring barrel; 48-hour power reserve
Functions: hours, minutes, subsidiary seconds; chronograph
Diameter: 30.4 mm; **Height:** 8.4 mm
Jewels: 26; **Balance:** screw balance
Frequency: 28,800 vph
Balance spring: flat hairspring
Shock protection: Incabloc
Remarks: related calibers: 2000 (without control wheel); with two or three totalizers ("tricompax") with or without date; various additional displays (moon phase, retrograde date hand, additional 24-hour sweep hand, power reserve indicator)

Caliber 8500

Manually wound; 1-minute tourbillon; column wheel control of chronograph functions; single spring barrel; 50-hour power reserve
Functions: hours, minutes, subsidiary seconds; split-seconds chronograph
Diameter: 31.3 mm
Height: 7.2 mm
Jewels: 31
Balance: screw balance
Frequency: 21,600 vph
Balance spring: flat hairspring
Remarks: very fine movement finishing

Caliber 8950-A

Automatic; 1-minute tourbillon; single spring barrel; 60-hour power reserve
Functions: hours, minutes
Diameter: 30.4 mm
Height: 6.7 mm
Jewels: 27
Balance: glucydur
Frequency: 28,800 vph
Balance spring: flat hairspring
Remarks: related caliber: 8950-M (manual winding); extensive personalization options for the finishing, accessories, and functions

Caliber 8000 (dial side)

Manually wound; 1-minute tourbillon; single spring barrel; 72-hour power reserve
Functions: hours, minutes
Diameter: 32.6 mm
Height: 5.7 mm
Jewels: 19
Balance: screw balance
Frequency: 21,600 vph
Balance spring: flat hairspring
Remarks: extensive personalization options for the finishing, accessories, and functions

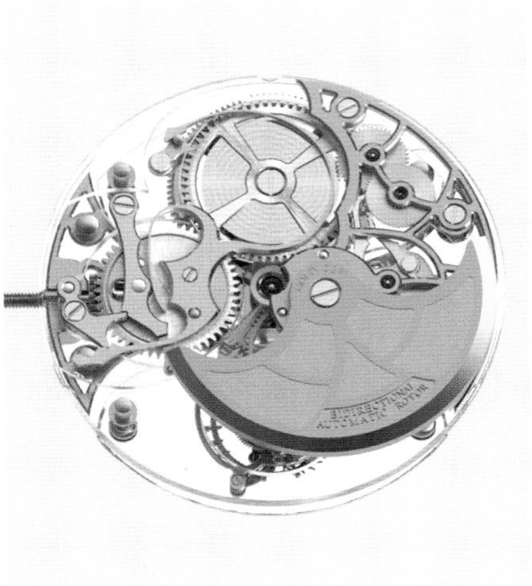

Caliber 8152

Automatic; 1-minute tourbillon; bridges and plate made of sapphire crystal; off-center, bidirectional rotor; single spring barrel; 72-hour power reserve
Functions: hours, minutes
Diameter: 32.6 mm
Height: 8.5 mm
Jewels: 25
Balance: screw balance
Frequency: 21,600 vph
Balance spring: flat hairspring
Remarks: extensive personalization options for the finishing, accessories, and functions

Caliber 8908-M (dial side)

Manually wound; flying 1-minute tourbillon; single spring barrel; 42-hour power reserve
Functions: hours, minutes
Diameter: 34.6 mm
Height: 6.6 mm
Jewels: 21
Balance: screw balance
Frequency: 28,800 vph
Balance spring: flat hairspring
Remarks: extensive personalization options for the finishing, accessories, and functions

ETA

This Swatch Group movement manufacturer produces more than five million movements a year. And after the withdrawal of Richemont's Jaeger-LeCoultre as well as Swatch Group sisters Nouvelle Lémania and Frédéric Piguet from the business of selling movements on the free market, most watch brands can hardly help but beat down the door of this full-service manufacturer.

ETA offers a broad spectrum of automatic movements in various dimensions with different functions, chronograph mechanisms in varying configurations, pocket watch classics (Calibers 6497 and 98), and manually wound calibers of days gone by (Calibers 1727 and 7001). This company truly offers everything that a manufacturer's heart could desire—not to mention the sheer variety of quartz technology from inexpensive three-hand mechanisms to highly complicated multifunctional movements and futuristic ETA-quartz featuring autonomous energy creation using a rotor and generator.

The almost stereotypical accusation of ETA being "mass goods" is not justified, however, for it is a real art to manufacture filigreed micromechanical technology in consistently high quality. This is certainly one of the reasons why there have been very few movement factories in Europe that can compete with ETA, or that would want to. Since the success of Swatch—a pure ETA product—millions of Swiss francs have been invested in new development and manufacturing technologies. ETA today owns more than twenty production locales in Switzerland, France, Germany, Malaysia, and Thailand.

In 2002, ETA's management announced it would discontinue providing half-completed component kits for reassembly and/or embellishment to specialized workshops, and from 2010 only offer completely assembled and finished movements for sale. The Swiss Competition Commission, however, studied the issue, and a new deal was struck in 2013, phasing out sales to customers over a period of six years. ETA is already somewhat of a competitor of independent reassemblers such as Soprod, Sellita, La Joux-Perret, Dubois Dépraz, and others thanks to its diversification of available calibers, which has led the rest to counter by creating their own base movements.

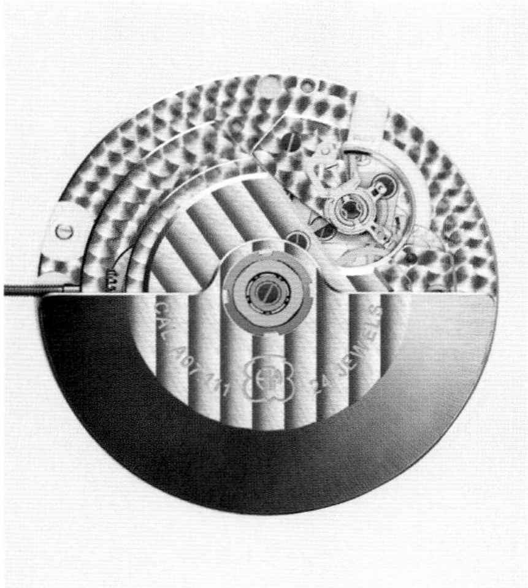

Caliber A07.111

Automatic; ETACHRON regulating system with fine-timing device, rotor on ball bearings, stop-second system; single spring barrel; 48-hour power reserve
Functions: hours, minutes, sweep seconds
Diameter: 37.2
Height: 7.9 mm
Jewels: 24
Frequency: 28,800 vph
Balance spring: flat hairspring
Shock protection: Incabloc
Remarks: related calibers: A07.161 (with power reserve display)

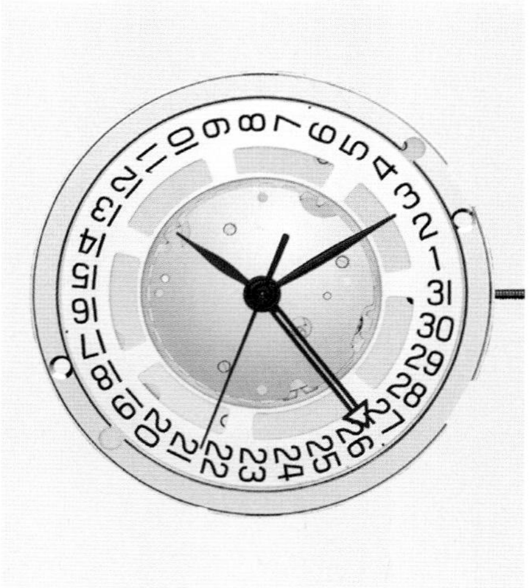

Caliber A07.171 (dial side)

Automatic; ETACHRON regulating system with fine-timing device, rotor on ball bearings, stop-second system; single spring barrel; 48-hour power reserve
Functions: hours, minutes, sweep seconds; 2nd time zone, additional 24-hour display (2nd time zone); quick-set date window
Diameter: 37.2 mm
Height: 7.9 mm
Jewels: 24
Frequency: 28,800 vph
Balance spring: flat hairspring
Shock protection: Incabloc

Caliber A07.211 (dial side)

Automatic; ETACHRON regulating system with fine-timing device, rotor on ball bearings, stop-second system; single spring barrel; 48-hour power reserve
Functions: hours, minutes, subsidiary seconds; chronograph; quick-set date window
Diameter: 37.2 mm
Height: 7.9 mm
Jewels: 25
Frequency: 28,800 vph
Balance spring: flat hairspring
Shock protection: Incabloc

Caliber 2000-1

Automatic; ball bearing–mounted rotor; stop-seconds, ETACHRON regulating system; single spring barrel; 40-hour power reserve
Functions: hours, minutes, sweep seconds; quick-set date window
Diameter: 20 mm
Height: 3.6 mm
Jewels: 20
Balance: glucydur
Frequency: 28,800 vph
Balance spring: flat hairspring
Shock protection: Incabloc

Caliber 2671

Automatic; ball bearing–mounted rotor; stop-seconds, ETACHRON regulating system; single spring barrel; 38-hour power reserve
Functions: hours, minutes, sweep seconds; date window
Diameter: 17.5 mm
Height: 4.8 mm
Jewels: 25
Balance: glucydur
Frequency: 28,800 vph
Balance spring: flat hairspring
Shock protection: Incabloc
Remarks: related calibers: 2678 (additional weekday window, height 5.35 mm)

Caliber 2681 (dial side)

Automatic; ball bearing–mounted rotor; stop-seconds, ETACHRON regulating system; single spring barrel; 38-hour power reserve
Functions: hours, minutes, sweep seconds; quick-set date window
Diameter: 20 mm
Height: 4.8 mm
Jewels: 25
Balance: glucydur
Frequency: 28,800 vph
Balance spring: flat hairspring
Shock protection: Incabloc

Caliber 2801-2

Manually wound; ETACHRON regulating system; 42-hour power reserve
Functions: hours, minutes, sweep seconds
Diameter: 26 mm
Height: 3.35 mm
Jewels: 17
Frequency: 28,800 vph
Related caliber: 2804-2 (with date window and quick set)

Caliber 2824-2

Automatic; ball bearing–mounted rotor; stop-seconds, ETACHRON regulating system; 38-hour power reserve
Functions: hours, minutes, sweep seconds; quick-set date window at 3 o'clock
Diameter: 26 mm
Height: 4.6 mm
Jewels: 25
Frequency: 28,800 vph
Related calibers: 2836-2 (additional day window at 3 o'clock, height 5.05 mm); 2826-2 (with large date, height 6.2 mm)

Caliber 2834-2 (dial side)

Automatic; ball bearing–mounted rotor; stop-seconds, ETACHRON regulating system; single spring barrel; 38-hour power reserve
Functions: hours, minutes, sweep seconds; quick-set date window, quick-set weekday
Diameter: 29.4 mm
Height: 5.05 mm
Jewels: 25
Balance: glucydur
Frequency: 28,800 vph
Balance spring: flat hairspring
Shock protection: Incabloc

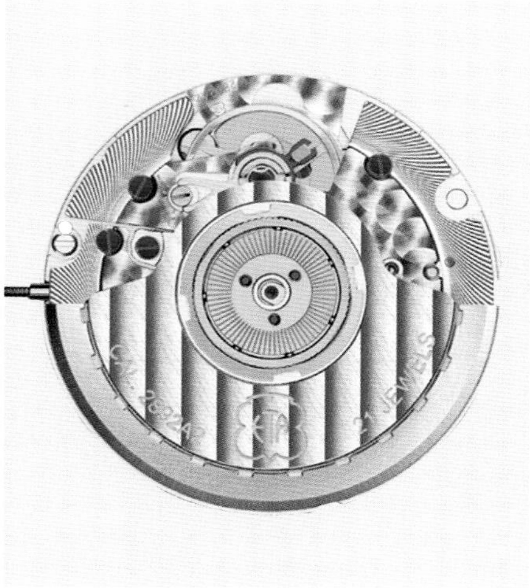

Caliber 2892-A2

Automatic; ball bearing–mounted rotor; stop-seconds, ETACHRON regulating system; single spring barrel; 42-hour power reserve
Functions: hours, minutes, sweep seconds; quick-set date window
Diameter: 26.2 mm
Height: 3.6 mm
Jewels: 21
Balance: glucydur
Frequency: 28,800 vph
Balance spring: flat hairspring
Shock protection: Incabloc

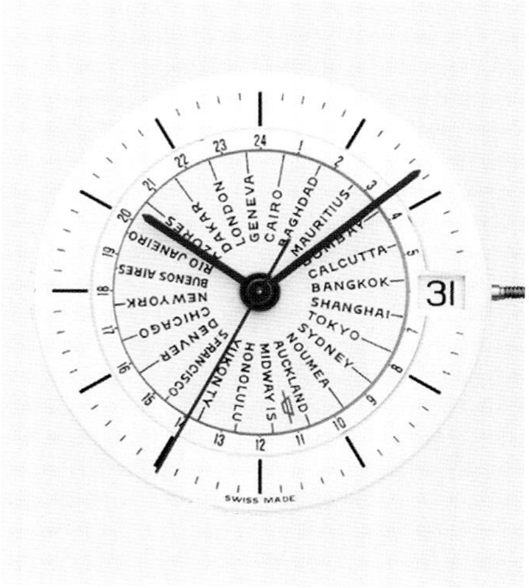

Caliber 2893-1 (dial side)

Automatic; ball bearing rotor; stop-seconds, ETACHRON regulating system; 42-hour power reserve
Functions: hours, minutes, sweep seconds; quick-set date window at 3 o'clock; world time display via central disk
Diameter: 25.6 mm
Height: 4.1 mm
Jewels: 21
Frequency: 28,800 vph
Related calibers: 2893-2 (24-hour hand; 2nd time zone instead of world time disk); 2893-3 (only world time disk without date window)

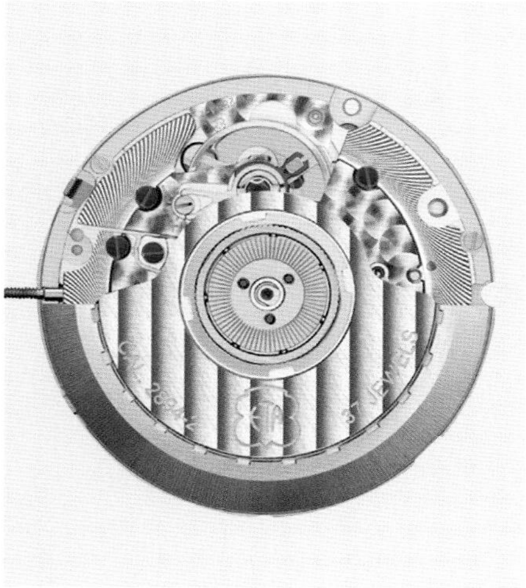

Caliber 2894-2

Automatic; ball bearing–mounted rotor; stop-seconds, ETACHRON regulating system; single spring barrel; 42-hour power reserve
Functions: hours, minutes, subsidiary seconds; chronograph; quick-set date window
Diameter: 28.6 mm
Height: 6.1 mm
Jewels: 37
Balance: glucydur
Frequency: 28,800 vph
Balance spring: flat hairspring
Shock protection: Incabloc
Related caliber: 2094 (diameter 23.9 mm, height 5.5 mm, 33 jewels)

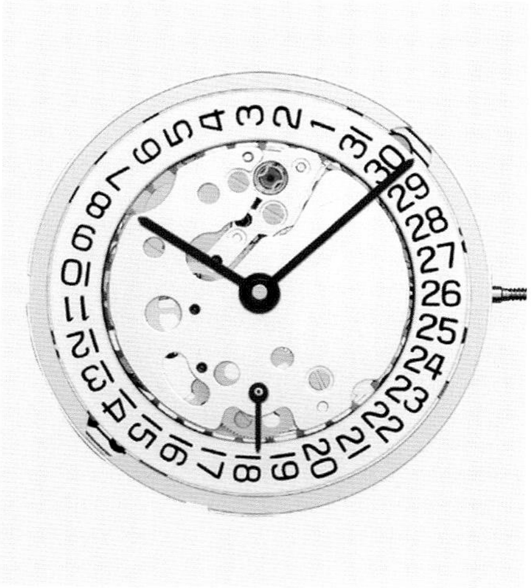

Caliber 2895-2 (dial side)

Automatic; ball bearing–mounted rotor; stop-seconds, ETACHRON regulating system; single spring barrel; 42-hour power reserve
Functions: hours, minutes, subsidiary seconds, at 6 o'clock; quick-set date window
Diameter: 26.2 mm
Height: 4.35 mm
Jewels: 27
Balance: glucydur
Frequency: 28,800 vph
Balance spring: flat hairspring
Shock protection: Incabloc

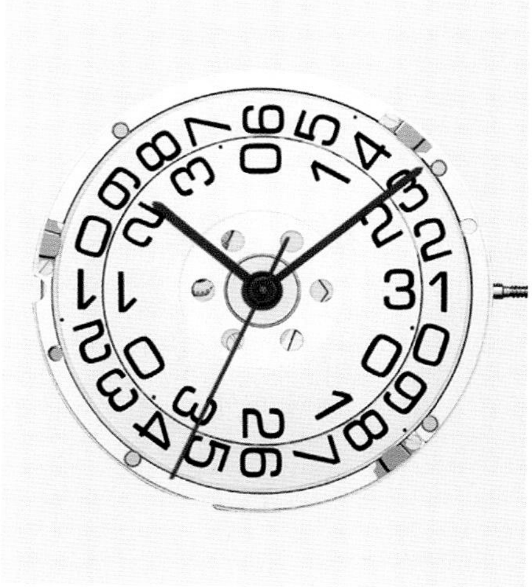

Caliber 2896 (dial side)

Automatic; ball bearing rotor; stop-seconds, ETACHRON regulating system; 42-hour power reserve
Functions: hours, minutes, sweep seconds; power reserve display at 3 o'clock
Diameter: 25.6 mm
Height: 4.85 mm
Jewels: 21
Frequency: 28,800 vph

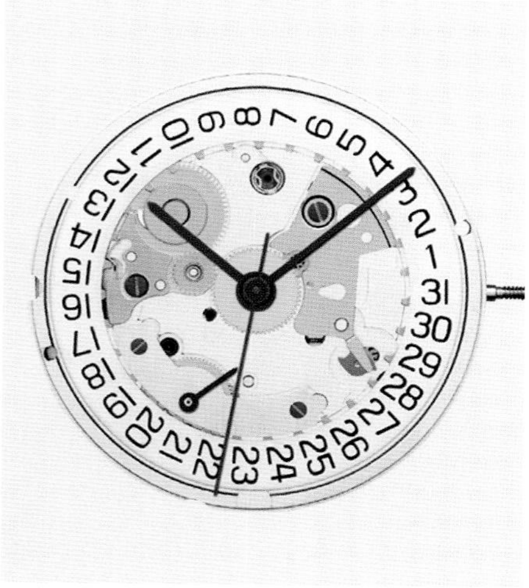

Caliber 2897 (dial side)

Automatic; ball bearing–mounted rotor; stop-seconds, ETACHRON regulating system; single spring barrel; 42-hour power reserve
Functions: hours, minutes, sweep seconds; power reserve indicator; quick-set date window
Diameter: 26.2 mm
Height: 4.85 mm
Jewels: 21
Balance: glucydur
Frequency: 28,800 vph
Balance spring: flat hairspring
Shock protection: Incabloc

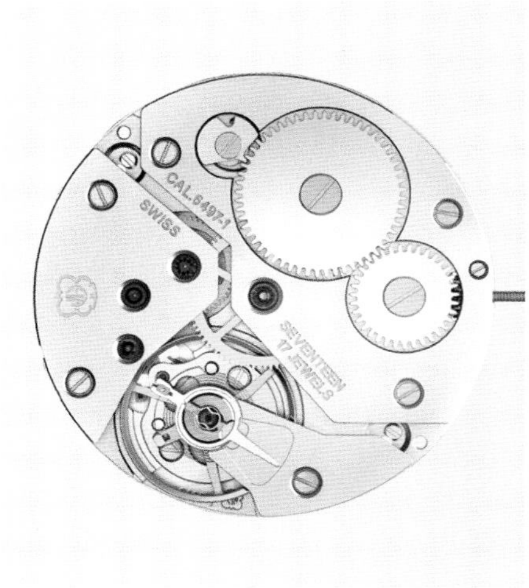

Caliber 6497-1

Manually wound; ETACHRON regulating system; single spring barrel; 46-hour power reserve
Functions: hours, minutes, subsidiary seconds
Diameter: 37.2 mm
Height: 4.5 mm
Jewels: 17
Frequency: 18,000 vph
Balance spring: flat hairspring
Remarks: pocket watch movement (Unitas model) in Lépine version with subsidiary seconds extending from the winding stem); as Caliber 6497-2 with 21,600 vph and 53-hour power reserve

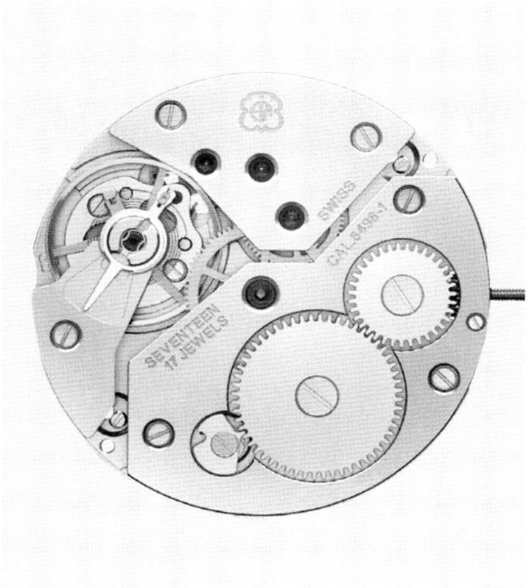

Caliber 6498-1

Manually wound; ETACHRON regulating system; single spring barrel; 46-hour power reserve
Functions: hours, minutes, subsidiary seconds
Diameter: 37.2 mm
Height: 4.5 mm
Jewels: 17
Frequency: 18,000 vph
Balance spring: flat hairspring
Remarks: pocket watch movement (Unitas model) in savonette version (subsidiary seconds at right angle to the winding stem); as Caliber 6498-2 with 21,600 vph and 53-hour power reserve

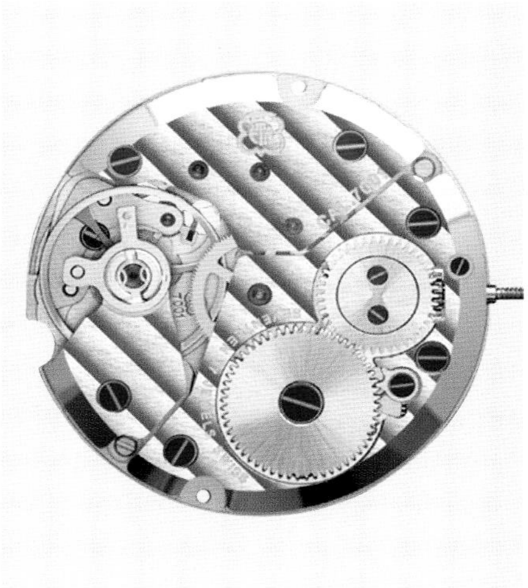

Caliber 7001

Manually wound; ultrathin construction; single spring barrel; 42-hour power reserve
Functions: hours, minutes, subsidiary seconds
Diameter: 23.7 mm
Height: 2.5 mm
Jewels: 17
Frequency: 21,600 vph
Balance spring: flat hairspring

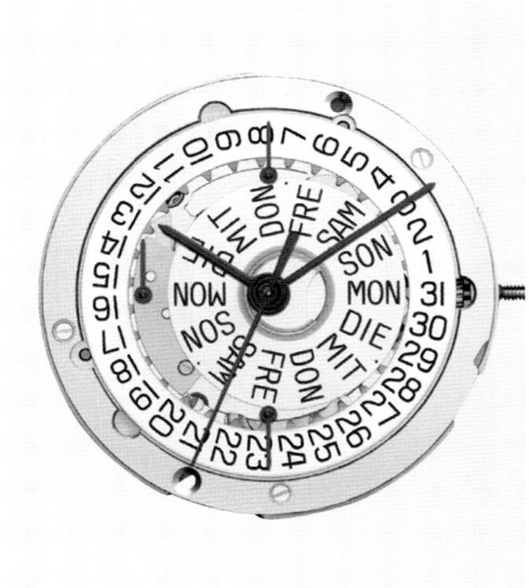

Caliber 7750 (dial side)

Automatic; stop-second system; single spring barrel; 42-hour power reserve
Functions: hours, minutes, subsidiary seconds; chronograph; quick-set date and weekday window
Diameter: 30.4 mm
Height: 7.9 mm
Jewels: 25
Balance: glucydur
Frequency: 28,800 vph
Balance spring: flat hairspring
Shock protection: Incabloc

Caliber 7751 (dial side)

Automatic; stop-second system; single spring barrel; 42-hour power reserve
Functions: hours, minutes, subsidiary seconds; additional 24-hour display; chronograph; full calendar with date, weekday, month, moon phase
Diameter: 30.4 mm
Height: 7.9 mm
Jewels: 25
Balance: glucydur
Frequency: 28,800 vph
Balance spring: flat hairspring
Shock protection: Incabloc
Remarks: related caliber: 7754 with sweep 24-hour hand (2nd time zone)

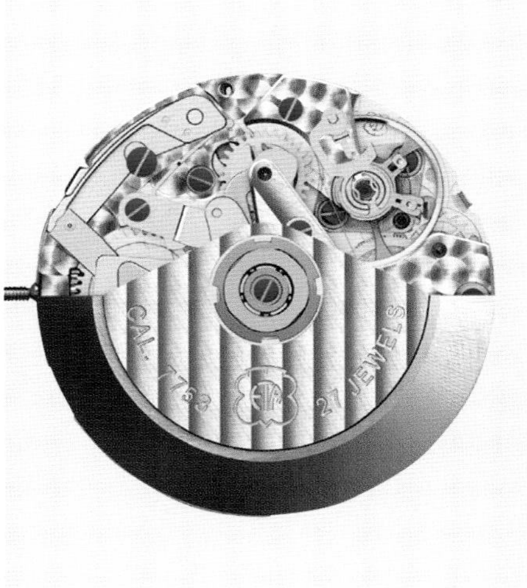

Caliber 7753

Automatic; stop-second system; single spring barrel; 42-hour power reserve
Functions: hours, minutes, subsidiary seconds; chronograph; quick-set date window with pusher
Diameter: 30.4
Height: 7.9 mm
Jewels: 25
Balance: glucydur
Frequency: 28,800 vph
Balance spring: flat hairspring
Shock protection: Incabloc
Remarks: variation of the Valjoux chronograph caliber with symmetrical "tricompax" layout of the totalizers

RONDA

Ronda is a Swiss company with a long tradition. It was founded by William Mosset, born in 1909 in the village of Hölstein, a man whose gift for micro-engineering declared itself early on when he invented a way to drill thirty-two holes in a metal plate in one operation and with great accuracy. The company was founded in 1946 in Lausen, a little town in the hinterlands of German-speaking Switzerland near Basel, where the first factory was built.

In the meantime the company has turned into a group with five subsidiaries: There are two production sites in Ticino, one in the Jura mountains, one operation in Thailand, and sales offices in Hong Kong. Overall, Ronda employs around 1,800 people in Switzerland and Asia.

The shareholders of the family enterprise, which is now in its second generation, value the company's absolute independence. This is undoubtedly a key advantage for the customer, since Ronda can continue defining its own strategy and can react decisively to customer needs.

That is why the company, which had already made a name for itself with quartz movements, decided to add a portfolio of automatic mechanical movements. The first product batches arrived on the market in early 2017; in the medium term, the mechanical Ronda Caliber R150 is to be produced in batches of six figures per year.

Caliber R150

Automatic; ball bearing–mounted rotor; stop-seconds, index for fine adjustment; single spring barrel; 40-hour power reserve
Functions: hours, minutes, sweep seconds; quick-set date
Diameter: 25.6 mm
Height: 4.4 mm
Jewels: 25
Frequency: 28,800 vph
Balance spring: flat hairspring
Shock protection: Incabloc

Caliber 5040.B

Quartz; 54-month power reserve; single spring barrel
Functions: hours, minutes, subsidiary seconds; chronograph, with add and split function; large date
Diameter: 28.6 mm
Height: 4.4 mm
Jewels: 13

Caliber 7004.P

Quartz; 48-month power reserve; single spring barrel
Functions: hours, minutes, subsidiary seconds; large date and weekday (retrograde)
Diameter: 34.6 mm
Height: 5.6 mm
Jewels: 6

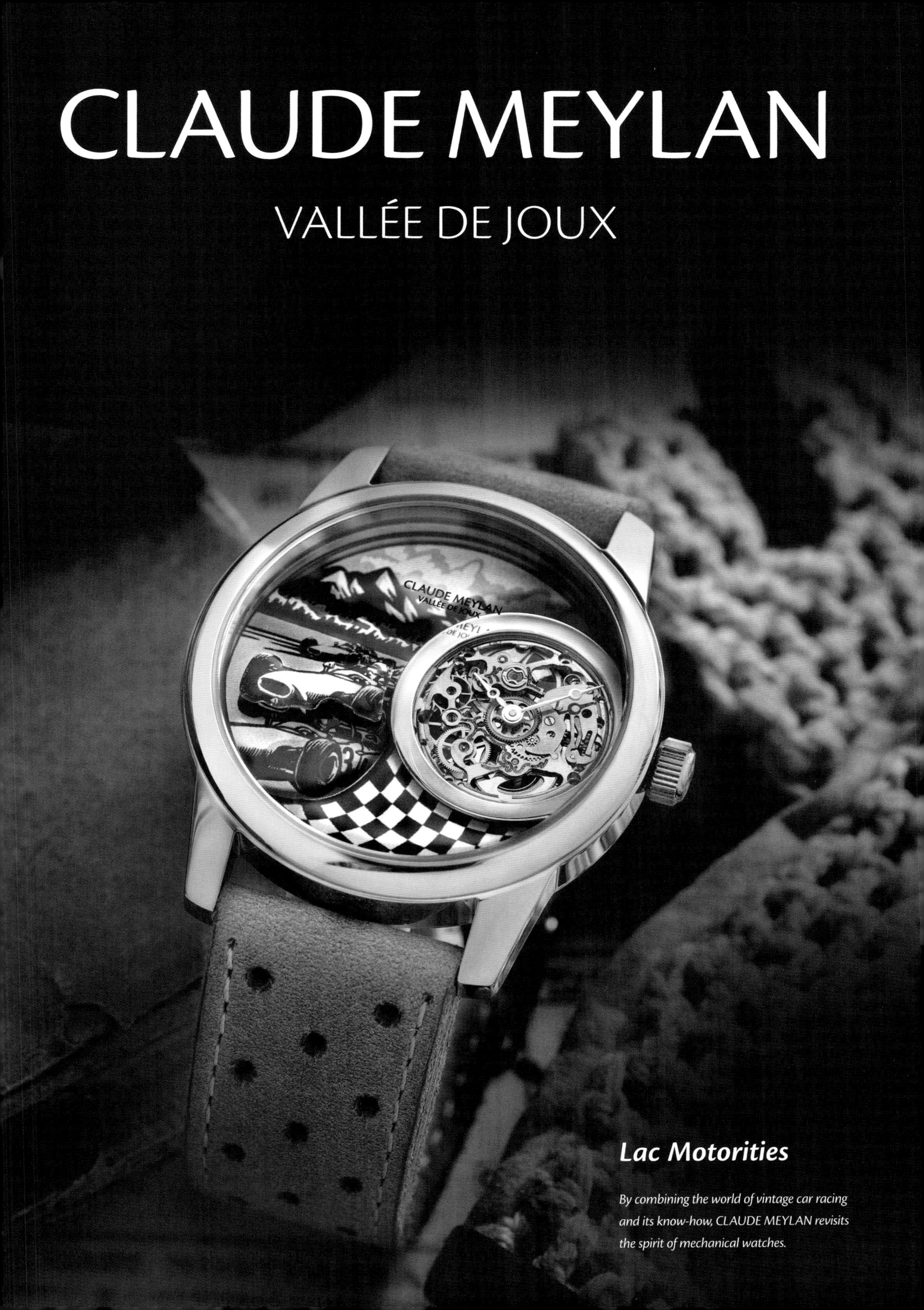
CLAUDE MEYLAN
VALLÉE DE JOUX
CLAUDE MEYLAN
VALLÉE DE JOUX
Lac Motorities
By combining the world of vintage car racing and its know-how, CLAUDE MEYLAN revisits the spirit of mechanical watches.

SELLITA

Sellita, founded in 1950 by Pierre Grandjean in La Chaux-de-Fonds, is one of the biggest reassemblers and embellishers in the mechanical watch industry. On average, Sellita embellishes and finishes about one million automatic and hand-wound movements annually—a figure that represents about 25 percent of Switzerland's mechanical movement production, according to Miguel García, Sellita's president.

Reassembly can be defined as the assembly and regulation of components to make a functioning movement. This is the type of work that ETA loved to give to outside companies back in the day in order to concentrate on manufacturing complete quartz movements and individual components for them.

Reassembly workshops like Sellita refine and embellish components purchased from ETA according to their customers' wishes and can even successfully fulfill smaller orders made by the company's estimated 350 clients.

When ETA announced that it would only sell ébauches to companies outside the Swatch Group until the end of 2010, García, who has owned Sellita since 2003, reacted by shifting production to the development and manufacturing of new in-house products.

He planned and implemented a new line of movements based on the dimensions of the most popular ETA calibers, whose patents had expired. The company now has a line of manually wound or automatic movements with little complications, like a date, weekday, GMT, or a second time zone, as well as chronographs with different display constellations. The new design types are all based on mature models. A whole new line of automatic movements was launched, the Caliber SW1000, which has no ETA parts at all. The way to identify these movements will simply be the four digits. The price range will be similar to that of other products offered by the company.

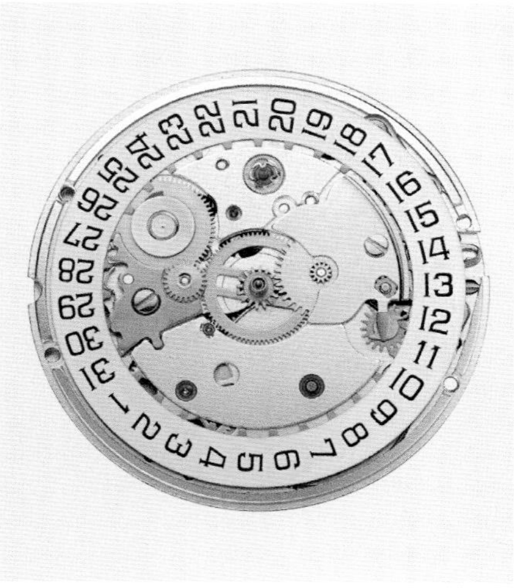

Caliber SW200-1

Automatic; ball bearing–mounted rotor; stop-second system; single spring barrel; 38-hour power reserve
Functions: hours, minutes, sweep seconds; quick-set date
Diameter: 25.6 mm
Height: 4.6 mm
Jewels: 26
Balance: nickel or glucydur
Frequency: 28,800 vph
Balance spring: Nivaflex
Shock protection: Novodiac or Incabloc

Caliber SW210-1

Manually wound; stop-second system; single spring barrel; 42-hour power reserve
Functions: hours, minutes, sweep seconds
Diameter: 25.6 mm
Height: 3.35 mm
Jewels: 19
Balance: nickel
Frequency: 28,800 vph
Balance spring: Nivaflex
Shock protection: Novodiac or Incabloc
Remarks: related caliber: SW215 (with window date)

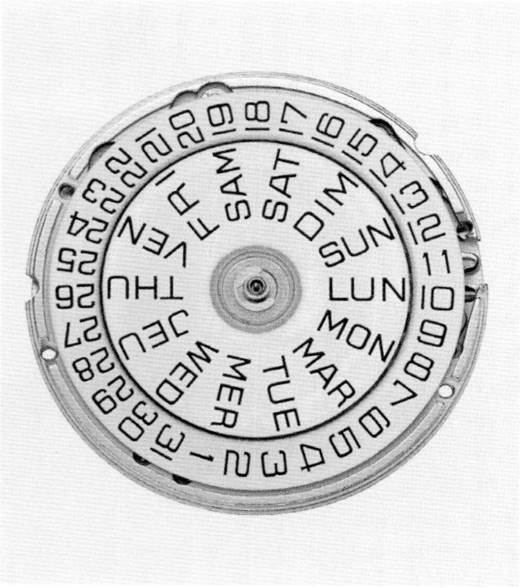

Caliber SW220-1

Automatic; ball bearing–mounted rotor; stop-second system; single spring barrel; 38-hour power reserve
Functions: hours, minutes, sweep seconds; quick-set date and weekday
Diameter: 25.6 mm
Height: 5.05 mm
Jewels: 26
Balance: nickel or glucydur
Frequency: 28,800 vph
Balance spring: flat hairspring, Nivaflex
Shock protection: Novodiac or Incabloc
Remarks: related calibers: SW221-1 (with hand date); SW240-1 with larger mainplate (ø 29 mm)

Caliber SW260-1

Automatic; ball bearing–mounted rotor; stop-second system; single spring barrel; 38-hour power reserve
Functions: hours, minutes, subsidiary seconds at 6 o'clock; quick-set date
Diameter: 25.6 mm
Height: 5.6 mm
Jewels: 31
Balance: nickel or glucydur
Frequency: 28,800 vph
Balance spring: flat hairspring, Nivaflex
Shock protection: Novodiac or Incabloc
Remarks: related caliber: SW290-1 (subsidiary seconds at 9 o'clock)

Caliber SW300-1

Automatic; ball bearing–mounted rotor; stop-second system; single spring barrel; 42-hour power reserve
Functions: hours, minutes, sweep seconds; quick-set date
Diameter: 25.6 mm
Height: 3.6 mm
Jewels: 25
Balance: glucydur
Frequency: 28,800 vph
Balance spring: flat hairspring, Nivaflex
Shock protection: Incabloc
Remarks: related caliber: SW360-1 (with subsidiary seconds, height 4.35 mm, 31 jewels)

Caliber SW330-1

Automatic; ball bearing–mounted rotor; stop-second system; single spring barrel, 42-hour power reserve
Functions: hours, minutes, sweep seconds; additional 24-hour display (2nd time zone); quick-set date
Diameter: 25.6 mm
Height: 4.1 mm
Jewels: 25
Balance: glucydur
Frequency: 28,800 vph
Balance spring: flat hairspring, Nivaflex
Shock protection: Incabloc

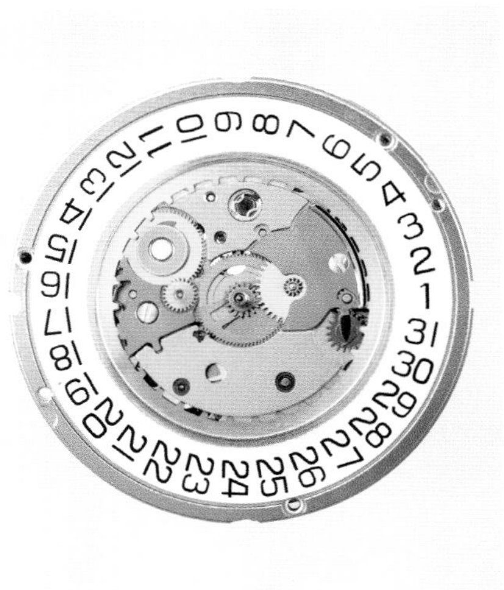

Caliber SW400-1

Automatic; ball bearing–mounted rotor; stop-second system; single spring barrel; 38-hour power reserve
Functions: hours, minutes, sweep seconds; quick-set date
Diameter: 31 mm
Height: 4.67 mm
Jewels: 26
Balance: nickel or glucydur
Frequency: 28,800 vph
Balance spring: Nivaflex
Shock protection: Novodiac or Incabloc

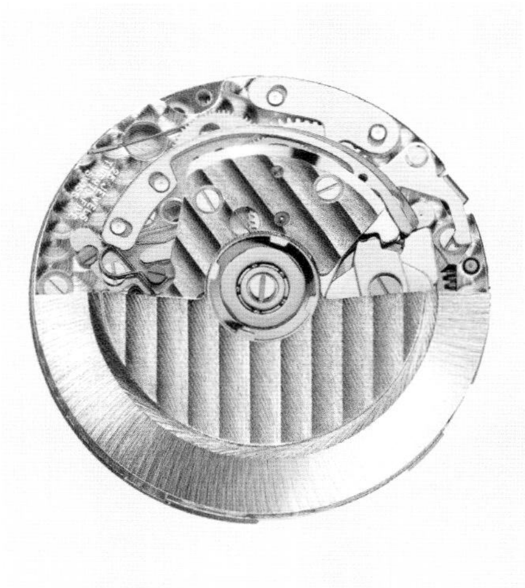

Caliber SW500-1

Automatic; ball bearing–mounted rotor; stop-second system; single spring barrel; 48-hour power reserve
Functions: hours, minutes, subsidiary seconds; chronograph quick-set date and weekday
Diameter: 30 mm
Height: 7.9 mm
Jewels: 25
Balance: nickel or glucydur
Frequency: 28,800 vph
Balance spring: Nivaflex
Shock protection: Incabloc

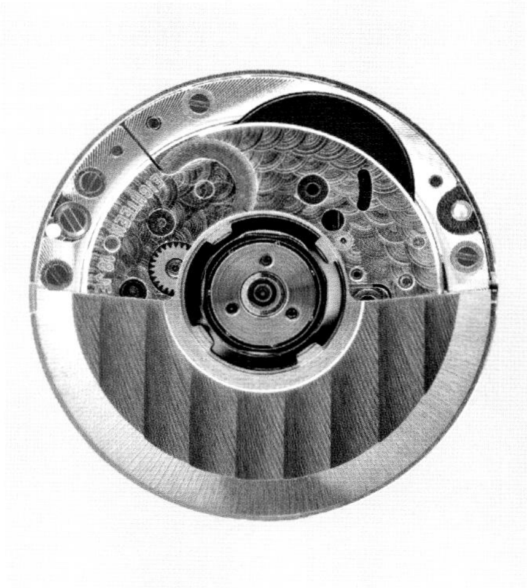

Caliber SW1000-1

Automatic; ball bearing–mounted rotor; stop-second system; single spring barrel; 38-hour power reserve
Functions: hours, minutes, sweep seconds; quick-set date
Diameter: 20 mm
Height: 3.9 mm
Jewels: 18
Balance: nickel or glucydur
Frequency: 28,800 vph
Balance spring: Nivaflex
Shock protection: Incabloc

Watch Your Watch

Mechanical watches are not only by and large more expensive and complex than quartzes, they are also a little high-maintenance, as it were. The mechanism within does need servicing occasionally—perhaps a touch of oil and an adjustment. Worse yet, the complexity of all those wheels and pinions engaged in reproducing the galaxy means that a user will occasionally do something perfectly harmless like wind his or her watch up only to find everything grinding to a halt. Here are some tips for dealing with these mechanical beauties for new watch owners and reminders for the old hands.

1. DATE CHANGES

Do not change the date manually (via the crown or pusher) on any mechanical watch—whether manual wind or automatic—when the time indicated on the dial reads between 10 and 2 o'clock. Although some better watches are protected against this horological quirk, most mechanical watches with a date indicator are engaged in the process of automatically changing the date between the hours of 10 p.m. and 2 a.m. Intervening with a forced manual change while the automatic date shift is engaged can damage the movement. Of course, you can make the adjustment between 10 a.m. and 2 p.m. in most cases—but this is just not a good habit to get into. When in doubt, roll the time past 12 o'clock and look for an automatic date change before you set the time and date. The Ulysse Nardin brand is notable, among a very few others, for in-house mechanical movements immune to this effect.

Bovet's barrier to pressing the wrong pusher.

2. CHRONOGRAPH USE

On a simple chronograph, start and stop are almost always the same button. Normally located above the crown, the start/stop actuator can be pressed at will to initiate and end the interval timing. The reset button, normally below the crown, is only used for resetting the chronograph to zero, but only when the chronograph is stopped—never while engaged. Only a "flyback" chronograph allows safe resetting to zero while running. With the chronograph engaged, you simply hit the reset button and all the chronograph indicators (seconds, minutes, and hours) snap back to zero and the chronograph begins to accumulate the interval time once again. In the early days of air travel this was a valuable complication as pilots would reset their chronographs when taking on a new heading—without having to fumble about with a three-step procedure with gloved hands.

Nota bene: Don't actuate or reset your chronograph while your watch is submerged—even if you have one of those that are built for such usage, like Omega, IWC, and a few other brands. Feel free to hit the buttons before submersion and jump in and swim while they run; just don't push anything while in the water.

3. CHANGING TIME BACKWARD

Don't adjust the time on your watch in a counterclockwise direction—especially if the watch has calendar functions. A few watches can tolerate the abuse, but it's better to avoid the possibility of damage altogether. Change the dates as needed (remembering the 10 and 2 rule above).

4. SHOCKS

Almost all modern watches are equipped with some level of shock protection. Best practices for the Swiss brands allow for a three-foot fall onto a hard wood surface. But if your watch is running poorly—or even worse has stopped entirely after an impact—do not shake, wind, or bang it again to get it running; take it to an expert for service as you may do even more damage. Sports like tennis, squash, or golf can have a deleterious effect on your watch, including flattening the pivots, overbanking, or even bending or breaking a pivot.

5. OVERWINDING

Most modern watches are fitted with a mechanism that allows the mainspring to slide inside the barrel—or stops it completely once the spring is fully wound—for protection against overwinding. The best advice here is just don't force it. Over the years, a winding crown may start to get "stickier" and more difficult to turn even when unwound. That's a sure sign it is due for service.

6. JACUZZI TEMPERATURE

Don't jump into the Jacuzzi—or even a steaming hot shower—with your watch on. Better-built watches with a deeper water-resistance rating typically have no problem with this scenario. However, take a 3 or 5 atm water-resistant watch into the Jacuzzi, and there's a chance the different rates of expansion and contraction of the metals and sapphire or mineral crystals may allow moisture into the case.

Panerai makes sure you think before touching the crown.

Do it yourself at your own risk.

7. SCREW THAT CROWN DOWN (AND THOSE PUSHERS)!

Always check and double-check to ensure a watch fitted with a screwed-down crown is closed tightly. Screwed-down pushers for a chronograph—or any other functions—deserve the same attention. This one oversight has cost quite a few owners their watches. If a screwed-down crown is not secured, water will likely get into the case and start oxidizing the metal. In time, the problem can destroy the watch.

8. MAGNETISM

If your watch is acting up, running faster or slower, it may have become magnetized. This can happen if you leave your timepiece near a computer, cell phone, or some other electronic device. Many service centers have a so-called degausser to take care of the problem. A number of brands also make watches with a soft iron core to deflect magnetic fields, though this might not work with the stronger ones.

9. TRIBOLOGY

Keeping a mechanical timepiece hidden away in a box for extended lengths of time is not the best way to care for it. Even if you don't wear a watch every day, it is a good idea to run your watch at regular intervals to keep its lubricating oils and greases viscous. Think about a can of house paint: Keep it stirred and it stays liquid almost indefinitely; leave it still for too long and a skin develops. On a smaller level the same thing can happen to the lubricants inside a mechanical watch.

10. SERVICE

Most mechanical watches call for a three- to five-year service cycle for cleaning, oiling, and maintenance. Some mechanical watches can run twice that long and have functioned within acceptable parameters, but if you're not going to have your watch serviced at regular intervals, you do run the risk of having timing issues. Always have your watch serviced by a qualified watchmaker (see box), not at the kiosk in the local mall. The best you can expect there is a quick battery change.

Gary Girdvainis is the founder of Isochron Media LLC, publishers of WristWatch *and* AboutTime *magazines.*

WATCH REPAIR SERVICE CENTERS

RGM
www.rgmwatches.com/repair

Stoll & Co.
www.americaswatchmaker.com

Swiss Watchmakers & Company
www.swisswatchland.com

Universal Watch Repair
www.universalwatch.net

Watch Repairs USA
www.watchrepairsusa.com

Glossary

ANNUAL CALENDAR

The automatic allowances for the different lengths of each month of a year in the calendar module of a watch. This type of watch usually shows the month and date, and sometimes the day of the week (like this one by Patek Philippe) and the phases of the moon.

ANTIMAGNETIC

Magnetic fields found in common everyday places affect mechanical movements, hence the use of anti- or non-magnetic components in the movement. Some companies encase movements in antimagnetic cores such as Sinn's Model 756, the Duograph, shown here.

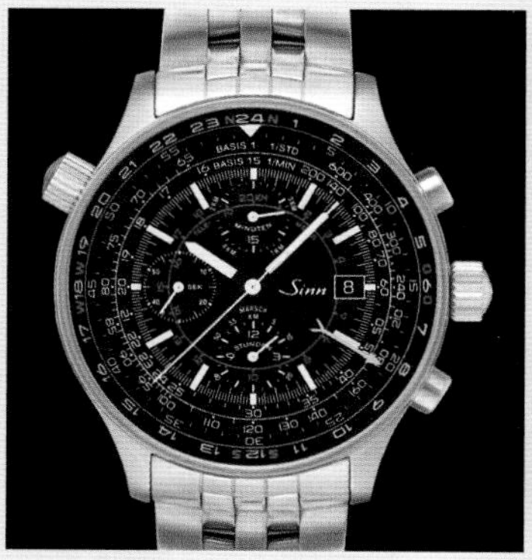

ANTIREFLECTION

A film created by steaming the crystal to eliminate light reflection and improve legibility. Antireflection functions best when applied to both sides of the crystal, but because it scratches, some manufacturers prefer to have it only on the interior of the crystal. It is mainly used on synthetic sapphire crystals. Dubey & Schaldenbrand applies antireflection on both sides for all of the company's wristwatches, such as this Aquadyn model.

AUTOMATIC WINDING

A rotating weight set into motion by moving the wrist winds the spring barrel via the gear train of a mechanical watch movement. Automatic winding was invented during the pocket watch era in 1770, but the breakthrough automatic winding movement via rotor began with the ball bearing Eterna-Matic in the late 1940s. Today we speak of unidirectional winding and bidirectionally winding rotors, depending on the type of gear train used. Shown is IWC's automatic Caliber 50611.

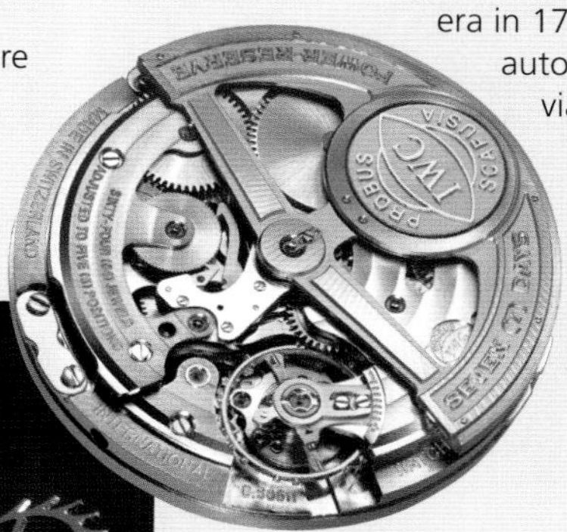

BALANCE

The beating heart of a mechanical watch movement is the balance. Fed by the energy of the mainspring, a tirelessly oscillating little wheel, just a few millimeters in diameter and possessing a spiral-shaped balance spring, sets the rhythm for the escape wheel and pallets with its vibration frequency. Today the balance is usually made of one piece of antimagnetic glucydur, an alloy that expands very little when exposed to heat.

BAR OR COCK

A metal plate fastened to the base plate at one point, leaving room for a gear wheel or pinion. The balance is usually attached to a bar called the balance cock. Glashütte tradition dictates that the balance cock be decoratively engraved by hand like this one by Glashütte Original.

BEVELING

To uniformly file down the sharp edges of a plate, bridge, or bar and give it a high polish. The process is also called *anglage.* Edges are usually beveled at a 45° angle. As the picture shows, this is painstaking work that needs the skilled hands and eyes of an experienced watchmaker or *angleur.*

BRIDGE

A metal plate fastened to the base plate at two points leaving room for a gear wheel or pinion. This vintage Favre-Leuba movement illustrates the point with three individual bridges.

CARBON FIBER

A very light, tough composite material, carbon fiber is composed of filaments comprised of several thousand seven-micron carbon fibers held together by resin. The arrangement of the filaments determines the quality of a component, making each unique. Carbon fiber is currently being used for dials, cases, and even movement components.

CALIBER

A term, similar to type or model, that refers to different watch movements. Pictured here is Heuer's Caliber 11, the legendary automatic chronograph caliber from 1969. This movement was a coproduction jointly researched and developed for four years by Heuer-Leonidas, Breitling, and Hamilton-Büren. Each company gave the movement a different name after serial production began.

CHAMPLEVÉ

A dial decoration technique, whereby the metal is engraved, filled with enamel, and baked, as in this cockatoo on a Cartier Tortue, enhanced with mother-of-pearl slivers.

CERAMIC

An inorganic, nonmetallic material formed by the action of heat and practically unscratchable. Pioneered by Rado, ceramic is a high-tech material generally made from aluminum and zirconia oxide. Today, it is used generally for cases and bezels and now comes in many colors.

CHRONOGRAPH

From the Greek *chronos* (time) and *graphein* (to write). Originally a chronograph literally wrote, inscribing the time elapsed on a piece of paper with the help of a pencil attached to a type of hand. Today this term is used for watches that show not only the time of day, but also certain time intervals via independent hands that may be started or stopped at will. Stopwatches differ from chronographs because they do not show the time of day. This exploded illustration shows the complexity of a Breitling chronograph.

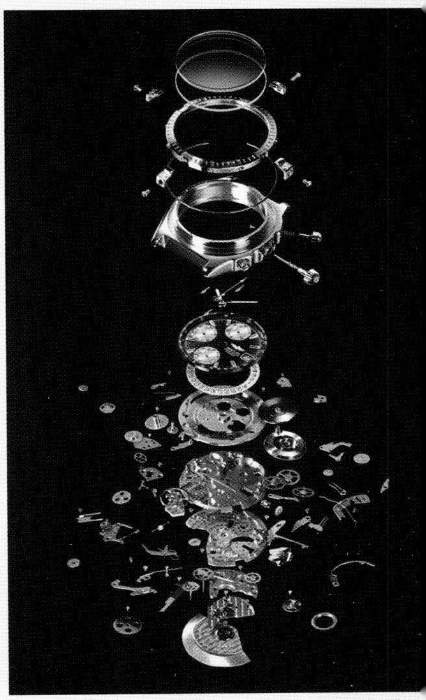

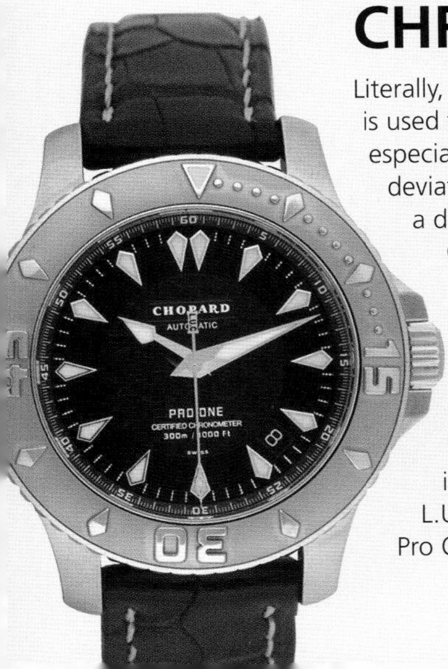

CHRONOMETER

Literally, "measurer of time." As the term is used today, a chronometer denotes an especially accurate watch (one with a deviation of no more than 5 seconds a day for mechanical movements). Chronometers are usually supplied with an official certificate from an independent testing office such as the COSC. The largest producer of chronometers in 2008 was Rolex, with 769,850 officially certified movements. Chopard came in sixth with more than 22,000 certified L.U.C mechanisms, like the 4.96 in the Pro One model shown here.

COLUMN WHEEL

The component used to control chronograph functions within a true chronograph movement. The presence of a column wheel indicates that the chronograph is fully integrated into the movement. In the modern era, modules are generally used that are attached to a base caliber movement. This particular column wheel is made of blued steel.

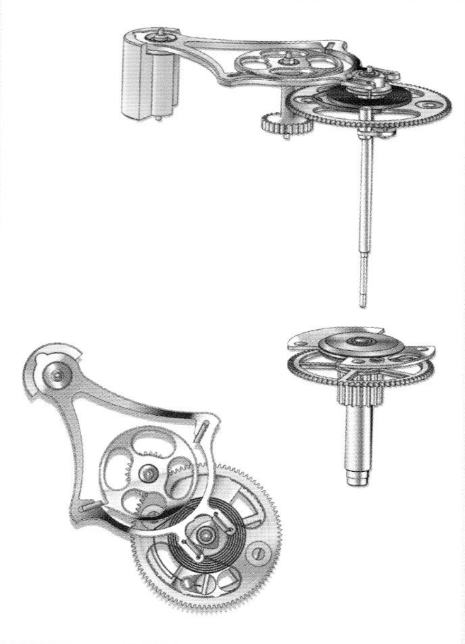

CONSTANT FORCE MECHANISM

Sometimes called a constant force escapement, it isn't really: in most cases this mechanism is "simply" an initial tension spring. It is also known in English by part of its French name, the *remontoir*, which actually means "winding mechanism." This mechanism regulates and portions the energy that is passed on through the escapement, making the rate as even and precise as possible. Shown here is the constant force escapement from A. Lange & Söhne's Lange 31—a mechanism that gets as close to its name as possible.

COSC

The Contrôle Officiel Suisse de Chronomètrage, the official Swiss testing office for chronometers. The COSC is the world's largest issuer of so-called chronometer certificates, which are only otherwise given out individually by certain observatories (such as the one in Neuchâtel, Switzerland). For a fee, the COSC tests the rate of movements that have been adjusted by watchmakers. These are usually mechanical movements, but the office also tests some high-precision quartz movements. Those that meet the specifications for being a chronometer are awarded an official certificate as shown here.

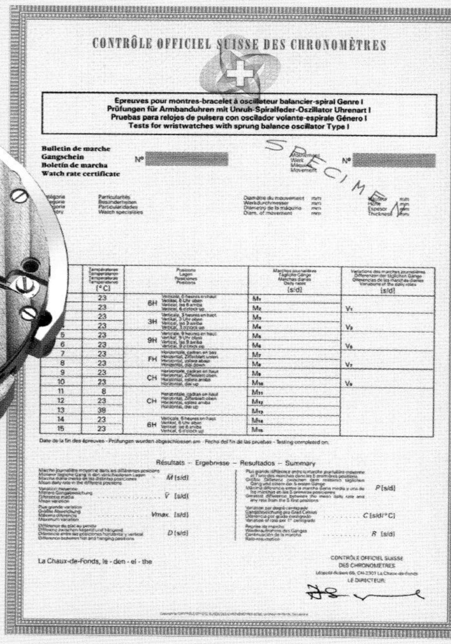

CÔTES DE GENÈVE

Also called *vagues de Genève* and Geneva stripes. This is a traditional Swiss surface decoration comprising an even pattern of parallel stripes, applied to flat movement components with a quickly rotating plastic or wooden peg. Glashütte watchmakers have devised their own version of *côtes de Genève* that is applied at a slightly different angle, called Glashütte ribbing.

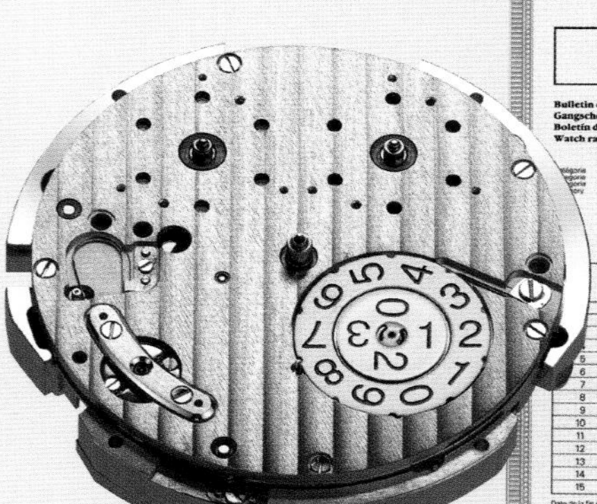

CROWN

The crown is used to wind and set a watch. A few simple turns of the crown will get an automatic movement started, while a manually wound watch is completely wound by the crown. The crown is also used for the setting of various functions, almost always including at least the hours, minutes, seconds, and date. A screwed-down crown like the one on the TAG Heuer Aquagraph pictured here can be tightened to prevent water entering the case or any mishaps while performing extreme sports such as diving.

EQUATION OF TIME

The mean time that we use to keep track of the passing of the day (24 hours evenly divided into minutes and seconds) is not equal to true solar time. The equation of time is a complication devised to show the difference between the mean time shown on one's wristwatch and the time the sun dictates. The Équation Marchante by Blancpain very distinctly indicates this difference via the golden sun-tipped hand that also rotates around the dial in a manner known to watch connoisseurs as *marchant*. Other wristwatch models, such as the Boreas by Martin Braun, display the difference on an extra scale on the dial.

ESCAPEMENT

The combination of the balance, balance spring, pallets, and escape wheel, a subgroup which divides the impulses coming from the spring barrel into small, accurately portioned doses. It guarantees that the gear train runs smoothly and efficiently. The pictured escapement is one newly invented by Parmigiani, containing pallet stones of varying colors, though they are generally red synthetic rubies. Here one of them is a colorless sapphire, or corundum, the same geological material that ruby is made of.

FLINQUÉ

A dial decoration in which a guilloché design is given a coat of enamel, softening the pattern and creating special effects, as shown here on a unique Bovet.

FLYBACK CHRONOGRAPH

A chronograph with a special dial train switch that makes the immediate reuse of the chronograph movement possible after resetting the hands. It was developed for special timekeeping duties such as those found in aviation, which require the measurement of time intervals in quick succession. A flyback may also be called a *retour en vol*. An elegant example of this type of chronograph is Corum's Classical Flyback Large Date shown here.

GEAR TRAIN

A mechanical watch's gear train transmits energy from the mainspring to the escapement. The gear train comprises the minute wheel, the third wheel, the fourth wheel, and the escape wheel.

GLUCYDUR

Glucydur is a functional alloy of copper, beryllium, and iron that has been used to make balances in watches since the 1930s. Its hardness and stability allow watchmakers to use balances that were poised at the factory and no longer required adjustment screws.

GUILLOCHÉ

A surface decoration usually applied to the dial and the rotor using a grooving tool with a sharp tip, such as a rose engine, to cut an even pattern onto a level surface. The exact adjustment of the tool for each new path is controlled by a device similar to a pantograph, and the movement of the tool can be controlled either manually or mechanically. Real *guillochis* (the correct term used by a master of guilloché) are very intricate and expensive to produce, which is why most dials decorated in this fashion are produced by stamping machines. Breguet is one of the very few companies to use real guilloché on every one of its dials.

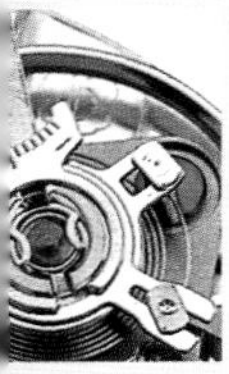

INDEX

A regulating mechanism found on the balance cock and used by the watchmaker to adjust the movement's rate. The index changes the effective length of the balance spring, thus making it move more quickly or slowly. This is the standard index found on an ETA Valjoux 7750.

JEWEL

To minimize friction, the hardened steel tips of a movement's rotating gear wheels (called pinions) are lodged in synthetic rubies (fashioned as polished stones with a hole) and lubricated with a very thin layer of special oil. These synthetic rubies are produced in exactly the same way as sapphire crystal using the same material. During the pocket watch era, real rubies with hand-drilled holes were still used, but because of the high costs involved, they were only used in movements with especially quickly rotating gears. The jewel shown here on a bridge from A. Lange & Söhne's Double Split is additionally embedded in a gold chaton secured with three blued screws.

LIGA

The word LIGA is actually a German acronym that stands for lithography *(Lithografie)*, electroplating *(Galvanisierung)*, and plastic molding *(Abformung)*. It is a lithographic process exposed by UV or X-ray light that literally "grows" perfect micro components made of nickel, nickel-phosphorus, or 23.5-karat gold in a plating bath. The components need no finishing or trimming after manufacture.

LUMINOUS SUBSTANCE

Tritium paint is a slightly radioactive substance that replaced radium as a luminous coating for hands, numerals, and hour markers on watch dials. Watches bearing tritium must be marked as such, with the letter *T* on the dial near 6 o'clock. It has now for the most part been replaced by nonradioactive materials such as Superluminova. Traser technology (as seen on these Ball timepieces) uses tritium gas enclosed in tiny silicate glass tubes coated on the inside with a phosphorescing substance. The luminescence is constant and will hold around twenty-five years.

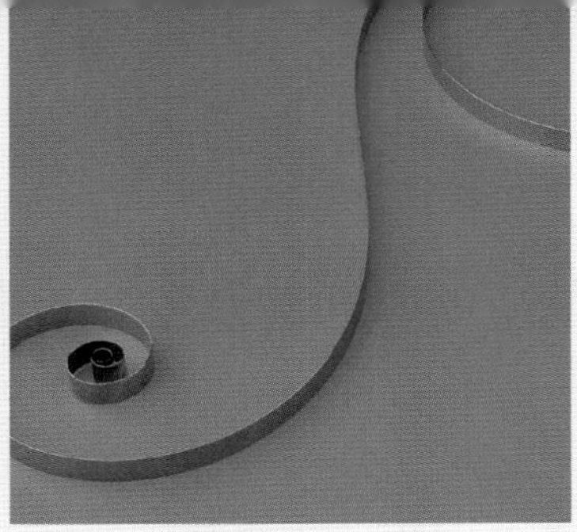

MAINSPRING

The mainspring, located in the spring barrel, stores energy when tensioned and passes it on to the escapement via the gear train as the tension relaxes. Today, mainsprings are generally made of Nivaflex, an alloy invented by Swiss engineer Max Straumann at the beginning of the 1950s. This alloy basically comprises iron, nickel, chrome, cobalt, and beryllium.

MINUTE REPEATER

A striking mechanism with hammers and gongs for acoustically signaling the hours, quarter hours, and minutes elapsed since noon or midnight. The wearer pushes a slide, which winds the spring. Normally a repeater uses two different gongs to signal hours (low tone), quarter hours (high and low tones in succession), and minutes (high tone). Some watches have three gongs, called a carillon. The Chronoswiss Répétition à Quarts is a prominent repeating introduction of recent years.

PERPETUAL CALENDAR

The calendar module for this type of timepiece automatically makes allowances for the different lengths of each month as well as leap years until the next secular year, which will occur in 2100. A perpetual calendar usually shows the date, month, and four-year cycle, and may show the day of the week and moon phase as well, as does this one introduced by George J von Burg at Baselworld 2005. Perpetual calendars need much skill to complete.

PERLAGE

Surface decoration comprising an even pattern of partially overlapping dots, applied with a quickly rotating plastic or wooden peg, as shown here on the plates of Frédérique Constant's *manufacture* Caliber FC 910-1.

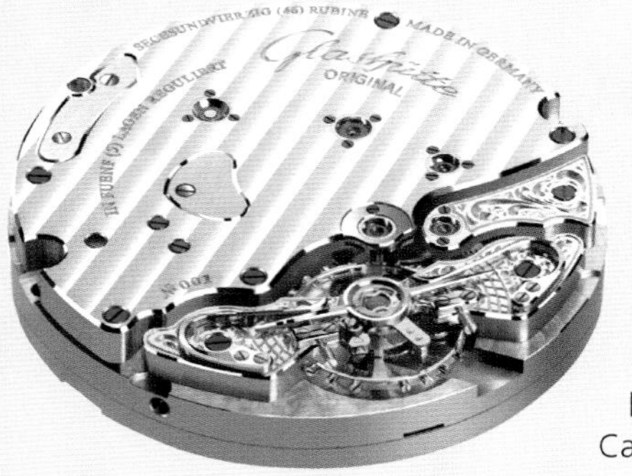

PLATE

A metal platform having several tiers for the gear train. The base plate of a movement usually incorporates the dial and carries the bearings for the primary pinions of the "first floor" of a gear train. The gear wheels are made complete by tightly fitting screwed-in bridges and bars on the back side of the plate. A specialty of the so-called Glashütte school, as opposed to the Swiss school, is the reverse completion of a movement not via different bridges and bars, but rather with a three-quarter plate. Glashütte Original's Caliber 65 (shown) displays a beautifully decorated three-quarter plate.

OWER RESERVE DISPLAY

A mechanical watch contains only a certain amount of power reserve. A fully wound modern automatic watch usually possesses between 36 and 42 hours of energy before it needs to be wound again. The power reserve display keeps the wearer informed about how much energy his or her watch still has in reserve, a function that is especially practical on manually wound watches with several days of possible reserve. The Nomos Tangente Power Reserve pictured here represents an especially creative way to illustrate the state of the mainspring's tension. On some German watches the power reserve is also displayed with the words "auf" and "ab."

PULSOMETER

A scale on the dial, flange, or bezel that, in conjunction with the second hand, may be used to measure a pulse rate. A pulsometer is always marked with a reference number—if it is marked with *gradué pour 15 pulsations*, for example, then the wearer counts fifteen pulse beats. At the last beat, the second hand will show what the pulse rate is in beats per minute on the pulsometer scale. The scale on Sinn's World Time Chronograph (shown) is marked simply with the German world *Puls* (pulse), but the function remains the same.

QUALITÉ FLEURIER

This certification of quality was established by Chopard, Parmigiani Fleurier, Vaucher, and Bovet Fleurier in 2004. Watches bearing the seal must fulfill five criteria, including COSC certification, passing several tests for robustness and precision, top-notch finishing, and being 100 percent Swiss-made (except for the raw materials). The seal appears here on the dial of the Parmigiani Fleurier Tonda 39.

RETROGRADE DISPLAY

A retrograde display shows the time linearly instead of circularly. The hand continues along an arc until it reaches the end of its scale, at which precise moment it jumps back to the beginning instantaneously. This Nienaber model not only shows the minutes in retrograde form, it is also a regulator display.

ROTOR

The rotor is the component that keeps an automatic watch wound. The kinetic motion of this part, which contains a heavy metal weight around its outer edge, winds the mainspring. It can either wind unilaterally or bilaterally (to one or both sides) depending on the caliber. The rotor from this Temption timepiece belongs to an ETA Valjoux 7750.

SAPPHIRE CRYSTAL

Synthetic sapphire crystal is known to gemologists as aluminum oxide (Al_2O_3) or corundum. It can be colorless (corundum), red (ruby), blue (sapphire), or green (emerald). It is virtually scratchproof; only a diamond is harder. The innovative Royal Blue Tourbillon by Ulysse Nardin pictured here features not only sapphire crystals on the front and back of the watch, but also actual plates made of both colorless and blue corundum within the movement.

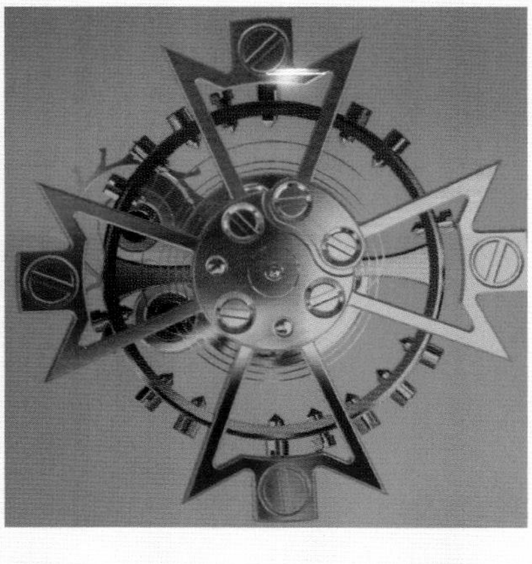

SCREW BALANCE

Before the invention of the perfectly weighted balance using a smooth ring, balances were fitted with weighted screws to get the exact impetus desired. Today a screw balance is a subtle sign of quality in a movement due to its costly construction and assembly utilizing minuscule weighted screws.

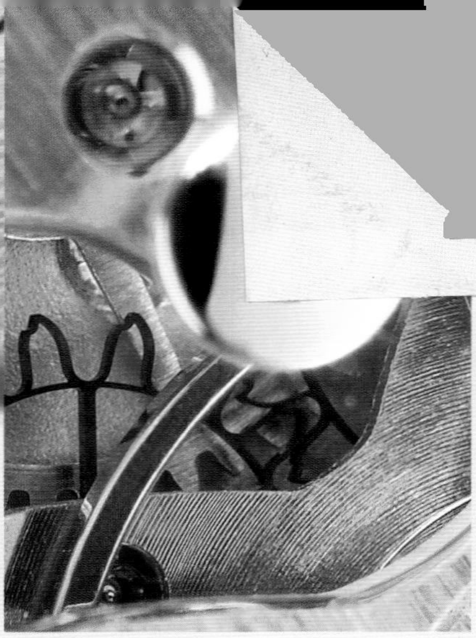

SEAL OF GENEVA

Since 1886 the official seal of this canton has been awarded to Genevan watch *manufactures* who must follow a defined set of high-quality criteria that include the following: polished jewel bed drillings, jewels with olive drillings, polished winding wheels, quality balances and balance springs, steel levers and springs with beveling of 45 degrees and *côtes de Genève* decoration, and polished stems and pinions. The list was updated in 2012 to include the entire watch and newer components. Testing is done on the finished piece. The Seal consists of two, one on the movement, one on the case. The pictured seal was awarded to Vacheron Constantin, a traditional Genevan *manufacture*.

SILICIUM/SILICON

Silicon is an element relatively new to mechanical watches. It is currently being used in the manufacture of precision escapements. Ulysse Nardin's Freak has lubrication-free silicon wheels, and Breguet has successfully used flat silicon balance springs.

SKELETONIZATION

The technique of cutting a movement's components down to their weight-bearing basic substance. This is generally done by hand in painstaking hours of microscopic work with a small handheld saw, though machines can skeletonize parts to a certain degree, such as the version of the Valjoux 7750 that was created for Chronoswiss's Opus and Pathos models. This tourbillon created by Christophe Schaffo is additionally—and masterfully—hand-engraved.

SONNERIE

A variety of minute repeater that—like a tower clock—sounds the time not at the will of the wearer, but rather automatically *(en passant)* every hour *(petite sonnerie)* or quarter hour *(grande sonnerie)*. Gérald Genta designed the most complicated sonnerie back in the early nineties. Shown is a recent model from the front and back.

SPLIT-SECONDS CHRONOGRAPH

Also known in the watch industry by its French name, the *rattrapante* (exploded view at left). A watch with two second hands, one of which can be blocked with a special dial train lever to indicate an intermediate time while the other continues to run. When released, the split-seconds hand jumps ahead to the position of the other second hand. The PTC by Porsche Design illustrates this nicely.

SPRING BARREL

The spring barrel contains the mainspring. It turns freely on an arbor, pulled along by the toothed wheel generally doubling as its lid. This wheel interacts with the first pinion of the movement's gear train. Some movements contain two or more spring barrels for added power reserve.

SWAN-NECK FINE ADJUSTMENT

A regulating instrument used by the watchmaker to adjust the movement's rate in place of an index. The swan neck is especially prevalent in fine Swiss and Glashütte watchmaking (here, Lang & Heyne's Moritz model). Mühle Glashütte has varied the theme with its woodpecker's neck.

TACHYMETER

A scale on the dial, flange, or bezel of a chronograph that, in conjunction with the second hand, gives the speed of a moving object. A tachymeter takes a value determined in less than a minute and converts it into miles or kilometers per hour. For example, a wearer could measure the time it takes a car to pass between two mile markers on the highway. When the car passes the marker, the second hand will be pointing to the car's speed in miles per hour on the tachymetric scale.

TOURBILLON

A technical device invented by Abraham-Louis Breguet in 1801 to compensate for the influence of gravity on the balance of a pocket watch. The entire escapement is mounted on an epicyclic train in a "cage" and rotated completely on its axis over regular periods of time. This superb horological highlight is seen as a sign of technological know-how in the modern era. Harry Winston's Histoire de Tourbillon 4 is a spectacular example.

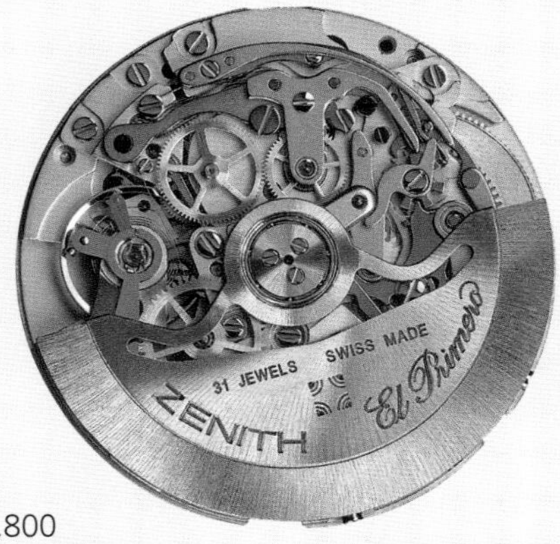

VIBRATION FREQUENCY (VPH)

The spring causes the balance to oscillate at a certain frequency measured in hertz (Hz) or vibrations per hour (vph). Most of today's wristwatches tick at 28,800 vph (4 Hz) or 21,600 vph (3 Hz). Less usual is 18,000 vph (2.5 Hz). Zenith's El Primero was the first serial movement to beat at 36,000 vph (5 Hz), and the Breguet Type XXII runs at 72,000 vph.

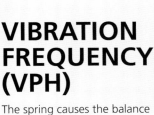

WATER RESISTANCE

Water resistance is an important feature of any timepiece and is usually measured in increments of one atmosphere (atm or bar, equal to 10 meters of water pressure) or meters and is often noted on the dial or case back. Watches resistant to 100 meters are best for swimming and snorkeling. Timepieces resistant to 200 meters are good for scuba diving. To deep-sea dive there are various professional timepieces available for use in depths of 200 meters or more. The Hydromax by Bell & Ross (shown) is water-resistant to a record 11,000 meters.

Editor-in-chief: Peter Braun
Editor: Marton Radkai
Production manager: Louise Kurtz
Copy editor: Virginia Carroll
Composition: Madeline Brubaker
Project management: North Market Street Graphics

For more information about advertising, please contact:
Gary Girdvainis
Isochron Media, LLC
25 Gay Bower Road, Monroe, CT 06468
203-485-6276, garygeorgeg@gmail.com

Printed and bound in Slovenia.

ISBN 978-0-7892-1399-0

Twenty-third edition
10 9 8 7 6 5 4 3 2 1

Library of Congress Cataloging-in-Publication Data available upon request

For bulk and premium sales and for text adoption procedures, write to Customer Service Manager,
Abbeville Press, 655 Third Avenue, New York, NY 10017, or call 1-800-ARTBOOK.

Visit Abbeville Press online at www.abbeville.com.

ISBN 978-0-7892-1399-0 U.S. $39.95
53995
EAN
9 780789 213990